MINING GEOLOGY

THE PRENTICE-HALL GEOLOGY SERIES

Norman E. A. Hinds, *Editor*

MINING GEOLOGY

by

Hugh Exton McKinstry

Professor of Geology, Harvard University

with sections by

Stanley A. Tyler

Professor of Geology, University of Wisconsin

and by

E. N. Pennebaker

Consulting Geologist, Consolidated Coppermines Corporation

and

Kenyon E. Richard

Geologist, American Smelting and Refining Company

Englewood Cliffs, N. J.

PRENTICE-HALL, INC.

Current printing (last digit):

18   17   16   15   14   13   12   11   10

PRINTED IN THE UNITED STATES OF AMERICA

58420—C

Foreword

As may be divined from its title, this book is about mining geology. Less evident, perhaps, is the fact that it seeks to cover a field rather different from that of texts entitled *Mineral Deposits* or *Economic Geology*. Those texts, concerned primarily with the origin and nature of mineral deposits and with descriptions of representative mining districts, provide the professional mining geologist with the scientific foundation for his work. They are admirably suited to that purpose and it is in no sense to their discredit that they leave the exact manner of applying this knowledge to the search for ore and the appraisal of mines largely to the ingenuity of the individual. Manifestly there is no substitute for ingenuity and personal judgment, especially in a vocation which, in the present state of its growth, is fully as much an art as a technology; yet mining geology has been a profession in its own right for a generation or more, and during this time many able men the world over have been devising techniques of investigation and developing philosophies of ore-search. It is true that some of this lore is to be found only in the minds of the seasoned practitioners and is best acquired through apprenticeship with them in the field. Nevertheless, much of it is common knowledge within the profession, even though not committed to paper, and much more is in print, though widely scattered in the technical literature.[1] Has not the time arrived when we can gather together some of the fruits of this experience for the assistance of younger geologists, as well as for others who wish to know more about how the mining geologist plies his trade?

Any attempt to explain what the mining geologist does and how he does it requires a survey of that incompletely charted borderland that lies between the respective domains of geology and mining. Of necessity the survey encroaches on both realms. Just how far it ought to venture into each, what subjects it should include, and how elementary or how exhaustive should be the treatment of each are questions on which no two authorities are likely to agree. Naturally each individual tends to set store by the notions and methods that have proved most useful in his own experience, and I can claim no immunity to personal predilections.

---

[1] Since this was written a very useful volume has appeared: Forrester, J. D., *Field and Mining Geology*. New York: John Wiley and Sons, Incorporated, 1946.

Although this book is intended for a reader who already has some acquaintance with the principles of structural geology and ore deposition, I have felt it advisable to review some of the basic geological principles, albeit from a standpoint somewhat different from that of the standard texts, in order to establish a sort of backsight from which to project the traverse.   Then, after having discussed the strictly geological applications of these principles, I could have halted at the boundaries of the claims already staked by mining engineering, mine valuation, geophysics, and engineering geology, merely pointing out the way and bidding the reader Godspeed to pursue his own further inquiries.   This, indeed, might have seemed the more discreet course were it not for the fact that mining geologists, more than most other professional men, find themselves working far from any library, even their own.   So, for their convenience, I have tried to assemble, in summary form, those essential principles and bits of information that they would seem most likely to use in the varied duties that fall to their lot.   And since, no matter where one stops or how far one goes, there are always fields beyond, I have tried to supply adequate references for readers who wish to venture farther.

Hidden, I suspect, behind capital I's in this book, are bits of the ideas and philosophies of many predecessors and associates.   Chief among these men are Waldemar Lindgren, who introduced me to mineral deposits, Louis Caryl Graton, whose challenging discussions compelled me to think about them, and Donald H. McLaughlin, who showed me how to study ore deposits in the field.   Some of the contributions of these and many other geologists have no doubt gone unacknowledged because the pages of the mind have inadequate spaces for source references; much that I fancy to be original might, if traced to its roots, turn out to be the property of one or another of the geologists and mining men with whom I have worked or talked in this or that mining field.

A number of my friends and colleagues have generously read and criticized various sections of the manuscript.   For their protection, I should make it clear that my expression of sincere gratitude to them does not carry the implication that they necessarily endorse all of the views expressed in this book or even in the sections that they have read. Some of those who have supplied information and suggestions are credited in appropriate places in the text, but I take this opportunity to thank a number of others whose help is not adequately acknowledged elsewhere, and to indicate the parts of the manuscript that they have been kind enough to read:

James S. Baker (Amenability of Ores to Treatment), D. W. Bantz (Acquiring Prospects), Francis Birch (Rock Pressure at Depth), Roland Blanchard (Types of Residual Limonite), Kirk Bryan (Physiographic Guides), Frederic M. Chace (Ore Guides), Rollin Farmin (Underground Mapping; Assembling Data), George M. Fowler (Churn Drilling), N. B. Keevil (Geophysical Investigations), L. C. Graton (Persistence of Ore in Depth), Robert D. Longyear (Diamond Drilling), C. V. Theis (Water Problems), George Tunell (Laboratory Methods and Mineralogical Guides), F. S. Turneaure (Persistence of Ore in Depth), W. T. Stuart (Water Problems), Harrison Schmitt (Mapping), C. O. Swanson (Erratic High Assays), S. A. Tyler (Exploration for Iron Ores), Robert K. Warner (Mine Valuation), and Kenneth K. Welker (Rock Bursts).   Edward Schmitz drew most of the illustrations.

HUGH EXTON McKINSTRY

Cambridge
April, 1948

Contents

Introduction

GEOLOGY IN THE MINING INDUSTRY

But as for us, though we may not have perfected the whole art of the discovery and preparation of metals, at least we can be of great assistance to persons studious in its acquisition.
— AGRICOLA DE RE METALLICA, 1550 [1]

"WHAT does a mining geologist do?"

In asking this question, people who are unfamiliar with the mining industry sometimes betray mild surprise that a science associated with dinosaurs, earthquakes, and uncommonly long names for common rocks can have any bearing on the job of digging metals out of the ground. Such a superficial answer as is appropriate to a dinner conversation evokes the response, "I think your work must be simply fascinating!" and doubtless leaves the interrogator with the impression that a mining geologist secures his results through some combination of witch-stick divining and an ability to see several hundred feet into the ground. This impression is, in a sense and in some slight degree, correct, although, of course, the method of performing such remarkable feats is not, as the dinner partner might imagine, through extra-sensory perception or even mental radar but through drawing logical conclusions from evidence laboriously collected. A prediction that a shaft will reach a certain bed of iron ore at a depth of 500 feet follows from careful measurement of the thickness of beds and the angle of inclination, together with the calculation of the length of the vertical leg of a triangle. Conclusions of a less elementary character, announced, one must sometimes admit, with a smaller degree of assurance and a larger reliance on judgment, are based nevertheless on the same sort of scientific facts and principles. The geologist has nothing up his sleeve.

---

[1] Translation by Herbert Clark Hoover and Lou Henry Hoover. London: The Mining Magazine, 1912.

"Pure" and Applied Geology

Geology, like other sciences, has both pure and applied aspects, but the distinction between the two is not as precisely defined as it is in some other disciplines. Biology, for example, has applied aspects, two of which are known separately as agronomy and bacteriology; physics is applied in such forms as strength of materials and electrical engineering. But in geology the applied aspects are inseparably identified with geology itself, perhaps because the arts of application are still youthful and just coming of age. While they are developing rapidly, they have not yet evolved into full-fledged precise techniques, and there are few cut-and-dried formulas into which one can substitute the variables and get the answers. Locke's remark [2] of seventeen years ago is still true in large degree: "It is as though doctors were provided with books only on physiology or engineers with books only on physics." Instead of finding all of its basic principles ready-made for application, mining geology has had to do its own pioneering research, especially in such fields as the identification of opaque minerals, the behavior of hydrothermal solutions, and the chemical reactions between groundwater and sulphides. In these and in many other fields of inquiry, mining geology, while pursuing its own career, cannot divorce itself from "pure" geology.

Fields of Applied Geology

Mining, of course, is only one of the fields in which geology finds practical application. In exploration for petroleum, the geological technique is considered indispensable. In the development of water resources, the phase of geology known as hydrology has been employed for many years. In civil engineering projects, geologists are called in to advise on all sorts of problems connected with rocks and soil—foundations for dams and bridges, conditions to be expected in tunneling, and sources of materials for highway construction.

Specialties within Mining Geology

As mining geology in itself covers a broad field, it is only natural that any one person should be better acquainted with some phases of it than with others, but as it happens, such specialization as there is does not seem to conform to any clearly defined boundaries. One might expect, for example, that since each metal presents problems of its own, there would be gold-mining geologists, lead-mining geologists, and so on. Actually, there is little deliberate specialization on individual metals and

---

[2] Locke, Augustus, The profession of orehunting: *Economic Geology*, Vol. 16, p. 345, 1921.

for a good reason: The problems peculiar to any particular metal lie more in the fields of purification and marketing than in finding and mining the deposits. The characteristics of natural occurrence are determined not so much by what metal a deposit contains as by what shape the deposit has and how it came into existence. Gold placers have more resemblance to tin placers than to gold veins; veins of the non-metallic mineral fluorite are more like veins of lead and zinc than like such non-metallic products as phosphate or mica.

Logically, then, specialization within the profession should follow the lines of genetic classes of deposits. If it is true that specialization promotes efficiency, we would be more efficient if we should qualify ourselves as pyrometasomatic geologists, supergene geologists, or syngenetic geologists. But, fortunately or unfortunately, specialization does not follow such logical lines. Actually it seems to fall largely to chance; the particular employer or company that the geologist happens to have worked for or the mines or districts in which he has gained his experience may determine the field of his specialization. A steel company's geologist is likely to be intimately acquainted with the occurrence of such diverse products as magmatic chromite, sedimentary manganese, and hydrothermal fluorite; the employee of a large metal-mining company may have specialized in placer gold, contact-metamorphic copper, and sedimentary deposits of coal; a state geologist may be an authority on sedimentary clays and epithermal fluorite for no other reason than that these are the important commercial products of his state.

So the spectrum of geological types of mineral deposits calls for some knowledge of nearly every phase of geology from *aa* to *zoning*, and the mining geologist cannot afford the easy but narrowing luxury of specialization in any limited phase of his science.

Importance of Epigenetic Deposits

While mining geology covers the whole field of mineral occurrence, there is one broad group of deposits about which more has been said and written than about all others put together. This is the group known as *epigenetic*—that is, ores and mineral products introduced into their surrounding rocks after the rocks themselves had already come into existence. The reason for this emphasis is not that such deposits have been the greatest producers, for a single class outside this group has turned out a far greater bulk of material, measured either in tons or in dollars. If this book seems to place chief emphasis on epigenetic ores, especially veins, lodes, and replacement deposits, it is because this group has been the object of most attention from the profession as a whole.

Such deposits are, by comparison, hard to find and follow, and, having a higher value per ton, have called for the services of more geologists and compelled the solution of more diverse and difficult problems than have deposits of other types.

The other broad group of deposits, *syngenetic* (mineral deposits formed along with the rocks that enclose them), are by no means without their geological problems; but those syngenetic deposits that occur in igneous rocks are for the most part either too simple to require geological guidance or too erratic to benefit by it. So they seem now, at least, although better technologies no doubt will be developed to deal with them more adequately. Syngenetic deposits in sedimentary rocks, which account for all of the coal, most of the outstanding deposits of iron and manganese, and the bulk of the non-metallic minerals, involve few problems which do not also face the student of epigenetic deposits— problems of sedimentation and stratigraphy and, in many cases, problems of structure (especially folding and faulting), although here again growing technology may evolve special techniques as the economic incentive becomes more conducive.

Geology in Mining

The mining industry in its task of finding, following, and extracting metallic ores has always made use of geology in one way or another. Writings on mining since medieval times all venture into discussions of ore genesis and ore localization; naïve and amusing as they may seem to us now, they were the best geology known at the time and were, even then, considered part of the knowledge essential to mining. Until geologists began to take an interest in the specialized problems of mining, each miner or engineer had to be his own geologist, applying as best he could, and often with marked success, the ideas that he gained from science or developed for himself. Only during the last century, and particularly during the last generation, have those aspects of geology that are applicable to mining been developed to such a degree as to form the basis for a separate profession.

In these days most projects for the exploration and development of metals are carried out under some form of geological guidance, whether it is supplied by professional geologists or by engineers who have themselves acquired a knowledge of geology, and whether it is based on original investigation or on surveys by government or scientific organizations.

Of the professional geologists who devote their attention to matters bearing on mining, many, but by no means all, are employed by mining companies. A large group are in government employ, and a few are engaged by organizations concerned with the financial aspects of mining.

Company-Staff Geology

Most large mining companies and many small ones maintain geological departments to investigate the geology of their mines and advise on exploratory and operating problems. As the functions of resident and consulting geologists are described in Chapter 19, and as the manner in which they collect information and draw deductions forms the main topic of this book, no further elaboration seems necessary at this point.

Geology in Litigation. In addition to duties concerned with finding, appraising, and mining ore, geologists are called occasionally as expert witnesses in lawsuits. In the United States, the extraordinary mining law based on the "right of apex" has been a fruitful source of litigation and calls not only for expert legal interpretation but for qualified scientific opinion as to whether, for example, a vein found underground is or is not identical with one exposed at the outcrop or "apex." Convincing testimony may require months of painstaking underground mapping, followed by the construction of elaborate maps and models.

There are those who feel that a geologist prostitutes his scientific integrity by taking a partisan position (especially if the fee is lucrative) and that the spectacle of two geologists swearing to opposing assertions does not elevate the dignity of the profession in the eyes of laymen who are unable to understand the honest differences of scientific opinion that are always possible even though no personal interests are at stake. Nevertheless, it must be said that only a geologist is competent to testify on questions of geology, and if honest men are not available, the work will fall to charlatans. Actually, men of unimpeachable integrity have given their services to litigants without visibly undermining their own mental honesty. Rarely have geologists sought such commissions after the manner of ambulance chasers, and any who did would find their professional reputations in jeopardy. Repeatedly, geologists of integrity have refused to accept cases unless convinced in their own minds that their clients were right, and not a few have been approached by both contending litigants and thus have had their choice as to which side they preferred to support. Fortunately, apex litigation is much rarer than it was a generation ago, and geologists, even those who have profited financially by it, will shed few tears at its passing.

The Work of Government Surveys

Less closely woven into the operating management of the industry than the "company geologist" but nevertheless highly important in mining development are the officials of the geological surveys of national, state, and provincial governments.

It is unlikely that economic geology would yet have attained full status as a science had it not been for the wealth of observation collected by government organizations and correlated by great leaders who have devoted all or part of their professional careers to government work. The study and comparison of mining districts on a scale that is possible only to a group with the authority and resources of a public organization have made it possible to evolve broad and sound theories of ore genesis. By carrying out mapping and scientific study over wide regions for a generation, the surveys have been able to solve large-scale structural and stratigraphic problems that could not have been answered by local investigation.

The pioneer work of the surveys blazes the trail for prospectors and singles out the districts that are most promising for investigation and development. The value of their work is illustrated by the achievements of the Ontario Department of Mines; rarely does a prospector go into the bush without one of the Ontario Survey's reconnaissance maps of the region to show him the areas of barren granite or of potentially productive greenstones and sediments. When prospecting activity touches a particular district, the Survey usually has men in the field immediately and issues a preliminary map before the end of the season. The prospectors and exploration companies make use of it at once as a guide in staking claims and laying out drilling programs.

Although government surveys have been criticized on the one hand for usurping the functions of private consultants and on the other for remaining aloof from practical problems,[3] the geological surveys need not, and usually do not, merit censure on either of these charges.[4] That the surveys' contributions to the search for metals is not entirely indirect and academic is demonstrated by the discovery of ore both in old districts and in virgin territory by government geologists on more than one occasion. During the second World War, when government agencies engaged directly in the search for strategic minerals, many gov-

---

[3] Farrell, J. H., Mining geology: *Mining and Metallurgy*, vol. 12, November, 1931, p. 490.

[4] Symposium: Relations between government surveys and the mining industry, participated in by Reno H. Sales, G. F. Loughlin, George H. Ashley, George W. Bain, Hugh M. Roberts, B. S. Butler, M. N. Short, William M. Agar. *Transactions of the American Institute of Mining and Metallurgical Engineers*, vol. 115, pp, 407–451, 1935.

ernment geologists found themselves undertaking the sort of detailed mapping and preparation of recommendations that would normally be the job of the company geologist. By and large they acquitted themselves well. Nevertheless, it is true that in normal times the efforts of public surveys to solve the ore-hunting problems of individual mines have not, in general, been spectacularly successful, partly because the time that can properly be devoted to the detailed study of a single mine is necessarily limited, and partly because of the experience and interests of survey men. Many of them enter government service directly from graduate school, and while a number subsequently shift from government to industry, relatively few transfer in the opposite direction to bring the operating outlook and the training in underground mapping which "company" geologists acquire. The situation is by no means regrettable, for the survey geologists develop instead a skill in reconnaissance mapping and a predominating interest in scientific problems that fit them admirably for their own special field of activity. That field, although it necessarily overlaps the activities of company geologists, does not compete with them. The government surveys have a function of extraordinarily useful service to industry that no single company is in a position to perform. The government surveys furnish the framework into which the company geologists can fit their more localized studies; the government geologists can and do develop the broader principles which the ore-hunters can particularize and apply.

"Geological Economists"

In recent years a great deal has been said and written about strategic minerals. Particularly when almost all useful minerals became strategic, governments realized the importance of accurate and up-to-the-minute information as to where metals and minerals occur, how rapidly they can be made available, and how long the ultimate supplies will last. In time of war such information is of critical importance, not only with regard to supplies accessible to ourselves and our allies but also with regard to sources available to the enemy. Plans for a lasting peace must also take into account the distribution of raw material supplies among nations.

World War II saw a large number of geologists employed in Washington, Ottawa, and other capitals, as well as in the field in all accessible parts of the world, working in partnership with mining engineers, economists, and business men in assembling information and putting plans into effect. The geologists' contribution was not strictly geological but grew out of acquaintance with varied mineral products, firsthand knowledge of the geography of many parts of the world, familiarity with deposits in remote regions, and facility in sizing up the potentialities of new and old districts either in the field or from descriptions.

Similarly, because of their acquaintance with mineral products and their experience in appraising mines, geologists have proved their usefulness as advisers and analysts to banks, investment houses, and commercial companies that have occasion to finance mining operations, invest in the stocks of mining companies, or deal in mineral commodities. In this type of work, the geologist becomes partly economist or business analyst. His work is in the home office or in the field, preferably alternating between the two. By astute reading of reports, he is able to weed out mining proposals that are based on incompetent or insufficient investigation. From the available geological description, he can form a guess as to whether the orebodies are of a type that can be economically mined and whether they will have extension beyond known reserves. From those proposals which appear attractive, he selects the ones which seem to be most worthy of further investigation. From his experience he can distinguish between sound, well-conceived exploration projects on the one hand and hare-brained promotion schemes on the other. In the field his greatest interest is in grade and costs, problems which are more in the line of the mining engineer than the geologist *per se;* his truly geological contribution is in sizing up the future possibilities—whether or not the mine or prospect is likely to grow up to be a larger producer and whether its life will be long or short.

Arrangement of the Book

In presenting the technique of applying geology to metal mining, Part I will be devoted to methods of collecting the necessary basic information by mapping and other means of investigation and to procedures in assembling the information from all sources into usable form. Part II is devoted chiefly to the relationship between ore and geology, with something of the philosophy of ore-search. Part III discusses methods of finding, developing, and valuing orebodies in the successive stages from prospecting to operation. Part IV describes the methods of converting run-of-mine ore into marketable products, with special attention to the manner in which mineralogy of the ore determines whether and how it can be processed and sold. The appendix contains miscellaneous geological and numerical data for the convenience of itinerant geologists.

Selected References

General Texts on Economic Geology and Mineral Deposits

Bateman, Alan M., *Economic Mineral Deposits*. New York: John Wiley and Sons, Incorporated, 1942.

Emmons, William Harvey, *Principles of Economic Geology*, 2nd Edition. New York: McGraw-Hill Book Company, Incorporated, 1940.

Lilley, Ernest R., *Economic Geology of Mineral Deposits*. New York: Henry Holt and Company, 1936.

Lindgren, Waldemar, *Mineral Deposits*, 4th Edition. New York: McGraw-Hill Book Company, Incorporated, 1933.

Ries, H., *Economic Geology*. New York: John Wiley and Sons, Incorporated, 1937.

Louis, Henry, *Mineral Deposits*. London: Ernest Benn, Limited, 1934.

Tarr, R. S., *Introduction to Economic Geology*. New York: McGraw-Hill Book Company, Incorporated, 1930.

Economic Geology as a Profession

Lindgren, Waldemar, "Economic Geology as a Profession," *Economic Geology*, 1919, Vol. 14, pp. 79–86.

Locke, Augustus, "The Profession of Orehunting," *Economic Geology*, 1921, Vol. 16, pp. 243–278.

National Roster of Scientific and Specialized Personnel, *Handbook of Descriptions of Specialized Fields in Geology*. Washington: War Manpower Commission, 1945.

Read, Thomas T., *Careers in the Mineral Industries*. New York: American Institute of Mining and Metallurgical Engineers, 1946, 30 pp.

Part One

ASSEMBLING GEOLOGICAL DATA

1

Geologic Mapping

Most recent discoveries of ore by geologic methods resulted from detailed studies of structural conditions and these had detailed large-scale mapping as their base. Few recent college graduates seem to have had training in mapping methods known to be effective. . . . The student is expected to acquire the needed skill somehow after graduation; yet it may mean his bread and butter for several years. Indeed he may never learn to map well and therefore be ineffective in exploration.

—HARRISON SCHMITT [1]

A MAP is a record of geological facts in their correct space relations—facts, be it noted, not theories. There must always be sharp distinction between observation and inference. You can see a contact where it is exposed but you cannot see it under covered ground. No matter how intelligent a guess you can make, it is still a guess and therefore not entitled to the degree of confidence that you can place in a record of what you have actually seen. This failure to distinguish between fact and inference is a criticism that can justly be leveled at some of the otherwise impeccable maps published by government surveys. "On many field maps, even where made with evident care, 'solid geology' lines alone are shown. Yet every [geological] surveyor knows that the validity of such lines is very different in different parts of their courses." [2] ". . . Indeed some surveyors plot their contacts throughout as solid lines, so that there is no means of telling how much was observed and how much inferred. This is a great mistake." [3] The geologist who fails to distinguish fact from inference on his maps is inconsiderate both of

[1] Schmitt, Harrison, On mapping underground geology: *Engineering & Mining Journal*, vol. 137, p. 557, 1936.
[2] Greenly, Edward, and Williams, Howel, *Methods in Geological Surveying*, p. 192. New York: D. Van Nostrand Co., 1930.
[3] *Ibid.*, p. 202.

1

other workers and of his own reputation. As successors cannot tell which localities supplied the evidence, they must search the whole area for exposed contacts. They must either accept all of the work, fact and theory alike, or reject it all and start the mapping from scratch. If new evidence indicates that an inferred boundary is wrong this is no reflection upon the ability of the mapper, *provided* the boundary was shown as an inferred one. But if no distinction is made, the geologist's records as well as his powers of observation become the subject of grave doubts.

Thus the map should always be drawn in such a manner that either the man who made it or someone else will later be able to eliminate all the interpretation, preserve all the observations and build up an en·· tirely new interpretation on the same set of facts. In any kind of mapping this is no more than sound scientific integrity; in mapping for mining purposes it is doubly important. New workings and drill holes are constantly adding new facts and either confirming or modifying the interpretations; indeed, economic geologists are more fortunate than other workers in this respect. "The expectation that predictions will eventually be tested by subsequent exploration imposes a wholesome restraint on vague and speculative ideas, especially after a few experiences that engender respect for the uncertainties and surprises that can be concealed only a few tens of feet beyond the face of a drift or below an outcrop." [4]

This does not mean that the geologist should go to the other extreme and show all, or almost all, boundaries as doubtful, for that would defeat the purpose of the distinction between fact and inference. Nor should he hesitate to interpret. It is his duty to offer interpretations at every opportunity for no one is in a better position to draw inferences than the man who has made the maps and studied the ground. It is not speculation or imagination that is to be discouraged, it is merely the failure to recognize and to indicate the element of uncertainty, a failure which carries not only mechanical but also psychological dangers. The misconception that one's theoretical interpretation is the only one possible is likely to be exposed by the propensity of nature to contrive an interpretation that the geologist had not foreseen.

Degree of Doubt

Not only should mere uncertainty be recognized, but the degree of

[4] McLaughlin, Donald H., and Sales, Reno, Utilization of geology by mining companies, in *Ore Deposits of the Western States* (Lindgren Volume), p. 686. New York: American Institute of Mining and Metallurgical Engineers, 1933.

uncertainty should be indicated on the maps and grasped by the mind. It is conventional to show observed facts in solid lines and interpretation, (e.g., contacts between crosscuts) in dotted or dashed lines. Greater degrees of uncertainty can be indicated by wider spacing of dots; highly speculative interpretations can be indicated by interrogation points.

In some mines two sets of maps are used, one a fact map on which nothing but observations are set down, the other, a set of "guess sheets" or "play sheets" on which the most plausible interpretations are indicated. These are constantly revised and altered as new information comes to light. Cross sections accompany the plans and serve as a check on interpretations; any interpretation shown on the plan must also make a convincing picture when plotted on cross sections.

What to Map

Any exposure of rock presents a wealth of detail. The proportions, sizes, and shapes of the grains of different minerals vary with each square inch, and the color varies correspondingly. The mass is cut by joints ranging in size from conspicuous to microscopic; they may be parallel or they may have no recognizable pattern. Bedding planes may be widely spaced and simple or they may be minutely spaced and intimately contorted. How much of this information is to be put on the map? A limit is imposed, of course, by the scale, yet the choice of scale should be determined by the amount of detail that is expedient, not the converse.

One school of geologists advocates omitting nothing. Thus, Schmitt [5] writes: "Most mining geologists with a number of years of experience in mapping believe that all details capable of being mapped should be recorded, including those which at first appear to be of remote significance. They may become significant when integrated and plotted on the office maps." Similarly Wilson,[6] says: "It is rare that the significant features, that is, those which may help to find ore, are all definitely known. It is only after details, no matter of how much present unimportance, have been mapped, studied and correlated that the essential ones can be selected."

Naturally this advice was written to be read with a sense of proportion. Being practical men, neither Schmitt nor Wilson would map on a scale of 1:1 which would be required if *all* details were to be recorded.

---

[5] Schmitt, Harrison, On mapping underground geology: *Engineering & Mining Journal,* vol. 137, p. 557, 1936.

[6] Wilson, Philip D., *Report on the Collection, Recording and Economic Application of Geological Data.* American Mining Congress, 25th Annual Convention, 1924.

Some choice of detail is unavoidable. "Geologic notes are a picture of the facts as filtered through the mind of the geologist. They cannot be wholly photographic." [7] "Geological maps are based on selection of subject; they can never be more than abstracts of Nature. But they can be truthful abstracts,—truthful, that is, in the sense of being according to what we may call the spirit of Nature." [8]

Selection of Detail

Perhaps this is a good place to draw the distinction between accuracy and exhaustiveness. If a finely stratified rock lies in complex dragfolds, it will be impossible to sketch each individual bed separately, but it will be perfectly possible to select certain beds and draw their shape as accurately as a sharp pencil and the scale of the map will permit. A folded bed will not appear as a mere wiggly line but as a replica which shows the actual inclination of each limb to the axial plane and the amplitude and wave-length of each fold reproduced to scale.

What to Map First

Since it is impossible, practically speaking, to put *every* feature on the map, are there not some *groups* of features which may safely be omitted?—subtle rock differences, for example, or insignificant-looking joints? In the ultimate sense, no, for in a large mine, operating through a long period of years, every kind of geological feature will receive study sooner or later.

It might therefore seem advisable to record all possible features foot by foot as the mapping progresses so that once any part of the mine or surface has been mapped the mapping of that section will be completed once and for all. This ideal, however, does not work out satisfactorily in practice. First, it is difficult to give effective attention to all features at once; second, some features can be recognized only after long acquaintance; and third, new observations repeatedly come to light and demand a review of the ground that has already been mapped.

The difficulty of giving attention to more than one feature at a time is likely to result in unintentional slighting of critical details. The geologist may make every effort to note "all" features, but later, when the occasion arises to assemble the data regarding some particular feature, it usually turns out that the notes are sketchy and indefinite. For ex-

[7] Billingsley, Paul, Utilization of geology by mining companies, in *Ore Deposits of the Western States* (Lindgren Volume), p. 720. New York: A.I.M.E., 1933.
[8] Greenly, Edward, and Williams, Howel, *Methods in Geological Surveying*, p. 205. London: Thos. Murby and Co., 1930; New York: D. Van Nostrand Co., 1930.

ample, if the feature is rock alteration the map may show "fresh rock" in one place, "strongly altered" in another, "fairly well altered" somewhere else, and in the critical place notes may be altogether absent. It becomes necessary to go through the mine again and map rock alteration separately according to some quantitative standard in order to get a picture that is accurate and consistent enough to be of practical use.

Some features, such as subtle variations in rock character, can be recognized only after months of association. In this respect rocks have some similarities to human beings. When one is introduced to a new crowd of people they all seem to look more or less alike. Then, with further acquaintance, one person after another emerges from the group and takes on individuality until finally the personalities are so distinct that one wonders that they could ever have been confused. Similarly, the rocks of an unfamiliar mine seem at first to be a single, monotonous assemblage. Then with close acquaintance, every formation and every alteration phase becomes so distinctly recognizable that the resident geologist fails to see how a visitor could confuse them. The visitor, on the other hand, suspects that the resident is merely imagining the differences that he is endeavoring to point out.

Thus it is that McLaughlin and Sales [9] remark: "Ability to see obscure but critical details comes only with repeated examinations of exposures and from actually living with the problems of a district."

In the Porcupine district, certain strips of yellowish dense rock were first noticed in highly deformed areas and were mistaken for altered phases of the fine-grained lavas with which they were associated. Later, when the same horizons were seen in a less disturbed locality, it was evident that the material was interbedded with carbonaceous shale and was part of a sedimentary horizon between two lava flows. This relationship made it necessary to return and study in detail the distribution of the yellowish dense rock with respect to the carbonaceous sediment and the varying textures of the enclosing lavas.

In ways such as this, new observations throw light on obscure problems. In this connection, Billingsley [10] says: "No one of us in Tintic has ever been able to reach a final correct geological understanding of a mine or an area upon the basis of a single examination, no matter how painstaking the mapping."

If the ultimate necessity of restudy and remapping is recognized at

---

[9] McLaughlin, Donald H., and Sales, Reno, Utilization of geology by mining companies, *Ore Deposits of the Western States* (Lindgren Volume), p. 686. New York: A.I.M.E., 1933.
[10] Billingsley, Paul, Utilization of geology by mining companies, *Ore Deposits of the Western States* (Lindgren Volume), p. 721. New York: A.I.M.E., 1933.

the outset, the growth of the geologic picture is accelerated and the efficiency of the whole mapping program is improved. The question becomes not "What shall we map?" but "What shall we map first?" When everything seems obscure and confusing it is a consoling thought that the rocks on the surface are likely to remain there for the duration of the present geological epoch, and that even underground there will be ample opportunity to return again and again to collect information that was not recorded in the preliminary mapping.

An exception is presented by underground workings in the immediate vicinity of active operations. Here there is danger that the evidence may be removed by mining, obscured by timbers, or marooned in a crosscut that will become inaccessible. In such locations every effort must be made to record "all" the evidence, yet with the full realization that, no matter how painstaking the mapping, it will later prove wanting in some particular.

There is a law of diminishing returns in geological mapping. Such features as veins, prominent fractures, and dikes can be put on the map with little loss of time. Others, such as subtle variations in rock type, minor differences in mineralization, and varying degree of alteration show less obvious progress per hour of mapping. Although the more obscure features may prove to be no less significant, the time required for their study delays the achievement of a general picture. This picture rounds itself out more rapidly if the definite and conspicuous features are assembled first.

Early results of practical value are worth securing even though they may need to be modified at a later stage. The geologist employed by a large company is sometimes permitted and even encouraged to indulge in studies whose bearing on the practical problems may not be apparent; yet his standing is improved if he is able at an early stage to be of direct assistance in the operation of the mine. This aspect takes on increasing importance in mines of smaller size where the expense of the geological department bulks large in the overhead costs, and the ore shortage is howling like a wolf at the door. Under such conditions one cannot afford to follow the methods of "the young geologist who spends months in study of rock alteration when the vein is lost at a fault." [11]

Two guiding principles will help to bring practical results at an early stage:

1. Give primary attention to the ore and to structures most obviously connected with it.

[11] Joralemon, Ira B., Mining geology today: *Mining Congress Journal*, December, 1940, p. 33.

2. Assemble first the facts that can be most quickly observed and recorded. When these observations have been pieced together and studied, the broader picture emerges and points to the problems that cry for immediate solution.

Reconnaissance vs. Detail

The attainment of a useful preliminary picture will be speeded by a judicious balance between local detail and broader structure, and between underground and surface investigation. Thus, when he begins his work in a new district, the first thing the mining geologist will wish to see is the ore—or at least what signs of it there are. But before settling in for a careful study of the ore deposit and its immediate vicinity, he will wish to have an idea of its broader setting. To this end, general geologic maps of the region are serviceable if they exist. Most parts of the United States and Canada are covered by the mapping of the federal and state or provincial surveys; in other countries mapping has been done by similar organizations, or at the worst, brief descriptions may be found in the technical journals. Depending on how thoroughly the region has been studied in the past, the available information may vary from extremely sketchy to highly detailed. Even though the area has been carefully mapped, the geologist will want to see some of the principal exposures himself, particularly unaltered rocks at a distance from mineralization, for an acquaintance with the fresh originals is usually essential to a recognition of the altered phases.

If the broader structure of the district has not already been deciphered, it will be well to do enough work of a reconnaissance nature to determine the general character of the rocks and their mutual relationships. The distance afield and the degree of detail to which this work is eventually pursued will depend on what bearing it may have on the problem of the ore deposit. Hence it is best to limit reconnaissance to a day or two in a car or on horseback, resuming this phase of the investigation later when a more advanced study of the ore deposit has shown what questions need to be answered.

A view of the region from the air is well worth the hire of a plane for an hour or two; it gives a comprehensive idea of the topography which can be obtained in no other way, and it often discloses broad geological features which would otherwise appear only after a protracted campaign of mapping.

Surface vs. Underground Mapping

The amount of surface mapping to be done at the outset may of course depend somewhat on the calendar and the climate. At high altitudes in Alaska the field season is extremely short, and surface work must be done within a two-month period or not at all; in most parts of Canada mapping progresses most rapidly during the few weeks between the melting of the snow and the appearance of the leaves (and incidentally of the "bush insects"). In sub-tropical climates, as in northern Mexico, the most favorable season is the winter, both for personal comfort and efficiency and for visibility in the brush covered slopes of the barranca country. Thus, under certain conditions, it may be advisable to gather all surface data that may be of possible use before the weather makes it difficult to get.

Surface and underground mapping supplement each other. On the surface the rocks are more weathered than in underground workings, yet weathering is not an unmixed curse; such features as bedding in shale, or breccia textures in volcanics, are sometimes visible only on weathered surfaces. Outcrops usually expose the rock less continuously than mine workings, yet such exposures as there are often fill gaps in the evidence from underground, for they are apt to be in places where the rocks are least likely to have underground workings beneath them. The mine workings, on the other hand, following zones of alteration, expose rocks which, unless silicified, are likely to have poor outcrops.

In short, maps of the surface and of the underground workings will both be needed, but whether the surface is mapped immediately or upon completion of the underground work will depend on climatic conditions and especially on what light it is likely to shed on problems of ore occurrence.

SURFACE MAPPING

Methods of mapping surface geology are described in many articles and textbooks which present excellent counsel and worth-while advice. But most of these writings, not being primarily for the mining geologist, devote their attention mainly to mapping on scales which, from his point of view, would be regarded as suitable only for rapid reconnaissance. Accurate location of significant features is essential for mining purposes; yet a balance between precision and speed may be gained by giving intelligent attention to *consistent* accuracy. Nothing is gained, for example, by measuring the position of an instrument station to an accuracy of a hundredth of a foot if it is to be used for locating points which can be plotted only to the nearest two feet.

Degree of Precision

The mining geologist's conception of detailed mapping is of quite a different order from that of the government geologist. An inch to a thousand feet, or the British Geological Survey's six miles to the inch, which government geologists would regard as a very large scale, are small scales for mining purposes and suitable only to generalized mapping. Accordingly the order of precision in measurement is quite different for the two types of work. On a scale of an inch to a mile a point can hardly be plotted to an accuracy closer than 40 feet, but this margin of error on the larger scales of mine maps would amount to something in the neighborhood of an inch. Furthermore, for academic purposes, the exact location of a contact is not significant so long as the general form of the contact and thicknesses of formations are correctly shown; but in mining work an error of a few feet in the location of a vein may raise questions of ownership or may cause a diamond drill hole to miss an oreshoot.

Choice of Scales

The scale of surface maps will depend on the purpose which they are intended to serve and the area to be covered. Large-scale maps covering the area over the mine workings will be on the same scale as the underground maps (p. 165). The surface is the top level of the mine, and a map uniform in scale and orientation with the set of underground maps permits drawing of cross sections and furnishes data to supplement and complete them.

Smaller-scale maps are used to cover an area extending a mile or a few miles from the workings. Their purpose is to show the relations of other veins and orebodies to the one in question and to depict the broader distribution and structure of the rocks. These maps are usually on a scale of 100 down to 500 or, exceptionally, 1000 feet to the inch.

Maps on a still smaller scale, one or two miles to the inch, comparable to those prepared by government surveys, are made for mining purposes only when the most generalized reconnaissance geology of a large area is required as "background."

Isolation of Outcrops

It is essential not only to locate the significant features accurately but to indicate clearly the areas in which no information can be obtained. Therefore, except under special circumstances, surface mapping for mining purposes should always be done by the "multiple exposure method,"

otherwise known as "isolation of outcrops," which consists in drawing in
the boundaries of all exposures, thus separating rock outcrops from concealed ground; geology only within the outcrops is mapped. Thus the
map consists of a series of islands surrounded by white space. Definite

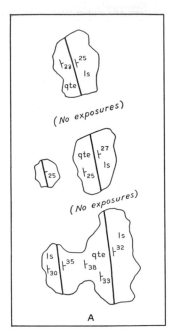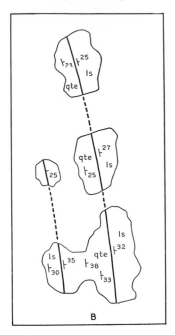

Fig. 1—Part of a map made by the "multiple exposure" method.
A: Observations as mapped. B: Contacts interpolated.

geological observations will be plotted only within the islands; the white
space will show only notes as to the probable nature of underlying rock
together with dotted lines indicating the inferred positions of contacts.
This method permits a ready distinction between observed and inferred
data [12] and has an important negative value [13] in indicating where veins
or contacts cannot possibly exist, thus placing limits on interpretation.

Although no observations are shown as facts in the white areas outside the outcrops, it is advantageous to plot the inferred position of contacts in tentative form before leaving the field, where visible topographic
features or the nature of the soil or rock fragments may serve as an aid
to conjecture. Where faulting is at all prevalent, the location of gullies
or of linear areas covered with soil under which faults may possibly exist
should be recorded.

[12] See pages 1 and 2.
[13] Cf. Irving, J. D., Substructure of geological reports: Economic Geology, 1913, vol. 8, p. 92.

Instruments and Equipment

For putting surface geology on the map, the most convenient instrument is a plane-table with telescopic alidade and stadia rod.

In place of stadia equipment, an open-sight alidade can produce sufficiently accurate results in the hands of a skilful worker, but it requires an excessive number of set-ups because points must be located either by taping, which limits the length of sights, or by intersection, which entails two sights from different set-ups for every point that is located.

The more rough-and-ready method of pace-and-compass traverse is not nearly accurate enough unless the topographic base map is highly detailed and shows identifiable points at close intervals.

So far as accuracy is concerned, a transit is equal to a plane-table but is not superior unless the distances between set-ups are measured by taping. Points for set-ups located by stadia are likely to be less accurate than similar points located by resection, a method to which the plane-table is admirably adapted but the transit is not. Many engineers prefer a transit to a plane-table but this is usually because they are not sufficiently experienced with the plane-table to take advantage of the many short-cuts and time-saving methods which it permits. It is prevalent belief that a plane-table cannot be used in wooded country, but experience shows that this impression is mistaken; a plane-table can be set up anywhere that a transit can. Bush may make the triangulation station invisible from a particular set-up, in which case the plane-table loses one of its advantages, but it is still as accurate as a transit, and side-shots can be plotted much faster.

Only in very rainy country is the plane-table inferior to the transit. Even so the plane-table can be made to serve by protecting it with an umbrella or canopy and using rough-surfaced celluloid sheets instead of paper.

The type of plane-table to be selected is largely a matter of individual taste. Personally, I find that a tripod equipped with the transit type of head is quicker to set up than either the Bumstead or the Johnson mechanism. An erect-reading alidade is easier to aim than an inverting one, although it transmits less light. A vertical arc that is visible from the eyepiece end of the instrument is a little more convenient than one that must be read from the side.

The rod that is available around a survey office is usually a levelling rod, which is quite unsuited to stadia work. Even rods made for stadia purposes are often unnecessarily heavy and not of the best design for long readings. A very satisfactory rod can be made by having the mine carpenter cut and plane a board ten feet long, four inches wide, and half an inch thick.   It is painted white, and then a design is put on it in black paint; additional colors are of little use, for red cannot be distinguished from black at a distance; figures have short visibility and lead to mistakes.   The most quickly legible design consists of a series of diamonds and triangles each 0.2 or 0.4 foot high.   These can be read by interpolation with an accuracy of 0.05 foot, corresponding to five feet of distance for long shots and with considerably better accuracy for short shots; for sights of under 1000 feet they can be read when only part of the rod is visible.   For short jobs, when there was not time for paint to dry, I have made a very serviceable rod by tacking squares and triangles of tar paper to a board.

Drawing paper, cloth-mounted, is used for plane-table sheets, and if it is tinted green or brown it relieves the eyes of painful glare.   Points are plotted with a hard pencil, 3H to 6H.   Strikes are plotted in the field with a protractor.

Topographic Base

As a base a topographic map of some sort is usually essential.   The accuracy and interval of contours, however, will depend on the geography and physiography.   In regions of gentle folding, where the dips are relatively flat, elevations are of great significance, and, if the country is at all rugged, the mapping gives only a misleading picture of the structure unless the topography is accurate.   On the other hand, where folding is tight and dips are steep, minor elevations make relatively little difference in the structural picture.   In much of the pre-Cambrian of

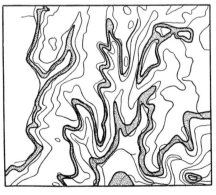

| A | B |

Fig. 2—Map showing gently dipping beds outcropping on uneven topography. A: Consistent accuracy between geology and topography. B: Topography less accurate than geology, giving erroneous impression that beds are folded.

the Canadian Shield, where the structure is on end and the difference in elevation between swamps and knolls amounts to little more than a hundred feet, it is hardly necessary to use contour maps except on the largest scales around important outcrops.

Under average conditions some contouring is required. There should be reasonable consistency between the precision of contouring and the precision of geologic mapping, otherwise weird and misleading effects are produced. (See Fig. 2) In B the false impression of irregularity of bedding is given by the attempt to map the contact with more precision than the accuracy of the contours permits, or, otherwise stated, the accuracy of the topography is insufficient for the geological detail.

Whether topography and geology should be mapped together will depend on the talent available and the value of the geologist's time. The aggregate amount of work is less if the contours are sketched in as the geology progresses; [14] the points used for geologic locations with a few additional shots on ridges and gulleys will serve for topographic control. This method, however, necessitates reading vertical angles and computing elevations for all sights, thus seriously retarding the geological phase of the work. So far as the geologist's own time is concerned, it is preferable to have a surveyor map the topography before geologic mapping commences.

For control, some system of accurately fixed points is necessary. Where the area to be mapped is small, the corners of patented claims which have been established by transit survey may be used, but in larger areas the control should be a triangulation system laid out accurately by transit from a carefully measured base line.[15]

Cerro de Pasco Method

General Features

The procedures used in plane-table mapping are described in most texts on surveying and on field geology. A variety of methods or combinations of methods may be used under varying circumstances and according to the preferences of the worker. It will be sufficient here to describe a particular method which provides a desirable combination of speed and accuracy under average conditions. I was introduced to it by Donald H. McLaughlin twenty years ago in Peru, and while it prob-

[14] For some useful hints, see Pelton, E. F., and Irwin, D. D., The plane table in geologic mapping (Discussion): *Economic Geology*, vol. 7, 1912, pp. 781–782.

[15] Methods for triangulation are described in texts on surveying listed at the end of the chapter.

ably did not originate there, it will be convenient to refer to it as the Cerro de Pasco method. It is a combination of standard plane-table methods which involves locating plane-table stations of the "first order" by resection from triangulation points and locating stadia stations of the "second order" from first order points. From each plane-table station,

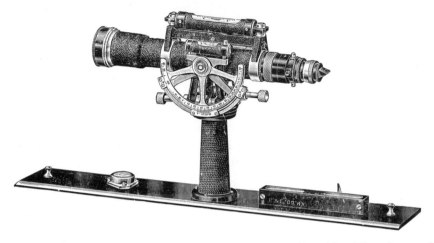

Fig. 3—Telescopic alidade for use with plane table. (*Courtesy of* Keuffel and Esser Company.)

geological points are located by short stadia shots. Since the table is always oriented by backsighting, "trial orientations" and locations by the three-point method are rarely necessary.

The method has only two disadvantages. The first is not serious: To begin work in any portion of the area it is necessary to climb up to a triangulation station. The second is that the geologist cannot sketch observations directly on the map. But he is never far from his map and can plot the geology on it from his notes while still in sight of the points he has located.

The locations of plane-table set-ups are accurate to within the thickness of a pencil line and any errors show up immediately. The sources of error which might be introduced by stadia traversing and compass orientation are avoided, as are the sources of delay in trial orientation, in solving the three-point problem, and in reading the vertical arc of the alidade (unless topography is being mapped along with geology).

Detailed Procedure

When you begin to map an area, select a series of points for plane-table "set-ups of the first order." Each of them should command a good view of the part of the area to be mapped. Mark each with a stake or other permanent landmark. Instruct a rodman to give sights on these in succession and then set up the plane-table on a triangulation station (A, Figure 4). To orient the table, lay the ruler-edge of the alidade on the line on the map connecting this triangulation point (which we will call No. 1) with another (preferably a distant one) and rotate the table until the vertical cross hair of the alidade bisects the distant station. Then clamp the table so that it will not rotate any farther and check the orientation by sighting on a third triangulation point. You are now ready to take a sight to establish the direction of the first substation (call it point A). Keeping the ruler-edge of the alidade on the point representing Triangulation Station No. 1 and using this point as a pivot, rotate the alidade until the cross hair bisects the stake, or the rod held on it, at point A. Draw a line (A-1) along the ruler-edge, extending the line the full length of the ruler or to the edge of the map, as a long line will give you an accurate backsight. While the rodman is moving from one point to the next it is helpful to take a number of sights on prominent rocks, claim-corners, and other landmarks which can later be located by triangulation from other stations.

You are now ready to move to the first substation. On arriving there, orient the table as before by placing the ruler-edge of the alidade on the line that was drawn from Triangulation Point No. 1 and turning the table until the cross hair bisects the triangulation point. Clamp the table. Then find the location of Point A by placing the edge of the alidade on the point indicating a second triangulation station and rotating it around this point until the cross hair cuts the second station. Draw a line along the ruler-edge, and the intersection of this line with the foresight line from Station 1 will be the location of Substation A. Check this location by placing the alidade on the point representing Triangulation Station 3 and drawing a line. If the location is correct, this line will pass through the intersection of the other two. Failing this, the three lines will form a "triangle of error" whose size will indicate the amount of inaccuracy and call for checking the orientation and sights. Assuming that the base map is correct, the error can be caused only by inaccurate orienting or by careless drawing of the lines from the resecting stations.

From the substation the surrounding geologic features are put in by stadia measurements, which give all the accuracy required provided the sights are not too long or too highly inclined.

The minimum crew consists of a geologist and an instrument man. The geologist carries a stadia rod and moves about freely making notes and observations. When he wishes to have a point located he sets up

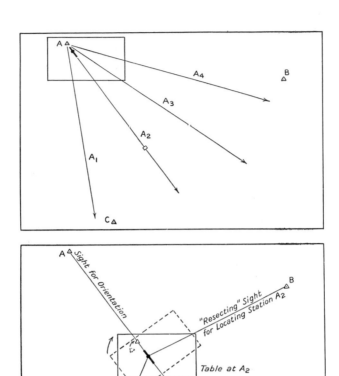

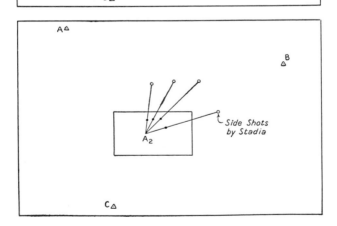

Fig. 4—Method of plane-table mapping by resection.   (*See* text.)

the rod. The instrument man places the alidade on the line, reads the distance between the stadia hairs and immediately signals "all right," leaving the drawing of the line of sight and the plotting of the distance until after the rodman has been released from his position. The instrument man numbers the points in succession, the geologist numbering his notes similarly. At every fourth or fifth point they should check by calling or signalling to make sure that they agree on the numbering.

Where necessary, the stadia reading is corrected for inclination, using a stadia table or a stadia slide-rule. The instrument man will soon learn what combination of angle and distance requires correction; no horizontal correction is necessary for short sights unless they are highly inclined. For instance, on a 200-foot sight the correction for 13° amounts to 5 feet. If a vein is being located, the correction needs to be made; if the point is only the margin of an outcrop which is not significant within 10 feet, an accurate correction is a waste of time.

After locating all the essential points within easy reach of the substation, the geologist returns to the instrument and plots his observations. This is always done before moving to the next station so that errors or inconsistencies can be checked or omissions that appear on the map can be filled in.

After the day's field work the permanent lines are inked in black, or in the appropriate color, and symbols and notes are re-lettered with ink. For several reasons it is advisable to do this inking before going into the field again: pencil notes may be blurred by subsequent work, errors and omissions may show up when the map is inked, and the trend of geologic structure becomes more apparent when the boundaries are emphasized by ink and color.

Personnel

As mentioned above, the minimum crew consists of a geologist and an instrument man. If no technically trained partner is available to operate the plane-table, the geologist can do his own instrument work, though at a considerable expense of time. He takes the rodman with him as he makes his circuit of geological observation and then returns to the instrument to take sights while the rodman repeats the circuit.

A larger party is more efficient. Two geologists making circuits on opposite sides of the set-up can keep an instrument man busy without seriously delaying each other. In countries where labor is not too expensive, it pays to have a rodman for each geologist; the rodman can be giving a sight while the geologist is making a new observation. Still another helper who can hold the rod for backsights and foresights or trim out brush when required can often save the party a great deal of time.

Other Methods

Hanover Method

The Hanover method described by Schmitt [16] is similar to the Cerro method except that points for plane-table set-ups are established by transit traverse between the triangulation points. This has advantages where visibility is poor or where accurate elevations are essential.

Transit instead of Plane-Table

The geologist sometimes finds himself in a situation where a plane-table is not available. Small companies do not always feel able to afford expensive instruments for a short job, or the geologist may be overtaken by the need of mapping in an outlying camp where he does not have his equipment with him. In such cases a transit is often available and can be pressed into service. Under these conditions it is best to put in an extra number of points by triangulation and establish substations by stadia location. If the triangulated points are not too far apart and the traverse is closed between them, the accuracy can be kept within satisfactory limits. I have, on occasion, used a method analogous to resection by carrying a map pinned to a board and plotting transit bearings with a protractor in the absence of an alidade. For short side-shots, an improvised open-sight alidade may be used for bearing, measuring distances by stadia through the transit-telescope.

Grid Methods

Some geologists prefer to be free of instruments while mapping. This can be arranged if identifiable points are established close enough together. For large-scale mapping Schmitt [17] recommends a grid system made by laying out squares 50 feet or 100 feet on a side and marking the corners with numbered stakes. Mapping within the grid is done by compass and tape. Similarly, H. J. C. Connolly mapped an intricate contact at the Coniaurum mine by having the surveyor lay off the outcrop in 25 foot squares, dropping a wooden tag at each intersection. The grid was run very rapidly and probably took less of the surveyor's time than would have been the case if he had been standing by to take sights as the geology progressed.

Grid methods become inevitable in thick bush where lines must be cut out for sighting. The lines are usually laid out on parallel bearings—

---

[16] Schmitt, Harrison, Cartography for mining geology: *Economic Geology*, vol. 27, 1932, p. 722.

[17] *Ibid.*, p. 724.

the most economical interval is usually 200 feet—and each line marked with stakes at 100-foot intervals.

If the foliage is thick there is a special method that requires a minimum of trimming out provided the sun is shining. The plane-table is set up on a station; a second instrument man, using a compass, goes to another point measured 100 feet ahead along the cut line. The geologist disappears into the bush in search of outcrops. When he wishes a point located he reflects the sun toward the instrument man's eyes with a mirror. While the instrument man is taking a sight on the mirror the compass man also takes a bearing on it and calls off the reading to the instrument man who plots the point formed by the intersection of the alidade line and the compass bearing. Sights of 100 feet or less can easily be taken in this way where a stadia rod could not possibly be read.

Air Photographs

Airplane photographs make the best possible base for mapping surface geology for scales of 500 ft. to the inch and smaller; some geologists who have used them declare that mapping without them is a shocking waste of time. Some of the advantages of airplane photographs over topographic maps are: greater speed and economy of preparation (except where the area is very small), abundance of landmarks (some but not all, readily identifiable), and capability of revealing geological features not recognizable on the ground. Lines of faulting, for instance, are often revealed by differences in vegetation and soil color. The geology sometimes shows up in surprising ways; geologists in South Africa noticed that dikes appeared on the air photos as pockmarked areas. Investigation showed that the pockmarks were ant-bear holes. It turned out that the dikes were more thoroughly decomposed and moister than the surrounding rocks, therefore more hospitable to ants and more attractive to ant-bears.

Even though it may not divulge any geological features, an airplane photograph provides an excellent record of the topography. The relief shows up best when the photographs are viewed in pairs through a stereoscope.

The actual taking of air photographs is a specialist's job and should be done by one of the companies thoroughly experienced and equipped for this type of work.[18] The geologist, however, should know something of the process of aerial photography.

In making aerial photographs the pilot flies over the area, following

[18] Commercial companies in the United States include: Fairchild Aerial Surveys, Incorporated, Los Angeles, California; Edgar Tobin Aerial Surveys, Inc., San Antonio, Texas; Abrams Aerial Surveys, Lansing, Michigan; Aero Service Corporation, Philadelphia; and Holmberg Aerial Survey Co., Chicago, Illinois.

equally spaced parallel lines, taking special care to fly a straight course and avoid tilt and variation in altitude. The photographer operates a special camera equipped to make exposures automatically at regular intervals. The intervals are pre-determined in accordance with the ground-speed of the plane so that each exposure overlaps the previous one by about 60%. Each traverse across the area results in a series of photographs called a strip; the traverses are so spaced that the strips overlap each other by about 25%. Each exposure records the position of a compass dial and bears a number.

After the negatives are developed the photographs are corrected, if necessary, for tilt and for differences in scale due to variation in altitude by re-photographing accompanied by slight reduction or enlargement as required. They are then fitted together into a mosaic by cutting out the central portion of each photograph and piecing these portions together, adjusting where necessary to fit into a control established by ground survey or triangulation.

For use in mapping country that is not too rugged, the actual photographs, either contact prints or enlargements, printed on rough-finish paper, are taken into the field. Geology is usually sketched directly on the prints, though some geologists use a cover-sheet of transparent paper. A small plane-table may be used for location, but this is not necessary if trees, bushes, mine dumps, and other landmarks are close enough together to afford an accurate location.

In mountainous country the difference in distance from the camera to the hilltops and the valley bottoms may cause serious local variation in scale. In this case it is necessary to make a topographic map from the photographs, adjusting for variation in scale. Thus part of the advantage of the air photograph is lost. Nevertheless, by employing an ingenious and complex stereoscopic instrument, contour maps of high precision can be made from air photographs at a cost much lower than can be achieved by ground-survey methods.

In the United States, especially in the West, airplane photographs

---

Fig. 5 (opposite)—Airplane photograph of part of the Inyo Range (T16S, R38E), Inyo County, California. The scale of the photograph is approximately one inch to two thousand feet. North is toward the bottom of the page. Shows sedimentary beds and volcanic flows (*cf.* Knopf, A., U.S.G.S. *Professional Paper 110*, Plate II). Formations, from lower left to upper right, are: Pennsylvanian and Permian limestones dipping toward the right (southwest) (light-colored); Triassic shales (light) with layers of massive limestone and conglomerate (dark); Triassic (?) volcanics (dark belt extending diagonally through lower center); Permian shales (light); Tertiary and Quaternary material, showing dissected pattern without discernible bedding. Faulting is present but not obvious in the photograph. (*Courtesy of* Fairchild Aerial Surveys, Inc.)

covering large tracts have been prepared by government agencies. The Department of Agriculture, through both the Agricultural Adjustment Administration and the Soil Conservation Service, has done extensive mapping. The U. S. Forestry Service has mapped large areas of mountain country in Colorado, Idaho, and elsewhere. These agencies supply prints at a very small charge.

UNDERGROUND MAPPING

Mapping underground geology is a blend of art and measurement. The emphasis is strongly on measurement, yet a natural ability to reproduce details accurately by sketching is a useful asset. Some individuals are better endowed in this respect than others, but no one will fail to improve with practice. (For examples of underground geologic mapping, see Plates I, II, and III, following p. 26.)

In order that the map may bear a faithful resemblance to the natural features in the rock, the actual plotting *must* be done underground. The practice of recording dips and strikes in a notebook and plotting them with a straight-edge in the office does not result in a geologic map; it gives merely a cubist's caricature of the structure which, except under the very simplest of conditions, is likely to be misleading.

"It is probably safe to say that natural lines are never straight . . . faults make nearer approaches to straightness than any other lines, but close attention to the ground always reveals slight curved oscillations. . . . In short, if we find ourselves drawing straight lines, or concentric curves, we shall be wise if we scrutinize our map very severely, for we may be tolerably sure that there is something wrong." [19]

The Base Map

The basis for underground mapping is a plan of the workings showing the survey stations and the outlines of drifts and crosscuts. For any but the most generalized work, the sidewall (or, as the miner calls it, the "rib") of the drift must be plotted in detail, not merely ruled in parallel to the line of sight between stations. The elevation of the track under each station should also be shown.

Such a base map will be available in most operating mines as a result of the work of the engineering department. In case it is not, the geologist may have to be his own engineer and prepare his base map by transit and tape according to the methods described in texts on mine survey-

[19] Greenly, Edward, and Williams, Howel, *Methods in Geological Surveying*, pp. 205–207. London: Thos. Murby & Co., 1930; New York: D. Van Nostrand Co., 1930.

ing. (See end of chapter.) For brief examinations or for preliminary work where time is more important than precision of results, a map made with a compass and tape will serve to show the general geological picture, but such a map should not be used for inferences regarding the dip between levels unless the traverse can be closed through raises.

Even if a transit survey is available, the geologist must satisfy himself as to its accuracy, for old maps, and even current ones, sometimes show evidence of laxity in surveying and plotting. Mistakes in distance if they exist will show up in the course of geologic mapping. Errors in bearing are harder to detect unless there are raises between the ends of the drifts, but if a level on a vein does not line up with the others in a cross section, the geologist should check it for a mistake in bearing before he jumps to the conclusion that there is a geological irregularity.

Work Sheets

For underground geologic mapping, a "work sheet" or "field sheet" is traced from the base map. A satisfactory material is a good grade of oiled tracing paper.[20] As an alternate a semi-transparent typewriter paper of 100% rag bond may be used. Tracing cloth is entirely unsuitable for this purpose as it does not take pencil line well and a little water ruins it. Blueprints do not show pencil lines and white prints are soft when they are moist.

Before going underground to start mapping geology, the outline of the workings is traced on sheets of standard size, usually 8½ x 11 inches, allowing an inch or so of overlap at the end of each sheet. As an alternative to standard-sized sheets, a strip 8½ inches wide and several feet in length may be folded accordion-fashion into sections 11 inches long. The workings, survey stations, and coordinates are traced in India ink, and, for convenience in plotting strikes, it is helpful to provide a generous number of north-south lines between the coordinates. If the ink is applied on the reverse side of the sheet, erasures can be made while mapping without destroying the outline of the workings, and furthermore, any geological lines that locally coincide with the wall of the drift can be distinguished. Very little extra time is required if the map is traced in pencil and then turned over for inking. Station numbers and lettering should, of course, appear on the face side of the map.

In order to keep up to date with development and to take advantage of clean exposures near the face, the company geologist may find it desirable to do his mapping before the engineers have had time to sur-

---

[20] Medium weight Colona or Ionic, made by the Keuffel and Esser Company, has proved satisfactory, as it is reasonably waterproof and takes both pencil and ink well.

vey and plot a new advance.   In this case he will have to make his own base map as he goes and later tie it into the new transit stations, locating them on his field sheets before posting the geology on the more accurate office map.

Equipment

The work sheet is held in an aluminum sheet-holder [21] with a hinged cover.   If the mine is at all wet, it is convenient to use a sheet of blotting paper the same size as the sheet-holder; it may be held to the top cover of the sheet-holder by a rubber band, or, as practiced by the geologists at Grass Valley, the blotting paper may be cemented to the lid of the sheet-holder.   At Butte and in other districts, a pencil-holder is riveted to the lower side of the sheet-holder.   It consists of a sheet of leather crimped to make pockets for half a dozen or more pencils; thus hard (3H to 5H) and soft black pencils and a variety of colored pencils are handily available.   Since the pencils must be kept sharp for drawing fine lines, some workers attach a strip of sandpaper to the lower side of the sheet holder.   Even better, according to Farmin, is a magneto-point file which may be laced through the pencil-holder.

For plotting veins and faults, some geologists use colored pencils,[22] which must be kept very sharp by frequent rolling on paper in order to give a fine line.   Others prefer to draw all lines in black, laying on color beside the line if necessary in order to identify it.

Measurements

The features that are to be plotted on the map are located by measuring their distance from a survey station or other accurately located point.   When stations are not too far apart, measurement by pacing may be precise enough for ordinary purposes, but taking into account the time consumed in adjusting small errors of closure, it is not much faster than measuring with a tape, and most geologists find it less satisfactory.

A cloth tape is quite accurate enough for geological locations.   As compared with a steel "chain" it is easier to read, less subject to snarling or kinking and less dangerous near trolley wires.   In measuring, one of a number of routines may be followed, depending largely on personal preference:

[21] The sheet-holder should be black enameled since uncoated aluminum soils and mars the sheets.—Schmitt, Harrison, personal letter.

[22] Farmin recommends for the blue, Golden Swan 8888 (Swan Pencil Co.) and for the red, Dixon Anadel, 1740.   For color conventions, see p. 170.

1. Stretch the tape out on the floor of the drift and glance down to read it whenever a location is needed. However, if the floor is muddy the tape soon gets illegibly dirty. Accordingly a modification of the method, practicable only where there is timber, is to hang the tape over nails or brackets.

2. Hang the zero end of the tape on a nail or hook opposite the survey station and carry the reel end. The chief inconvenience here is that the geologist already has more equipment and instruments in his hands than he can juggle; furthermore, if he has to move back and forth along the drift he must be constantly winding and unwinding the tape in order to keep it off the floor.

3. Do the measuring in advance of mapping, placing numbers on the wall in chalk or lamp smoke at ten-foot intervals. A stitch sewed into the tape at each ten-foot mark can be felt with the fingers and thus saves looking for the figures in the semi-darkness. For most purposes, location of points between the ten-foot marks can be judged by eye with an error of one foot or less, but, if a feature must be located more accurately than this, a small tape or a graduated hammer-handle may be used.

If necessary, the geologist can do the measuring and marking by himself but he can save time by borrowing one, or preferably two, helpers who can be released to other duties as soon as a length of drift sufficient to keep the geologist busy for a day has been measured off.

On the map, the 10-foot intervals are marked off with a scale, and for ordinary purposes the scale need not be used further in the mapping. Thus one more instrument is in the pocket and out of the way.

Washing Walls

Since the walls of mines are usually covered with dust and smoke, it is a regular practice in many mines to wash them before mapping. As Brock [23] says: "The cost is a mere trifle in comparison to the amounts spent on blind crosscutting, drifting and drilling." This method not only saves a great deal of the geologist's time, which would otherwise be consumed in chipping the rocks, but reveals structures which would be missed entirely if the walls were concealed. Washing alone, without the assistance of geology, has been known to disclose the tail of an orebody that had previously been overlooked. Where running water is piped through the workings for supplying leyner drills, washing is not difficult to arrange. For use in places where excess water would flow into stopes and cause trouble, W. H. Pritchard and I devised an airspray constructed somewhat on the plan of a Bunsen burner. Just enough water is fed into the nozzle to make a dense fog and change the dust to thin mud which is blown off by the force of the compressed air.

[23] Brock, R. W., Scientific ore finding: *Economic Geology*, vol. 19, 1924, p. 675.

In crosscuts it is usually sufficient to wash a horizontal strip a foot wide on one or both walls; in drifts where a vein is exposed it is best to wash the back.

If rocks are not perfectly exposed or if features are hard to decipher, it is well to trace out contacts in advance of mapping and outline them in chalk or lamp-smoke. This leaves the geologist's hands and mind free to concentrate on the mapping itself without interruption.

Plane of Projection

In mapping a level, it is important to project all geological features to a uniform horizontal plane, and this necessity takes on special importance if fractures or bedding have a gentle dip. The plane is usually the height of the observer's belt (which is half the height of a standard square set for stope floors), though some prefer breast height.

Under special conditions, however, it is advisable to use the elevation of the back of the drift as a plane for mapping. This is especially true if the features to be mapped appear to best advantage in the back. Suppose, for example, the mineralization follows gently pitching folds which are cut by faults dipping flatly in the opposite direction. If you were mapping waist high, the fold might appear on your map some ten feet from where you observe it in the back, while a fracture might appear ten feet away in the opposite direction. In order to put these features on your map, you would be constantly solving problems in descriptive geometry, but by making a plan of the vein as it appears overhead, you can map what you see and not what you imagine. If this datum is used, however, it is important to make some such note as "plane mapped is back." However, where most of the features are steep and moderately regular, the projection involves little opportunity for error, and the waist-high plane can be used consistently. No matter what plane is used, the geologist should not neglect to examine the wall from top to bottom. Everyone sees the upper part of the face, but too few people bend over to look at the lower part of a drift.

Where veins or beds dip gently, say 30 degrees or less, any irregularities show up in exaggerated form on a plan, and to map them accurately requires projection for many feet beyond the limit of workings. While such projections are necessary if the geology is to be shown on plans at all, the simplest way to record data in such cases is to do the mapping in section, or to carry both a plan and a section as the mapping proceeds.

Taking Dips and Strikes

The method of measuring the attitude of any structural plane such as a bed, vein, fault or fracture will be familiar to every geologist, but

100 feet

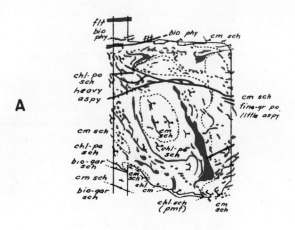

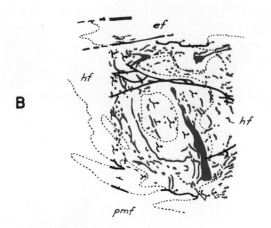

PLATE II

Two maps of a stope in the Homestake Mine, Lead, South Dakota.
A—Observed features. B—Generalized Map. *Courtesy of* J. A.
Noble, Homestake Mining Company.

PLATE I

GEOLOGIC MAP

OF

PART OF A LEVEL OF A MINE

Courtesy of Rollin Farmin

Scale ~ 1": 50'

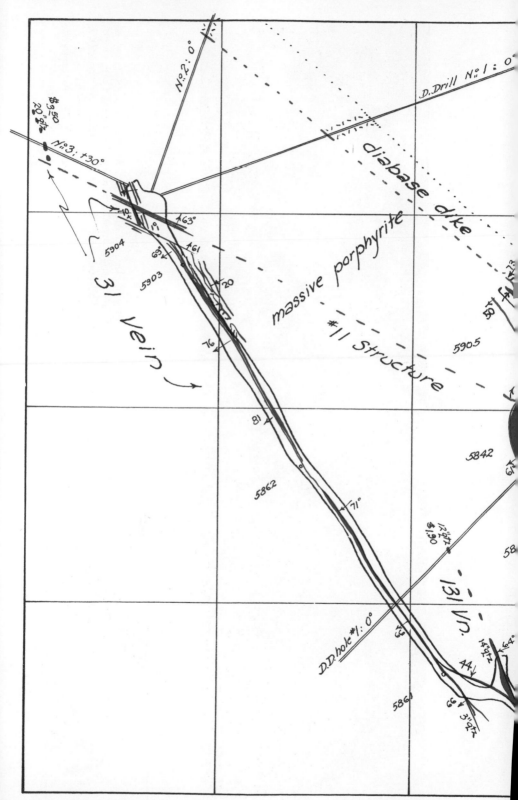

PLATE III

An example of detailed mapping. Above is a photograph of the wall of a stope in the Homestake Mine, Lead, South Dakota. The horizontal distance is 68 feet. At the left is a detailed map of exactly the same area. *Courtesy of J. A. Noble, Homestake Mining Company. Note:* Arsenopyrite (blue dots) was shown in green on the original map.

there are a few tricks that are especially applicable to underground work. To describe the methods we might assume that the strike and dip of a fracture are to be measured.

The *strike* may be taken if (a) the traces of the fracture appear on both walls, (b) the fracture is visible in the back, or (c) the rock has broken in such a way as to expose the surface of the fracture.

(a) If the fracture is visible on both walls, stand with your back to one wall and the back of your head against the fracture. Select a point just level with your eye on the fracture as it appears in the opposite wall. In case the dip of the fracture is gentle, it may be advisable to select this point accurately by setting the clinometer of the compass at zero and using it as a level. When the point has been selected, sight on it with the compass and read the bearing. A much quicker but less accurate method is to stand with your elbow against the fracture and "shoot from the hip."

(b) If the fracture is exposed in the back or roof, hold the compass vertically below it and parallel to it and read the bearing.

(c) If the surface of the fracture is exposed, hold the compass horizontal, with its edge against the fracture, and read the needle. In case the dip is gentle, an error may be introduced by failure to hold the compass perfectly level, *i.e.*, the compass may touch the rock surface along a line which is not exactly horizontal. This error may be avoided by first finding the line of true dip by using the compass as a clinometer in the manner to be described shortly, marking this line by a scratch on the rock if necessary. The strike may then be taken accurately by holding the compass horizontal, with its edge touching the rock along a line at right angles to the dip line.

Another way to take the strike of an exposed rock surface is to stand across the drift from the exposure and, holding your lamp at the level of your eye, move it back and forth until it just fails either to illuminate the surface or to cast a dark shadow on it. Standing with your eye in the position that the lamp occupied, you can then take a bearing horizontally across to the fracture.

In order to have a check on your plotting, it is well to observe the footage at which the fracture intersects each wall. In fact, some geologists plot fractures without the use of a compass, using merely the footages on the two walls. This is quite sufficient for some purposes, but when the strikes are critical data, the combined methods afford a double check.

In mines where local magnetic attraction makes compass readings unreliable, the strike can be measured by reading the magnetic bearing of the fracture and then, holding the compass in the same place, taking the magnetic bearing of the center line of the drift.[24] An alternative

[24] Schmitt, Harrison, On mapping underground geology: *Engineering and Mining Journal*, 1936, vol. 137, p. 558.

method is to measure the strike with a large clinometer or protractor from a string stretched between two survey plugs.

Dips are measured with the clinometer that forms part of the Brunton compass. Beginners should, perhaps, be reminded that only in the special case in which the strike is at right angles to the drift does the trace of the fracture as it appears in the wall ever represent the true dip; hence, in all cases it is necessary to take the strike into account when measuring the dip. If the fracture is exposed on both walls, place your eye in the projection of the plane of the fracture (as explained in the directions for measuring the strike) and, holding the instrument at arm's length, line its edge in with the trace of the fracture.

If the rock has broken away from one side of a fracture in such a manner as to expose its surface, the dip may be taken by holding the compass edge against the actual fracture plane. If the dip is very gentle, a significant error may be introduced by failure to have the compass in a truly vertical plane. In order to avoid this error, rotate the compass through a small arc, keeping its edge against the rock surface. The maximum inclination that you read will be the true dip.

Sometimes an accurate measurement must be made of the dip of a structural plane which is not exposed in vertical section. Suppose, for example, that a vein appears in the back (roof) of a drift and also on the lower part of the wall. The measurement may be made by stretching a string from a nail driven into a crack in the rock, at the edge of the vein in the back, down to the corresponding part of the vein on the side of the drift. The inclination of the string is then measured. The place at which the lower end of the string should be attached may be found by describing a circle on the wall with the lower end of the string and picking the lowest point on the circle. Another method of measuring the dip is to suspend a plumb bob from the vein in the back and measure the horizontal distance from the plumb line to the lower segment of the vein. The length of the plumb line divided by the horizontal measurement will be the tangent of the angle of dip.

After taking the necessary readings, the vein or fracture is then plotted on the map with a protractor. The alternative procedure, sketching the fracture and noting its strike with the idea of doing the actual plotting later in the office, is amateurish and usually a confession that the observer has not acquired the manual skill necessary to deal with lamp, map, pencil, and protractor using only the available two hands; only by plotting it on the spot can its correct relation to other features be accurately recorded. It is well to write down the strike in figures in addition to plotting it for several reasons: it affords a check against mistakes in plotting, it provides a better basis for projection of the fault than the mere short line appearing on the map, and finally, if a number of parallel fractures have the same strike, the fact is more quickly appreciated.

Most fractures are not plane surfaces but show more or less curvature. If the curvature is less than can be shown on the scale of the map, the method just described is adequate. But if the fracture changes its strike from one side of the drift to the other, this fact needs to be recorded; the strikes on both walls of the drift are measured and plotted, and the two strikes are connected by a curved line resembling as closely as possible the curve which the fracture actually describes. Similarly, branch fractures are sketched in, using their measured strikes as control.

In the case of sedimentary beds, highly accurate measurements of dip and strike may be desirable, particularly if the bedding is uniform over long distances and thus capable of being projected. In highly contorted bedding, however, extremely accurate readings are not significant, since greatly varying dips might be obtained within a foot or two. In such cases the important thing to record is the form of the fold rather than precise readings of dip, for the attitude of the axial plane and the plunge of the axial line are likely to be more significant than the local dip of the bedding.

Mapping Raises

It is usually essential to map raises in order to obtain accurate data for the construction of cross sections. Yet base maps or sections of raises are seldom available; the geologist must make his own base. He can do so most easily by stretching a cord from the top to the bottom of the raise (or between intermediate points if the raise is so crooked that the string touches the walls). The inclination of the string may be measured with a Brunton compass or a clinometer, allowing for sag. In raises of flat inclination it will be necessary to take the bearing of the string as well as its inclination. The detailed shape of the raise may be plotted by measuring the distance from the walls to the string at intervals. Elevations are conveniently determined by suspending a tape in the raise, but if extreme accuracy is not required, the ladder rungs can be counted and the total count corrected to the known distance (horizontal and vertical) between fixed points on the upper and lower levels.

Mapping Stopes

Stopes present special problems in mapping because they are so often irregular in shape and not susceptible to simple representation on either a plan or a section.

When the orebody is on a steep and relatively narrow vein, the available base on which geology may be plotted usually consists of a projection of the stope outlines on a vertical longitudinal section which the engineers bring up to date at monthly or fortnightly intervals. Survey stations (plugs) are sometimes available, but usually they are not.

When mining is by flat-backed stopes, the method of mapping is similar to that in a drift, but the geologist may have to make his own base plans as the engineers do not usually plot stope detail on horizontal sections. When mining is by rilled stopes, *i.e.*, where the back is inclined rather than horizontal, the geologist must locate himself by making measurements between points which are usually not at the same elevation. This requires measurement of the inclination of the line by sighting with a Brunton compass or, for more accurate work, by stretching a mason's cord between the points and measuring its bearing and inclination with a hanging ("German") compass[25] and inclinometer. Measuring the bearing as well as the inclination is necessary, of course, wherever the line that has been taped is not parallel to the plane of projection. Plotting the geology will require the construction of horizontal projections at successive elevations or of vertical cross sections at successive coordinates, depending on the attitude of exposures and the structure of the vein.

Broad stopes necessitate locations in two horizontal dimensions as well as in the vertical. This is essential for plotting geology even when plans of the stope-outline at successive floors are available. I have found that for mapping broad flat-backed stopes a small plane table with an open-sight alidade is very convenient. The procedure is much as in surface mapping except that the distances are always measured by tape.

In stopes timbered with square-sets, the mapping is greatly simplified, since the timbering provides a three-dimensional coordinate system. Schmitt found that even in this case, however, it is sometimes necessary to measure the position of each floor with a string compass. In Butte and other districts where square-set stopes are numerous, the usual practice is to map the stopes on standard sheets of coordinate paper

[25] Schmitt gives directions for converting a Brunton compass into a hanging compass for this purpose in his article, On mapping underground geology: *Engineering and Mining Journal*, 1936, vol. 137, p. 558.

using a sheet for each stope floor. The sheets when assembled in a loose-leaf binder form a series of horizontal sections at regular vertical intervals, usually 7.7 or 8 feet.

A stope on a bed or vein which is gently inclined calls for some contemplation in order to determine the best method of portraying the geology. If the ore layer is regular in dip and strike, the simplest picture may be a projection in the plane of the inclined layer, but if the layer is folded or warped, this scheme is unsatisfactory. The alternative, projection to a horizontal or a vertical plane, is more practical but demands a considerable amount of descriptive geometry or trigonometry, because most of the measurements have to be made along inclined lines. James[26] has devised what he calls the "profile technique" for mapping horizontal and vertical projections of room and pillar stopes in the flattish limestone replacement deposits in New Mexico, and this method with appropriate modifications can be used in a wide variety of inclined stopes. It has the great advantage that plans and sections can be plotted underground without delaying completion of the maps pending office computations. Furthermore, the graphic solution of the three-dimensional problem remains on record in systematic form. The essential features of the technique are that (1) measurements in the stope are made by means of tapes stretched between wall points and temporarily fixed in positions, horizontal or inclined as circumstances dictate, and (2) the vertical and horizontal distances between the points are ascertained by plotting a profile at the side of the map as the work proceeds. On the profile (not to be confused with a vertical section) the measured lines are plotted in their true length and inclination so that each point on the line appears at its proper elevation.

Figure 6 represents a stope mapped by this method. The distance from X to 1 along the main gallery was measured by stretching a tape between these two points.[27] The length and inclination of the line X–1 were plotted in the profile at the bottom of the sketch, and the horizontal distance between X and 1 was scaled from the profile. Knowing also the bearing of the line X–1, the point 1 was plotted in its true position on the plan. Without removing the tape, a second tape was stretched from point 2 to point 3 in the first room. As it happened, it passed below the first tape at the point *b* (shown on the second tape as *b'*). So the vertical distance between the two tapes was measured and, having

[26] James, Allan Harris, Profile technique useful in mapping stope geology: *Engineering and Mining Journal*, vol. 147, no. 11, November, 1946, pp. 74–75.

[27] For survey stations, lead-headed roofing nails were driven into cracks in the rock. The lead head, by cushioning the hammer blow, lessens the tendency of the nail to bend.

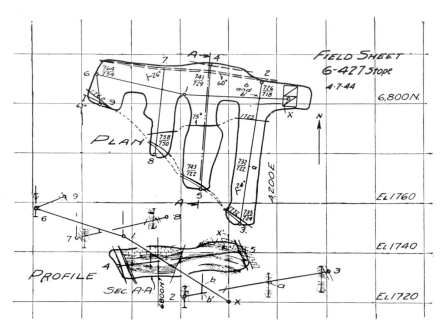

Fig. 6—Profile method of mapping flat stopes. (*After* James, Allan H., *E. and M. J.*).

located *b'*, the line 2–3 could be plotted on the profile.   This permitted scaling the horizontal distance 2–3 and from this and the measured bearing of the line 2–3, the points 2 and 3 were plotted on the plan. It will be noted that this line 2–3 could have been plotted either from right to left or from left to right; which direction is followed does not matter because the horizontal positions of points on the profile are not significant except with respect to the particular lines on which they appear.   However, consistency increases the clarity of the notes.   Here, for example, measurements in the gallery (X–1 and 1–6) are plotted from right to left, while measurements in the rooms (2–3, 4–5, and 7–8) are plotted from left to right.

Intermediate points of geological interest along the line 2–3 were plotted on the profile and then transferred to the plan.   Thus at *a* on the profile there appears a geologic column from roof to floor, and the elevations of the roof and floor are shown in their correct vertical positions.   These elevations, scaled from the profile, have been recorded numerically on the plan as 732 and 722 respectively at the point *a*.

When all data for the first room (2–3) had been recorded, the tape was removed to the second room and the points 4 and 5 established in a similar manner.   At the same time, vertical geological sections such as the one through the room 4–5 were prepared.

One small disadvantage inherent in any horizontal projection of a set of inclined workings is that strikes of features such as the fault shown at points 3, 5, 8 and 9, do not line up, since they are observed at different levels. Despite this disadvantage, it is probably best in the original record to plot such features at the points at which they are observed and with their true strikes. In addition, it may be feasible to measure the bearing of the trace of the fault on some geological surface such as a well-defined roof and plot this in, say, as a dashed line.

Recording Notes

The work sheet is an excellent place for recording incidental notes and making sketch sections of special features. Some restraint should be used, however, when it comes to putting this material on the permanent map. All data which can be shown graphically should be recorded by a convention rather than in words; too much "literature" in the form of long notes and descriptive matter tends to clutter the map with detail and obscure the structural picture. If, for example, the nature of rocks is a subject of mapping, it is best to reduce rock types to a series of categories which can be recorded by abbreviations or conventions. Thus in an igneous rock, grain size and alteration might be expressed in terms of one of a half-dozen standards of classification; "lt grn 2mm cl 3" might mean "light green, grain size 2 millimeters, chloritic alteration of medium intensity." The abbreviated note, always mentioning the features in the same order, not only occupies less space on the map but can be read more quickly than the extended note, once you are accustomed to your own conventions, and it can be given a more quantitative significance than a verbal description.

Reducing features to be mapped to a quantitative basis wherever possible facilitates recording and, what is more important, eliminates the subjective factor. Thus grain size is not just "coarse" or "fine" but is expressed in millimeters or in screen sizes; as standards for comparison, Schmitt[28] has used sands sized by standard Tyler screens and glued to cards. Colors of rocks, limonite gossans, and other materials may be designated by Ridgway standards.[29] Such methods are definitely in line with the present trend toward the quantitative throughout the whole science of geology.

[28] Schmitt, Harrison, Outcrops of ore shoots: *Economic Geology*, vol. 34, 1939, p. 659.
[29] Ridgway, R., *Color Standards and Nomenclature*. Baltimore: A. Hoehn and Co., 1912.

SELECTED REFERENCES

Topographic Mapping

Breed, C. B., and Hosmer, G. L., *Principles and Practice of Surveying* (2 vols.) 7th Edition. New York: John Wiley and Sons, Incorporated, 1938.

Beaman, W. M., *Topographic Instructions of the U.S. Geological Survey.* U.S.G.S. Bulletin 788-E, 1928.

Davis, Raymond E., Foote, Francis S., and Rayner, W. H., *Surveying Theory and Practice,* 2nd Edition. New York: John Wiley & Sons, Inc., 1934.

Airplane Photography

Bagley, Jas. W., *Aerophotography and Aerosurveying,* New York: McGraw-Hill Book Company, Incorporated, 324 pp. 1941.

Cobb, Genevieve C., Bibliography on the interpretation of aerial photographs: *Bull. G.S.A.,* vol. 54, pp. 1195–1210, 1943.

Eardley, A. J., *Aerial Photographs,* New York: Harper and Brothers, 1942.

Hart, Cecil A., *Air Photography Applied to Surveying,* New York: Longmans, Green and Company, 1940.

Loel, Wayne, Use of aerial photographs in geologic mapping: *Tr. A.I.M.E.,* vol. 144, pp. 356–409, 1941.

Smith, H. T. U., *Aerial Photographs and their Applications,* New York: Appleton-Century Company, 1943.

Talley, Benj. B., *Engineering Applications of Aerial and Terrestrial Photogrammetry,* New York: Pitman Publishing Company, 1938.

VanNouhuys, J. J., Geological interpretation of aerial photographs: *A.I.M.E. Tech. Pub. No. 825,* 1937; *Tr. A.I.M.E.,* vol. 126, pp. 607–624, 1937.

Geologic Mapping

Greenly, Edward, and Williams, Howel, *Methods in Geological Surveying,* London: Thos. Murby and Company, 1930; New York: D. Van Nostrand Company, 1930.

Lahee, F. H., *Field Geology,* 4th Edition, pp. 420–426, Geologic Surveying (The Compass and Clinometer), New York: McGraw-Hill Book Company, Incorporated, 1941.

Mather, Kirtley F., Manipulation of the telescopic alidade in geologic mapping: *Bull. Sci. Laboratories of Dennison University,* Grenville, Ohio, vol. 19, pp. 97–142, 1919.

Ransome, F. L., *et al.,* Symposium on geologic mapping. A series of articles in *Economic Geology* through vols. 7 and 8, 1912 and 1913.

Schmitt, Harrison, Cartography for mining geology: *Econ. Geol.,* vol. 27, pp. 716–736, 1932.

Schmitt, Harrison, On mapping underground geology: *Engineering and Mining Journal,* vol. 137, pp. 557–561, November, 1936.

2

Sampling Ore and Calculating Tonnage

Sampling is the process of taking a small portion of an article such that the consistency of the portion shall be representative of the whole.
—Baxter and Parks [1]

ALTHOUGH the usual reason for sampling a mine is primarily economic, the resulting assay returns constitute data of a truly geological character. Only the most pedantic of geologists would scorn assay results as hum-drum pragmatic statistics; the earnest seeker after the truth considers them quite as essential to purely scientific deduction as are mineralogical and petrological observations. Moreover, the results of sampling are much more quantitative in their nature than most other available geologic data. In no other branch of the science does the investigator have before him such a wealth of detailed and accurate information in regard to the distribution of one or more elements throughout a rock mass as does the mining geologist when he studies an assay map.

If geology benefits from sampling, it also contributes to it, for sampling can never be reduced to blind rules of thumb; it must be carried out in conformity with geological principles. Every engineer who does an intelligent job of sampling must adjust his cuts to the structure of the vein and calculate his averages with due regard to the nature of the orebody; otherwise his results can be sadly misleading. Recognizing the intimate relationship between geology and sampling, many mining companies place the sampling crew under the direction of the chief geologist. Even a geologist who does not have supervision of the sampling of an operating mine will have occasion to take plenty of samples

---

[1] Baxter, C. H., and Parks, R. D., *Mine Examination and Valuation.* Houghton: Michigan College of Mines and Technology, 1939.

when he examines prospects.   Therefore he needs an understanding of
the principles of sampling as part of the equipment for the practical
phases of his work.   Indeed a knowledge of these principles is an asset
to any geologist, whether or not he is engaged in mining, for not a few
studies in "pure" geology, especially in the realm of petrography and
stratigraphy, would be better for an application of the philosophy of
sampling and a wider employment of sound sampling technique.

GENERAL PRINCIPLES

An orebody is a mixture of minerals in proportions that vary in different parts of the mass.   As a consequence the proportion of contained metals also varies from place to place.   Therefore, a single sample
taken in any particular place would not contain the same proportion of
metals as does the orebody as a whole except by a highly improbable
coincidence.   The probable error, which would be very large if only
one sample were taken, decreases with the number of samples, but it
never disappears completely unless the samples are so numerous and so
large that their aggregate is equal to the orebody itself, in which case
the orebody would be completely used up in the process of sampling.
Since carrying sampling to such an extreme would defeat its own purpose, some probable error is always present in actual cases and the practical objective is to reduce this probable error to allowable limits.   This
means balancing the number of samples against the desired accuracy;
if there are not enough samples the result is unreliable; if there are too
many, the time and expense of taking them is excessive.

In an actual orebody, the accuracy of sampling depends not alone on
the number of samples but also on proper distribution of them throughout the orebody, for it would obviously be incorrect to take all of the
samples either in a rich part or a lean part.   Therefore it is important
to select the places in such a way that all parts of the orebody will be
represented.

Theoretically it might be permissible to combine all of the samples
into a single composite for assay, but since it is essential to learn not
only the average grade of the whole orebody but the grades of different
parts of it, the common practice is to assay each sample separately and
combine the results by appropriate methods of calculation.

To determine accurately the proper number of samples and the proper
places in which to take them would, in the nature of the case, call for
assumptions as to the values and their distribution—assumptions that
would have no accurate basis until the sampling was completed.   There-

fore there is no infallible way of deciding the matter in advance, although once a reasonable number of samples has been taken it is possible to judge whether or not they are sufficiently numerous and properly placed.

The experience of the profession, in sampling thousands of mines, provides a basis for deciding what the proper position and spacing should be, subject, of course, to modification for any individual mine after taking preliminary samples. This experience has developed methods which eliminate, so far as possible, the personal element in selecting the material that is to constitute the sample. The standard methods of sampling include the use of various types of drills, as discussed in subsequent chapters, but if ore is exposed on the surface or in underground workings, the usual practice is to break out systematically selected portions of it. The conventional method of doing this is by channel sampling.

CHANNEL SAMPLING

This method consists of cutting channels across the face of exposed ore and collecting the resulting chips, fragments, and dust from each channel to make up a sample.

Procedure

Preparing the Surface. Before cutting the sample the exposure has to be cleaned to remove dust, slime and soluble salts.[2] This may be done by washing the rock thoroughly with a hose or scrubbing with a stiff brush. It is usually better, however, to chip off the outer part of the rock along the band within which the sample is to be taken. This is especially true in copper sulphide bodies where a "skin" of post-mine oxidation may have attained a thickness of a large fraction of an inch or, exceptionally, several inches. Moreover, chipping the surface and removing projecting points and ridges prepares a comparatively plane surface in which to cut the sample.

When the surface is clean, the next step is to mark out the location of the channel by inscribing two parallel lines on the rock a few inches apart, using as drawing material the smoke of a carbide lamp or else chalk or paint. The lines should be from three to six inches apart, de-

---

[2] Dust from blasting may contain fine rich sulphides. Efflorescences of metallic salts may penetrate fractured or porous rock to a depth, in extreme cases, of several inches and cause serious errors in sampling. See Roland Blanchard, Chemical migration, post-mine phenomena in New Guinea: *E. & M. J.*, vol. 134, no. 9, p. 365 and no. 10, p. 425.

pending on the nature of the rock and ore. After these preliminaries the job of cutting begins.

Cutting the Channel. The tools are few but formidable: a hammer and a moil. The hammer is a "single jack" three or four pounds in weight. The moil is a piece of drill steel eight to eighteen inches long with one end drawn to a point and tempered. Instead of the hammer and moil a prospector's pick is convenient for very soft rock but it cannot cope with hard vein-matter.[3]

The width and depth of the channel should be as nearly uniform as the nature of the rock permits. To insure uniformity I have, on occasion, used as a gauge a block of wood, say one inch thick and four inches wide. When the block fits into the groove flush with the adjoining rock surface, the width and depth of the channel are accurate. Such ideal width and regularity may not be attainable in blocky ground where the moil unavoidably loosens large chunks. The best remedy in this case is to cut a channel so wide and deep that the irregularities are small in proportion. But in most types of ore, even very hard ore, it is perfectly possible to cut neat, well-defined channels, although this takes time and "elbow grease." Rickard's example in which six men, three of them moiling, took a whole shift to cut a twelve foot length of channel is not extreme where the rock is hard. Far from being a mere ideal to be read about in textbooks, the cutting of good channels has for more than a generation been standard practice among engineers who pride themselves on the thoroughness of their work. The time and expense is fully repaid in accuracy of results.

In some operating mines the sampling process is speeded by using a light air-operated machine-drill equipped with a pointed or chisel-shaped bit. Another method of reducing the labor of chipping off samples makes use of blow torches to heat and crack the rock. A. E. Walker[4] of the M. A. Hanna Company describes the method as follows:

"The method seems to work quite well on any very dense rock, and the principle is similar to making pop-corn. The full force flame of an ordinary gasoline blow torch is held on the rock for a few minutes, and plates or slabs of the material spall off in thicknesses from $\frac{1}{8}''$ to $\frac{1}{4}''$ and a few inches in diameter.

"I designed wire frames to hold the torches at the proper distance from the ore or rock with screen wings on each side, which kept the spalls from flying very far away and from injuring the sample man.

---

[3] See discussion in Rickard, T. A., *Sampling and Estimation of Ore in a Mine*, pp. 17, 145, 213. New York: Hill Publishing Co., 1907.

[4] Personal communication.

"One man can handle two torches at a time on fairly flat outcrops. The process can be speeded up by using hammers before and after the heat is applied."

Collecting the Sample. Taking a sample is usually a two-man job; one man wields the hammer and moil while the other holds a receptacle to catch the fragments of rock and ore. This is ordinarily a powder box or a collapsible canvas bucket.[5] Alternatively, a sheet of canvas spread on the floor of the workings or on a platform will catch the chips as they fall, but unfortunately it may also catch dust and loosened blocks from outside the channel.

Labeling Samples. The collected sample is placed in a canvas sack along with an identifying label or tag. Lest damage to the label by moisture or abrasion should render the sample worthless, one must be sure that the labeling is enduring. Some engineers use numbered metal discs; others use blocks of soft wood on which a number is written with a hard pencil and protected by covering the writing with another block and tying the two together. However, paper labels properly protected are usually adequate. A designating number written with soft pencil on a large piece of good paper which is then folded like a package will generally reach the assay office in good condition. This is better than putting the tag in an envelope whose seams will come unstuck if the sample is moist. The sack containing the sample and its number is tied with twine and, in examination work, is sealed with wax or with a lead seal of the type used by express companies.

The number on the label corresponds with the record in the sampler's notebook. It is best to use a system of simple consecutive numbers. A, B, C, etc., can be used as suffixes without causing complications, but decimals and letters interspersed among digits are likely to confuse the assayer and lead to mistakes. Even if nothing worse results, the assayer is likely to list the samples in an unexpected and inconvenient order on the assay certificate.

Location of Samples

Most orebodies have some semblance of banding or layering. Vein-matter usually shows banded or ribbon-structure rudely paralleling the walls; sediments and replaced sediments are bedded; deposits of other types may display foliation, streaking, or other parallel arrangement. Since the distribution of metals is apt to follow such banding, a sample taken across it so as to include all of the bands is likely to be the most

---

[5] Herzig, C. S., *Mine Sampling and Valuing.* Mining and Scientific Press, 1914. A bucket is described and illustrated on p. 22.

representative.   Although a sample taken at right angles to the plane of
layering will give the shortest length of cut, the channel may cross the
layers at any convenient angle so long as it cuts all of the layers and cuts
them all at the same angle.   In drifts on steeply dipping veins the most
convenient practice is to cut the samples across the back of the drift.
However, the back may not expose all of the vein, in which event it may
be necessary to extend the sample to include part or all of one wall of
the drift.   Where this is the case, or where the back is arched, a problem
arises because it is then impossible to cross all of the bands at a uniform
angle.   Some engineers meet this situation by varying the width or depth
of the channel in order to give a larger sample in the part most nearly
normal to the dip, thus preserving the principle that the sample should
contain equal weights of material for equal portions of the vein-width.
But this involves considerable judgment and it seems sounder to subdivide
samples of this sort (see p. 41).   In crosscuts, the sample may be cut
either horizontally or inclined perpendicular to the dip.   If such a cut
does not cover the full width, adjoining cuts may be offset (Figure 7).

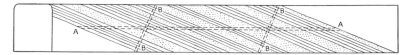

Fig. 7—Channels for sampling gently dipping formation in a crosscut.   (Vertical section)   Either the inclined channels, *B-B*, or the horizontal channel, *A-A*,
   would be proper.   *B-B* requires less cutting; *A-A* may be more convenient.

Subdividing Sample Channels

If an orebody has a width of much more than five feet, the conventional practice is to take two or more samples from each channel, sub-

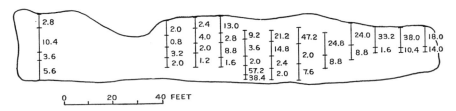

Fig. 8—Plan of a stope sampled by subdivided channels.   Numbers represent dwt. in gold.
   Balatoc Mine, P.I.   (*After* Hezzelwood, Geo. W., *A.I.M.E. Tech. Pub. 1407*)

dividing the channel in such a way that no individual sample represents
a width of more than five feet.   Thus a vein 20 feet wide would be
sampled in four five-foot sections.   This shows, at least in a general way,

which parts of the vein are richer and which are leaner, information that may be useful in mining. Although the conventional five-foot width, or any other uniform figure, simplifies calculation, it does not, as a rule, yield the most accurate information regarding the distribution of values, and there are distinct advantages in making the subdivision not at arbitrary footages on the measuring tape but at natural boundaries between contrasting types of rock or vein matter.[6] Some of the advantages are:

I. Accuracy of sampling.

A. If a vein consists of streaks contrasting in richness, the natural human tendency is to take too much from the richer parts or, in an effort to avoid this temptation, to lean over backward and take too little from a rich band. But sampling each band separately evades these possible sources of inaccuracy.

B. If the orebody consists of hard and soft streaks, there is a similar tendency, whether from laziness or overconscientiousness, to take disproportionate amounts of the hard and soft, a danger which is not present if each band is sampled separately.

C. Where the back is arched or where, for other practical reasons, the channel does not cross the vein at a uniform angle, subdividing the channel at changes in angle avoids the necessity of varying the number of pounds per foot to correspond with the width of vein represented.

II. Accuracy of information.

A. Breaking the sample to accord with bands of contrasting mineralogical nature affords valuable geological evidence regarding the association of metals with different types of vein matter and may also afford a useful record of the detailed structure of the orebody.

B. Explicit information regarding the distribution of values in the orebody may influence methods of mining. For example, in the case of a wide orebody, it may show that not all of the width should be mined. In the case of a narrow vein, separate samples of the footwall, the vein itself, and the hanging wall will indicate the extent to which dilution in stoping will affect the grade of the ore and may give an idea of the possibilities of hand-sorting and resuing.

These methods of subdividing will result in a larger number of samples and consequently a higher bill for assaying than the conventional method of arbitrary five-foot widths, but the advantages usually compensate for the greater expense.

Measuring Sampled Widths

Whether or not the sample has been cut normal to the walls of the vein, the width recorded should ordinarily be the true width, that is,

---

[6] Cf. Burnham, M. Howard, *Modern Mine Valuation*, p. 82 ff. London: Griffin, 1912.

the width as measured along a line perpendicular to the vein walls. Measuring between projected planes of the walls or between the projections of points at which the channel has been subdivided is usually adequate, but if great accuracy is desired it is sometimes possible to make the projection by stretching a string from the vein wall, as exposed in the

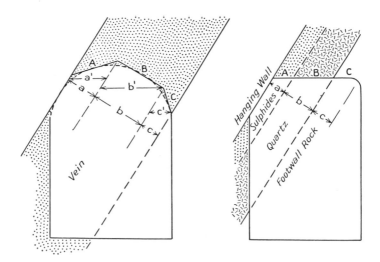

Fig. 9—Subdivided channel sample across a vein. *Left:* Subdivided because of irregularity of back. *Right:* Subdivided because of contrast in type of material.

back of a drift, to the same wall as exposed on the side or rib, and to measure the width at right angles to the string. Alternatively one may make the actual measurement along the channel, and take the inclination of the channel with a clinometer, correcting to true width by trigonometry. Of course, it is also possible to make all measurements horizontally. Then in estimating the volume of the ore the area of a horizontal section is multiplied by the vertical distance between the top and bottom of the block since horizontal width times vertical height gives the same result as true width times inclined height. (See p. 60.)

Spacing the Channels

The proper distance between channels depends on the uniformity of the ore. For average ore, the samples are customarily spaced five feet apart along the vein. The interval may have to be as small as three feet if the ore is rich and spotty, but it can be as great as ten feet if the ore is exceptionally homogeneous. Preliminary samples need not be spaced as closely as this, and one may save work in an examination by taking first a set of samples at 20 foot intervals, with the intention of cutting intermediate samples in the sections where the first returns show appreciable values. Whatever the interval, it should be uniform in any given section of the mine, and samples should be cut exactly where the measurements fall, since equal spacing not only simplifies calculation but eliminates any personal element in selecting the places for cutting channels. In narrow rich veins like those at Cobalt, Ontario, where many of the veins are not more than a few inches wide, it may be well to take a continuous channel along the vein instead of interval-channels across it. In such cases, auxiliary samples should be cut to test the wall-rock.

Measurements should be tied to some permanent location such as the intersection of a drift with a crosscut or, preferably, to a survey station. The face of a drift is a poor landmark as the heading may later be extended.

Floor Samples. Although the back and walls are the most convenient places to sample, it may happen that the ore above a drift has been stoped out or for some other reason is inaccessible and the only ore that is left to furnish evidence regarding a deeper block is in the floor of the drift. Unfortunately floor samples are not only inconvenient to take, because of rails, ties, and, often, water, but they are likely to be unreliable. If ore from a face or from stopes has been trammed through the level, fines may have accumulated on the floor and sifted into cracks in the rock. Consequently it is usually safer and not much more expensive to put down short winzes at intervals or, if conditions permit, to bore hammer-drill holes at an angle to the vein. Where there is no alternative it is perfectly feasible to sample the floor, however, by taking up the track, cleaning the surface as thoroughly as possible, and cutting channels in the ordinary manner. If the values are contained in solid ore rather than along fractures it is best to wash each piece that forms a part of the sample. But if the values are in veinlets of friable minerals, the danger of losing fines in washing must be balanced against the risk of salting by extraneous "dirt." If water is flowing down the drift it may need to be diverted into a launder by building across the drift a dam of planks nailed to the side-posts and chinked with clay.[7]

Reducing the Bulk of Samples

Since the samples as sent to the assayer need not consist of more than a few ounces[8] each, the possibility of reducing weight by keeping only

[7] Levy, Ernest, Sampling the floor of a wet level, in Rickard, T. A., *Sampling and Estimation of Ore in a Mine*, p. 124. New York: Hill, 1907.
[8] The standard charge for fire assaying is an "assay ton" (29.166 grams). Additional charges may be required for duplicate assays, check assays, or additional determinations.

part of the sample and discarding the rest is not to be dismissed lightly if
the engineer must pack the samples out of the bush on his back.   Even
if transportation is no problem, duplicate samples may be desirable as
checks or as material from which to make up composite samples for
more complete analysis or for metallurgical testing.   (Composites are
prepared by weighing out a portion from each sample proportional to
the sample width or to the tonnage that the sample represents.)

Separating a sample into smaller parts is, in effect, sampling a sample
and must be carried out systematically in order that the sub-sample may
be truly representative of the whole.   This means that all fragments
must be crushed to such size that any particle may be included in the
sub-sample or omitted from it as chance dictates without changing the
grade by more than a permissible margin of error.   The size depends
on the weight and grade of the largest particle (which may happen also
to be the richest) compared to the weight and grade, respectively, of
the sub-sample.   Richards'[9] tables, and also Brunton's[10] mathematical
and experimental work, indicate that in a two-pound sub-sample no
piece should be larger than 24 mesh (about .03″) in medium grade ore
and 42 mesh in rich or "spotted" ore.   These "safe" sizes are very conservative, and most ores give reasonably accurate results if sampled at
much coarser diameters.   Brunton's tables readily explain, however, why
"duplicate" samples of some ores, especially those containing native gold,
fail to check each other when reduced by ordinary methods.   Another
table published by Henry Louis[11] and based, apparently, on experience
is more in line with the common practice of engineers:

Weight of Sample, Lb.	Size of Largest Piece Inches, Diameter
1000	$1\frac{3}{4}$
200	1
40	$\frac{1}{2}$
10	$\frac{1}{4}$
under 10	$\frac{3}{16}$

For samples of one or two pounds, the size should be much smaller.
These sizes are intended to apply to ordinary ores.   In rich, precious-
metal ores, pieces should be smaller than those indicated by the table; for
homogeneous ore like iron ore or pyrite, they may be somewhat larger.

9 Richards, Robert H., Ore Dressing: New York, E. & M. J., 1903, vol. 2, p. 852.   Also
Bugbee, E. E., Textbook of Fire Assaying, p. 51.   New York: Wiley, 1940.
10 Brunton, D. W., Theory and practice of ore sampling: Tr. A.I.M.E., vol. 25, pp. 826–
844, 1896.
11 Louis, Henry, Mineral Valuation, p. 147.   London: Griffin, 1923.

Samples may be crushed and split very rapidly if a small power crusher and a Jones riffle sampler are available.   On prospect examinations, however, such luxurious equipment may be lacking and the examiner is reduced to the more laborious method of crushing the pieces with a hammer on an old car wheel or stamp shoe.   The sample is then subdivided by the method known as "coning and quartering."   Coning consists of making the ore into a conical pile by pouring successive shovelsful or scoopsful onto a particular spot on some smooth surface such as a sheet of steel or a platform of boards covered with canvas or oilcloth.   The fines pile up to form the apex of the cone while the coarser particles roll down evenly on all sides.   Then the cone is spread into a flat disc-shaped pile by drawing portions of the sample out radially in all directions from the center.   Quartering, the final process, consists in marking the disc into quarters as in cutting a pie and then combining two opposite quarters to make one sub-sample while the other two quarters form a duplicate.[12]

OTHER SAMPLING METHODS

Channel samples are the accepted standard in most operating mines and in all but very sketchy examinations, but other types of samples are used in some cases, either instead of channel samples or in addition to them.

1. *Chip samples.*   A series of chips of rock is taken either in a continuous line across the exposure or at random intervals over a face.   The method is less laborious than channel sampling and, in a few mining districts, comparative tests have shown that in the hands of samplers trained in a particular mine it can give comparable results.   This is rather exceptional, however, and the method should never be used until it has been thoroughly checked against channel sampling or milling results for the same mine.   It has no place in examination work except perhaps when quick preliminary returns are needed.

2. *Muck samples.*   A grab-sample of the muck pile after blasting is sometimes taken instead of a channel sample of a face.   This is usually done very crudely by picking up pieces of rock of convenient size.   While it is theoretically quite unreliable, a muck sample may give correct results in some ores whose values are evenly distributed or are independent of breaking-qualities.

3. *Car samples.*   A shovelful of ore or a series of pieces selected either at random or according to a prearranged system is taken from each car that

[12] A quicker method which is sufficiently accurate under most conditions is to roll the ore into a long pile and separate it into two parts by lifting a stick under the canvas sheet.   See Wilkins, E. G., "Some Notes on Crushing, Mixing, and Reducing Samples," *Mining Mag.*, p. 276, Nov., 1930.

comes from the face.   Since this gives a fairly large sample it stands a chance
of being reliable though the usual tendency is to take too much either of the
coarse or of the fine material.   A check may be obtained by averaging all
the car samples for a day and comparing with the corresponding mill-head
sample, for the daily mill-head sample is likely to be correct, especially if
taken by automatic methods after crushing.   Even with this check, however, the car sample from a single heading may be incorrect though balanced
by compensating errors from other sources.

4. *Drill-hole samples.*   Sampling by hammer drills, diamond drills, and
churn drills is described in Chapter 3.

AVERAGING ASSAYS

General Method

The grade of ore throughout a portion of a mine is estimated by
averaging together the assay returns of the samples that have been taken.
In order to follow the method of computation, let us consider first a
series of samples spaced at equal intervals along a vein.   If the vein is
of uniform width, then the average grade will be the simple arithmetical
average of the assays.   But few veins are of uniform width, and, since a
sample across a wide portion represents a larger tonnage than one across
a narrow portion, it is necessary to weight each assay in accordance with
its width, thus:

Sample Number	*Width Feet*	*Assay % Cu*	*Width × Assay*
1	3.2	6.2	19.84
2	6.4	7.3	46.72
3	5.3	8.5	45.05
4	2.1	6.4	13.44
Total	17.0 (a)		125.05 (b)
Average	4.25	7.35 (b ÷ a)	

If the ore is to be mined to a minimum stoping width and portions of
the vein are narrower than this minimum it will be necessary in stoping
to break some of the wall-rock adjoining the narrower portions of the
vein.   Therefore in calculating the grade of the material that will be
broken in stoping it is necessary to add appropriate amounts of wall-
rock to each of the narrower samples.   Where the wall-rock is assumed
to carry no values the computation can be carried out simply by substituting the minimum mining width for the width of any samples
whose measured width is less than this.   This substitution is made not
in the calculation of width × assay but at the stage at which widths

are added together in order to divide the sum into the width-value product. Thus in the example given above, if the minimum stoping width is 5 feet:

Sample Number	Minimum Stoping Width	Measured Width	Assay % Cu	Measured Width × Assay
1	(5.0)	3.2	6.2	19.84
2	6.4	6.4	7.3	46.72
3	5.3	5.3	8.5	45.05
4	(5.0)	2.1	6.4	13.44
Total	21.7 (a)	17.0		125.05 (b)
Average	5.4		5.76 (b ÷ a)	

If a sample channel has been subdivided, assays of the fractions are first averaged together, weighting each for its own width in order to get the value for the full channel; then the values of the individual channels are averaged together as explained above.

If, as before, the channels are spaced at equal intervals, the calculation may be carried out in simple fashion by computing a weighted average of all the fractions. Average vein width is obtained by dividing the aggregate width of fractions by the number of channels.

	Width Feet	Value Ounce Au	Width × Value
Channel 1	1.2	.06	.07
	3.0	.54	1.62
	1.4	.08	.11
Channel 2	1.3	.04	.05
	3.2	.68	2.18
	4.0	.05	.20
Channel 3	1.2	.23	.28
	3.4	.24	.82
	2.3	.30	.69
Total	21.0		6.02
Average	6.7	.29	

If the richer or leaner fractions represent streaks or bands which are continuous from channel to channel there may be advantages in calculating the average value of each streak separately, whether as a matter of geological information or as a guide to mining. But any attempt to correlate a rich fraction in one channel with a similar one in the next is dangerous unless geologic mapping indicates that the individual bands are actually continuous.

If, instead of being spaced at uniform distances along the vein, the channels have been cut at irregular intervals, some of the samples will be obliged to represent greater lengths along the vein than others. Each sample must therefore be weighted by the length which it represents, a length which is equal to half the distance to the next sample on one side plus half the distance to the next sample on the other. If not only the sample intervals but also the vein-widths are non-uniform, both of these factors must, of course, enter into the calculation with the result that each sample will be weighted for the area that it represents, i.e., length × width.

Thus the average grade would be:

$$\frac{\Sigma \ (\text{width} \ \times \ \text{interval} \ \times \ \text{assay})}{\Sigma \ (\text{width} \ \times \ \text{interval})}$$

The average width would be:

$$\frac{\Sigma \ (\text{width} \ \times \ \text{interval})}{\Sigma \ (\text{interval})}$$

All of these calculations assume that there is no significant difference in the specific gravities of different types of material, and thus that equal volumes represent equal weights. The assumption is usually not far from the truth, but if certain portions of the orebody consist of material that is considerably heavier or lighter than the average, it may be necessary to weight the samples not only for volume but for specific gravity. To take an extreme case, consider a vein composed of equal widths of pure galena (sp. gr. 7.58, Pb 86%) and gangue (sp. gr., say 2.6, Pb nil). The unweighted average of the two halves would be 43% Pb but the average, weighted for specific gravity, would be 64% Pb.

Precise application of the principle of weighting for specific gravity would require a specific gravity determination for each sample, a practice which is not common and, ordinarily, is hardly warranted. In some ores the specific gravity is closely related to the assay value so that it is feasible to construct a curve based on a limited number of determinations and then read off the specific gravity corresponding to any given metal content. This method may not be applicable to mixed ores or to ores containing a considerable but undetermined percentage of pyrite or of other accessory heavy mineral, but it is entirely practical with most iron ores and some others whose mineralogical character is simple. However, the increase in accuracy is not always sufficient to compensate for the extra labor in calculation.

Erratic High Assays

The usual methods of calculating the average of a series of samples, as used in the foregoing examples, embody the assumption that from each channel to the next the grade of ore changes at a uniform rate or, what amounts to the same thing so far as numerical results are concerned, that each assay represents the value of the ore for an interval extending halfway to the next sample on each side. Although such an assumption usually yields a perfectly satisfactory approximation, it rarely if ever is in strict accordance with the facts and it can lead to serious error if one or a few samples are notably richer than the rest, a condition which is not uncommon in precious-metal ores and not unknown, though less common, in base-metal ores.

Consider a list of channel samples taken along a drift on a gold-bearing vein:

$5.25, $4.00, $17.85, **$480.10**, $49.20, $22.40, $6.00, $10.15, $1.40, $.70

The arithmetical average of these ten samples, including the high sample assaying $480.10 is $59.70. Omitting the high sample, the average of the remaining nine is $12.99. The critical part that the high sample plays in determining the average prompts the question: Is it proper to include such a sample at its full value in averaging a series? In general it is not. Neither is it correct, as a rule, to ignore it.

First, of course, one must eliminate the possibility that the high assay is simply a mistake arising through faulty splitting of the sample or through accidental salting in the laboratory. Careful reduction and reassay of the duplicate half of the original sample should settle this question. Recutting the sample is not always a fair check because some orebodies owe their value to scattered high spots; to recut high samples would eliminate these but might be unfair to the orebody because if the low samples had also been recut they might have disclosed high values where the original sampling did not show them. Some earlier authorities recommend discarding high samples altogether on the ground that this affords a factor of safety. The answer to this is that an underestimate of grade is almost as misleading as an overestimate; in any case a safety factor should not be a hidden one but, where used, should be introduced deliberately and labeled clearly in the estimate.[13]

How to deal with erratic high samples is one of the knottiest problems in ore estimation. Since attempts to establish standard procedures have

---

[13] *Cf.* Rickard, T. A., *The Sampling and Estimation of Ore in a Mine*, p. 212. New York: Hill Publishing Co., 1907.

not proved wholly satisfactory, most authorities dismiss the subject with a statement that choice of a method must depend on judgment and experience.   Truer words were never written, but they are cold comfort to those whose experience in such matters is limited.   In order to build up a background of judgment it is well to examine some of the conditions which give rise to erratic high assays.

Erratic or Merely High?   In considering high assays it is important to distinguish between assays that are erratic and assays that are high though relatively numerous, for if high samples are numerous, they are not erratic.   In the Colquijirca silver mine in Peru, the first sampling yielded so many assays running 200 to 500 ounces that additional samples were taken, either in the same channels or within a few feet of them. Invariably the recuts confirmed existence of high-grade ore, although in some cases they gave results as much as 50% higher or lower than the originals.   Since the high samples were numerous and were shown to represent substantial masses of ore, they were not "cut" in averaging, nor should they have been since subsequent mining showed that the yield was remarkably close to the estimate.

Modes of Distribution of High Values.   The reason why no rules of thumb can apply to all cases is that, no two orebodies being alike, erratic highs may reflect any one of a number of conditions depending on the manner in which valuable minerals are distributed throughout the orebody.   Thus the problem is fundamentally geological[14] rather than purely mathematical.   In order to examine the alternative possibilities, we may consider an oversimplified example in which nine samples show negligible values and one gives $1000 per ton.   To make the example concrete we shall assume that the sample channels are three feet apart and that each channel is 0.3 feet broad, 0.1 feet deep and (as measured across the vein) 5 feet long.   Now it is possible that our $1000 sample represents a length of high-grade ore which attains a peak value of $1000 at the sample channel and declines uniformly to zero at the adjoining channel on each side (b, Figure 10).   Should this be true we would be correct in averaging the samples arithmetically in order to calculate the average *for the surface exposed by the drift.*   This average would be $100.   Alternatively,[15] and more probably, the $1000 sample

---

[14] The best discussion to date of high assays from a geological point of view is a recent paper by C. O. Swanson: "Probabilities in Estimating the Grade of Gold Deposits," *Can. Inst. Mining and Metallurgy Tr.,* vol. 48, pp. 323–350, 1945.   I have made free use of Swanson's ideas in preparing the present text.

[15] The further possibility that the arrangement of values may be asymmetrical, with a peak-value higher than $1000 on one side of the sample and a correspondingly more rapid decline to zero beyond this peak (d, fig. 10) will not be considered for the purpose of the present illustration, nor will the more general and realistic case of interrupted and irregular decline from a peak.   (e, fig. 10.)

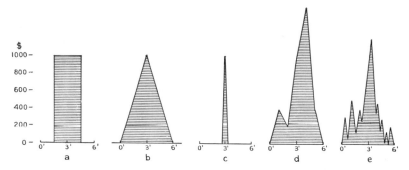

Fig. 10—Assay graphs to illustrate alternative modes of distribution of values for a $1000 sample at Footage 3 between barren samples at Footages 0 and 6.

is due to one or a few small spots of exceptionally rich material (c, Fig. 10). For example, a sphere of native gold 0.4 inches in diameter and weighing about 0.4 ounces would alone confer a value of $1000 per ton on a sample of the specified dimensions. If this is the arrangement (and assuming that no other piece of gold exists anywhere between the sample channels), the influence of the $1000 sample should not extend beyond the limits of its own channel, equivalent to 1% of the total distance covered by the sampling. The average in this case would be calculated:

Percentage of Length	Value	Product
99%	0	0
1%	$1000	10
100%		10

Hence the weighted average would be $10 a ton. Clearly then the correct average value might lie anywhere between $10 and $100 depending on the manner in which the high values decline on both sides of the high sample, a question to which the assays themselves offer no clue.

But if we were to take additional intermediate samples so closely spaced that the channels lay side by side like piano keys we would have an accurate indication of the distribution of values along the drift. We would then have 90 additional samples and any number of them, from none to 90, might show high values. If our original sampling turned out to be representative we would have among the 90, nine $1000 samples.[16] Such a satisfactory confirmation of the original sampling would, of course, be highly fortuitous in the present example, but if the

[16] For simplicity we are making the improbable assumption that all samples assay either $1000 or $0.

length of drift sampled had been vastly greater and the number of original samples correspondingly more numerous, a reasonable check would not be surprising. We shall therefore assume, in continuing the discussion, that the original sampling has been proved to be representative and the weighted average is $100 a ton.

Distribution of Values Within a Block. We have been calculating the average value of the ore exposed by the drift, a slice of ore extending upward above the drift for only 0.1 feet, *i.e.,* the depth of a sample channel. What about the ore in the whole block above the drift? The conventional method of estimation embodies the assumption for purposes of calculation that ore equivalent in average value to that exposed by the drift extends upward halfway to the next level, or, let us say in this case, 30 feet vertically. This, in turn, involves the assumption that the $1000 ore extends upward in the form of a vertical strip or column. Of course the values are not really arranged in any such bizarre fashion, but the assumption would lead to the correct mathematical result provided the high spots occur throughout the vein in a random manner. If so, a row of samples taken on any imaginary sublevel would contain the same proportion of $1000 assays as does the row on the main level.

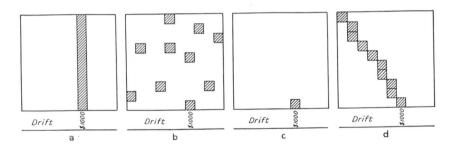

Fig. 11—Alternative modes of distribution of high-grade patches in a block of ore. On the level, all would be represented by a single rich sample. *a:* Implication of conventional method of averaging. *b:* One of many possible types of random distribution, giving same average as *a*. *c:* Implication of the frequency weighting method of averaging. *d:* Elongated shoot, giving same average as *a*. (Conventionalized diagrams)

Similarly, if the patches had been part of an elongated shoot, whether vertical or inclined, the distribution would have been equivalent to a strip-like arrangement and an arithmetical average would have been proper.

But suppose that, instead of occurring in a vertical strip or its equivalent, the $1000 ore extends upward only to a distance roughly equal to its horizontal dimension, viz. 3 feet. This, in fact, is the type of distribution that we might expect in the absence of evidence to the contrary.   If this is actually the mode of distribution, the high-grade ore occupies not 1/10 of the volume of the block but 1/100 and hence the value of the block would be based not on the proportion of high-grade samples in the drift but on the square of this proportion.   If the $1000 ore constitutes 1/100 of the volume of the block, the average grade of the block would be $10 per ton.   We get the same result if we reduce the high sample to the arithmetical average of the group and then re-calculate the average: ($100 + $0)/10 = $10.   Also we will get roughly the same result if we weight each assay by its "frequency," [17] *i.e.,* the number of samples having a given assay-value divided by the total number of samples taken.   Thus:

Number of Samples (N)	Frequency (F)	N × F	Assay	Product
9	.90	8.1	$ 0	0
1	.10	.1	1000	100
		8.2		100

Average: $12.19

We have been assuming that our original ten samples are representa-tive, an assumption which we confirmed by taking additional samples so close together that no space remained between them.   Such close sampling, of course, is hardly practicable, but there is another (though less reliable) way to obtain similar information.   Since the manner of distribution of high values through the orebody as a whole is likely to be analogous to that in the section in question, we would expect from a consideration of probability that 90 samples from other parts of the same orebody would contain about the same proportion of exceptionally high assays as would 90 samples from the area originally channeled. This is so because the proportion of high-grade assays should be the same as the proportion of vein-matter which carries high values.   This is the basis of the frequency-weighting principle.   Although in our ex-ample we inferred the frequency from only ten samples (substantiated by an additional ninety) the method is really valid only when the fre-quency is calculated from a much larger number of assays.

Random vs. Shootlike Distribution.   For the sake of simplicity we have been considering a preposterous type of orebody in which all values are either $1000 or nothing, but the same principles apply to realistic ex-amples in which assays range in value from low to high.

---

[17] This method will be explained in greater detail on a subsequent page.   Another way of performing the same operation is to weight the assay value of the group (*e.g.,* $0 and $1000) by the square of its frequency.   The discrepancy between $12.19 and $10 arises from the fact that the sum of the squares of two numbers is not equal to the square of their sum.

We have seen that, if the high-grade ore occurs in a single, roughly equidimensional shoot, the assay might properly be weighted by the square of the frequency in calculating the average value of the block. If, in contrast, the high-grade ore occurs in spots roughly equal in diameter to the width of a sample channel (in this case 1/10 of the sample interval), and if these spots are distributed at random throughout the orebody, the chances are that similar spots occur within the block in about the same proportion as along the exposure sampled. In this case the assay should be weighted by the frequency and not by the square of the frequency.

Test for Random Distribution. Which of the alternative modes of distribution is the actual one, or, indeed, whether either one corresponds with actuality, is not disclosed either by the series of ten samples, nor from frequency data even from a larger number. However, Swanson [18] has devised a useful test for random distribution of values. He divides the samples from an entire deposit into a large number of groups based on location, so that each group represents a particular part of the orebody. Treating the average value for each group as though it were a single sample, he computes the probable error [19] for the average of the groups and compares this with the probable error in an average made from individual samples. If the two probable errors are of the same order of magnitude, the distribution is random and not shoot-like.

Applying this principle to the Box Property on Lake Athabaska, Swanson concluded that the values there have random distribution. Averages for the property gave the following results:

Average, weighted for frequency and assay [20]	$ .56
Average after cutting high assays to double the mean [21]	.88
Arithmetical average (unweighted)	1.89
" " after allowing 10% for dilution	1.70
Mill heads	1.70

[18] Swanson, C. O., Probabilities in estimating the grade of gold deposits: *C.I.M. Tr.*, vol. 48, pp. 323–350, 1945.

[19] Probable error is determined from the formula:

$$E = 0.6745 \sqrt{\frac{\Sigma d^2}{n\,(n-1)}}$$

where d is the deviation of each sample from the mean, and n is the number of samples. This may be simplified for approximation to:

$$E \propto D/\sqrt{n}$$

where D is the average deviation.

[20, 21] The significance of these items will be evident from succeeding paragraphs.

The satisfactory check between the arithmetical average and the mill heads substantiates the assumption that the distribution is random.

Calculation by the Frequency-Weighting Method. The principle of estimating the grade of a block of ore by weighting the assays for frequency of occurrence has been illustrated for a simplified example, but the application of the technique to a large number of samples merits a more specific description. In calculating the average grade of ore in a section of a Rand mine, from values expressed in inch-pennyweights (width in inches $\times$ gold content in dwt.), Watermeyer[22] first constructed a frequency curve from all stope assays taken over a 12-month period by arranging them in order of value and subdividing the list into groups, each covering a range of 50 inch-dwt. (*e.g.*, group 1, 0–50 dwt., group 2, 50–100 dwt., etc.) and calculating the frequency for each group, *i.e.*, the number of samples within each, divided by the total number of samples. The curve[23] with frequencies plotted as ordinates and values as abscissae, made it possible to read off the appropriate frequency for any assay value. Then, in averaging the values from any part of the mine or for any period, he weighted each value by its corresponding frequency:

$$\frac{\Sigma \ (\text{assay} \ \times \ \text{width} \ \times \ \text{frequency})}{\Sigma \ (\text{width} \ \times \ \text{frequency})} = \text{average assay}$$

Calculated in this manner, the averages of stope assays from the Van Ryn mine for successive months (estimate taken as 100) compare with mill returns ("mill yield plus pulp") as follows:

108.6, 105.1, 105.4, 105.8, 102.4, 99.8.

For six mines the estimates for a single month's production compared on the same basis: 99.8, 85.2, 101.7, 104.2, 99.3, 94.2. Although Watermeyer does not offer for comparison the results of simple arithmetical averages, he states that they are always too high and implies that estimates by the frequency method gave much more accurate and consistent results.

In comparing the mechanics of the Watermeyer method with that of a simple arithmetical average it is important to note that the arithmetical average actually embodies a weighting for frequency. Thus, instead of

[22] Watermeyer, G. A., Application of the theory of probability in the determination of ore reserves: *Journal Chemical, Metallurgical and Mining Society of So. Africa*, 1919, vol. 19, pp. 97–107.   Discussion, pp. 107–108, 132, 181–187, 202–209, 251–252, 273–282.

[23] Actually, before plotting the curve, Watermeyer adjusted the calculated frequencies to a mathematical curve in accordance with what is known as the Compound Gaussian Law. The curve, however, does not vary widely from the one which would be obtained by "smoothing out" the graph of computed figures.

adding the individual values and dividing by the number of samples, one might subdivide the list into value-groups, compute the average for each group, multiply this by the frequency for the group, and add the products. The Watermeyer method, viewed on the same basis, multiplies twice by the frequency, *i.e.*, weights by the square of the frequency.

Arithmetical Average vs. Frequency Weighting. On checking the results obtained by the two methods (arithmetical average and frequency-weighting) against the mill returns from mining operations, it appears that, while each method applies satisfactorily to certain orebodies, weighting by the frequency usually gives too high a result whereas weighting by the square of the frequency gives too low a result.[24] From this Swanson has concluded that in most ore deposits the high values do not occur either in purely random arrangement nor yet in perfectly defined shoots, but rather they partake of the nature of both modes of distribution. That is, there is a tendency toward grouping in rudely equidimensional shoots; yet in combination with this there is an element of random distribution.

Weighting by Frequency and Assay. Recognizing that the frequency-weighting method often is too drastic, but reaching his conclusion by a different train of reasoning, Truscott[25] introduced an additional weighting factor, namely the value of the assay itself. He maintained that a higher assay is evidence of greater local intensity of mineralization and this "more intense mineralization will manifest itself over a greater area." In other words, rich ore should extend farther on all sides from a high sample than from a lower one, and, therefore, value should be considered in determining the area to which the assay value should be assigned. Truscott's formula would thus be:

$$\frac{\Sigma \ (\text{frequency} \times \text{assay} \times \text{assay})}{\Sigma \ (\text{frequency} \times \text{assay})} = \text{average value}$$

In at least three instances, averages by the Truscott method have given satisfactory results.

	Shamva[26]	Sumatra[27]	Hollinger[28]
Arithmetic mean (unweighted)	8.2 dwt	7.05 dwt	——
Average weighted for frequency only	2.7 "	3.54 "	——
" " " " and assay	4.4 "	5.05 "	$5.29
Mill returns	4.5 "	5.12 "	$4.88

[24] Swanson, C. O., Probabilities in estimating the grade of gold deposits: *Can. Inst. Mining & Metallurgy Tr.*, vol. 48, pp. 323–350, 1945.

[25] Truscott, S. J., *Mine Economics*, p. 67. London: Mining Publications, Ltd., 1937. *Also* The computation of the probable value of ore reserves from assay results: *Tr. I.M.M.*, vol. 39, p. 482, 1930.

[26] Truscott, S. J., *Mine Economics*, p. 71. London: Mining Publications, Ltd., 1937.

Since weighting by assay and frequency is very laborious, two short-cut methods developed by Jones in his study of assays in the Hollinger mine may prove useful. The two methods are independent of each other:

1. Arrange the assays for any stope in order of their value. Select the sample which occurs 82% of the way along the list (*e.g.*, if there are 1000 samples, select no. 820). Divide the value of this sample by two and the result is approximately equal to that obtained by the "frequency × assay" method of calculation.

2. Select the sample which occurs 88% of the way along the list. Cut all higher assays to this value and compute the arithmetical (*i.e.*, unweighted) average. This average is approximately equal to that obtained by the "frequency × assay" method.

These percentages (82 and 88) hold for all stopes in the Hollinger mine even though the average grades of ore in individual stopes range from $3 to over $16. These methods are based not on any theory but on purely empirical observation and depend on the frequency curve that is characteristic of the Hollinger mine. Whether or not similar percentages would hold in other mines or indeed whether the method could be used at all could be determined only by trial.

"Texture" of Value-Distribution. In contemplating the manner in which high values occur throughout the ore, we may recognize what might be called the "texture" [29] of the variations in grade. In a "fine-textured" distribution, the high assays which some of the samples yield are attributable to small spots of rich material. Recutting the sample or taking additional samples on both sides of it will in general fail to duplicate the high assay but will not disprove the existence of rich spots. Increasing the bulk of each sample, however, tends to reduce the range of sample values and to give results which are more nearly representative.

In a "coarse-textured" distribution the high assays actually represent sizable rich portions within the deposit. Here recutting the sample serves the useful purpose of confirming the presence of rich material; the new samples on each side indicate its size and consistency. The rich portions may prove to be distributed at random and conform to Swanson's criteria based on calculation of probable error, or they may be arranged according to some pattern. If it is possible to recognize distinctly localized rich and lean areas within the orebody, the samples from

---

[27] Grey, D. W. J., Notes on the Balimbing Mine, West Coast, Sumatra, *Tr. I.M.M.*, vol. 45, p. 243, 1936.

[28] Based on one month's mill-run. Jones, W. A., Estimation of the average value of gold ore: *Tr. Can. I.M.M.*, vol. 46, pp. 209–225, 1943.

[29] This concept was suggested by C. O. Swanson in personal correspondence.

each should be averaged separately. Geological observation is the best guide to such localization, and no juggling with mathematical formulas is a substitute for it.

Resumé. An arithmetical average is proper:

(*a*) if the high-grade spots occur in random arrangement.

(*b*) if the high values occur in the form of an elongated oreshoot traversing the ore-block under consideration. (But in this case it is preferable to treat the shoot separately in calculation.)

An arithmetical average is incorrect:

If the high values constitute a roughly equidimensional oreshoot or form the core of an oreshoot. In this case either the Watermeyer or the Truscott method may give a more accurate result.

Pragmatic Methods. Contemplation of statistical and frequency-weighting methods gives an insight into the nature of high assays and the manner in which they influence the average grade. But although they find application in special cases, frequency methods are not widely used, partly because they involve laborious calculations and partly because they are applicable only where a large fund of assay data is available. Instead, most engineers use one of a variety of simpler but more arbitrary methods depending on the manner of distribution of the high values:

1. Taking auxiliary samples on each side of the high one and substituting for the high the average of the three. An alternative method is to include in the average the next two samples on each side, thereby combining the results of five samples.

2. Calculating the mean of the whole series of samples, reducing all the highs to this mean and then calculating the "cut" average. This usually gives too drastic a reduction. Consequently, highs are cut to one and a half or two times the mean.

3. Cutting all high samples to an arbitrary value, say $25 or $50.

4. Applying a percentage correction to the arithmetical average.

Any one of these may give satisfactory results in a particular case, but it would be unsafe to place final reliance on any one method without confirming its applicability to the orebody in question. The final check is the value that the ore yields on mining and milling or smelting. In an operating property such a check is readily available through test mill-runs or trial smelter shipments. In an inactive property one may need to mine out material for bulk shipments from areas that have been sampled. If costs or transportation difficulties prohibit shipping, an alternative is to take systematic bulk samples and crush them down to the proper size for quartering or splitting.

In examination work, however, it is often necessary to make a preliminary estimate before bulk sampling can be undertaken or indeed before its expense can be justified.   In this case the examiner has no alternative but to select the method which, in the light of his experience, seems best adapted to the particular orebody.

CALCULATING GRADE AND TONNAGE OF ORE

Average Grade

The average grade of a block of ore is calculated from the average grades of the sampled openings which bound it.   In a typical vein deposit the openings consist of drifts on the levels that form the top and bottom of the block plus raises that connect the levels and form the ends of the block.   The usual method of calculating the value of the block is illustrated in the following example:

	Length (L)	Width (W)	L × W	Assay (A)	L × W × A
Level 3	110'	5.2'	572	12.2%	6978.4
Level 4	130'	6.8'	884	10.3%	9105.2
Raise J	180'	6.1'	1098	8.1%	8893.8
Raise K	190'	5.4'	1026	9.2%	9439.2
Sum	610		3580		34416.6
Average		5.87'		9.61%	

If there is much discrepancy in the values of different sides of the block, a more accurate result may be obtained by dividing the block into triangles as in Figure 12.   Either method is necessarily an approxi-

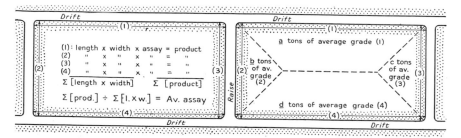

Fig. 12—Two methods of estimating the average tenor of a block of ore.   (Longitudinal section on a vertical vein)

mation which may give incorrect results with special and peculiar modes of ore distribution.   For example, a rich patch at the corner of a block will unduly raise the assays for two of the sides.   In general, wherever any part of a block is distinctly divergent in grade from the whole, it is best to calculate its value separately and then combine the result with the value of the rest of the block in proportion to volume.

Volume

The weight of a block of ore is estimated by first calculating the volume and then applying a factor to convert volume into tonnage.

Volume is average thickness times area. The average thickness will have been determined while computing the average assay. Area is either calculated by mensuration or is measured on the longitudinal section by means of a planimeter. If widths have been measured horizontally, the area is measured directly on a longitudinal section, but if true widths are used the area as shown on the longitudinal section needs to be divided by the sine of the dip in order to correct for the foreshortening in the projection. Although the procedure just outlined is for ore on a steep vein, analogous methods would be used, of course, for a flat-lying orebody depicted on a composite plan.

For the volumes of thick or pipe-like orebodies, it may be convenient to use the prismoidal formula:

$$V = \frac{A_1 + 4A_2 + A_3}{6}h$$

where A_1 is the area of the upper surface,
A_2 is the area of a mid-section,
A_3 is the area of the bottom surface, and
h is the height of the prism.

Tonnage

Conversion of volume into tonnage is very simple where metric measurements are in use. All that is necessary is to multiply the volume in cubic meters by the specific gravity to get metric tons. If the volume is expressed in cubic feet, divide it by the tonnage-volume factor (the number of cubic feet in a ton of ore). This factor may be obtained in one of several ways:

1. Weigh the ore from an excavation of known dimensions. If this information is not available from past mining operations, tests may be made by measuring one, or preferably several, faces before and after blasting and weighing the cars of ore that come from each face. Alternatively, a small-scale test may be made by excavating a hole a few feet in dimensions, weighing the material from it, and determining its volume by filling it with a measured quantity of shot, grain, or other material. Plaster of Paris may be used to make a cast of the hole. When the cast has been coated with paraffin,

its volume may be measured by water displacement.[30]   The small-scale test is satisfactory if the ore is uniform but it must be repeated in many places if the ore is variable in density.

2. Weigh several cars of broken ore even though its original volume in place is not known.   Correction is then made for voids, which amount to about 35% of the volume, but this percentage varies with uniformity of particle-size, and thus constitutes a source of error if a precise factor is required.

3. Measure the specific gravity of samples.   Specific gravity of powdered ore is easiest to measure but gives too high a result if the ore is porous or vuggy. Specific gravity of a specimen (coated with paraffin or shellac if necessary) gives better results but does not take large vugs or cavities into account.

4. Estimate the specific gravity from the mineralogical composition.   (See Tables 1 and 2.)   This is subject to the same errors as Method 3, plus any inaccuracy in estimating the percentage of each mineral.   The mineralogical composition of simple ores can be calculated from the assay or the chemical analysis.

Since ore-estimates are always on a "dry" (moisture-free) basis, any test on "natural" ore should be corrected for moisture-content.   Actually, small errors in the tonnage-volume factor are less serious than errors in grade, since they do not affect the profit per ton.   What they do affect is the life of the mine, which in any case cannot be estimated precisely except in plenemensurate deposits (see p. 477).

The tonnage and average grade of each block having been calculated, the tonnages of the individual blocks are added together and their average is determined by weighting the grade of each block by the tonnage:

	Tons	Grade	Tons × Grade
Block 1	1760	6.1%	10736
Block 2	2384	8.4%	20026
Block 3	5760	7.4%	42624
Total	9904		73386
Average		7.41%	

Ore Sampled by Drilling

When the grade and tonnage of an orebody are to be estimated from vertical drill holes, as is common in thick, flat-lying orebodies, the method of calculation depends on the manner in which the holes are spaced.

Holes spaced at uniform intervals are, of course, the simplest to deal with.   Whether the holes are drilled on a rectangular coordinate system

---

[30] Baxter, Charles H., and Parks, Roland D., *Mine Examination and Valuation*, p. 65.   Houghton: Mich. College of Mines and Technology, 2nd Ed., 1939.

TABLE 1

WEIGHT AND TENOR OF ORE MINERALS *

(For formulas of less common ore minerals, see Glossary)

Mineral	Formula	Metal Content		Spec. Gr.	Lb. per Cu. Ft.	Cu. Ft. per Short Ton
		Calculated	By Analysis			
Copper		$Cu, \%$				
Native Copper	Cu	100.0	—	8.95	556	3.58
Bornite	Cu_5FeS_4	63.33	63.0–63.3	5.06–5.08	316–318	6.30–6.32
Chalcocite	Cu_2S	79.86	79.3–79.7	5.5–5.8	344–362	5.83
Chalcopyrite	$CuFeS_2$	34.64	31.5–33.6	4.1–4.3	253–269	7.84
Chrysacolla	$CuSiO_3.2H_2O$	36.1	—	2.0–2.4	125–150	13.3–16.0
Enargite	Cu_3AsS_4	48.42	45.7–49.0	4.43–4.45	276–278	7.23–7.24
Malachite	$Cu_2CO_3(OH)_2$	57.4	—	3.9–4.0	243–250	8.0–8.2
Tetrahedrite	$(Cu,Fe,Zn,As)_{12}Sb_4S_{13}$	45.77	22.1–45.4	4.6–5.1	287–319	6.27–6.95
Gold		$Au, \%$				
Native Gold	Au	100.0	50–98.8	19.3 (15.0–19.3)	1205 (937–1205)	1.66–2.14
Iron		$Fe, \%$				
Goethite	FeO(OH)	62.9	61.7–62.8	4.37	272	7.35
Hematite	Fe_2O_3	69.94	—	5.26	328	6.10
"Limonite"	$FeO(OH).nH_2O$	—	—	3.6–4	(267–303) 213–238	(6.6–7.5) 8.4–9.4

* Compositions and specific gravities mostly from Dana (Palache) and Dana (Hurlbut).

TABLE 1 (*Continued*)

WEIGHT AND TENOR OF ORE MINERALS

Mineral	Formula	Metal Content		Spec. Gr.	Lb. per Cu. Ft.	Cu. Ft. per Short Ton
		Calculated	By Analysis			
Iron			Fe, %			
Magnetite	Fe_3O_4	72.36	56.0–72.0	5.18	329	6.08
Pyrite	FeS_2	46.55	45.0–46.5	5.02	286–313	6.4–7.0
		(53.45% Sulphur)				
Pyrrhotite	$Fe_{1-x}S$	63.53	57.5–63.4	4.58–4.65	286–290	6.9–7.0
Siderite	$FeCO_3$	48.2	—	3.85	240	8.38
Lead			Pb, %			
Anglesite	$PbSO_4$	68.3	—	6.2–6.4	386–400	5.0–5.17
Cerussite	$PbCO_3$	77.5	—	6.55	408	4.9
Galena	PbS	86.60	—	7.4–7.6	426–465	4.3–4.7
Mercury			Hg, %			
Cinnabar	HgS	86.2	—	8.10	505	3.95
Nickel			Ni, %			
Pentlandite	$(Fe,Ni)_9S_8$	34.22	34.2–34.8	4.6–5.0	288–312	6.4–7.0

TABLE 1 (*Concluded*)

WEIGHT AND TENOR OF ORE MINERALS

Mineral	Formula	Metal Content		Spec. Gr.	Lb. per Cu. Ft.	Cu. Ft. per Short Ton
		Calculated	By Analysis			
Platinum		Pt, %				
Native Platinum	Pt	100.0	73.0–90.0	21.45 (14–19)	1340 (874–1170)	1.49 (1.69–2.29)
Sperrylite	$PtAs_2$	56.58	52.0–56.0	10.58	—	—
Silver		Ag, %				
Native Silver	Ag	100.0	50–98	10.5	655	3.14
Argentite	Ag_2S	87.06	71.0–87.0	7.3	455	4.38
(Tetrahedrite)	(See p. 62)	—	0–18	4.6–5.1	287–319	6.27–6.95
Tin		Sn, %				
Cassiterite	SnO_2	78.6	70.0–76.7	6.8–7.1	425–443	4.5–4.7
Stannite	$Cu_2FeSn_2S_4$	27.61	27.2–27.5	4.4	275	7.3
Zinc		Zn, %				
Hemimorphite	$Zn_4Si_2O_7(OH)_2 \cdot H_2O$	54.2	—	3.4–3.5	212–219	9.2–9.45
Smithsonite	$ZnCO_3$	52.06	—	4.35–4.40	272–275	7.3–7.4
Sphalerite	ZnS	67.10	38.0–66.9	3.9–4.1	244–253	7.8–8.2

TABLE 2

WEIGHT OF GANGUE MINERALS AND ROCKS

	Specific Gravity			Lb. per Cu. Ft.			Cu. Ft. per Short Ton		
Gangue Minerals									
Quartz	2.65			166			12.2		
Calcite	2.72			170			11.8		
Dolomite	2.85			178			11.25		
Barite	4.5			280			7.12		
Igneous Rocks *									
	Low	Mean	High	Low	Mean	High	Low	Mean	High
Granite	2.52	2.67	2.81	157	167	175	11.5	12.0	12.7
Granodiorite	2.67	2.72	2.78	167	170	178	11.6	11.8	12.5
Diorite	2.72	2.84	2.96	170	177	185	10.8	11.3	11.75
Diabase	2.80	2.96	3.11	175	185	197	10.3	11.85	11.45
Gabbro	2.85	2.98	3.12	178	186	195	10.35	10.8	11.25
Sedimentary Rocks †									
Sand (unconsolidated)	1.37–1.75			86–119			18.35–28.2		
Gravel "	1.36–2.00			85–125			25.6–27.7		
Sandstone	1.65–2.50			103–156			12.8–19.4		
Quartzite	2.48–2.63			155–164			12.2–12.9		
Shale	2.00–2.65			125–165			12.1–16.0		
Schist	2.64–2.68			165–168			11.95–12.2		
Limestone	2.40–2.70			150–169			11.9–13.4		
Marble	2.66–2.86			166–178			11.2–12.1		

* Density data from Daly, R. A., in Handbook of Physical Constants, G.S.A. *Special Paper 36, 1942,* p. 14.

† Density data from Spicer, H. Cecil, Handbook of Physical Constants, G.S.A. *Special Paper 36, 1942,* pp. 19–26.

Extreme and unusual values omitted from range.

or on the corners of 60 degree triangles (theoretically the most economical design since each hole is at a uniform distance from all of its neighbors), the grade is a simple average, weighted only for thickness. The average thickness is an arithmetical mean of all thickness-measurements. A more common and adaptable method of calculation, however, is to draw up a series of cross sections through parallel rows of holes, calculating the area and average grade of ore shown in each cross section. The method can be used even if the rows are not at equal distances apart nor the holes uniformly spaced along them. The average grade is calculated by combining the average grades of the respective cross sections, weighting each by its area and (if the intervals between cross sections are unequal) by the sum of the half-distances to the two adjoining cross sections. A set of cross sections drawn at right angles to the first set gives a good means of checking the result. Volumes are computed by averaging the areas of each pair of adjoining sections and multiplying by the distance between them. Extensions beyond the extreme end-sections are assumed or omitted depending on the probable shape of the ore-boundary.

Where the holes are not in rows but on an irregular grid, the relative positions of the holes must be taken into account. There are two common ways of doing this:

1. The area is divided into triangles, each hole forming the corner of a triangle. The average of the holes at the corners of each triangle is the grade of the triangular prism. The grades of the triangular prisms are averaged together, weighting each for its volume.

In applying this method it is important to lay out the triangles judiciously in order to avoid having too many triangles grouped about a single hole, especially if the grade at this hole is exceptionally high or low.[31] If there are large variations in the thickness of the ore, a contour plan is helpful in laying out the triangles in such a way that the bottom (or top) of each triangular prism has as nearly a uniform slope as possible.[32]

2. A polygon is constructed around each hole by drawing its bounding lines perpendicular to and bisecting the line connecting each pair of holes.[33] This polygon is the plan of a polygonal prism of ore to which is assigned the grade and thickness of ore of the hole at its center. The areas of the polygons are measured either with a planimeter or by dividing the polygon into triangles. The polygons are averaged together, weighting each for its volume.

[31] Weighting each hole by the number of degrees by which the angle at the hole differs from 60 degrees has been recommended. See Harding, James E., Calculation of ore tonnage and grade from drill-hole samples: *Tr. A.I.M.E.*, vol. 46, pp. 117–126, 1921. For certain cases, as where one or more of the holes has a zero value, Harding points out that the method has to be modified. His recommended modification is too long to describe here.

[32] Baxter, C. H., and Parks, R. D., *Mine Examination and Valuation*, 2d Ed., p. 46. Houghton: Mich. College of Mines and Technology, 1939.

[33] Poston, Roy H., Methods and cost of mining at No. 8 Mine, St. L. S. and R. Co., Southeast Mo., lead district: *U.S.B.M. Information Circular* 6160, pp. 5–7, 1929.

Jackson, Charles F., and Hedges, J. H., Metal mining practice: *U.S.B.M. Bull.* 419, pp. 68–69, 1939.

Read, T. T., Estimating ore by the polygon method: *E. & M. J.*, vol. 144, no. 8, pp. 84–85, August, 1943, points out mathematical inaccuracies in the polygon method.

Harding, James E., How to calculate tonnage and grade of an orebody: *E. & M. J.*, vol. 116, pp. 445–448, 1923.

PRECAUTIONS AGAINST SALTING

Interested persons occasionally consider it to their advantage to arrange matters in such a way that the assay returns will prove more encouraging than the true value of the ore would warrant. This may be achieved either through collusion with an obliging assayer or by surreptitious introduction of extraneous material into the samples, an art which is known less grandiloquently to the profession as intentional salting. The methods that have been employed are so varied and ingenious that accounts of the handiwork of salters make entertaining reading.[34] Sometimes before the samples are taken the ore is salted in place either by injecting a solution or suspension of metallic salt into the cracks or by shooting finely divided metal at the ore by means of a shotgun, pistol, or stick of dynamite. However, this method is extravagant because a large amount of metal is required to prepare all of the surface that may be sampled, and it is not always effective since a good engineer may be so uncooperative as to chip or blast away the surface material before sampling. A more economical method is to make sure that the "salt" gets into the samples by waiting until the samples have been cut, and actually putting it there either by opening the sacks at the mouth or on a seam or by injecting liquid or suspended material with a syringe. The material that is used may be finely divided metal such as gold filings, placer gold, or silver precipitate or else a solution or suspension, as of gold chloride or of silver chloride, nitrate or cyanide. All of these materials have been employed in one instance or another.

The subsequent operations of quartering, testing, and assaying all offer opportunities for artificial enrichment, perhaps by gold contained in cigarette ashes, pipe ashes, or tobacco juice.

Fortunately the "nefarious art" never enjoyed wide popularity even in the roaring days when mines changed hands rapidly at high cash prices. It is even rarer under modern conditions because, when ample time is available for checking sample results and even doing development work before payments are due, the skill of the salter is less likely to reap its reward. Nevertheless, since rackets have a way of adapting themselves to new environments, it is not safe to assume that salting is a completely lost art.

[34] Rickard, T. A., Salting: *E. & M. J.*, vol. 142, no. 3, p. 42, March; no. 4, p. 52, May; no. 5, p. 50, June; all 1941.

Hammond, John Hayes, *Autobiography*, pp. 168–170. New York: Farrar and Rinehart, 1935.

McDermott, Walter, Mining reports and mine salting: *Tr. I.M.M.*, vol. 3, pp. 108–130, 1894–5.

The only sure method of preventing salting is to keep the samples under observation at all times, day and night. Such watchfulness is inconvenient at best and becomes impossible on a large examination where, of necessity, many hands must help with the sampling. Most engineers, while conceding that the complete prevention of salting is difficult if not impossible, follow well-established practices which, although not guaranteed to foil a resourceful salter, tend to discourage him by making his handiwork more difficult. Such precautions as sealing sacks with wax or lead seals, placing the sacks in a locked leather mailpouch (proof against a syringe) and storing the samples in a trunk or room under the examiner's padlock or in his own automobile are so much a part of good engineering practice that a mine owner should not consider them a reflection on his integrity. Since places to be channelled, if marked out far in advance of cutting, are an invitation to doctoring, it is well to keep measurements only a shift or less ahead of the samplers.

Some engineers, however, take few if any measures to prevent salting but instead concentrate their attention on detecting it when and if it occurs. Such methods as the following are usually effective:

Dummy samples. A piece of rock or other material known be barren is crushed and sacked as one of the samples. Naturally it should not show values on assay.

Unequal splits. If it is certain that no salting has occurred up to the point at which samples are quartered down, one or more samples are split into "duplicates" having unequal weights. From here on it is difficult to salt so scientifically that the duplicates will give equal assays.[35]

Resampling. As a second sample from the same channel will probably have a different weight from the first, it will be difficult to salt both of them consistently. While it is true that the recuts will not necessarily give values identical with the originals, the average of a second set should correspond with the average of the first. Webber[36] recommends a systematic method of recutting. He places numbers on all the channel samples underground but not in numerical order. Then he selects some for recutting, changes the numbers on them, and keeps a secret register of the old and new numbers. It would thus be difficult to salt the recuts convincingly without knowing which originals they correspond to. This method has the advantage that after changing the tags underground, the list of numbers to be recut can be handed to an assistant.

Panning. Panning the sample reveals the presence of any gold filings or other extraneous metal.

[35] Hoover, Theodore J., *The Economics of Mining*, p. 75. Stanford: Stanford University Press, 1933.

[36] Webber, Morton, The detection of salting, M. & S. P., November 8, pp. 673–6, 1919.

Washing. Washing samples before assay removes soluble salts and finely divided metal. Unfortunately it also removes any legitimate values that may occur in the form of fines.

Recording the nature of the ore. Probably the best precaution against salting, as well as against accidental interchanging of samples and other gross blunders, is to keep detailed descriptive notes of the material in each sample. This is effective not because one can estimate closely the content in base metal sulphides, much less precious metals, but because in most mines high-grade and low-grade ore have their own characteristics of texture, mineralogy, color and general appearance. An assay result widely inconsistent with the description will immediately suggest reexamining the channel and recutting the sample.

Comparison with past production records. Assay returns which give a very much higher average than records of past production may or may not be correct but in any case they call for an explanation.

Selected References

Baxter, Charles H., and Parks, Roland D., *Mine Examination and Valuation,* 2nd Edition, pp. 18–77. Houghton, Michigan: Michigan College of Mines and Technology, 1939.

Herzig, C. S., *Mine Sampling and Valuing.* San Francisco: Mining and Scientific Press, 1914.

Jackson, Chas. F., and Knaebel, John B., *Sampling and Estimation of Ore Deposits,* U. S. Bureau of Mines, Bull. 356, 1932.

Hoover, Theodore Jesse, *The Economics of Mining,* Chapters 3, 4, and 6. Stanford University, Cal.: Stanford University Press, 1933.

Prescott, Basil, Sampling and estimating cordilleran silver-lead deposits: *Trans. American Institute of Mining and Metallurgical Engineers,* vol. 72, pp. 665–676, 1925.

Rickard, T. A., *Sampling and Estimation of Ore in a Mine.* New York: Hill Publishing Company, 1907.

Sharwood, W. J., and von Bernewitz, M., *Bibliography of Literature on Sampling* (to July, 1921). U. S. Bureau of Mines, Publication No. R. I. 2336, 1922.

Swanson, C. O., Probabilities in estimating the grade of gold deposits: *Canadian Mining and Metallurgical Bulletin* No. 397, May, 1945. Same article in *Trans. Can. Inst. Min. and Met.* vol. 48, pp. 323–350, 1945.

3

DRILLING

Acclaim properly went to Sir Edgeworth David and his associates for drilling to learn the subsurface structure of Funi Futi, and to the Geophysical Laboratory for putting down short holes in the Yellowstone to ascertain what goes on below the hot-spring orifices. What of the mining geologist who directs one or a dozen diamond drills that run day and night year after year in order, even like David and Fenner, to test the soundness of geological reasoning from the known into the unknown?

—L. C. GRATON [1]

INTRODUCTION

DRILL holes make it possible to investigate blocks of ground that by any other means would be accessible only at much greater expense, if at all. In some investigations, drill holes are intended merely to secure geological information—the position of a contact, the attitude of a formation, or the sequence in a stratigraphic column. In others they are designed to determine the presence or absence of veins or other guides to ore. In still others, drill holes are used to take samples of the ore and to provide all the information that is required for an estimate of tonnage and grade.

At many mines the resident geologist is in complete charge of drilling, from designing the exploration and making the contracts, to logging and storing the cuttings and core. This arrangement has many advantages, provided the geologist is amply supplied with assistance and is not kept so busy with details and executive duties that he lacks time for analysis and speculation. At some properties the geologist is relieved of the mechanical routine, but he usually has, and always *should* have, the responsibility for recommending the location of drill holes

[1] Graton, L. C., Ore deposits, *Geology, 1888–1938*, Geol. Soc. of America, Fiftieth Anniversary Volume, p. 505, 1941.

and of recording the results of the work. He should therefore be familiar with the possibilities and limitations of the types of drills most commonly used and with the principles on which they operate. While the technique of drill operation is hardly an appropriate subject for this book, the handling of samples, the interpretation of results, and something of the philosophy of exploration by drilling merit discussion from the geological point of view.

Types of Drills

Diamond drills and churn drills are the types most widely used for sampling and exploration in connection with metal mining. Hammer drills are used occasionally, especially underground for testing the walls of drifts in wide orebodies. Shot drills have been used, notably in the Northern Rhodesian copper fields. Rotary rigs for core drilling, so extensively used in oil exploration and designed for speed and economy in deep holes of large diameter, have so far found very limited use in testing metal deposits.[2]

Certain methods employing inexpensive equipment [3] are used for boring shallow holes in soft ground. Wash-boring rigs in which the material is removed from inside a casing by the force of a jet of water, serve to test loose material or determine the depth to bedrock. Hand augers are used to prospect unconsolidated material, and frequently to sample mill tailings. The Empire type of drill, in which a toothed casing is rotated by manpower, is used especially to test placer deposits in regions where labor is cheap and where difficult transportation demands a light machine.

CHURN DRILLING

By E. N. Pennebaker and Kenyon E. Richard

Introduction

The churn drill now generally used for mineral exploration is a variation of the American standard cable rig, a portable rig first used in

---

[2] Rotary rigs were tried out thoroughly at Kimberly, Nevada, in boring through 700 to 1000 feet of rhyolite, rhyolite breccia, and monzonite porphyry. Progress was satisfactory, but costs were high and good core samples in the mineralized zone were difficult to secure. The drilling through zones high in pyrite was extremely unsatisfactory. Under a combination of favorable circumstances, the rotary rig could probably be used to advantage.—E. N. Pennebaker (Personal communication).

[3] Peele, Robert, *Mining Engineers' Handbook*. New York: John Wiley & Sons, 1941. Sec. 9, pp. 02–08.

1878 in Pennsylvania and developed there for drilling oil and gas wells. Near the close of the last century its principles were adopted on the Mesabi iron range, where such rigs were used as substitutes for diamond drills.   In the Tri-State (Joplin) and the Platteville, Wisconsin, mining districts, churn drills were first used for prospecting for lead and zinc ores about 40 years ago.   In 1926 there were 400 of these units in use in the Tri-State mining district. More recently they have been widely applied there to determine the stratigraphy which is a requisite in preparing structure contour maps.

Prospecting for ore in bedrock by churn drilling was first undertaken in the far west near Ely, Nevada, in the search for disseminated copper deposits.   Systematic churn drill prospecting at Ray and Inspiration, Arizona, followed in 1908.

The churn drill digs a vertical hole, employing a bit hung on a cable to which motion is imparted by one of various types of power units.   The bit is lifted a few feet and dropped. The churning motion of the bit abrades the ground, and so a hole is dug.   The cuttings of rock thus produced form a mud or slurry with water; this "sludge" is removed from the hole at regular intervals and constitutes the sample.

Fig. 13—Churn drill in operation. Keystone Model 53. (*Courtesy of* Keystone Driller Company)

Great care must be taken in order to procure an accurate sample, and errors from "salting" and other sources must be watched for with vigilance, particularly in the case of deposits with a high and variable sulphide, or heavy mineral, content, or where variations in the hardness of the ground are frequent.

Churn Drill Equipment

Modern churn drill equipment is made up in two principal sizes, both of which are portable and embody the same mechanical design.   The smaller size is used for shallow drilling, commonly in placer deposits. Depths of 500 feet are attained without difficulty in a moderately soft rock similar to altered granite, and 600 or 700 feet can be reached under favorable conditions. This type of drill is also employed for drilling blast holes in quarry and pit mining. The larger size "swings" a weight of tools up to 6000 pounds and normally drills to depths of 1000 or 1200 feet. Under favorable conditions, in which the rock is evenly firm with a relative absence of faults, shear zones, joints, bedding plane partings, etc., depths of 2000 feet or more can be gained.

Drilling is accomplished by imparting a rectilinear motion, with a magnitude of 18 inches to 3 feet, and a speed of 30 to 60 strokes per minute, to the cable or rope on which the bit is suspended. On earlier rigs the drilling cable was attached to one end of a center-pivoted walking beam actuated by a crank and rod. Power was supplied by a steam engine. Present models employ internal combustion or electric power, and the stroke is imparted to the drilling cable directly by a lateral pull from a crank, rod, and pulley assembly. This type of machine is more compact and portable. The choice of power, internal combustion or electric, is dependent on local conditions. It is the opinion of some drillers that the internal combustion engine, due to power lag, imparts a better "snap" to the cable than does the electric motor.

A wide assortment of accessory equipment is usually required. As drilling progresses, the hole is successively reduced in diameter, requiring a set of bits and casing for each size of hole. Too, a great variety of "fishing" tools must be employed when the cable breaks and tools or bailer are dropped in the hole, or when the casing breaks or becomes unjointed. A complement of these special tools is needed for each hole size.

Under normal conditions a hole is begun with a bit from 8 to 12 inches in diameter. Successive 2-inch reductions in bit diameter are made as the hole is deepened and strings of casing are installed. Under particular conditions the hole may be started with a bit as large as 26 inches in diameter. Holes have been finished with bits as small in diameter as $2\frac{1}{2}$ inches; although the speed of drilling a hole with such small diameter tools is very low, the cost is high, and the sample is less reliable.

The larger size rig requires preparation of a level area about 30 feet by 75 feet adjacent to the location to be drilled.

Drill rigs are usually mounted on self-propelled wheels or caterpillar treads, but occasionally they must be pulled from one location to another by truck or tractor. In any case, a road is graded to the drill site.

The size and power of the drill rig governs the road gradient, sharpness of turns, etc. However, some of the newer models can negotiate very steep and tortuous roads.

Operation of the Churn Drill

Under normal drilling conditions a crew of three men operates the drill when it is being used to sample a mineral deposit. For blast-hole drilling when no sample of the rock is taken, two men are sufficient. The driller is in authority and operates and regulates the machine during drilling, bailing, etc. The driller's helper keeps the equipment in order, dresses the bits, and assists the driller during bailing and bit-changing operations. The sampler is responsible for handling the sludge after it is dumped from the bailer; his duties involve splitting, drying, sacking, and labelling. The sampler's job is very important because slovenliness and inattention to the details of the procedure may render the entire results unreliable.

Drilling

The drilling cycle is relatively simple. If the rock being drilled contains water, the bit is lowered to the bottom of the hole and drilling is begun. If the formation is dry, water is lowered to the bottom of the hole in a bailer and dumped. Water is not poured from the collar, since this procedure tends to wash rock from the sides of the hole, introducing foreign material into the succeeding sample. Drilling is performed by rhythmic raising and dropping of the bit on the bottom of the hole. The striking end of the bit is relatively blunt, and the rock is crushed rather than chipped by the impact of the bit. At the start of its downward cycle the bit is allowed to fall freely until it is close to the bottom of the hole. At this point the return motion of the cable is inaugurated with the result that as the bit hits the rock the cable is stretched and the bit rebounds quickly. This "snap" is a prime requisite for proper drilling. The driller adjusts the speed of the cycle and the rate at which the cable is fed into the hole by judging the "snap" as he holds his hand on the cable.

Bailing

In most cases, after every five-foot depth of hole has been drilled, the bit is hoisted above the collar and the bailer is lowered into the hole on a light cable. The bailer is filled with the sludge of drill cuttings and water, hoisted to the collar, and discharged. This procedure is repeated several times until all of the sludge is removed from the hole, or, if water stands in the hole, bailing is continued until only a small amount of slime remains in the water bailed.

The dart valve type bailer is most commonly used because the valve is sturdy and functions easily. However, this valve is situated 1 foot to 18 inches above the bottom of the bailer, and so there is a small percentage of the sludge which cannot be recovered from the bottom of the hole. If, as is most often the case, the valuable material being sought is a heavy mineral, it is possible that this remaining few gallons of sludge in the bottom of the hole might contain more than a true proportion of the mineral due to gravity concentration. Consequently, it should be removed if possible and added to the sample. This can be accomplished in two ways: (1) A bailerful of water is lowered to the bottom of the hole, mixed with the sludge, and then bailed out again. (2) A bailer of either the "sand pump" or "flat valve" type is used to get this last bit of sludge. Neither of these types is very satisfactory when used for the entire bailing procedure. The flat valve bailer is difficult to discharge when completely full of sludge, or if the sludge contains much sand. The sand pump type employs a plunger which sucks the sludge into the bailer in the manner of a syringe. This mechanism tends to become clogged and difficult to operate.

Casing

Rarely does a mineral deposit occur in rock that is uniformly firm so that the walls of the hole do not slough while the hole is being drilled. Fault structures and zones softened by alteration are frequently encountered. Also, the formation may be too soft to support itself, or it may spall when exposed to air or water for a short time, or fragments may be knocked off by cable or tools. This tendency for the walls of the hole to cave, if slight, may not impede drilling. Therefore, if accurate samples of certain portions of the hole are not needed, a slight amount of caving can be ignored. However, if an accurate representation of each segment of rock drilled is required, dilution of the sample by rock fragments caving from higher in the hole must be prevented by casing.

Casing consists of lengths of iron or steel pipe, of slightly smaller diameter than the hole, which are threaded together and lowered down the hole to its bottom. The hole may be filled up several feet with cavings, in which case considerable bailing must be done before the casing extends to the bottom of the hole. After the hole is cased, drilling is continued with the next smaller size bit. When the hole again caves, a string of smaller diameter casing is telescoped within the first, and so on.

A deep hole in difficult ground may require many strings of casing, entailing considerable expense. Removal of this casing after a hole is completed is commonly a difficult process.

If a hole enters a zone which quickly caves and casing is put down through the caved material to the bottom of the hole, when drilling is resumed the casing will usually follow down close to the head of the bit until firm rock is reached. Thus the caving zone is blocked off, and drilling may be continued.

Normally a small amount of caving from the walls of a hole cannot be detected by the driller. Under conditions in which the rock contains no water and all drilling water is lowered down the hole, the volume of sludge bailed will give an approximation of the amount of caving being experienced, provided the rock is even in hardness and texture and a hole of precisely uniform diameter is developed. If the need for accuracy of sampling is great enough, the casing should always follow down close to the bottom of the hole. If the rock is relatively soft, a heavier type of casing may be used and driven down to the bottom of the hole at intervals of 5, 10, or 25 feet.

If the rock is hard or contains hard ribs, the procedure of keeping the casing close to the bottom becomes very difficult and time-consuming. After a small segment of hole has been drilled below the bottom of the casing, the shoulder on which the casing rests must then be cut down to the bottom of the hole. This is accomplished with an "under-reamer" bit, which consists of cutting edges which are held in against a spring while being lowered through the casing and expand when below the casing. Before the under-reaming procedure is begun the casing must be raised several feet above the shoulder to allow room for the churning action of the under-reamer. After a zone of very badly caving rock is crossed, under-reaming cannot again be employed until a smaller string of casing is put into the hole, because if the casing is raised off the shoulder to this zone of caving rock, the bottom of the hole will then be filled again by cavings.

Samples

The advisability of keeping the casing close to the bottom of the hole is a compromise between the local requirements for economy and the demands for accuracy of sample.

Taking the Sample

It is the practice of many churn drillers and drill contractors to advance the hole as rapidly as possible and establish themselves as efficient operators. Many foremen of churn drill crews crowd the drilling in order to attain good cost-per-foot records. This practice is detrimental to proper sampling procedure. The geologist should carry proper authority to outline and guide the sampling and any of the details of drilling, bailing, and casing which could affect the accuracy of samples taken. He should exercise this authority with vigilance.

The frequency of sampling is largely dependent on the distribution in the rock of the valuable mineral being sought, although it is usually impractical to drill more than 10 feet without bailing. An interval of 5 feet is commonly utilized if the mineral is distributed through the rock with moderate regularity. Otherwise, intervals as low as two feet are used. In many circumstances the structure overlying the orebody is well enough known to permit drilling nearly to the orebody before sampling is begun, thus increasing speed and lowering costs.

Sludge consistency bears an important relation to sampling. Thick sludge goes through the splitter with difficulty, and the necessary addition of water to wash it through tends to separate the heavy and light minerals. Thin sludge passes through the splitter easily and, in general, is more satisfactory. Tests conducted at Kimberly, Nevada, indicated a more uniform distribution of sulphide minerals through thin sludge than through thick sludge. When the bit is hoisted to the collar of the hole after drilling, the driller can determine the consistency of the sludge in the bottom of the hole by inspecting the material clinging to the bit. If the sludge appears to be too thick, it can be diluted by water lowered in the bailer to the bottom of the hole. On the other hand, if the valuable mineral is a very heavy one, such as gold, concentration may occur through settling. A thick sludge tends to retard this effect.

The bailer is discharged into a launder which conveys the sludge to the point where it is sampled. This launder should be of sufficient capacity to avoid runover when the larger sizes of bailer are being used and the sludge is very thin, in which case the discharge is rapid and voluminous.

There are numerous methods of sampling the sludge from the launder. Rarely, all of the sludge is collected in large cans, dried, weighed for theoretical weight comparison, and reduced to a small volume, for assay, by the Jones riffle sampler or other acceptable method. Common practice employs a composite type of Jones riffle sampler, or "splitter," in which the sludge is successively halved as it pours through 3 tiers of riffles, an eighth of the original volume of sludge being caught in a tub. If a 10- or 12-inch hole is being drilled, several tubs may be filled from a run of 5 feet. These can be allowed to stand and settle and the clear water decanted; or they can be poured back through the splitter and further reduced in volume. In the event two equivalent samples are needed, a dry one for assay and a wet one for metallurgical tests or geological inspection, the splitter can be designed to save both halves of the final riffle split. The sample for assay is dried and carefully sacked. If sulphides are present, drying is done over a slow fire to avoid roasting.

Oil and grease from the drilling cable tend to foul the wet sample for flotation tests.

Before tubs are removed from the splitter discharge, the sludge clinging to the launder and splitter should be washed through and the proper proportion included in the sample. When extreme care is being applied the bit and bailer are washed in the launder.

The principal sources of error in the above procedure are due to the high specific gravity of some ore minerals and the friability of others. The tendencies to slime due to friability or concentrate due to high specific gravity are enhanced by the use of too much water in flushing out the splitter.

To compensate for the lack of good rock samples from churn drill holes, a number of methods are used, chiefly in the oil fields, for determining the nature of the material penetrated by this drill. Various cable-tool core barrels are available for taking core samples from the hole. These have been used with variable success to take samples at selected intervals.

Measurement of the electrical properties [4] of the wall rock affords evidences of the nature and even of the attitude of rock formations. "Electrical logs" known to the profession as "slumberjays" [5] are graphs of resistivity and self-potential at successive depths. For taking samples [6] a cylindrical bullet can be fired into the wall from a "gun" suspended in the drill hole and the cylinder containing the sample recovered by means of an attached spring. A camera [7] small enough to oper-

---

[4] Heiland, C. A., Geophysical Exploration, pp. 825–836. New York: Prentice-Hall, Inc., 1940.

[5] Americanization of the French pronunciation of the names of C. and M. Slumberger, who developed the method.

[6] Leonardon, Eugene G., and McCann, D. C., Exploring drill holes by sample-taking bullets: A.I.M.E. Tech. Pub., No. 1062, 1939.

[7] Low, Bela, and Kelly, Sherwin F., A borehole camera: Mining & Met., February, 1932, p. 81.

ate in a 5½-inch borehole has been devised in Holland for photographing the bedding in the walls of waterwells. Measurement of the radioactivity [8] of successive beds has been used in stratigraphic correlation. All of these methods, some employed in the oil industry consistently, some experimentally, have been used to a very limited extent, if at all, in connection with metal mining.

Handling Samples in the Geologic Laboratory

As a rule, a wet sample of the churn drill sludge is sent to the geologic laboratory at regular intervals corresponding to the assay interval, which is commonly every 5 feet.

Various methods of caring for and examining the sludge are employed, depending upon the purpose of the drilling. The sludge may merely be examined and discarded with brief notes taken for the log. In other instances the sludge is panned to remove the mud and fine particles, and the clean rock and metallic mineral fragments are then examined. These are sometimes discarded, or they may be saved for future reference by one of several methods: (1) The fragments may be glued to strips of cardboard or wood; (2) they may be placed within glass tubes in their proper sequence; or samples from each interval may be saved in individual glass bottles.

Considering the cost of obtaining the sample and the advantage of being able to refer back to the sample for purposes of rock classification or mineral identification, it is very desirable to keep permanently a portion of the sludge. Besides this, rejects of the assay pulp should be kept permanently on file. One western mining company uses the following procedure:

The sludge for each sample interval is carefully panned, and the clean rock fragments and sulphide minerals are segregated and slowly dried on a hot plate. Various fractions are removed for mineral grain examination under the microscope, for thin sections of rock fragments, and for briquettes of the metallic mineral grains. Rock fragments from each sample interval are then cemented on a clean pine board, each one-half inch on the board representing five feet of hole. Sulphide minerals are affixed beside the rock fragments on the board, roughly according to their abundance. Footage intervals and assay values are recorded on the board. The boards, each 4 feet and 3 inches long, 3 inches wide, and ⅜ inch thick, are filed in sequence in cabinets and can be referred to readily.

[8] Jackson, Warren J., and Campbell, John L. P., Some practical aspects of radioactivity well logging: *A.I.M.E. Tech. Pub.*. No. 1923, 1945, pp. 1–27.

Records and Logs

It is standard practice to compile a composite log showing the pertinent information acquired from drilling the hole. The log is drawn to scale, and the various data are plotted at appropriate sample intervals or depths. Although conditions of drilling and the kind of information accumulated vary from district to district, all logs of drill holes include certain essential data and such additional detail as judgment considers expedient. In districts where churn drilling has been conducted for many years, experience has demonstrated that compilation of a good amount of detail on one log rather than several separate records is often rewarded many times over. Conversely, failure to record any but the most obvious data, may, years later, result in the need to redrill the hole.

Information comprising a complete log may be grouped as follows: (1) engineering, (2) assaying, (3) geological, (4) metallurgical, (5) operational. The following paragraphs enumerate most of the features which might be included under each of these headings. Of course, these data are not necessarily applicable to all situations.

Engineering. In this category are contained the location of the hole (coordinates), name of claim or property on which it is situated, collar elevation, depth, and date of drilling. The amount of sludge recovered may be recorded here.

Assaying. This includes assay returns of individual samples for valuable constituents, results of composite samples, and occasional returns for unusual elements.

The engineering and assaying data may be considered the bare essentials of a log.

Geological. The information included here is based on a study of the rock cuttings after removal of slimes by panning. The amount of detail recorded varies at different properties. Such information as the kind of rock, type and strength of alteration and mineralization, relative amounts of ore and gangue minerals, and any unusual or diagnostic features should be recorded for each sample interval.

Metallurgical. The summarized results of metallurgical tests on any of the wet samples or composites can be recorded on the drafted log.

Operational. Operating data are normally supplied on a form which the driller or drill foreman fills out for each shift. The information is very helpful to the geologist for locating structures or soft zones of alteration which are not apparent in the panned rock fragments. This "driller's log" should contain space for comment on such features of each sample as hardness of the rock, caving of the hole, reliability of the sample, number of bailerfuls for each sample, depth of any ground water standing in the hole, color of sludge, drilling time, and a casing record including depth to bottom of each string of casing, size of casing, and whether or not the casing is following down as the hole is being drilled. Also there should be comments on all unusual features encountered.

Determining Structure

Information yielded by churn drilling, in addition to giving the assay value of the rock, may be used to decipher major structural features of the district. Boundaries of rock units can be determined by a careful examination of the sludge. Gouge from large faults can sometimes be identified during the panning of the sludge. Such features of mineralogy as changes from the oxidized zone to the zone of secondary enrichment and from that to the primary ore zones are readily shown. Insoluble residues, prepared by treating sludge with acid, are widely used in correlating limestone formations.

Many small but important structural features are unfortunately destroyed in the pulverized sludge.

Cost and Speed

The costs and speed of churn drilling vary widely depending upon: (1) hardness of the ground, extent of its fracturing, and its ability to stand without caving; (2) the care and manner in which the hole is cased in order to ensure reliable samples; (3) the speed with which casing can be recovered and the rig can be moved to a new set-up; (4) the diameter of the hole and the depth to which it is drilled; (5) the manner of sampling and the special precautions taken, and (6) the skill and experience of the drill crew and foreman in the particular district being explored. As can be readily imagined, these factors vary widely.

Under favorable conditions holes can be rapidly drilled to 1000 or 1200 feet at moderate cost. Deeper holes require heavier equipment.

In general it may be stated that shallow holes (about 300 feet in depth) in which average sampling precautions are maintained, should cost from $1.00 to $2.50 per foot. In the Tri-State zinc district, where the average depth of holes is about 300 feet, all drilling is done by contract at a present (1947) cost of $1.40 to $1.50 a foot.[9] Elsewhere, holes up to 1000 feet in depth in good drilling ground and with average precautions for taking samples should cost from $2.50 to $4.50 per foot. Deep holes in which exceptional care in casing and sampling has been maintained may exceed $20.00 per foot.

[9] Fowler, George M., Written communication.

Geologist's Duties

The geologist has a number of duties with respect to churn drill exploration for mineral deposits. He must decide on the proper spacing of holes and lay out the drilling program accordingly. He should supervise the taking and handling of samples at the drill. In the laboratory it is his duty to prepare and examine the samples for information to go on the geologic log of the hole. He will very likely prepare and keep a portion of the sample on file for future reference.

It is the geologist's job to construct the drilling and geologic log of the hole. The results of drilling must be combined with other geologic and engineering information on maps and sections. The tonnage and grade of orebodies are calculated, and the possibility of extending the orebody is always his active responsibility.

DIAMOND DRILLING [10]

In diamond drilling, a ring-like bit, armed with small diamonds, rotates and cuts out a cylindrical core of the rock through which it passes. The bit is mounted on the end of a shaft consisting of hollow flush-jointed rods. The rods not only convey motion and pressure from the impelling mechanism (the drilling machine) to the bit but serve as a pipe to conduct a stream of water which flushes away the cuttings and ground-up rock. These cuttings afford a supplementary sample.

Periodically, as boring progresses, the driller pulls the rods out of the hole, unscrewing the joints where necessary, and removes the core which has accumulated in a cylindrical chamber (the core barrel) just behind the bit. The core, which constitutes the principal sample, is placed in a container for transportation to the laboratory or the core-shed.

The Bit

Until recent years, bits were set by hand with large Brazilian carbonado diamonds, but efficiency and costs have lately been improved by using small stones (bortz), similar in nature to gem diamonds though less precious because of their minor size and lack of perfection. Bits used at the Hollinger Mine carry from 140 to 225 stones (depending on the size of the bit), each stone weighing 1/70 carat on the average.[11]

[10] This section has had the benefit of reading and criticism by R. J. Longyear and E. N. Pennebaker.

[11] Dunbar, W. Roy, Diamond drilling at the Hollinger Mine: *Canadian Institute of Mining and Metallurgy*, vol. 43, pp. 42–54, 1940.

Dougherty, J. W., and Douglas, J. M., Mining practice at the Hollinger Gold Mine, *A.I.M.E. Tech. Pub. 1159*, 1940.

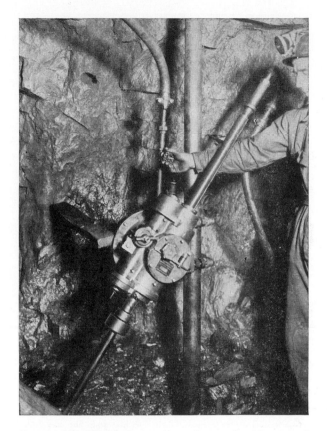

Fig. 14—Diamond drill operating underground. (*Courtesy of* E. J. Longyear Company)

Longyear bits use somewhat larger stones, averaging 15 to 20 to the carat.[12]   A reaming shell set with a few larger bortz stones is attached above the bit and helps maintain the gauge of the hole.   The new type of bit permits speeds up to 1000 or 2000 R.P.M. and requires a relatively small amount of pressure on the bit during drilling.[13]

In the bits just described the stones are embedded in the surface of the metal that constitutes the bit.   Another type of bit recently developed is made by heating a mixture of powdered tungsten carbide, powdered metallic cobalt and bortz in a mold under pressure.[14]   This produces a hard matrix impregnated throughout with diamonds.   Drilling is carried out under heavy pressure.

[12] Longyear, R. D., Personal letter.
[13] Longmore, H. J., Diamond drilling today: *Min. & Met.*, vol. 21, pp. 335–336, 1940.
[14] Weslow, W. C., Use of diamond impregnated cemented carbide for core bits: *A.I.M.E. Tech. Pub. 1172*, 1940.

Fig. 15—Gasoline-driven diamond drill. Drilling rods not attached. Long-year Junior Straitline with twin hydraulic swivel head. Cat Head or Spool Hoist. (*Courtesy of* E. J. Longyear Company)

The Core Barrel

The core barrel is a cylindrical chamber for receiving and retaining the core as drilling progresses. One end of it carries the bit and the other is attached to the string of drill rods. The older type of core barrel consists of a single hollow cylinder but for better protection of the core a double tube barrel has come into common use. This employs an inner cylinder which, in some models, is permitted by ball bearings to rotate or to remain stationary independent of the outer tube so that the core is freed of any friction or twisting action. In order to prevent the water that descends through the rods from washing any of the core out of the barrel, the water is not allowed to pass through the inner core tube but is circuited through the space between the inner and the outer tube.

Exceptionally complete core recovery under unusually difficult conditions is claimed for a special core barrel so designed that as soon as the core jams in the inner barrel, whether because the barrel is full or because the core has become wedged inside it, the flow of water is automatically cut off and the increasing pressure at the pump warns the driller to stop the machine and pull the rods.[15]

Coring of very soft material has recently been achieved on the iron ranges by freezing, using pre-chilled kerosene instead of drill-water.[16]

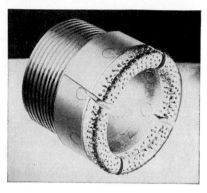

Fig. 16—Diamond-drill bit set with bortz stones. (*Courtesy of* E. J. Longyear Company)

Fig. 17—Diamond-drill bit and reaming shell, both set with bortz stones. (*Courtesy of* E. J. Longyear Company)

Samples

The Core

As it is removed from the core barrel, the core consists (one hopes) of one or more cylindrical pieces of rock. In exceptionally solid ground

---

[15] Duffield, C. F., Core recovery devices used in South Australian drilling practice: *Australian Inst. Mining & Met.*, New Series, Nos. 131–132, 1943. Abstract, *Mining Magazine*, pp. 113–114, August, 1944.

Burrows, L. J., Improved barrel and bit increases core recovery: *E. & M. J.*, vol. 147, Nov., 1946, pp. 80–81. The Pickard core barrel incorporates similar features; see news article, *E. & M. J.*, vol. 148, Oct., 1947, p. 192.

[16] Tyler, Stanley A., Oral communication.

it may be in a single piece the length of the core barrel, *i.e.*, 5, 10 or even 20 feet long, but more often it consists of sections from a foot or more down to an inch or less in length or even small fragments and compact clay. The driller places the core in a box having longitudinal compartments of the proper size to accommodate it, and dividing each "run" from the next by a small block of wood marked with the footage. The depth of the hole is ascertained by keeping track of the number of drill rods (which are of standard length) and correcting for the distance between the collar of the hole and the top end of the last rod. As the last piece of core may remain in the hole, perhaps still attached to the underlying rock, it is a good plan to measure the distance from the face of the bit to the bottom of the core in the core barrel so that when the piece of core is recovered it can be put in its proper place.[17] An even more precise method, applicable only to steep downward holes, is to measure the depth to the top of the remaining core by letting a weighted steel tape down the hole.[18]

Splitting

In order to preserve a continuous sample of the core for the geological record and at the same time obtain an assay of it, each section of core for which an assay is desired should be split longitudinally; half of it is preserved and the other half is sacked and sent to the assay laboratory.

When much core is to be split a mechanical device is economical. A mechanical splitter[19] consists of a clamp to hold the piece of core and a blade to which force can be applied with a hammer. For short jobs the more laborious process of placing the core in a piece of angle-iron and splitting it longitudinally with a hammer and cold-chisel may be necessary. A slightly more convenient method is to take a piece of pipe a little larger than the core and slit it along one side to allow the insertion of a chisel.

Regarding the assaying of core, the practice varies among different mines. In some cases, all of the core is split, and half of it sent for assay whether the material is ore or not. In other cases the core is not assayed except for intervals in which the sludge assays show values. In still others the core goes to the assay office only when it shows mineraliza-

---

[17] Longyear, Robert D., Recovering and interpreting diamond core drill samples: *Min. & Met.*, p. 239, May, 1937.

[18] MacLachlan, D. K. F., The sampling and estimation of bore-hole cores and sludges: *Trans. Inst. Mining and Metallurgy*, vol. 40, p. 179, 1931.

[19] Longyear Co., Minneapolis.

tion. The latter practice is safe enough in base-metal mines and even in precious-metal mines if the character of the ore is well known, but if there is any doubt it is better to assay too much than too little. It would be poor economy to save the price of an assay by taking the remotest chance on missing the indication of an orebody. Even low assays, when correlated with other facts, may disclose valuable information.

Logging

Before splitting the core, the geologist examines it carefully, and since certain features show up best on the broken surface, he also examines it after splitting. Usually the texture of the rock is brought out better by wetting it. The identification of rocks should not be left to the drill runner's ideas of lithology, yet the drillers' own log, containing a record of the hardness or softness of ground and the places where the motion of the machine indicates that core is being

Fig. 18—Core splitter. (*Courtesy of* E. J. Longyear Company)

ground up, may be of great help in interpreting results.

The geologist's log is a "foot by foot" description written in a notebook or, preferably, on a standard form that can be filed with others. As in mapping, the description can be expressed most systematically and quantitatively by symbols, but any unusual rock should be fully described in words. Besides the type and appearance of the rock, the following facts usually deserve recording:

Percentage of core recovered in each run
Grain size, expressed quantitatively
Recognizable minerals
Type and degree of alteration
Angle between structural planes and the axis of the core:
   Cleavage and schistosity

> Bedding
> Joints
> Veinlets or stringers
> Location of sections in which the core is crushed or broken or where only
> clay or mud is recovered (This may indicate a fault.)

To form a record more accurate in most respects than verbal description, John E. Kiser [20] has developed a method of photographing the core on 35 mm. color film under standard illumination.

Supplementary to the description in words or photographs, a graphic log depicts the hole with its dip corrected for deflection and shows wall-rock in a color convention, positions of veins, and assays of core and sludge. Each hole has a sheet to itself as this makes for easier handling than a large sheet on which several holes have been plotted.

In addition the holes should be plotted in the proper projection on the standard plans, cross sections and longitudinal sections of the mine. In some cases, special methods of projection are helpful; for example, in Ducktown,[21] drill holes are plotted on plans by projecting them not vertically, but up or down the dip. Thus, the projection shows the geologist what the hole would have passed through if it had been drilled horizontally.

Storage

Core is usually filed for permanent storage in flat trays fitted with cleats dividing the tray lengthwise into compartments $\frac{1}{16}''$ to $\frac{1}{8}''$ wider than the diameter of the core. It is a mistake to make core-boxes too long; core is heavy and a box much more than six feet long can hardly be handled by one man. Core boxes are often piled one on top of another, but they are much more accessible if a rack is constructed, so that any box can be taken out without unpiling the ones on top of it. Each box should be plainly marked with the number of the hole and the footage, preferably in paint rather than crayon, thus: "Box 24, D. D. H. 15, 675'–714'." A serial number on the box and a corresponding record in the log makes it easier to find a particular section of core and facilitates putting the box back in its correct position.

The value of the proper treatment of core is emphasized by contrast in the following description of bad practice quoted from a private report by an engineer who recently examined a property in the Michigan iron country:

[20] Kiser, John E., Drill cores logged by color photography: E. & M. J., vol. 146, No. 9, pp. 82–4, 1945.
[21] Kendall, H. F., and Ffolliott, J. H., Geology applied to mining in the Ducktown district: Min. & Met., vol. 14, p. 175 ff., April, 1933.

"Note: The core in the file is selected core,—*i.e.*, only one piece for each run was saved; consequently a ½" to 1" piece of core may represent from 1' to 10' of drilling. In some places core is missing entirely—either was not recovered originally or has been lost since. The core was marked with adhesive labels, but being stored in a building which is alternately damp and then dry, many of the labels have come off for long consecutive footages, hence it was often impossible to be sure of the footage."

Core deserves respectful treatment and perpetual care. The few dollars a foot that the drilling has cost is not a fair index to the true value of the core; it may hold information that will lead to the discovery of

Fig. 19—Galvanized iron box for storing core. (*Courtesy of* E. J. Longyear Company)

a million dollars' worth of ore, or, if fortune is less smiling, it may at least save tens of thousands of dollars of useless expenditure. When a new problem comes up for study, no written description is as satisfying as a look at the core itself, for no matter how carefully the core has been logged, fate too often decrees that the particular observations that are needed for a special purpose have been overlooked. Even a photograph does not fill the requirements if, for example, heavy-mineral determinations are desired. The common practice of saving representative portions from each run as a permanent sample is only partially satisfactory because no one can be sure just what parts may disclose information of incalculable value. Although special facilities and even a special building may have to be provided, the expense is small in proportion to the possible value of the information that they preserve.

The Sludge

During diamond drilling, water is pumped down the inside of the rods and comes up on the outside, emerging between the rods and the collar of the casing.   The rock fragments that it brings up are collected and form the sludge sample.   If the core has been recovered intact, the sludge sample is not necessarily assayed unless the run has been in ore, although in precious-metal mines it is good practice to assay all of the sludge, even though the core "doesn't look like ore."   If bad luck occasions a poor core recovery, sludge samples become doubly precious.

Many operators are inclined to disregard sludge because in their experience its assays have not been consistent with those of the core. But failure to obtain a check between the core and the sludge usually indicates faulty technique in collection of sludge samples.   Discrepancies may be caused by (1) incomplete washing of the hole between runs, (2) loss of drilling water (3) either salting or dilution from material from higher in the hole, (4) overflow of fines from the sludge boxes, (5) adherence of metallic particles to greased rods.   These contingencies merit brief discussion:

(1) If the hole is not washed thoroughly at the end of each run, heavy metallic particles, especially gold, are likely to accumulate in the bottom of the hole until an extra surge of water during a subsequent run flushes them up.   Unfortunately the column of water rising in the drill hole serves as an effective classifier, with the result that the light material comes up first, making the water turbid; the heavier particles, which are usually the most valuable, come up later after the water has begun to clear.   Matson and Wallis [22] find that it sometimes takes 45 minutes of washing to bring all of the sludge up.   They recommend examining the wash water in a beaker at three-minute intervals until it is completely free from mineral particles. Recovery of heavy particles may sometimes be improved by "reverse" pumping, i.e., pumping the water down between the rods and the casing to return upward through the inside of the rods.[23]

(2) If any of the water that is pumped down the hole escapes through fissures or permeable channels in the rock, it takes sludge with it and may cause an enrichment or impoverishment of the sample.   Loss of water is detected by measuring the amount pumped down and comparing it with the amount returned.   Serious loss must be prevented by stopping up the openings in some way; such varied materials [24] as bran, oatmeal, sawdust, tallow, and horse manure, are used on occasion, but the most positive remedy is to place quick-setting cement in the hole.   If the water is escaping from the upper part of the hole, it may be retained by a casing.

(3) Rods may grind against the wall of the hole, especially if the hole is crooked, and if the rock is locally rich it can salt the sludge sample.   Simi-

[22] Matson, H. T. and Wallis, G. Allan, Drill sampling and interpretation of sampling results in the copper fields of Northern Rhodesia: A.I.M.E. Tech. Pub. No. 373, 1931.

[23] MacLachlan, D. K. F., The sampling and estimation of borehole cores and sludges: Trans. Inst. Mining and Metallurgy, vol. 40, p. 184, 1931.

[24] Walker, Harlan A., Diamond drilling in El Potosi Mine, Chihuahua, Mexico: E. & M. J., vol. 114, p. 896, 1922.

larly, pieces of the wall may be dislodged in the course of raising and lower-ing the rods. Therefore, if accurate sludge samples are required, it is good practice to case the hole down to the beginning of the ore-section before proceeding to drill through it. In fact, Lake Superior iron-ore practice calls for reaming the casing to the bottom of the hole after each five-foot run.

(4) If turbid water overflows from the sludge-collecting boxes, it carries away light particles and effects a concentration in the sludge sample. On the other hand, oil or grease can make the sludge-box into a flotation cell and carry off some of the metallic particles.

Where reliable sludge is essential, enough barrels or sludge boxes are used to collect *all* of the return water from each run and the ensuing washing. Matson and Wallis [25] used ten or more boxes, arranged in a semi-circle, fed by a launder that could be rotated to fill each box in turn. As the sludge settles, the clear water is decanted, or siphoned, off. Settling of colloidal material is hastened by adding either a strong solution of alum or a solution of lime. (The residue of spent carbide has been found effective and handy.)

(5) To prevent metallic particles from adhering to the rods, a soap solu-tion is commonly used instead of grease for lubricating the rods when drill-ing in ore. Before applying it, the rods are cleaned inside and out with kero-sene or gasoline.[26]

The settled sludge from each run is collected from the boxes and combined. It is then dried over a fire or a steam table; stirring with a wooden paddle prevents it from caking.

TABLE 3

STANDARD SIZES OF CORE-BARREL BITS [27] (*in inches*)

| Designation | Core-Barrel Bit | | Hole * | Core |
	Inside Diam.	Outside Diam.	Approx. Diam.	Approx. Diam.
EX	$7/8$	$1 7/16$	$1 1/2$	$7/8$
AX	$1 7/32$	$1 27/32$	$1 7/8$	$1 1/8$
BX	$1 11/16$	$2 5/16$	$2 3/8$	$1 5/8$
NX	$2 3/16$	$2 15/16$	3	$2 1/8$

* Assuming hole $1/32$ inch larger than bit and listing diameters to nearest $1/8$ inch.

[25] Walker, Harlan A., *op. cit.*
[26] MacLachlan, D. K. F., The sampling and estimation of borehole cores and sludges: *Trans. Inst. of Min. & Met.*, vol. 40, p. 185, 1931.
[27] *Diamond Drill Core Fittings*, Commercial Standard CS17–47, 4th Ed. National Bureau of Standards, 1947. Slightly different standards are in use in eastern Canada.

Combining Assay Returns from Sludge and Core

The material which the drill has passed through is thus represented by two types of samples: the core and the sludge. If both are completely recovered, their assays should check unless, through irregular distribution of minerals in the ore, the core happens to have included rich grains or stringers that the sludge missed or vice versa. As the sludge represents a large cross-sectional area of rock—usually larger, in fact, than the core—it is by no means negligible and in theory at least, the two assays should be combined mathematically. If core recovery is complete it matters little how the combining factors are determined so long as logical principles are followed, but it will be convenient to outline the alternative methods here, since they will serve as a basis for dealing with incomplete recoveries.

The factors for combining core and sludge [28] may be derived from either (1) theoretical diameter of core and of hole (see Table 3) or, (2) measured volumes or weights of core and sludge. For the core, the weight is determined by actual weighing; the volume by measuring the diameter with calipers. Either the weight or the volume is sufficient as one can be converted into the other by using the specific gravity. For the sludge, the weight may be determined by weighing the dried sludge; the volume, if required, is calculated from it by a specific gravity conversion.

If core recovery is incomplete, as unfortunately it very often is, the sludge sample assumes real importance. The presumption is that the unrecovered part of the core was ground up and became a part of the sludge; therefore the calculation must take into account the percentage of core recovery. This may be estimated by one of the following methods:

> *a.* The pieces of core are fitted together and their combined length is measured.
> *b.* The core is weighed and compared with the weight of core that should be cut by a bit of the size used.[29]
> *c.* In addition to the weight, the specific gravity of the core is determined by weighing in water and the diameter of the core is measured at frequent intervals.[30] The recovery is computed by comparing actual weight with the

---

[28] Greenhalgh, C. W., Calculations from diamond drill sampling—a comparison of methods: *A.I.M.E. Tech. Pub. 1784, Mining Technology,* pp. 1–8, January, 1946.

[29] Weller, John M., Interpretation of sludge and core assays: *E. & M. J.,* vol. 139, p. 37, July, 1938.

[30] Matson, H. T., and Wallis, G. Allan, Drill sampling and interpretation of sampling results in the copper fields of Northern Rhodesia: *A.I.M.E. Tech. Pub. No. 373,* p. 9, 1931.

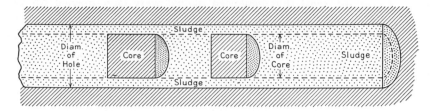

Fig. 20—Sectional view of a diamond drill hole to illustrate source of core and sludge where core recovery is incomplete. (Idealized diagram)

estimated weight for 100% recovery, calculated from the volume and specific gravity according to the formula:

$$\frac{\text{weight of core} \times 100}{\text{Length of run} \times \pi(\text{diam.}/2)^2 \times \text{sp. gr.} \times 62.5}*$$

Having determined the percentage of core recovery, the factors for computing the ratio of combination can be calculated from this and from the total volume of the hole as indicated by the size of the bit. To facilitate calculation, tables and graphs are published showing relative volumes for varying percentages of core recovery.[31] However, combining sludge and core in proportion to the volumes of rock represented is valid only if sludge recovery is 100 per cent. If some of the sludge has been lost or if material from outside the proper boundary of the hole has entered the sample, the sludge is a poor sample and as Moehlman pertinently remarks: "No amount of mathematical calculation can make a poor sample good." Still, a poor sample may be better than none (though this statement is open to argument) and if recoveries are not too seriously incomplete or overcomplete, Moehlman's [32] method of weighting the sludge sample by its percentage of recovery (or by the reciprocal of recovery if it is over 100%) is a plausible method of making use of the assay. The percentage of sludge recovery is determined by weighing the dried sludge and comparing with the theoretical amount that should have been recovered, as calculated from bit-diameter and core recovery.

The importance of combining sludge and core in order to get the correct results is illustrated by data from the Colquiri tin mine in Bolivia,[33]

---

* Weight of a cubic foot of water.

[31] E. J. Longyear & Co., *Bulletin No. 46*, Minneapolis, Minn. Moehlman, R. S., Diamond drilling in exploration and development: *A.I.M.E. Tech. Pub. No. 1858*, p. 8 ff., 1946.

[32] Moehlman, R. S., Diamond drilling in exploration and development: *A.I.M.E. Tech. Pub. 1858, Mining Technology*, p. 11, January, 1946.

[33] Turneaure, F. S., Personal communication.

where a series of veins that had been drilled were later opened up and sampled by channeling. (The purpose of drilling was not, in this case, to make an accurate determination of grade but to indicate whether or not to develop certain veins). In twelve drill-hole intersections, core recovery averaged 84.3%, most of the missing core representing sections of friable vein-matter. Core assays averaged 1.44% Sn; core and sludge assays, combined in proportion to theoretical volume, averaged 1.87% Sn as compared with channel samples for the same veins, though not in the identical places, which averaged 1.89% Sn. On narrow veins (averaging 0.8 meters) the check was less satisfactory but likewise confirmed the soundness of combining the assays for sludge and core: for eight veins, core assays averaged 1.83% and combined assays 2.82%, compared with 2.68% for channel samples.

Example of Methods of Calculation

Data: length of run: 5 ft.   Bit, AX.   Sp. gr. of rocks: 2.63.

	Recovered			*Assay*
	Length	*Weight*	*Percentage*	*% Cu*
Core	1.2 ft.	1.4 lb.	(24%)	0.50
Sludge		7.2 lb.	(50%)	1.10

(Figures in parentheses are computed.)

For an AX bit the factors for volume and weight would be calculated as follows (also available from tables):

	Diameter	*Area* (cross section)	*Vol. per* Ft. of Length	*Wgt. per* Ft. of Lgth. (sp. gr. 2.63)	*% of* Vol. of Hole
Hole	1⅞" = 1.875"	2.76 sq. in.	.0192 cu. ft.	3.15 lb.	100
Core	1⅛" = 1.125"	0.99 " "	.0069 " "	1.13 "	36
Sludge		1.77 " "	.0123 " "	2.02 "	64

Method 1. Weighting for theoretical volume (disregarding incompleteness of core and sludge recovery).

	Percent of Vol. of Hole	Assay	Product
Core	36	0.50 % Cu.	18.0
Sludge	64	1.10 % Cu.	70.4
	100		88.4

Average assay: .88% Cu.

Method 2. Weighting for theoretical volume (taking incompleteness of core recovery into account).

Note: Since only 1.2 ft. of core was recovered from a 5 ft. run it is assumed that the unrecovered part of the core was ground up and became part of the sludge. The core, therefore represents 24% of 36% or 8.64% of the volume of the hole. The sludge represents 100 — 8.64% = 91.36% of the volume of the hole.

	Percent of Vol. of Hole	Assay	Product
Core	8.6%	0.50 % Cu.	4.30
Sludge	91.4%	1.10 % Cu.	100.54
	100.0%		104.84

Average assay: 1.05% Cu.

Method 3. Weighting by weights of products actually recovered.

	Weight	Assay	Product
Core	1.4 lb.	.50 % Cu.	.70
Sludge	7.2 lb.	1.10 % Cu.	7.92
	8.6 lb.		8.62

Average assay: 1.00% Cu.

Method 4. Weighting by theoretical volume taking into account incompleteness of both sludge and core (as proposed by Moehlman).

	Theoretical Vol. (see Method 2)	% of Theoretical Vol. Recovered [34]	Prod.	Assay	Prod.
Core	8.6	100	8.60	0.50	4.30
Sludge	91.4	50	45.70	1.10	50.27
	100.0		54.30		54.57

Average assay: 1.00% Cu.

Comments on the Four Methods: Method 1 would be satisfactory if both core and sludge recovery were complete or nearly so. Method 2 would be satisfactory if sludge recovery were complete. Methods 3

[34] Sludge recovery was calculated as follows: The amount of sludge recovered *should* have been 5 × (2.02 lb. + 76% of 1.13 lb.) = 14.4 lb. The amount actually recovered being 7.2 lb., the recovery is 50%.

and 4 both give lower rating to the sludge assay because of its incompleteness and both will give the same result so long as sludge recovery is less than 100%. If sludge recovery had been, say 150%, method 3 would give a disproportionately high rating to what is, because of overcomplete recovery, a poor sample. Method 4 would weight the sludge sample more nearly in proportion to its reliability: the weighting would be $\frac{100}{150}$ or 66.7% instead of 150%.

Deviation of Holes

In order to draw correct inferences from drill-hole data it is essential to know the orientation of the hole throughout its entire course. The inclination and bearing at the collar do not tell the whole story because diamond drill holes are never ideally straight. In short holes the deviation is usually negligible but in holes over 200 feet long it is likely to be quite appreciable and for lengths of 2000 feet it may amount to as much as 25 degrees or even more. Exceptional but not unique is a hole in the Metalline District (Washington) which was started vertically downward but had deviated by 70 degrees at a depth of 1000 feet.[35]

Careful drilling [36] minimizes the tendency to crooked holes but even with the best technique some curvature is unavoidable. The direction of deviation is often influenced by the nature and structure of the rock. Holes at a small angle to bedding may curve toward parallelism with the bedding plane, but when a drill hole intersects bedding or cleavage at a large angle it tends to assume a direction at right angles to the laminated structure. Apart from this influence, horizontal holes tend to curve upward, perhaps because of sag in the rods behind the bit. It is hard to straighten a hole that has started to curve, but often local experience makes it possible to anticipate deviation when laying out the drilling program and thus hit the target through a curved trajectory.

Although the usual intention is to drill holes as straight as circumstances permit, it is entirely feasible to cause deflection intentionally [37]

[35] Sampson, Edward, and Griggs, Allan B., Deviation of diamond drill holes in the Metalline District, Washington: *A.I.M.E. Tech. Paper 1825, Mining Technology,* p. 1, January, 1946.

[36] Collins, John J., Some problems involved in the interpretation of diamond-drill-hole sampling and surveying: *A.I.M.E. Tech. Pub. No. 1842,* 1946. This paper gives a list of suggestions by A. R. Kinkle, Jr., for discouraging the wandering of drill holes. Collins' paper is an excellent summary of various aspects of drill-hole interpretation and carries a very full bibliography.

[37] Hoffmann, J. I., Recent practice in diamond drilling and borehole surveying: *Tr. Inst. Mining & Met.,* vol. 21, p. 481, 1912.

Allen, R. E., Theory and practice of directed drilling: *Min. & Met.,* vol. 14, p. 501 *ff.,* 1933.

Yates, Arthur B., Surveying and controlling diamond drill holes: *A.I.M.E. Tech. Pub. 1950,* pp. 1–2, January, 1946.

usually by lowering a metal wedge into the hole. Thus a change in direction may intersect the vein at a better angle, or after a vein has been cut, a branch hole will give a second penetration and an additional sample.

Surveying Holes

The amount of curvature can be determined, approximately at least, by "surveying" the hole after drilling.[38] Several methods are in use. To determine inclination, the commonest way is to use a glass tube partly filled with hydrofluoric acid. This is enclosed in a steel or bronze case which for purposes of the survey is substituted for the core barrel of the drill and lowered into the hole. The acid etches a line on the glass in the position at which the liquid stands and thus gives a record of the inclination of the tube. The tube is emptied of acid as soon as it comes from the hole, and the angle of inclination is measured by filling the tube with the proper amount of water or colored liquid and tilting in a clinometer [39] until the liquid coincides with the etched line. Correction for the small error introduced by capillarity is made with the aid of a chart provided for the purpose.

The azimuth of the hole, indicating the horizontal component of deviation, is measured with some type of compass. The one most commonly used is the Maas compass [40] consisting of a small magnetic needle on a pivot attached to a cork which floats in gelatine. The gelatine is placed in the same glass tube as that used for the dip measurement, separated from the hydrofluoric acid chamber by a rubber stopper or plug in the middle of the tube. The whole is enclosed in a bronze rather than a steel casing. The gelatine is in the form of a warm solution of just the right consistency to remain liquid during the time required to lower the rods and then set within twenty minutes or half an hour after the instrument is lowered. For deep holes where a long time is required for lowering, a small thermos jacket may be used to keep the gelatine warm; where the wall-rock is hot, agar agar is sometimes used instead of gelatine, since it solidifies at a higher temperature. (A gasoline stove of the Primus type is convenient for heating the water underground.)

---

[38] Storms, W. Rex, Surveying diamond drill holes: *E. & M. J.*, vol. 134, pp. 157 *ff.*, 1933.

[39] A transit may be adapted for use as a clinometer by fitting a brass cap over the telescope tube to hold the survey bottle. Kendall, H. F., and Ffolliott, J. H., Geology applied to mining in the Ducktown district: *Min. & Met.*, vol. 14, p. 175 *ff.*, 1933.

[40] White, E. E., Surveying and sampling diamond drill holes: *Trans. A.I.M.E.*, vol. 44, p. 69, 1912.

Storms, W. Rex, Surveying diamond drill holes: *E. & M. J.*, vol. 134, pp. 157 *ff.*, 1933.

The manufacturers of the Maas compass will sell or lease it. The agent in the U. S. is E. L. Derby, Ishpeming, Mich.

Instead of gelatine and hydrofluoric acid, photographic methods are sometimes used. One type of instrument records the position of the compass needle on sensitized paper illuminated by a flashlight bulb which is operated by a dry cell and turned on and off by a timing clock.[41]

Another photographic instrument [42] designed by A. B. Yates, L. B. Wright, and A. A. Lease, consists of a compass in a cubical binnacle small enough to fit into a cylindrical brass case. The compass needle bears radioactive material which registers the attitude of the needle on a photographic film placed in the box. The dip of the hole is measured similarly on another film which records the position of a line of radioactive material drawn on the outside of the suspended compass box.

Compass methods involve a considerable margin of error because of the necessarily short length of the needle in holes of small diameter; also where there is local magnetic attraction they may be quite deceptive. A gyroscopic bore-hole compass,[43] which is independent of magnetic effects, has been devised but has not as yet been widely used in connection with mining. A method of determining the bearing from the etch-tube alone without the use of a compass has been developed for surveys in magnetic rock. Its essential feature is that during the lowering and raising of the tube, the rods are not permitted to rotate, hence the orientation of the etch-ellipse is known in terms of a plane (distorted into a twisted surface) which passes through the axis of the rods and is vertical at the collar of the hole. The technique and methods of calculation are described by Dahners and Cohen.[44]

Deductions from Drill Samples

Grade

Provided core recovery is complete, a drill hole assay is comparable in significance to a channel sample; it is inferior in that its bulk is smaller; it is superior in that it is likely to have more uniform dimensions. Therefore, a series of drill holes will afford an accurate sampling of any orebody if a series of channel samples similarly spaced could be regarded as a satisfactory sample of the same orebody. Whether or not such is the

[41] Humphreys, F., Borehole surveying instruments: *Jour. Chem. & Met. Soc. So. Africa,* May 1934. Abstract, *Mining Mag.* Aug. 1934, pp. 112 *ff.*
   McFarland, Harry F., Surveying a borehole with improvised apparatus: *E. & M. J.,* vol. 140, November, p. 41, 1939.
[42] Wright, L. B., Borehole surveying at the Homestake: *E. & M. J.,* vol. 126, p. 57, 1928.
   Storms, W. Rex, Surveying diamond drill holes: *E. & M. J.,* vol. 134, p. 157, 1933.
[43] Muller, F. G. D., Trouble caused by crooked holes: *Oil Weekly,* April 19, 1924.
[44] Dahners, L. A., and Cohen, C. J., A method for surveying drill holes by oriented drill rods: *U. S. Bur. Mines,* Report of Investigations, 3773, 1944.

condition depends on the uniformity of the ore; the probability can be determined by plotting the spacing of the drill holes on tracing paper and laying the tracing in various trial positions on the sample map of an area of similar ore.   The probability factor should be faced honestly and coldly; it is only human to place great confidence in a rich intersection and discredit a lean one, but the geologist must guard against this type of wishful thinking.

In precious-metal deposits, especially narrow gold veins, drill holes are not satisfactory for determining the average grade of the ore unless they are more numerous and more closely spaced than is likely to be economical. Nevertheless, assays of the core may give some indication as to whether or not a vein is minable.   An analysis of the results of diamond drilling in a large gold-quartz mine indicated that of 100 holes through veins which were later opened up, only 15 had shown ore-grade where minable ore did not exist and only 12 passed through ore without yielding ore grade assays.[45]   The fact that 12 passed through ore without indicating the fact in terms of assay-returns is a warning against trusting negative results too implicitly as experience in drilling many other gold deposits abundantly emphasizes.   A mine manager in Grass Valley used to point out a sizable stope on the map, bring from the safe a collection of specimens gleaming with gold and remark: "There was a drill hole within ten feet of that and it showed a blank."   The fault, perhaps, was not in having put in drill holes but in putting in too few of them.   Yet the number of holes necessary to exhaust the possibilities might have been more expensive than cutting up the ground by drifting.   The odds that holes a given distance apart may have straddled an orebody large enough to be of interest can be reduced to mathematical probability if the habits of orebodies in the district are known.

Even if assays have to be discredited completely, the mineralogical nature of the vein-matter in the core may indicate whether or not a vein is worth developing.   Also, where orebodies are surrounded by haloes of altered rock, a drill intersection may indicate the proximity of ore even though it does not actually encounter values.

Vein-Width

Obviously the distance between vein-walls as measured along the core is not, in the general case, the true width of the vein; it is necessary to correct the measurement for the amount by which the intersection between borehole and vein varies from a right angle.   In a newly dis-

[45] Chase, P. W., Personal communication.

covered vein whose attitude is not known, the drill cores must be interpreted with caution; a three-inch stringer may give the impression of
being a two-foot vein if its attitude cannot be measured.

The angle between the drill hole and the orebody may be determined
in one of two ways. In a narrow vein with well-defined regular
tight walls, the angle of intersection is
visible in the core itself; this observation
is more reliable if the angles at both walls
check closely. The attitude of streaking in a banded vein may provide cor-
roborative evidence. Even though the
direct observation may not be very definite it should always be recorded, where
possible, as a check on other evidence.
The second basis of calculation is the
inclination and bearing of the drill hole
compared with the dip of the vein. The
dip is determined by drawing a cross section of the vein through its outcrop or
underground exposures and the point of
intersection. On irregular veins this
may involve some error and all data as

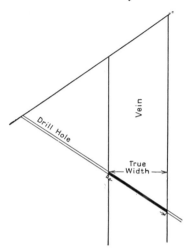

Fig. 21—Relation between true width
of a vein and width as measured along
drill hole. (Idealized diagram)

to the shape of the vein shown in various plans and sections must receive consideration in arriving at the most probable attitude.

In very wide orebodies it may be necessary to correct not only for angle
of intersection but for curvature of the hole, as the length of an arc is
greater than the length of a chord.

The probability that a single drill hole or a limited number of holes
will afford a correct measure of the average width of an orebody depends
on the habits of the ore, that is, whether widths are habitually regular
or irregular. The probability may be determined on a statistical basis
in the same manner as reliability of grade.

Structure

Apart from their use as indicators of ore, diamond drill holes give
valuable structural information. They not only determine the location
of rock contacts, but they are capable of furnishing evidence as to the
attitude of contacts and other structural planes. To save words we shall,
for the moment, refer to any structural plane as a bed, although the same
geometrical considerations apply to a vein, cleavage plane, fault or any
other approximately plane surface. If a particular bed can be identified

in three holes, its dip and strike can be calculated by the familiar three-point method. This consists merely in taking the point which is intermediate in elevation (as compared with the others) and computing the position of a point of equal altitude along the line between the other two.

Fig. 22—Relation of core sample to rock. Original orientation of core has been lost through rotation. (*Courtesy of* E. J. Longyear Company)

A new line joining the two points of equal altitude is the strike and from this the dip can be readily calculated.

A somewhat different problem arises when no particular bed is identifiable yet bedding planes are visible in the core. The attitude of bedding can then be determined from the core-bedding angles in three non-parallel holes. The principle involved is that the bedding plane must be tangent to a cone whose axis is the drill hole and whose apical angle is twice the core-bedding angle. Since only angular relations are involved, all three holes may be regarded as though they had been drilled from the same station so that the three cones have a common apex. The true attitude of bedding is that of a plane tangent to all three cones.

While three holes are necessary to solve the most general problem, two will, in certain

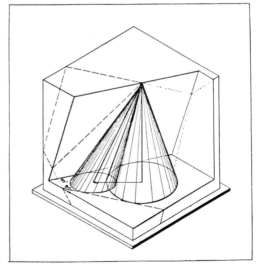

Fig. 23—A vertical and an inclined drill hole. The cone surrounding each hole is the locus of all lines making a given angle with that hole. The possible attitudes of bedding are the common tangents to the two cones. (*After* Mead, *Economic Geology*)

cases, give a unique solution and in other cases offer a choice between two, three, or four possible attitudes. The example of two holes, one vertical and the other inclined, has been discussed by Mead [46] and by subsequent writers.[47]   Stein derives the formula:

$$\cos E = \tan H \tan V \mp \frac{\sin I}{\cos H \cos V}$$

where
   E is the angle between the bearing of the inclined hole and the directions of dip of the possible planes of bedding,
   H is the plunge of the inclined drill hole from horizontal,
   V is the core-bedding angle in the vertical drill hole, and
   I is the core-bedding angle in the inclined drill hole.

The angle E, which gives the bearing of the dip-line, may have two possible values, depending on whether the angle is measured clockwise or counterclockwise from the bearing of the inclined hole.   Furthermore, the magnitude of E may have two solutions, depending on whether the minus-or-plus sign in the equation is taken as positive or negative.   One of these values may lie outside the limits of the cosine function (*viz.* — 1 to + 1) and therefore be imaginary.

The more general case in which three non-parallel holes are requisite to a definite solution is more complex but can be solved either by determinants [48] or by a stereographic projection.[49]

If data are available from only one hole, the angle which the bed makes with the axis of the core can be useful, although, since the core has been rotated from its natural position by an unknown amount, it does not in itself furnish full evidence unless the core-bedding angle happens to be 90 degrees.   Thus, in the general case, the attitude of the bed is indeterminate, but if the strike is known from other data, there are only two possible angles of dip, and the geologist may perhaps feel confident in selecting one of them as the more probable if he knows enough

[46] Mead, Warren J., Determination of attitude of concealed bedded formations by diamond drilling: *Economic Geology*, vol. 16, pp. 37–47, 1921.   Mead presents graphic solutions and describes an instrument which he invented for solving the problem mechanically.

[47] Stein, Herbert A., A trigonometric solution of the two-drillhole problem: *Economic Geology*, vol. 36, pp. 84–94, 1941.

Fisher, D. Jerome, Drillhole problems in the stereographic projection: *Economic Geology*, vol. 36, pp. 551–560, 1941.

[48] Mertie, J. B., Jr., Structural determinations from diamond drilling: *Economic Geology*, vol. 38, pp. 298–312, 1943.   Presents a solution by spherical geometry involving the use of determinants.

[49] Bucher, Walter H., Dip and strike from three not parallel drill cores lacking key beds: *Economic Geology*, vol. 38, pp. 648–657, 1943.   Solution of the problem by stereographic projection.

Gilluly, James, Discussion: Dip and strike from three not parallel drill cores lacking key beds: *Economic Geology*, vol. 39, pp. 359–363, 1944.   Suggests a short-cut in Bucher's solution.

about the local structure. Wisser [50] has prepared charts giving the possible combinations of dip and strike for various hole-inclinations.

In many districts there are planar or linear structures that have a uniform orientation over considerable distances and can be used to determine what position the core occupied when it was in the ground. Regional cleavage, for example, is likely to be nearly constant even though the bedding changes in attitude abruptly from place to place. Similarly, linear structure, such as parallelism of hornblende prisms, may vary little throughout a district. When either of these structures is placed in its correct geographical position, the attitude of bedding may be read directly. There are special cases, however, in which orientation by this method is indeterminate. If the planar structure is parallel to the axis of the core, there are two possible orientations. If planar structure is normal to the core-axis the number of possible orientations is infinite. If linear structure is perpendicular to the core-axis there are two possible orientations. But if linear structure is parallel to the core-axis the number of possible orientations is infinite.

A method [51] of orienting the core by locating the direction of magnetic polarization is applicable to most rocks, although a few, such as limestone and dolomite, do not contain enough magnetic material. A piece of the core, which can be as small as ¾ inch in diameter, is slowly rotated in a special instrument containing a delicate magnetometer, and the orientation of the magnetic field is recorded on sensitized paper. Comparing this direction with the attitude of the local terrestrial magnetism makes it possible to reorient the core in its natural position.

Speed and Cost

The speed of drilling and the cost per foot are roughly reciprocal and vary widely with the nature of the rock; other things being equal, soft rock is of course drilled faster and more cheaply than hard. Unevenness of texture, as, for example, veinlets or knots of quartz in a partly decomposed rock, can cause more trouble than hardness alone. The principal source of delay and expense is "grief" of one sort or another. In fractured

[50] Wisser, Edward, An aid in the interpretation of diamond drill cores: *Economic Geology*, vol. 27, pp. 437–449, 1932.

For examples, see Hawkes, H. E., and Holtz, P. E., Drill-hole correlation of the magnetites of the Jersey Highlands, New York and New Jersey: *U.S.G.S. Bull. 955-A*, 1947.

[51] Lynton, A. A. P. G. Bulletin 21 (5), pp. 580–615, 1937.

Webb, E. Ray, Subsurface dip and strike determined by newly developed polar core orientation: *Mining and Metallurgy*, vol. 21, pp. 553–554, 1940.

Roberts, Dwight C., and Webb, E. Ray, Polar core orientation: paper presented at Oil World Exposition, Houston, Texas, 1939, Sperry-Sun Well Surveying Co., Philadelphia.

ground, the bit may stick and even get detached or "lost"; [52] in permeable ground, the failure of return water may demand interruption of the work to allow plugging or cementing.

Speeds differ so much under differing conditions that average figures are of little significance.   Rate of advance, including delays, varies from 8 feet or less to 30 or 40 feet per shift.

Holes of large diameter are more expensive than small ones.   Long holes are more expensive per foot than short because of the time required to raise and lower the rods between runs, though with very short holes the time consumed in moving the drill becomes an important factor in the cost.   Of the three types of drilling—diamond drilling for blast holes, exploratory drilling underground, and exploratory drilling from surface—the first is the cheapest, the second is a little more expensive because of care in core recovery, and the third may cost still more because of transportation and other factors.

Some of the lowest costs are obtained in the large Canadian mines where the rock cores well.   Here holes are of small diameter and of short to medium length, and many machines are in operation at once.   In the Hollinger Mine, where over 250,000 feet of drilling is done every year, the cost is reported as 58 cents a foot, including labor, repairs, air, depreciation, social services, and all expense that can properly be allocated to drilling.[53]   In general, costs of less than a dollar are considered low, and from this they may range up to three or four dollars a foot, with still higher costs for large, long, and difficult holes.   On prospects, drilling may usually be contracted for $2 to $4 a foot plus the cost of casing, cementing, moving, and transporting the machine from the nearest rail point.   The foregoing figures are based on pre-war experience.   For present (1948) conditions about 50% should be added and, where diamond loss is high, the increase in costs is still greater.

The Geologist's Duties

In addition to laying out the holes, logging the core, and interpreting the results, the geologist should keep in close touch with the actual drilling operation by visiting the drill at frequent intervals.   In one large company it is the rule that when the drill encounters evidence of a vein, the work is suspended and the geologist is summoned no matter what

[52] Poston, Roy A., Recovering stuck diamond drill bits: *Engineering and Mining Journal*, vol. 119, p. 451, March 14, 1925.

[53] Dunbar, W. Roy, Diamond drilling at the Hollinger Mine: *Canadian Institute of Mining and Metallurgy Transactions*, vol. 43, p. 53, 1940.

Dougherty, J. W., and Douglas, J. M., Mining practice at the Hollinger gold mine: *American Institute of Mining and Metallurgical Engineers Technical Publication* 1159, 1940.

the time of day or night. When attending a "delivery case" of this sort, the geologist's duty is to:

1. Check the measurement of footage.

2. See that the drillers pull the rods at frequent intervals (usually two feet for narrow orebodies; five feet for thick orebodies such as porphyry coppers).

3. See that the pieces of core go into the core box in correct order and right-end-to when the driller empties the core barrel.

4. Supervise the collection of sludge samples, making sure that no fines are lost in the overflow, that all of the sludge goes into the sample, and that the sludge boxes are properly cleaned between runs.

5. Watch the return water, panning the sludge at intervals and noting any change in the mineral content.

If the geologist has been given the authority to direct drilling, he can be held responsible, and properly so, for the correctness of the results. His responsibility does not end with mere mechanical care, but extends to the choice of proper methods and the exclusion of any of the sources of error and misinterpretation that drilling is heir to.

SHOT DRILLING

In principle, shot drilling is similar to diamond drilling, but the cutting medium, instead of set diamonds, consists of loose chilled-steel shot fed into the rods with the wash-water and rolling under the bit. Shot drill holes are usually larger than diamond drill holes, in fact enormous bores five feet in diameter, for use as mine shafts, have been sunk successfully at Grass Valley, Cal.,[54] and Zenith, Minn.,[55] by placing the rotating mechanism down in the hole. In Northern Rhodesia, where the shot drill has found its greatest use in exploration, cores were four inches in diameter.[56] The rods are considerably smaller than the bit, which means that the ascending return water slackens in velocity above the bit, and the heavy particles in the sludge fail to rise to the collar. Accordingly, the sludge is collected in a sediment tube or calyx (hence the alternative name Calyx drill), an open-topped hollow cylinder which forms an upward extension of the core-barrel. Along with the sludge, used shot and particles of steel accumulate. The larger pieces of steel are removed with a magnet [57] from the coarse portion of the

[54] Newsom, J. B., Shaft boring found inexpensive and safe: *Engineering and Mining Journal* vol. 137, pp. 443–446, 1936.

[55] Newsom, J. B., and Haselton, W. D., Borehole at the Zenith Mine, Ely, Minn.: *American Institute of Mining and Metallurgical Engineers Technical Publication* 1068, pp. 1–14, 1939.

[56] Truscott, S. J., *Mine Economics*, p. 95. London: Mining Publications, Ltd., 1937.

[57] Matson, H. T., and Wallis, G. Allan, Drill sampling and interpretation of sampling results in the copper fields of Northern Rhodesia: *American Institute of Mining and Metallurgical Engineers Technical Publication* 373, p. 8, 1931.

sludge, and a correction for the remaining free iron is made by comparing the percentage of iron in the sludge-assay with that in the core-assay.

HAMMER DRILLING

Pneumatically operated hammer drills of the type employed for drilling the round for underground blasting can be used for purposes of sampling and exploration.[58] The cuttings from the hole constitute the sample. Holes as much as 250 feet deep or, exceptionally, even deeper, have proved satisfactory. Since the length of a single piece of standard drill steel is limited and, especially, since the restricted space in underground workings would interfere with the use of long rods, any holes more than 22 feet deep require sectionalized rods. Therefore it is convenient to describe the methods under "shallow holes" (those less than 22 feet deep) and "deep holes" (those more than 22 feet deep).

Shallow holes are usually drilled dry, with a canvas bag held around the collar of the hole to catch the cuttings. The drill steel passes through a hole in the bottom of the bag and leakage is prevented by a rubber gasket around the steel on the inside of the bag. Hammer drill holes are well adapted to testing the rock in the walls of workings; thus they have been used in wide lodes such as those at the Homestake and Ducktown. Their use in veins which are not wider than a drift is limited by the physical difficulty of setting up the drill in a position where it can bore a hole across the full width of the vein. Hammer drill holes may be either more accurate or less accurate than channel samples. At Miami, Arizona, they proved to be more accurate; channel samples were 13% too low. In some other mines, however, hammer drill sampling is less accurate. Which is better depends on the nature of the ore and rock, and only a comparative test will answer the question.

Deep holes are drilled with steel in sections 3 to 9 feet long connected by threaded sleeves which allow the butts of the steel to take up the shock of drilling yet transmit rotation. The sleeve holds the rods together when they are withdrawn from the hole. For an accurate sample one must collect *all* of the cuttings and send for assay a fraction that is truly representative. Since long holes are drilled wet, it is not feasible to catch the cuttings in a bag. Instead, pans are held under the collar of the hole. For holes of gentle inclination, a more satisfactory method is to drill an auxiliary hole upward at a steeper angle to tap the main

[58] Knaebel, John B., Sampling and exploration by means of hammer drills: *U. S. Bureau of Mines Information Circular 6594*, February 1932, pp. 1–29.

hole at a depth of a few inches.   Then a pipe, one end of which is fitted into the auxiliary hole and the other split open to form a launder, conducts the sample to the receptacle.   The most convenient angle for deep holes is 5 to 30 degrees upward.   In more highly inclined holes, there are serious difficulties in collecting the sample, but in downward holes the cuttings may be removed by injecting air and water alternately into the hole through the hollow steel, thus employing the air-lift principle.

The "deep hole" method is economical [59] for drilling a large number of closely spaced holes.   Under these conditions, hammer drills bore faster and more cheaply than diamond drills, though they have the disadvantage of not furnishing a core for inspection.

PLANNING A DRILLING CAMPAIGN
Choice of a Drilling Method

Whether drilling is designed to test the grade and width of an orebody, to find new ore, or merely to secure geological information, the choice of a method usually lies between churn drilling and diamond drilling. The principal factors which influence the choice are the nature of the information required, the shape and attitude of the target, and the physical nature of the ground.   The respective advantages of churn drills and diamond drills are indicated in Table 4.

The chief advantage of the churn drill apart from possible economy is that it cuts a hole of relatively broad diameter and thereby yields a large and representative sample.   The best results and costs are obtained in rocks that are soft to medium hard, provided they do not slump or cave readily into the hole.   But, with heavy equipment, rather hard rocks can be penetrated without great difficulty.   The churn drill is used to best advantage in drilling prospect holes through flat and moderately inclined mineralized zones of considerable horizontal extent, in which the valuable metal content is rather evenly distributed.   Therefore, churn drills, with various modifications, are widely used for prospecting placer deposits, for blast-hole drilling, for prospecting mineral deposits in bedrock, and to determine stratigraphy.   The so-called "porphyry copper" deposits have been explored largely by churn-drill operations.[60]

Much of the preliminary prospecting for ore in the Tri-State zinc

---

[59] At Broken Hill, N.S.W., holes averaging 20.6 feet cost 4 shillings 5 pence per foot, compared with about 7 shillings sixpence for diamond drilling. Garrety, M. D., Sampling with the long-hole rock drill at North Broken Hill: *Proceedings Austr. Inst. Min. and Met.*, n.s. no., 124, December 31, 1941, Abstr., *Mining Magazine* (London), vol. 67, pp. 223–225, 1942.

[60] This paragraph is from a written communication by E. N. Pennebaker and Kenyon E. Richard.

TABLE 4

COMPARISON OF DIAMOND AND CHURN DRILLS

Diamond Drill	*Churn Drill*
1. Can drill in any direction—downward, horizontal, inclined, and (from underground workings) upward.	1. Can drill only vertical downward holes. Usually drills from surface but can drill from underground if large station is prepared.
2. Core sample gives valuable geological information: texture of rock, distribution of mineral grains, attitude of bedding, cleavage, veinlets, etc. to axis of core.	2. No core sample. Cuttings (sludge) examined in laboratory give considerable information *re* nature of rock and mineralization.
3. Sample is small, though shape and diameter are uniform.	3. Sample more accurate insofar as size is larger. Shape and diameter more subject to variation.
a. In gold deposits, gives accurate sample if core is good.	a. Large gold particles difficult to raise though performance improved by thick mud and suction bailer.
4. Slower than churn drilling under average conditions.	4. Faster, at least up to 1000 or 1200 feet.
a. Successful in hard rock.	a. Slow and expensive in really hard rock.
b. In fractured, blocky ground gives incomplete core and slow progress.	b. Successful in fractured blocky ground.
c. Suffers "grief" and serious bit-wear in poorly consolidated conglomerate, or soft rock with hard veinlets and nodules.	c. Progress satisfactory in conglomerate (if not too hard) and chert-bearing limestone.
d. Gives unsatisfactory core in unconsolidated material.	d. Gives good samples in unconsolidated material (sand, gravel, and clay).
5. Hole usually serves no purpose other than testing.	5. Hole being large may later serve for ventilation, drainage, or (in open pits) for blasting.

region since 1928 has been done by boring churn-drill holes about one-quarter mile apart in order to determine the stratigraphy, mineralization, and other pertinent data, and scores of square miles have been prospected by this method. More than 50,000 drill holes have been completed in the district to date. The drilling depth ranges from a few feet to 500 feet, the average depth being about 300 feet.[61]

Diamond drilling competes with churn drilling under conditions where reasonably good core recovery can be expected, and under these conditions, for example, in the "porphyry" copper deposits, the present trend appears to be in favor of diamond drilling, partly because of the increased speed and economy of the modern type of bit, partly because the sample, although smaller than that from a churn drill, is more uniform in cross section and therefore, under favorable conditions, more accurate, and partly because of the advantage of recovering a sample intact in the form of a solid core. But if the rock is decomposed or friable or badly fractured, it does not yield a good core, and if the ground is very broken and cavernous, the bit gets wedged in the hole or the water escapes and fails to "return." In these unfavorable conditions, diamond drilling is slow and expensive. In really hard rock, the diamond drill makes faster progress than the churn drill, provided the rock is uniform, but if it consists of hard veinlets or nodules in a soft matrix, the effect on bits is disastrous. In the Tri-State district, where the limestone contains chert and jasperoid in nodules and irregular masses and the rock is shattered in and around the orebodies, the diamond drill cannot compete with the churn drill.

Shot (calyx) drilling can compete with diamond drilling in rocks which are uniform and not too hard. In Northern Rhodesia, one of the few places where it has been used extensively in exploration for metals, it proved faster and cheaper than diamond drilling. However, the holes are less uniform in diameter,[62] tend to deflect more,[63] and cannot be drilled satisfactorily at angles flatter than 35 degrees from the vertical.[64] Shot drills would be unsuitable for drilling iron ore because of the contamination of the sludge sample by particles of shot.

Combinations of diamond and churn drilling are sometimes advantageous. Thus on the Mesabi Range, a churn drill may be used to dig a hole to bedrock, after which a diamond drill bores through the cherty taconite, and churn drilling is resumed when friable iron-formation is reached. For this purpose a string of rods similar to diamond-drill rods and equipped with a chopping bit is used instead of the usual

[61] Fowler, George M., Written communication.

[62] Truscott, S. J., *Mine Economics*, pp. 95 and 97. London: Mining Publications, Ltd., 1937.

[63] MacLachlan, D. K. F., The sampling and estimation of borehole cores and sludges: *Transactions, Institution of Mining and Metallurgy*, vol. 40, p. 178, 1931.

[64] Taggert, Arthur F. and Lewis, Robert S., in *Peele's Mining Engineers Handbook*, sec. 9, p. 61. New York: John Wiley and Sons, Inc., 1941.

churn-drilling cable and tools; the sludge is recovered by a stream of water as in diamond drilling.[65]   In the modification known as "structure drilling," [66] the water is pumped down between the rods and the casing and rises through the inside of the rods.   This method recovers cuttings in the form of relatively large fragments, which are desired for testing the susceptibility of iron ore to concentration by "washing."

The diamond drill meets with no competition from the churn drill, of course, where the target can be reached most advantageously by flat or inclined holes.   Therefore, diamond drilling is virtually the only method used in testing steeply dipping veins.

Hammer drilling may compete successfully with diamond drilling both in speed and cost, where a large number of closely spaced short holes is needed.   It is inconvenient for steep holes, especially upward, and its greatest disadvantage is that it does not yield a core sample.

Drilling for Sampling Purposes

Drilling, by whichever of the methods is best suited to the conditions, affords a satisfactory means of sampling and blocking out ore if the orebody can be drilled at a sufficient number of places at reasonable cost. This depends on the depth of the ore and on the spacing necessary to give an accurate indication of grade.

In shallow flattish deposits a large area is within reach of short holes, and where the tenor is relatively uniform, as in iron ores and in the "porphyry" coppers, the holes need not be closely spaced.   "General practice in some of the 'porphyry-copper' districts is to space churn drill holes from 150 to 200 feet apart.   Where possible, they should be drilled at the corners of a regular grid laid out on coordinate squares. In some instances in thin supergene ore bodies of rather erratic tenor, spacing at 75 foot intervals has been necessary.   In 'porphyry' deposits, a number of scout holes should be carried down at intervals well below the general bottom of drilling, as considerable primary ore has been found in recent years below what was earlier thought to be the bottom of commercial mineralization." [67]

In steeply inclined deposits the amount of ore within reach of the surface, even by inclined diamond drill holes, is limited, but if the grade is uniform, as in the Northern Rhodesian copper deposits, so that the

---

[65] Jackson, Charles F., and Knaebel, John B., Sampling and estimation of ore deposits: *U. S. Bureau of Mines Bulletin 356*, 1932, p. 23.

[66] Bolthouse, H. C., Structure drilling as applied in Western Mesaba mining practice: *Mining Congress Journal*, vol. 22, p. 44, November 1936.

[67] Pennebaker, E. N., and Richard, Kenyon E., Written communication.

holes need not be too numerous, diamond drilling may afford a satisfactory means of sampling to depths of 1000 feet or more as well as in such deeper horizons as may be reached from underground stations. With less uniform ores the advisability of attempting to estimate the grade from drilling results is open to question.

Angle of Intersection

In laying out diamond drill holes, it is often economical to drill several holes from one station, because moving the machine and setting it up again forms a sizable item of cost. This is especially true in underground workings, where an expensive drill station has to be excavated for each new set-up or where, indeed, no additional vantage point may be available. One factor that limits the number of holes that can be "fanned" from a single station is, of course, the length of the hole necessary to reach the more remote points, but the principal factor is the angle at which the hole will intersect the plane of the vein. Since the accuracy of a borehole as a measure of width decreases rapidly with the angle of intersection, too acute an angle should be avoided. Thirty degrees is usually the minimum permissible, and 45 degrees is safer. Calculating the limiting position may involve a neat problem in descriptive geometry. Its solution is based on the consideration that the locus of all boreholes intersecting the vein at a given angle is the surface of a cone whose apex is at the drill station and whose axis is a line from the station normal to the plane of the vein.

There are exceptional circumstances, however, as where the width of the vein is known from other data, in which it is proper to drill the hole to cut the vein at a very acute angle in order to get a longer and therefore more accurate sample of the vein-matter.

Drilling for New Ore

In drilling for the purpose of finding new orebodies, there are two rather contrasting methods of planning the campaign. One is to test a given block of ground completely by drilling holes on a pre-arranged geometrical pattern. The other is to "feel your way" by letting the results of each hole determine the position of the next.

The fixed, preconceived program has its definite advantages. Since the number of holes and the depth of each have been planned, the operator may provide the proper number of machines to give the best costs and speed. Operating several machines at once makes for economy in supervision and servicing. A machine of large capacity can be used for long holes, and a machine of smaller capacity for short holes. But such a program should never be undertaken unless it is certain to be carried to completion, as discouraging results in the early holes are not a fair test of the ground.

The method of "feeling your way" is much more flexible. Since it gives scope to judgment and to the application of the geological knowledge which develops in the course of the work, it is likely to yield more information with a smaller footage of drilling. Under most conditions, however, a compromise between the two methods is better than either one alone. This may well take the form of a pre-designed skeletal pattern, leaving the order in which the holes are drilled and the decisions to omit some and drill others to be determined as the work progresses.

There is naturally an advantage in finding ore at an early stage in the program and devoting further work to testing its extent rather than probing blindly in unknown ground. If the first holes indicate enough ore to warrant underground development, the drilling of additional holes may be superfluous. If there is a large area in which ore *may* occur, but within which there is no definite reason to believe that one place is more favorable than another, it is best to explore the entire area in reconnaissance fashion by widely spaced holes, thus avoiding the danger of drilling all of the early holes in barren ground. If any ore is found, the adjoining holes are drilled in order to test its extent. If the whole structure has been tested by wide spacing and nothing found, the results may be so discouraging that further drilling is not warranted, but it must be remembered that the possibility of finding ore is not excluded until the whole area has been drilled at intervals appropriate to the size of the expected orebodies.

A knowledge of the habits of the ore in any district will afford a measure of the widest permissible spacing to avoid missing an orebody. Suppose that the smallest oreshoot that would be of interest is 100 feet broad, measured in the plane of a vein. Then holes spaced to cut the vein at intervals somewhat less than 100 feet would penetrate any orebody that existed. If the oreshoots are long horizontally and short vertically, the holes may be spaced farther apart horizontally than vertically. If, on the other hand, the oreshoots have steep pitches, the spacing should be wide vertically and close horizontally. Similar considerations apply of course to elongated orebodies in a flat-lying horizon like the "runs" of ore in the Mississippi Valley deposits. If there is a definite target to shoot at, whether the extension of a known orebody or a structure that is considered favorable, the first holes should be aimed at this target. Its position, however, may be known only within limits.

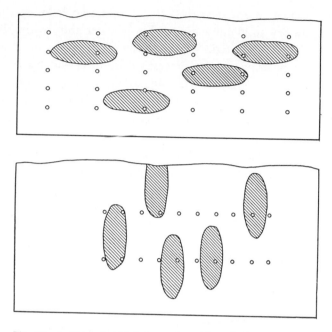

Fig. 24—Spacing of drill holes varies with probable size and orientation of ore-shoots. Small circles represent drill holes. Cross-hatched areas represent ore-shoots. (Diagrammatic)

It is then advisable to locate the drill holes in such a way as to: (1) Test the most likely place first, and (2) exhaust the possibilities with as few holes as possible. From Figure 25 it is evident that a hole at *A* is

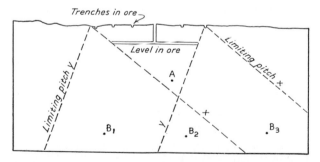

Fig. 25—Spacing of drill holes to test an orebody whose pitch is known only within limits. Hole *A* is within area of overlap of alternative angles of pitch. To test at depth *B*, at least three holes are necessary. (Diagrammatic)

within the area in which the limiting projections overlap. This is the strategic position provided it gives enough depth to be of interest. If the drilling is laid out to test the vein at depth *B*, a hole vertically below the oreshoot might miss the ore; at least two holes at this depth would be necessary to avoid a miss.   The greater the depth, the larger the number of holes required.[68]   Where the pitch of the oreshoot is not known, it may be expedient to determine its direction by one or two shallow holes (even though they might cut the vein in an upper leached zone) before undertaking deeper drilling.[69]   Preliminary shallow holes may be desirable also if the dip of the vein is questionable or subject to change, since an unexpected steepening would greatly increase the depth at which a steeply inclined hole would cut it.   Failing to find the vein where expected, the driller might give up before reaching it.

Selected References

Bibliography of Diamond Drilling, 1947 Edition.   Minneapolis: E. J. Longyear Company, 1947.

Breckon, L. S., Sampling churn-drill sludge at the Utah copper mine: *Engineering and Mining Journal*, vol. 126, pp. 491–492, 1928.

Collins, John J., Some problems involved in the interpretation of diamond-drill-hole sampling and surveying: American Institute of Mining and Metallurgical Engineers, Technical Publication No. 1842, *Mining Technology*, January 1946.   Gives good bibliography.   See also articles in same issue of *Mining Technology* by Greenhalgh, C. W.; Sampson, Edward, and Griggs, Allan B.; Moehlman, Robert S.; Yates, Arthur B.; Davidson, D. M.

Haddock, M. H., *Deep Borehole Surveys and Problems*.   New York and London: McGraw-Hill Book Co., Inc., 1931.

Hitchcock, C. H., Diamond drilling practice: *Can. Inst. Min. and Met.*, vol. 36, pp. 253–285, 1935.

Joralemon, Ira B., Sampling and estimating disseminated copper deposits: *Trans. Am. Inst. Mining and Metallurgy*, vol. 72, pp. 607–620, 1925.

Lahee, Frederic H., *Field Geology*, 4th Edition, Chapter 18, pp. 559–593, "Subsurface Geological Surveying."   New York: McGraw-Hill Book Company, Inc., 1941.

Longyear, Robert D., Recovering and interpreting diamond core-drill samples: *Mining and Metallurgy*, vol. 18, pp. 238–243, May, 1937.

MacLachlan, D. K. F., Sampling and estimation of borehole cores and sludges: *Trans. Institution of Mining and Metallurgy* (London), vol. 40, pp. 177–192, 1931.

Matson, H. T., and Wallis, G. Allan, Drill sampling and interpretation of sampling results in the copper fields of Northern Rhodesia: *Am. Inst. Mining and Met. Engrs. Technical Publication No. 373*, 1931.

Rice, E. R., Churn drilling of disseminated copper deposits, *Engineering and Mining Journal*, vol. 111, pp. 1058–1064, vol. 112, pp. 11–18, 1921.

---

[68] This conception has been developed and applied repeatedly by H. J. C. Connolly.

[69] Moehlman, R. S., Diamond drilling in exploration and development: *American Institute of Mining and Metallurgical Engineers, Technical Publication 1858*, pp. 2–3, 1946.

4

Geophysical Investigations

In short . . . geophysics, like the microscope, is another geological tool.
—Harrison Schmitt [1]

Geophysical prospecting, except in its simplest forms, involves specialized techniques and gives consistent results only in the hands of a scientist who has a thorough understanding of the principles and construction of the instruments and of the mathematics of interpreting the results. A geologist, unless he has made a special study of geophysical prospecting, can hardly expect to carry out the more complex types of surveys himself, but it is well for him to know enough about their possibilities and limitations to be able to exercise judgment as to the conditions under which they may be applicable, to distinguish truly scientific from pseudo-scientific methods, and to correlate the geophysicist's results with geological conditions.

Although individual operators have their own refinements in technique, all of the geophysical methods that are based on sound scientific principles are well known to the profession. Mysterious and miraculous methods smell of "doodlebuggery," and a practitioner who refuses to disclose and explain the method he employs may be suspected of fear that his method will be recognized as unsound, or of not knowing himself just what he is attempting to do.

METHODS

The principal methods used in geophysical exploration are:

Magnetic	Seismic
Electrical	Gravimetric

[1] Schmitt, Harrison: *E. & M. J.*, vol. 141, p. 78, February 1940.

Of these, the magnetic and electrical methods are the ones which have found most use in connection with mining; seismic and gravimetric methods have had relatively little application in the metals field, although they are widely used in petroleum exploration. A special method, measurement of radioactivity, is of use in prospecting for radium and uranium.

Magnetic Methods

Applicability

Ores which consist of magnetic minerals exert a direct effect on suitable instruments. Iron ores in which the principal mineral is magnetite have been sought and found by the use of a magnetized needle since the 17th century; but even hematitic and limonitic ores usually contain enough magnetite to permit exploration by this method. For geological interpretation of magnetic observations on iron ores in the Lake Superior District, see Chapter 16.

Commercial ore-minerals other than iron oxides are not directly detectable by ordinary magnetic means, but this fact does not necessarily exclude the use of magnetic methods in the search for them, because magnetic minerals occur as accessories in some ores of the non-ferrous metals. As an example, the work that has been done in the Sudbury nickel district is very instructive. There, extended surveys with the magnetometer,[2] made throughout the potential ore-bearing area by both the International and the Falconbridge Nickel Companies, following accurate and detailed geologic mapping, have led to the discovery of at least two important new orebodies. The method was applicable because pyrrhotite, which exerts a notable magnetic effect, accompanies the nickel and copper minerals.

Apart from the direct effect of the ore minerals themselves, magnetic methods may afford structural information that leads to the discovery of ore. The phenomenal westward extension of the Rand was the result of cooperation between an experienced mining geologist, the late Leopold Reinecke, and a sound geophysicist, Dr. Rudolf Krahmann.[3] Both the structural concept and the geophysical observations were simple (or at least so they appear in retrospect). The geophysical portion of the program consisted in tracing with a magnetometer the sub-outcrops

[2] Galbraith, F. M., The magnetometer as a geological instrument at Sudbury, *A.I.M.E. Tech. Pub.*, No. 1482, July 1942.

[3] Krahmann, R., Magnetometric observations on the west Rand: *Jour. Chemical Metallurgical and Mining Society of South Africa*, March, 1936. Abstract: *Mining Magazine*, vol. 54, pp. 370–373, June, 1936.

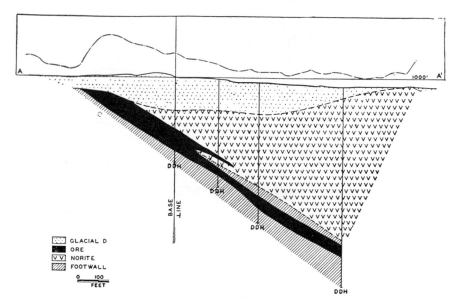

GLACIAL D
ORE
V V NORITE
FOOTWALL

0   100
FEET

Fig. 26—Magnetic profile (*A-A'*.) and geological cross section through a nickel-bearing pyrrhotite orebody, Sudbury district, Ontario. (*After* F. McIntosh Galbraith, American Institute of Mining and Metallurgical Engineers)

of sedimentary iron formations (ferruginous shales) which occupy positions a known distance stratigraphically below the gold-bearing conglomerate "reef." The sub-outcrop was covered unconformably by a dolomite formation, fortunately relatively free of those basic intrusives which elsewhere complicate the magnetic field. Knowing the location of the magnetic bed and the approximate dip of the gold-bearing formation, the location of the Main Reef under cover of 2000 feet was estimated and later confirmed by deep diamond drilling.

Magnetic methods have been used to advantage for tracing geological contacts under covered ground. They are usually applicable to basic igneous bodies which contrast physically with sediments that adjoin them, and have proved particularly useful in the pre-Cambrian shield where contrasts in magnetic susceptibilities of lavas, sedimentary rocks, and intrusive rocks are frequently sufficient to trace contacts, reveal discontinuities, or provide "markers" for outlining structure. In the Lake Superior "Copper Country" magnetic methods have been very useful for tracing out the basaltic flows,[4] a process which is made possible by the concentration of magnetic material in certain horizons in the flows.

[4] Aldrich, H. R., Magnetic surveying on the copper-bearing rocks of Wisconsin, *Econ. Geol.*, vol. 18, pp. 562–574, 1923,

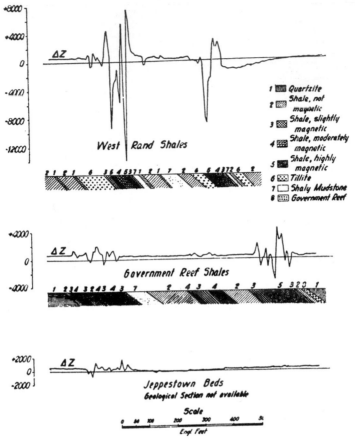

Fig. 27—Magnetometric traverse (vertical intensity) across lower portion
of the Witwatersrand System about 20 miles west of Johannesburg (looking northeast). The goldbearing Main Reef Series is about 5000 feet
stratigraphically above the Government Reef Shales (middle section).
(*After* Krahman, as reproduced by Heiland)

In the Canadian pre-Cambrian shield magnetic methods have been used
on at least 1000 different mining properties with considerable success.
A number of orebodies have been located in conjunction with geological
and diamond-drilling programs, but as gold is the metal usually sought,
the chief use of the geophysical survey is to trace geological contacts
and structural features by means of magnetic contrasts in underlying
rock.   The secret of the success of geomagnetic methods in Canadian
mining camps is the nearly vertical dip of the formations in most districts.   This situation presents the relatively simple problem of segregat-
ing formations of different magnetic susceptibility, obscured only by
a mantle of glacial drift, generally uniformly weak in magnetism.   In-

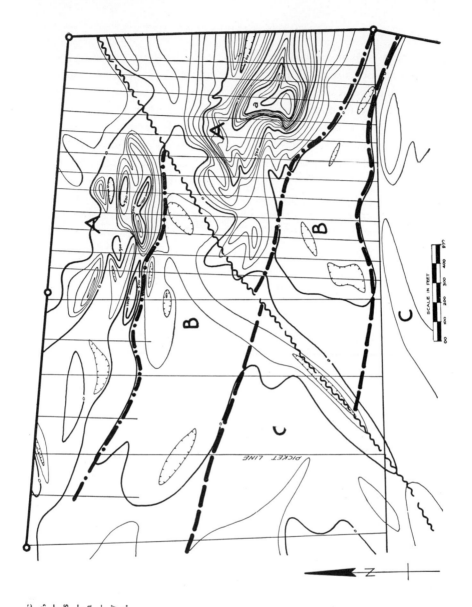

Fig. 28—Part of a geomagnetic survey of Bourlamac Township, Quebec. Contours indicate magnetic intensity. Dot-and-dash lines are contacts separating rock formations: *A*, andesite and diorite with some sulphides; *a*, diorite; *B*, dacite; *C*, acid volcanics. The wavy line is a fault. (*Courtesy* of N. B. Keevil)

terpretation cannot be considered to be fool-proof, however, because contrasts are not always all that is to be desired, and because of the very complexity of pre-Cambrian geology itself.   The best interpretations are made when the magnetic data are correlated with a known geological occurrence and extended into covered ground, or where a reasonable amount of data from surface outcrops or from diamond drilling are available.   The quality and usefulness of the interpretations of such geomagnetic surveys have improved a great deal during the past few years, owing partly to increased experience of the practitioners but chiefly to the entrance into the field of geophysicists with a sound background in practical geology.

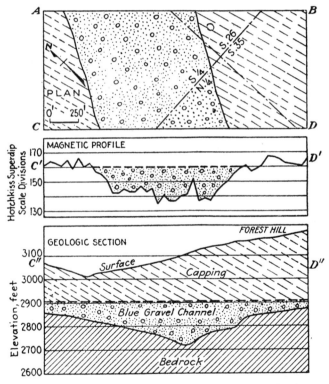

Fig. 29—Magnetic low over placer channel on magnetic bedrock, California. (*After* E. W. Ellsworth, reproduced by Heiland)

Magnetic methods have been used also in delimiting the channels of placer deposits.[5]   The significance of readings depends on whether the bedrock is more magnetic or less magnetic than the alluvial material

---

[5] Jenkins, Olaf P., and Wright, W. Quinby, California's goldbearing Tertiary channels, *E. and M. J.*, vol. 135, p. 502, November, 1934.

of the channel. In channels cut in basic rock the bedrock is usually more magnetic, and the channel is marked by a zone of low magnetic intensity. But if the gravel contains much magnetite ("black sand") and the bedrock has low magnetic intensity, the magnetic readings give a direct indication of the location of heavy concentrate in the channel.

Operation of the Dip Needle

The instruments commonly used in magnetic exploration are the dip needle, the Hotchkiss superdip, and the magnetometer. The dip needle is such a simple instrument and so widely used by geologists that the following directions for its use, prepared by S. A. Tyler, should not be out of place here:

The magnetic element of the dip needle consists of a thin magnetized needle suspended at its center of gravity by points whose ends rest in adjustable jewel bearings. The needle swings within a graduated circle which carries a bubble for levelling at its base. A thumb-screw release opens and closes a spring clamp which holds the needle, protecting the jewels and points when the instrument is not in use. With the exception of the needle, all parts of the instrument are made of brass.

In taking an observation, first hold the instrument in a horizontal plane and release the needle with the thumb and forefinger. Orient yourself facing magnetic west so that your body stands in the plane of the magnetic meridian. Then clamp the needle with the north end always at the same point, 10 or 20 degrees above zero. Raise the instrument into a vertical plane at the level of the eyes, center the level bubble and release the needle so that it swings freely. As it swings, compute mentally the mid-points of the first two or three swings and if they check closely, record the reading. The entire operation requires about fifteen seconds. In order to obtain reliable results, always reproduce every step in the observation in exactly the same manner each time you take a reading, releasing the needle from the same point and with the same twisting motion and holding the instrument steady while the needle is swinging.

To yield significant interpretations, magnetic observations must be taken systematically at regularly spaced intervals. The spacing depends largely on the detail that a particular problem demands; for reconnaissance work it may be from 100 to 130 feet, whereas for very detailed work it may be 5 to 10 feet.

In reconnaissance work the points at which readings are taken may be located by pace and compass, but in detailed work they usually need to be taped. The compass used in locating stations is a sundial compass rather than a Brunton, because magnetic deflections over iron-bearing rocks are generally very pronounced. The magnetic declination indicated by the sundial compass should be recorded at regular intervals, for this information is of value in determining the horizontal component of the magnetic field.

The magnetic readings are plotted directly on the outcrop map in order to integrate them with geological observations. Although the hundreds or thousands of magnetic readings on a map would be difficult to interpret directly, a pattern usually emerges out of the apparent chaos on contouring the readings in a manner analogous to the contouring of elevations.

Airborne Magnetometer

A very rapid and economical type of magnetic reconnaissance from the air [6] was developed during the war. A "bird" towed below an airplane carries a magnetometer which is connected electrically with a recording device inside the plane where a needle traces a continuous profile of magnetic intensity. Operated normally at an altitude of about 1000 feet, the instrument escapes the disturbing effects of purely local attraction from such objects as rails or small near-surface concentrations of magnetite. Its usefulness, so far, is limited to reconnaissance; ground surveys are still required for detailed exploration. It has been tested over magnetite deposits in the Adirondacks, iron deposits in Minnesota, nickel in Sudbury and elsewhere with most encouraging results.

Still more recently Hans Lundberg has been making magnetic observations from a helicopter,[7] for which he claims the advantages of greater maneuverability and ability to fly at lower altitudes.

Electrical Methods

Applicability

Electrical methods had their first spectacular success in northern Sweden [8] where conditions were ideal for this type of prospecting; the country is relatively level, introducing no large corrections for topography, the overburden is thin and the ore consists of bodies of massive sulphide. Many orebodies were found in the region; the largest of them is the Boliden Mine where the arsenopyrite-chalcopyrite ore carries 2½ per cent copper and 10 grams per ton in gold. Another well-known district where electrical prospecting was successful is Buchans in Newfoundland. There, following the original discovery, additional bodies of lead-zinc ore were located by equipotential methods.

[6] Balsley, J. R., Jr., The airborne magnetometer, U.S.G.S. Geophysical Investigations Report 3, 1946.

[7] Unsigned article, Detailed magnetometer surveys quickly made from helicopters, *Mining and Metallurgy*, vol. 27, p. 474, 1946. Lundberg, Hans, Mining geophysics, *Mining and Metallurgy* (Annual Review Number), vol. 28, p. 95, February 1947. Also papers presented verbally.

[8] Eklund, Josef, Electrical Prospecting in Sweden, *Mining Magazine*, vol. 36, p. 265, May, 1927.

Electrical methods have been used successfully in outlining the contour of the bedrock surface in placer deposits [9] and in locating quartz veins.[10]

Principles

Electrical methods of prospecting depend for their success on the contrast in electrical properties between an orebody and the rocks that surround it. If they are used in deciphering structure, instead of searching for an orebody itself, they depend on contrast in electrical properties between different rock formations. The principal electrical property involved is conductivity, which may express itself in determining the paths that the current follows in flowing through a rock mass (more accurately described as the field of flux) or in the drop in potential from point to point within the field. Some of the other properties that may be measured are electrostatic capacity, inductance, and magnetic permeability.

Massive sulphide bodies are highly conductive and the most spectacular successes have been achieved with ores of this sort. The conductivity of most rocks is much lower than that of massive sulphides, yet there is a wide variation as between one type of rock and another. Graphitic beds are strongly conductive, whereas massive quartz veins are highly resistant. Water, if it contains dissolved salts as most groundwater does, is a much better conductor than rock itself, hence the conductivity of rocks is determined largely by the water held in pores and fractures and, therefore, by the porosity and texture of the rock. Faults and shear zones, since they are likely to be water-courses, are usually zones of good conductivity.

Lines of Flow. The principles of electrical prospecting may be illustrated by describing one of the simpler methods. If we introduce current into the earth through two electrodes several thousand feet apart, connected to the terminals of a generator by insulated wires, electric current flows through the ground from one electrode to the other. If the ground is ideally homogeneous, some of the current will flow in a straight line between the two electrodes, but this will be only one of an infinite number of lines of flux which radiate outward from one electrode and gather inward toward the other. So long as the ground is

---

[9] Jakosky, J. J., and Wilson, C. H., Examining a placer by geophysical methods, *E. & M. J.*, vol. 135, pp. 71 ff., February 1934, also Geophysical studies in placer and water-supply problems: *A.I.M.E. Tech. Pub.* 515, 1934.

[10] Kelly, Sherwin F. and Low, Bela, Discovering gold-quartz veins electrically, *Mining and Metallurgy*, vol. 15, pages 251–256, June 1934.

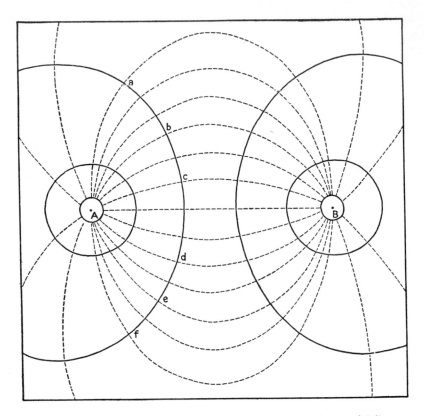

Fig. 30—Current flow-lines (broken lines) and equipotential lines (solid lines) about two electrodes, *A* and *B*. (Idealized diagram) (*After* Billings)

homogeneous the lines of flux are smooth curves symmetrically arranged. But let us suppose that somewhere in the area there is a body of highly conductive sulphide. The curves take advantage of this good conductor, swinging out of their ideal paths to converge toward it. If, in contrast, there is a mass of solid, highly resistant quartz the lines diverge around it and only a small proportion of the current flows through it. These "anomalies"—distortions of the symmetrical pattern of flux lines —are the areas of interest.

Equipotential Lines. Since tracing the actual flow lines is not a convenient procedure, in practice other features are mapped which express the pattern in a somewhat different manner. A common method is to survey equipotential lines, an equipotential line being the locus of all points having the same electromotive potential and, therefore, of points between which no current will flow.

Methods of Application

For simplicity of description a direct-current field has been assumed; actually alternating current is more commonly used for reasons which will appear later. The methods just described, in which current is introduced directly into the ground are known as *galvanic* methods. Instead, the ground may be energized by setting up induced currents in it.

What with the variety of methods that can be used to energize the ground and the variety of methods of measuring the effects, a large range of combinations is available to the geophysicist. Those most commonly used in mining may be classified as follows:

I. According to method of energizing the ground.

A. Self-potential methods.

In this case no artificial power is applied; the feature that is measured is the natural E.M.F. generated by electrochemical reaction in the ground. A sulphide body, if chemical or mineralogical conditions at its opposite ends are dissimilar, reacts with the ground-water to form a gigantic electric battery which sets up electric currents of its own. The currents are usually detected at the surface by measuring the potential drop between pairs of copper electrodes each of which is placed in a porous pot containing saturated copper sulphate solution. The pots are placed in good contact with the ground 25 to 100 feet apart. Important anomalies between 100 and 500 millivolts may be distinguished from normal background fluctuations up to 50 millivolts.

B. Galvanic methods.

(1) *Direct current methods.* Current is supplied by a battery, or more commonly a direct-current generator, and introduced into the ground through a pair of point electrodes (as already described) or through "line electrodes" consisting of a pair of bare wires laid out parallel to each other on opposite sides of the area to be surveyed, grounded at frequent intervals by electrodes sunk into the earth. Direct current methods have the advantage of simplicity, but the electrolytic action resulting in polarization of the electrodes introduces complications. One way of overcoming this is to use nonpolarizing electrodes (porous cups), as in self-potential measurements.

(2) *Alternating current methods.* Current is supplied by an A.C. generator and introduced into the ground through either "point" or "line" electrodes.

As compared with direct currents, alternating currents introduce certain mathematical complications, due to surface effects, inductance and electrostatic capacity. For this reason, however, if properly interpreted, they permit the observation of electrical properties which direct currents fail to reveal. They have practical advantages in that they can be easily amplified and recorded on rugged meters or if a frequency within the audible range is used, they can be detected by earphones. The frequency that is selected depends partly on the depth of penetration that is desired. High frequencies (over 10 kilocycles) penetrate only to short distances below the surface and for most mining purposes have not proved very satisfactory. Low and intermediate frequencies (5 to 100 cycles) are used in potential methods and particularly where deep penetration is desired.

C. Induction methods. In contrast to galvanic methods in which the source of power is connected directly to the earth, induction methods employ an insulated circuit. The flow of current through an insulated cable sets up a magnetic field and this, in turn, induces currents in the earth in the same way that the primary circuit of an induction coil or transformer sets up a magnetic field and induces current in a secondary circuit. Either the magnetic field or the induced current may be measured.

The primary circuit is a loop of insulated cable which may be horizontal—laid on the ground in a circular or rectangular shape—or vertical. Theoretically, a vertical loop would be better for detecting steeply dipping orebodies, but such an arrangement is difficult to set up.

II. According to method of detecting the electrical properties. The current (or lack of current) in the ground can be detected either by direct measurement or by induction.

For *direct measurement*, probing electrodes are used. Usually two probing electrodes are connected through some device for detecting or measuring the current. It may consist of a galvanometer, earphones (in the case of alternating current within the audible range), voltmeter, potentiometer, or milliammeter. When the ground is energized by induction, the surveying instrument may be equipped with a compensator to cut out the direct effect of the primary circuit, leaving only the induced current to be measured.

In the *equipotential* method of surveying, the probing electrodes are used to trace out a series of points. One probing electrode, inserted into the ground, may remain temporarily fixed while the other is moved from point to point until a place is found where no current flows between the two electrodes. This means that the two points are on the same equipotential line. Then a third point on the same line is sought, and so on, until the line has been traced out. Alternatively, readings may be taken along parallel picket lines and the equipotential contours drawn later.

By *resistivity* methods, the resistivity (reciprocal of the conductivity) of component portions of the area are determined by measuring the potential difference and the current intensity between each pair of points. The resistivity is calculated according to Ohm's law, $I = E/R$ (or the corresponding modification of it for alternating currents).

In *potential-drop-ratio* methods a traverse is run across the area and the drop in potential for each interval is compared with the drop in the next interval.

In *electromagnetic* methods, the current in the ground is not measured directly, but the magnetic field is surveyed by means of portable coils in which it sets up induced currents. By rotating a detecting coil one can measure not merely the horizontal but also the vertical component of the magnetic field.

Choice of Methods. The large number of methods and combinations of methods offers a wide choice of means of surveying. No one method is "best"; the method selected should be the one best suited to the particular problem in hand.

In general the galvanic methods work best where the rock-conductivity is relatively high, whereas induction methods are advantageous in rocks of low conductivity or rocks that are covered by thick overburden.

Of the methods of surveying, the equipotential measurements are well-adapted to the detection of broad conductive orebodies and to determining the strike of concealed formations whose dip is steep.

Resistivity methods are widely used for structural studies of beds having greatly differing resistance, particularly for determining the depth of flatly dipping formations.

Potential-drop methods give sharp indications at the contacts of steep formation boundaries. They have been used extensively in locating quartz veins in the course of exploration for gold.

Electromagnetic methods have been successful in locating bodies of heavy sulphide but can also be applied to disseminated sulphides. They are useful for determining the depth of beds or other sheetlike bodies of gentle dip.

Combinations of Methods. It is often desirable to survey the same ground by more than one electrical method, for example, self-potential followed by electromagnetic. Thus one method serves as a check on the other and the one may bring out characteristics that the other fails to show. Similarly, electrical methods may be supplemented by other geophysical methods; for example, an electrical method may locate a conductive body and a magnetic method may determine whether it is a magnetic ore, such as magnetite or pyrrhotite, or a non-magnetic ore such as pyrite. Or a magnetic survey may be made to outline the general geological picture, and electrical methods be applied locally to possible structures or contacts. Gravimetric methods have been used to determine whether a conductive body suspected of being sulphide is massive or disseminated. If the possible types of ore which may be expected in a district are known, geophysical information may tell whether the deposit under investigation is likely to be of commercial interest or not.

Seismic Methods

The seismic method consists of detonating a charge of dynamite or other explosive and measuring the reflection or refraction of the artificial earthquake waves set up by the shock. In connection with mining it has been used to determine the depth to bedrock preparatory to diamond drilling. In oil geology it has been used very widely and successfully to determine the depth to key stratigraphic horizons, and there is no reason why it could not be used to solve similar problems in connection with mining geology. Most of the mining geologists' problems, however, involve much more complex structural conditions on a smaller scale.

Gravimetric Methods

Gravimetric methods are based on local variations in the direction and intensity of the earth's gravitative field. Heavy masses attract the plumb-bob and, conversely, light masses allow the plumb-bob to be deflected away from them. Instead of the simple plumb-bob, delicate instruments are used. One of the most familiar is the Eötvös torsion balance, which measures the horizontal rate of change in the configuration of the earth's gravitative field. In recent years, this has been replaced by gravimeters of various types.

Gravimetric methods have been used widely in petroleum geology but until recently have found little use in ore-search, partly because the rough topography characteristic of so many mining districts complicates the interpretations. However, the method has been successful in finding a large body of chromite in Cuba, where it was favored by a combination of factors: low physiographic relief, shallow depth of ore (150 feet), and strong contrast in specific gravity between the massive chromite and the surrounding serpentine.

Very spectacular success in selecting areas to be tested by drilling has been achieved in connection with exploration for gold in the Orange Free State.[11] There, as on the Rand, the gold-bearing reefs occur in the Witwatersrand series. But in the Orange Free State this series is

---

[11] Frost, A., McIntyre, R. C., Papenfus, E. B., and Weiss, O., The Odendaalsrust Goldfield: *South African Mining and Engineering Journal*, October 12, October 26, November 2, 1946. Digest, *Mining Magazine*, vol. 75, pp. 389–391, 1946.

covered in places by 5000 to 7000 feet of basic lavas (the Ventersdorp Series) so that it can be reached by drilling only in places where the lavas are thin or missing. A still younger unconformable cover of Karroo sediments over the whole area makes it impossible to recognize such places by surface mapping, but a survey with the torsion balance to determine the approximate thickness of the heavy lava disclosed an area 4½ miles long in which the lava is absent. Here the Ventersdorp had been elevated in a horst block and removed by erosion, leaving the Witwatersrand Series exposed on an old erosion surface until it was covered by the capping of Karroo sediments. Drilling in this area through about 1000 feet of Karroo intersected gold-bearing reefs with extremely encouraging values. On the basis of about a hundred drill holes in this and other favorable locations within the district, company officials predict that over an area of 200 square miles a number of new mines will be developed, some of which will be quite rich.[12] This achievement is all the more impressive because the nearest outcrop of known Witwatersrand rocks is 70 miles away and, so far as surface evidence would indicate, gold might occur anywhere or nowhere through all of northern and northwestern Orange Free State.

Radioactivity [13]

Ores of uranium and radium may be detected by measuring the effects of their radioactivity. A simple method used in the early days of the development of the Great Bear Lake District (N.W.T.) consisted of wrapping photographic plates in lightproof material, laying them about at intervals over the area and then collecting and developing them.[14]

More modern methods of greater sensitivity employ ionization chambers, or the Geiger-Mueller counter, a device equipped with meters, earphones or count registers, which make it possible to "see" or "hear" the gamma rays. The tests can be applied either in the field, under water, or in drill holes, or on specimens of soil and rock in the laboratory.

Radioactivity can be detected in extremely minute amounts, but its use for detecting hidden ore is limited by the blanketing effect of rock cover, as even the most penetrating natural radiation is absorbed by a few yards of soil. The location of ore at greater depths by radioactivity instruments must, therefore, depend upon the migration of radioactive

[12] Annan, Robert, Speech of the chairman at annual meeting, Consolidated Gold Fields of South Africa: *Mining Magazine*, vol. 74, company meetings section, p. 41, December, 1946.

[13] Much of the information presented in this section was supplied by N. B. Keevil in personal correspondence.

[14] Kidd, D. F., Personal communication.

elements from the source, either by transport in solutions during or following ore-deposition, or by diffusion of radon, the only gaseous member of the radioactive series. Such processes may result in an aureole, or in localization of radioactivity along faults or fissures and thus provide somewhat greater depth penetration to radioactive methods. At least a limited use of such methods has been shown by locating through shallow overburden radioactive ore in Colorado, Great Bear Lake, N.W.T., and in Russia. The possibility of tracing the source of radioactivity in relatively radioactive fans in glacial overburden has been suggested and subjected satisfactorily to limited tests by soil and plant analyses by N. B. Keevil and F. Senftle (manuscript in preparation).

Ridland [15] tested the Geiger-Mueller counter at Great Bear Lake over two known radium-bearing veins. The gamma ray count increased notably within 100 feet of the veins and immediately over them gave such intense activity as to endanger the instrument. This was true even though the ore on one of them did not come to within 60 feet of the surface. Traverses over nine additional shear zones gave results which warranted recommendation of exploratory programs on three of them. The outcome of these recommendations is not yet published, but later applications of radioactive methods in this area are reported to have met with some success.

Aside from their use in the search for uranium-bearing ores, the use of radioactive methods has been suggested as an aid in correlation of formations and in deciphering geologic structure.[16]

Rocks are radioactive in measurable degree, the acid rocks more so than the basic as a general rule, and there is sufficient variation between one formation and another to permit correlation of certain beds—for example, formations in churn-drill holes. Furthermore, certain groundwaters have an appreciable content of radon and of soluble radioactive material, so that faults containing such water might be recognized and traced by measuring variations in radioactivity. However, this application is of limited use as yet and should be considered only where relatively radioactive material is known to exist below.

LIMITATIONS OF GEOPHYSICAL METHODS

Deducing geological structure from geophysical observations is inevitably a matter of interpretation. The instruments measure the physi-

[15] Ridland, G. Carman, Use of the Geiger-Mueller counter in the search for pitchblende-bearing veins at Great Bear Lake, Canada, A.I.M.E. Tech. Pub. No. 1610, 1943.

[16] Krasnow, Shelley, Application of radioactive methods to geological exploration. Paper presented before Washington Section, A.I.M.E., May 23rd, 1945.

cal properties of the ground but do not in themselves tell what rocks or minerals are present; ordinarily a set of geophysical data is susceptible to various alternative interpretations, some geologically probable and some improbable. As Davidson [17] says, "An essential or at least highly desirable prerequisite to the useful application of geophysics is a good geological picture of the area concerned. Without this, any interpretation of results is of doubtful value and may result in the expenditure of money on interpretations which are geologically impossible." An interpretation can be made with most confidence when the survey can start on exposed rock and trace a contact or other feature under covered ground. It is least reliable in large covered areas where little is directly known about the geology. There is still room for much progress in the interpretation of geophysical data. Most skilled practitioners of applied geophysics are not sufficiently trained in mining geology to appreciate all of the possible alternative interpretations that may be placed on geophysical data, while most geologists have so little skill in mathematical physics that they are obliged to rely on the geophysicist for their structural deductions. What is needed is a new generation of geophysical geologists or geological geophysicists, who can bridge the gap between the two techniques.

Assuming that the structure is correctly interpreted from the geophysical data, the usefulness of the results depends on how closely the ore is related to structure—in other words, the definiteness of structural control. Here mining is at a disadvantage as compared with oil geology. Mines are usually in regions of complex structure which, at best, is difficult to interpret from geophysical data. Furthermore, the step from structure to ore-control is a longer one than the corresponding step from rock structure to an oil-pool. For these reasons, geophysical methods have played a much less vital role in mining than in oil exploration.

On the whole, geophysics, with the exception of magnetic methods, has so far proved somewhat disappointing. This has been due not so much to any fault in the methods themselves as to the over-hopeful attitude aroused in the mid-'twenties by the sales campaigns of the purveyors of the art and by the natural enthusiasm of explorers for a new and rather mysterious method. A few itinerant impostors and "screw-balls" who appeared out of nowhere and disappeared whence they had come did not help the situation in the minds of those operators who were not quite able to distinguish sincere science from hocus-pocus.

[17] Davidson, Stanley, Modernized exploration technique in eastern Canadian mining fields, *Can. Inst. of Mining & Metallurgy, Bull.* No. 381, p. 50, January, 1944.

Furthermore, it is only fair to recognize that in the decade of the 'thirties, when geophysical methods were ready for testing and development in the field, the attention of the mining world turned to gold, the metal that is probably least susceptible to detection by geophysical methods. Greater interest in base metals, affording a more favorable opportunity to test the science, should result in a more significant advance in techniques and a higher percentage of successes in directly locating hidden ore.

In brief, geophysical methods can serve a very useful purpose in mining exploration, first in locating ore of the limited number of types susceptible to direct detection and second as a geological tool in tracing contacts and in affording evidence of geologic structure. It must be emphasized that, except in special cases, geophysics is a tool for the geologist to use and only one of the tools at his disposal. It can be a useful aid to geology, but it is not a substitute for it. At the same time, it is a tool that should be considered whenever there is any uncertainty about underlying geology, and particularly when outcrops are sparse.

SELECTED REFERENCES

Heiland, C. A., *Geophysical Exploration*.   New York: Prentice-Hall, Incorporated, 1940.

Jakosky, J. J., *Exploration Geophysics*.   Los Angeles: Times-Mirror Press, 1940.

Nettleton, L. L., *Geophysical Prospecting for Oil*.   New York and London: McGraw-Hill Book Co., Inc., 1940.   (Although concerned primarily with petroleum, the methods described include those applicable to ore search.)

5

Laboratory Methods

But somehow he hasn't got hold of it quite
Or the liquid you pour on it first isn't right
So that's why he works at it night after night
'Til he knows he can do it for certain.

—A. A. MILNE [1]

IN THE mine or in the field, the geologist's observations are limited to what he can see with his two eyes aided, where necessary, by a simple hand lens. He will recognize many rocks and minerals at sight, but from time to time he will find some unfamiliar species. The laboratory, with its chemical and optical equipment, makes it possible to confirm or reject his hunches or to determine the identity of a mineral that is totally strange to him. Grains and textures that are too fine for the hand lens to resolve will reveal themselves under the high-power microscope.

Sooner or later the identity of every mineral found in a mine ought to be determined. Each may throw light on the origin of the ore or may even reveal minerals of commercial value in places where they had not been suspected. In Leadville, Colorado, an inconspicuous white mineral went unnoticed for forty years until an assayer had the intellectual curiosity to identify it.[2] When it proved to be hemimorphite (calamine), the camp enjoyed a sensational revival as a producer of high-grade zinc ore. The practical value of routine examination by microscopic methods is illustrated in a spectacular way by the discovery of

---

[1] "The Alchemist," from *When We Were Very Young*. New York: E. P. Dutton, 1924.
[2] Henderson, Charles W., Geology and ore deposits of the Leadville Mining District, Colorado: U.S.G.S. Professional Paper 148, 1927, page 123. Some accounts credit the discovery not to an assayer but to miners who had become familiar with oxidized lead-zinc ores in other districts.

tungsten at Yellow Pine, Idaho, in 1940. Donald White of the United States Geological Survey, while studying thin sections of cores recovered in a drilling campaign which was designed to increase the reserves of antimony ore, recognized scheelite in one of the slides and immediately examined all the rest of his specimens under the ultraviolet light. Further exploration based on his observations resulted in the discovery of the richest tungsten deposit in the United States, just at a time when the metal was urgently needed in the war effort.

Studies of paragenesis may lead in unexpected ways to ore discovery. In the Hanover district of New Mexico (Pewabic mine), microscopic study showed that sphalerite is later than garnet and replaces it preferentially; thus the presence of garnet has been a factor in localizing the zinc ore. This observation gave Schmitt confidence to recommend exploration of a garnetized zone and as a result, a large tonnage of ore was found. Identifying minerals and determining their textural relations may not always lead to spectacular discoveries, but they afford an insight into the processes of ore deposition and thus promote constructive reasoning.

Aside from its facilities for identifying minerals and investigating textures, the laboratory serves as a place for assembling and comparing specimens from different parts of the district. Systematic classification and comparison is likely to disclose similarities and differences which might escape notice unless typical varieties of rocks and ore are studied side by side.

The extent to which laboratory investigations can be carried is likely to be limited by the available equipment. A blowpipe and the reagents for chemical identifications will probably be at hand or may be acquired at negligible expense. Microscopes, either polarizing or reflecting, however, are rarely to be found except in the offices of the largest companies, and unless the geologist supplies his own equipment he is unlikely to have an instrument available. Nevertheless, even smaller companies would find it good economy to appropriate the few hundred dollars required to provide laboratory equipment in cases where it offers promise of solving pertinent problems.

HAND SPECIMENS

Study of hand specimens with a lens or an inexpensive binocular microscope is capable of yielding more information than most geologists realize. Many features such as the shapes and contact-relations of mineral grains and the arrangement of layers in vugs are too small to be clear to the naked eye yet too large to come within the field of the high power microscope. Therefore scrutiny with a lens or binocular should not be omitted even though the specimens are later to be studied in polished and thin section under higher magnification.

Fig. 31—Stereoscopic (binocular) microscope. (*Courtesy of* Spencer Lens Company)

Under the binocular any small mineral grain, crystal, or flake may be isolated for further examination by detaching it with a needle and picking it up on a tiny taper made of beeswax. It is then ready for further investigation whether by immersion methods under the petrographic microscope, by microchemical technique, by blowpipe tests, or by X-ray diffraction methods.

MICROSCOPIC METHODS

Two types of high power microscopes are used for mining work: the petrographic microscope for gangue and transparent minerals, and the reflecting microscope for sulphides and other opaque minerals. A single instrument, fitted with interchangeable accessories, can be made to serve either pupose.

Petrographic, "mineragraphic," and other laboratory methods have developed into such highly specialized techniques that a description of the principles and practice in sufficient detail to be of use would occupy much more space than is appropriate in this book. As most university graduates in geology are trained in some or all of these methods, the purpose of the present chapter is to remind the reader of the variety of means of investigation at his disposal, call attention to some of the types of problems that they can solve and present references to the most convenient sources of information.

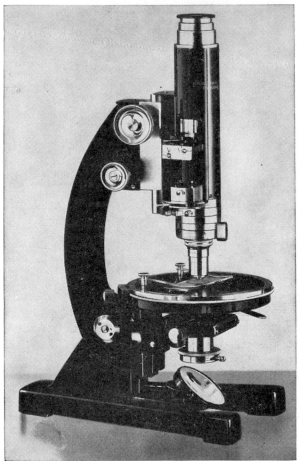

Fig. 32—Petrographic (polarizing) microscope. (*Courtesy of* Bausch and Lomb Optical Company)

PETROGRAPHIC METHODS

The petrographic microscope,[3] employing transmitted polarized light, is used for studying fresh and altered rocks. It is also employed for investigating gangue minerals and determining their relations to ore minerals. For mere identification, the material may be examined in the form of fine grains or powder. This method permits the use of liquids

---

[3] For works on petrography and optical crystallography, see *Selected References* at the end of this chapter.

of known refractive index in order to measure the indices of the minerals by the immersion method.

Thin sections are used when the textural relations of the minerals are to be determined.

The preparation of thin sections requires a certain amount of specialized equipment and no little skill and patience. Under ordinary conditions it hardly pays the geologist to grind them himself, as a number of firms [4] are equipped to prepare them commercially.

When a hand specimen is collected in the field or underground it is well to take at the same time a chip about an inch square from which a thin section can be made. Alternatively a corner can later be sawed out of the hand specimen. Either method avoids shattering the hand specimen which becomes doubly valuable if it represents material from which a thin section has been made. Before the chip is sent to the preparator it is important to mark on it in crayon the plane in which the thin section is to be cut unless the orientation is of no significance.

When an oriented section is desired (*see* Petrofabric Studies), the usual practice is to break out the specimen with a hammer or moil, fit it back into its natural position in the rock and attach a piece of adhesive tape [5] bearing a horizontal line to indicate the compass direction and an arrow to indicate either the nadir or a line whose inclination is recorded.

Morgan [6] recommends marking the specimen before breaking it loose, ruling a line on it with a dental pick by using a Brunton compass as a straightedge. He makes an arrow on one end of the line to act as a precaution against reversing the specimen end-for-end and takes the bearing of the line.

The actual study of the specimens should preferably be made by the geologist himself, assuming that he has had adequate petrographic training. If the necessary equipment is not at hand he will do well to make a pilgrimage to the nearest university or museum. He may save time, however, by engaging a professional petrographer to make a preliminary examination of the slides, since a large share of the time consumed in petrographic work is occupied in making accurate identifications of the

[4] George S. Rev, Box 25, Schermerhorn Hall, Columbia University, New York, 27, N. Y.
Reid & Mergner, Washington, D. C.
W. Harold Tomlinson, 260 N. Rolling Rd., Springfield, Pa.
Rudolph von Huene, 865 N. Mentor Ave., Pasadena, Cal., makes both polished and thin sections.
[5] Cloos, Ernst, The application of recent structural methods in the interpretation of the crystalline rocks of Maryland: *Md. Geol. Survey*, vol. 13, 1937, page 86.
[6] Morgan, Ray E., A method for collecting oriented ı...neral specimens: *Econ. Geol.*, vol. 38, 1943, pp. 603–608.

minerals. Wherever warranted by the requirements, the petrographer will make determinations which are at least roughly quantitative. Instead of stating vaguely that a rock consists of feldspar and pyroxene, he will report the approximate percentage of each mineral and that the pyroxene is, let us say, pigeonite and the feldspar is bytownite, An_{75} in grains, .5 mm in diameter.

Beyond accurate identification and description he will be very hesitant in spinning hypotheses regarding rocks that he has not seen in the field. Some "office petrographers" are prone to build up the whole history of a district on half a dozen thin sections, a practice which is likely to be useless if not downright misleading. For example, a professor, of national reputation, examined a suite of specimens from a remote mining district and reported that the original rock was peridotite, whereas the field relations clearly indicated that it was a contact-metamorphosed limestone.

Microscopic determination of the minerals present in a rock and of their relative proportions permit a correct identification of the rock. The identification may or may not be of practical value. Of greater importance than merely tagging the rock with its precise name is the ability to distinguish between two different igneous (or for that matter sedimentary) bodies, a matter which can be of critical importance if one rock is "favorable" and the other not. It is sometimes possible to correlate dikes or flows by accurate determination of their feldspars or ferromagnesians. Such identifications can be useful for solving fault problems and for other purposes. Although this method is always worth trying, it is not always successful; an attempt to apply it to the lava flows of Keweenaw Point in Michigan showed, rather surprisingly, that the pyroxenes of all of the flows that were studied had identical optical properties.[7]

The petrographic microscope is especially useful in studying altered rocks. Even in materials which would appear to be altered beyond recognition, patches of sericite may represent the original feldspar phenocrysts, and patches of chlorite and carbonate may represent the original ferromagnesians, thus giving a clue to the nature of the rock from which the alteration product was derived. In some of the basic lavas of northern Ontario, the size of the aggregates of leucoxene (derived from ilmenite or from titanium-bearing ferromagnesians) is a reliable index to the grain size of the original rock; variation toward fine grain indicates approach to a flow-top or flow bottom, and unusually

[7] Hardin, George, Personal conversation.

large patches of leucoxene are typical of the centers of especially thick flows.

In certain districts it is of practical importance to distinguish between alteration which is regional and alteration which represents part of the process of ore deposition. For example, Gustafson[8] recognized two varieties of chlorite in the vicinity of the Homestake mine, one broadly distributed in the Homestake formation and the other confined to rock intimately associated with the orebodies.

Features which the microscope discloses are often highly enlightening, but their usefulness is still further enhanced when they can be correlated with features visible to the naked eye. Sometimes a particular rock-type or alteration phase is overlooked in preliminary mapping but disclosed by microscopic study. Once seen, it can be recognized underground by some characteristic of color or texture so that further mapping is possible without repeated recourse to the microscope.

PETROFABRIC STUDIES

In rocks that have been deformed under differential pressure, there is usually an approach toward a parallel orientation of elongate grains or of mica flakes or of the optic axes of such minerals as quartz and calcite. This "preferred orientation" may not be evident to the eye, but it is disclosed by examining a suite of thin sections cut from specimens whose natural attitude in their original setting is a matter of record. Using a microscope equipped with a universal stage, the orientation of each mineral grain is measured and the results are plotted on a statistical graph. The methods, developed by Sander[9] and other Continental geologists are summarized and discussed in English by Knopf and Ingerson[10] and by Fairbairn.[11]

The preferred orientations clearly have a relation to the deformation that the rock has experienced although the significance of the orientation in terms of tectonics is, in some respects, still a matter of opinion.[12] So far, it has not been widely used in mining geology, but there is no

[8] Gustafson, John K., Metamorphism and hydrothermal alteration of the Homestake gold-bearing formation: *Econ. Geol.*, vol. 28, 1933, p. 123.

[9] Sander, Bruno, *Gefügekunde der Gesteine.* Vienna: Julius Springer, 1930.

[10] Knopf, Eleanora Bliss, and Ingerson, Earl, *Structural Petrology*, Geol. Soc. of America, Memoir 6, November 1938.

[11] Fairbairn, H. W., *Structural Petrology of Deformed Rocks.* Cambridge, Mass.: Addison-Wesley Press Inc., 1942.

Billings, Marland, P., *Structural Geology.* New York: Prentice-Hall, Inc., 1942, pp. 332–355.

[12] Griggs, David T., Experimental flow of rocks under conditions favoring recrystallization: *Bull. G.S.A.*, vol. 51, p. 1003, 1940.

reason why it should not be helpful in solving certain complex structural problems.

A method of ascertaining the direction of movement on a fault by observing the position of microscopic shears and the distortion of mica flakes in oriented thin sections taken adjacent to the fault zone has been described by Fraser.[13]

HEAVY MINERAL STUDIES

In recent years the technique of correlating sedimentary formations by means of their "heavy accessories" has made rapid progress.[14] The method consists of crushing or otherwise disintegrating the rock and concentrating the scanty amounts of such minerals as garnet, ilmenite, magnetite, and zircon by settling in heavy liquids or by hydraulic classification. Any given stratigraphic horizon is likely to carry these minerals in roughly constant proportion and with constant size and shape of grain, a fact which can be used in recognizing the horizon wherever it is met in the district.

The same method has been extended to the correlation of igneous rocks. Here zircon is the most useful index mineral. Through comparison of the colors and shapes of zircon grains, two and possibly three different ages of granite have been distinguished among the pre-Cambrian intrusives of the Lake Superior Region.[15]

Heavy mineral studies of pulverized churn drill sludges have been successful in identifying rock formations. At Kimberley,[16] Nevada, where highly altered and mineralized sandstone, limestone and monzonite porphyry were difficult to distinguish from one another, the following quick test was devised: The sludge is panned and the heavier non-metallic section is scraped off to one side. The sulphides are then panned out and set aside. The heavy non-metallic fraction which con-

---

[13] Fraser, Donald M., Interpretation of fault movements from mineral fractures: E. & M. J., vol. 133, December, 1932, p. 621.

[14] Milnor, H. B., *Sedimentary Petrography*, 3rd Edition. T. Murby & Company, London; Nordeman Pub. Co., New York, 1940.

Twenhofel, W. H. and Tyler, S. A., *Methods of Study of Sediments*. New York: McGraw-Hill, 1941.

Krumbein, Wm. C., and Pettijohn, F. J., *Manual of Sedimentary Petrology*. New York, London: Appleton-Century Co., 1938.

[15] Tyler, S. A., Marsden, R. W., Grout, F. F., and Thiel, G. A., Studies of the Lake Superior pre-Cambrian by accessory mineral methods: Bull. G. S. A., vol. 51, 1940, pp. 1429–1538.

Morgan, J. H. and Auer, Marianna L., Optical, spectrographic and radioactive studies of zircon: Am. Jour. Sci., vol. 239, 1941, pp. 305–311.

Krynine, Paul D., The Tourmaline group in sediments: Jour. Geol., vol. 54, 1946, pages 65–87.

[16] Pennebaker, E. N., Personal letter.

sists of the coarser rock fragments and fine grained heavy minerals is somewhat further segregated by tapping on a card and then examined under the microscope. Sandstone shows detrital zircon in rounded grains; monzonite porphyry yields euhedral zircons with sharp crystal faces; limestone gives no zircon but commonly an abundance of contact metamorphic silicates. Identity of the zircon may be further confirmed under the ultra-violet light either with or without the use of the binocular microscope.

MINERAGRAPHIC STUDIES [17]

Polished sections of ores are studied under the reflecting microscope in order to identify the minerals and determine their texture and sequence of deposition.

Techniques

Methods of identification, as outlined in the standard determinative tables,[18] are based on hardness,[19] color,[20]

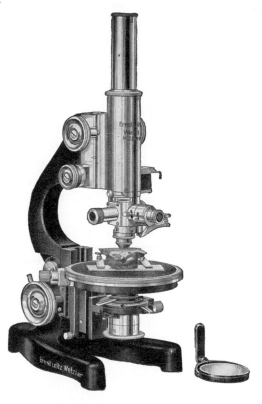

Fig. 33—Reflecting (metallographic) microscope. (*Courtesy of* E. Leitz, Inc.)

and appearance in polarized light (*i.e.* whether isotropic or anisotropic), together with response to a series of etching reagents. The standard routine reduces the possibilities to a small group of species which react

[17] "Mineragraphy" and "mineralography," both clumsy words, have been proposed as names for the study of minerals in polished sections. Unfortunately nothing has come of Lindgren's suggestion (Editorial: Microchemical Reactions, *Econ. Geol.*, vol. 19, 1924, page 764.) that a prize be offered for a better term.

[18] Short, M. N., Microscopic determination of the ore minerals: *U.S.G.S.*, Bull. 914, 1940.
Farnham, C. M., *Determination of the Opaque Minerals*. New York: McGraw-Hill, 1931.
Schneiderhöhn, Hans and Ramdohr, Paul, *Lehrbuch der Erzmikroscopie*. Berlin: Gebrüder Bornträger, 1931.

[19] Talmage, Sterling B., Quantitative standards for hardness of the ore minerals: *Econ. Geol.*, vol. 20, 1925, p. 531.

[20] Talmage, Sterling B., The diagnostic value of color in polished sections: *Econ. Geol.*, vol. 20, 1925, p. 168.

similarly; additional tests are often necessary in order to distinguish between members of the group. To this end, qualitative microchemical tests [21] for suspected elements are usually diagnostic, but in difficult determinations, special properties such as electrical conductivity,[22] susceptibility to electrolytic etching,[23] the effect of light [24] (in the case of silver-bearing minerals) and iridescent filming [25] are of aid. But X-ray methods are finding increasing use as a supplement to other tests or as a substitute for them.[26]

In some research problems, whether geological or metallurgical, it is desirable to determine which minerals or grains contain specific metals or other elements. For this purpose, two techniques, one by chemical treatment, and one by X-ray methods have been developed recently.

The X-ray technique consists in reflecting rays from the surface of a polished section and focussing them on a sensitized film by means of a curved crystal surface The resulting photograph shows a row of images of the polished surface, each image depicting the pattern of distribution for an individual metal.[27]

The chemical technique consists of coating the surface of the specimen with a film of acid or other solvent and pressing against it a piece of gelatine-coated paper, which is then "developed" in a reagent which reacts with a specific element and produces a "print" showing in color the areas in which the element is present.[28]

Polished specimens for rough-and-ready use can be prepared rather rapidly by hand methods on rotating laps.[29] Such specimens, however,

[21] Short, M. N., *op. cit.*, pp. 173–251.

Frazer, H. J., and Dreyer, Robert M., Mutual interference in the microchemical determination of ore minerals: *Am. Mineralogist,* vol. 22, 1937, pp. 949–976.

[22] Harvey, Roger D., Electrical conductivity and polished mineral surfaces: *Econ. Geol.,* vol. 23, 1928, pp. 778–803.

[23] McKinstry, H. E., Magnetic electrochemical and photochemical tests in the identification of opaque minerals: *Econ. Geol.,* vol. 22, 1927, p. 669.

Dodge, Daniel V., Identification of the opaque minerals by electrochemical methods: *Am. Mineralogist,* vol. 28, 1943, pp. 103–108.

[24] McKinstry, H. E., Magnetic electrochemical and photochemical tests in the identification of opaque minerals, *Econ. Geol.,* vol. 22, 1927, p. 669.

[25] Gaud'n, A. M., Identification of sulphide minerals by selective iridescent filming: *A.I.M.E. Tech. Pub. 912,* 1938.

[26] Further reference to X-ray methods will be found later in this chapter.

[27] v. Hámos, L., X-ray image method of chemical analysis: *American Mineralogist,* vol. 23, pp. 215–225, 1938.

[28] Gutzeit, Gregoire, Determination and localization of metallic minerals by the contact print method: *Tr. A.I.M.E.,* vol. 153, 1943, pages 286–299.

Yagoda, Herman, Analytical patterns in the study of mineral and biological materials, *Ind. Eng. Chem. Anal. Ed.,* vol. 15, 1943, page. 135. Localization of copper and silver minerals in polished sections by the potassium cyanide etch pattern, *Amer. Mineralogist,* vol. 30, 1945, pages 51–64.

[29] Hatton, J. H., An inexpensive table for polishing ores, *Am. Mineralogist,* vol. 21, 1936, pages 800–809.

have the disadvantage that hard minerals stand out in relief and make it difficult to focus on their contacts, which often harbor interesting minerals. Moreover, soft and fragile minerals are likely to be plucked out by the grinding. Therefore, polished surfaces of high quality require special preparation by more elaborate equipment [30] than is available at most mines, and for exacting work the geologist will do best to have his specimens polished at a laboratory where specialized apparatus is installed.[31]

For studying the relations of transparent as well as opaque minerals in the same specimen, thin sections having a polished surface often prove useful.[32]

Sequence of Deposition

Textures observed in polished sections may indicate the order in which the minerals were deposited and lead to inferences regarding the history of ore deposition. The history may afford an insight into the origin of the deposit and serve as a background for geological reasoning. Apart from theoretical considerations it may open a way to the direct solution of ore-hunting problems. If, for example, certain valuable minerals have been introduced at a late stage during a period of reopening, the

[30] Vanderwilt, J. W., Improvements in the polishing of ores: *Econ. Geol.*, vol. 23, 1928, pp. 292–316.

Graton, L. C., Technique in mineralography at Harvard: *Amer. Min.*, vol. 22, 1937, pp. 491–516.

Murdoch, Joseph, A polishing apparatus for ore minerals: *Econ. Geol.*, vol. 33, 1938, pp. 542–553.

Stillwell, F. L., Bakelite press for mounting mineral grains and ores: *Australasian Inst. of Mining and Metallurgy*, Proc., N.S. no. 90, 1933, p. 327.

Krieger, P., and Bird, P. H., Mounting polished surfaces in bakelite: *Econ. Geol.*, vol. 27, 1932, pp. 675–678.

Fuller, H. C., Mounting polished surfaces in bakelite: *Econ. Geol.*, vol. 28, 1933, pp. 393–395.

Staff of Lakeshore Mine, Milling investigations into the ore as occurring at the Lake Shore Mine: *Can. Inst. Min. and Met.*, vol. 39, 1936, pp. 398–401. (Describes a simplified modification of the Graton-Vanderwilt machine.)

Fuller, J. Osborn, Mechanical polishing with a film of abrasive: *Econ. Geol.*, vol. 36, p. 199, 1941.

Bird, Paul H., Mounting concentrates and tailings for microscopic study: *Eng. and Mining Jour.*, vol. 136, pp. 233–234, 1935.

[31] Charles F. Fletcher, Rotch Building, Cambridge 38, Mass., prepares polished sections to order.

[32] Donnay, J. D. H., Thinned polished sections: *Econ. Geol.*, vol. 25, 1930, pp. 270–274.

Grondijs, H. F., and Schouten, C., Polished thin sections of ore and rock: *Econ. Geol.*, vol. 26, 1931, pp. 343–345.

Rankama, K., An improved technique for the making of thinned polished sections: *Econ. Geol.*, vol. 36, 1941, pp. 561–563.

Kennedy, George C., The preparation of polished thin sections: *Econ. Geol.*, vol. 40, 1945, pp. 353–360.

microscope is likely to reveal the fact and point to an investigation of the mechanics of fracturing in order to determine which parts of the orebody have been reopened.

Criteria of Sequence [33]

Since translation of textures into paragenesis involves a technique that is hardly more than thirty years old, it is not surprising that there are still differences of opinion as to the significance of certain features and that some of the mistaken assumptions of the early stages are only now being corrected. Naturally, controversial matters are the ones that are most discussed, and there is actually much less disagreement among authorities than the diverse opinions expressed in the literature might suggest. On the simpler and more obvious criteria there is little if any difference of opinion and these we shall consider first.

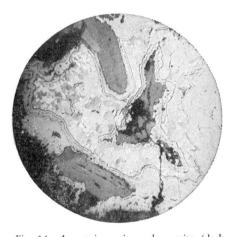

Fig. 34—A vug in pyrite and enargite (dark gray blades) is lined successively by marcasite (light gray mottled) and pyrite. The center of the vug is filled with tetrahedrite. Cerro de Pasco, Peru. Crossed nicols (×20). (*Photo by* S. I. Bowditch and E. B. Dane, Jr., Harvard Laboratory of Mining Geology)

Common Textures

I. *Open-Space fillings.*

A. *In vugs, vesicles, and solution cavities.* Obviously, in simple filling the mineral that forms the innermost lining of the cavity is the youngest and the order of deposition is the order of arrangement of the bands from the rock-wall inward.

B. *In veinlets.* Veinlets formed by the filling of open spaces are of such shape that their walls would fit together if the filling were removed, due allowance being made for the possibility of movement in a direction not parallel to the polished surface and for loss of fragments torn from the walls. Deposition begins at the walls and the minerals in the center are the youngest.

II. *Replacement Textures.*

A. *Replacement veinlets.* The borders of microscopic (or submicroscopic) fractures may be replaced by a new mineral. The replaced zone may be of such uniform width that the walls match and the veinlet re-

---

[33] Schwartz, G. M., Microscopic criteria of hypogene and supergene origin of ore minerals: *Econ. Geol.,* vol. 27, 1932, pp. 533–553.

Bastin, E. S., Graton, L. C., Lindgren, Waldemar, Newhouse, W. H., Schwartz, G. M., and Short, M. N., Criteria of age relations of minerals with especial reference to polished sections of ores: *Econ. Geol.,* vol. 26, pp. 561–610, 1931.

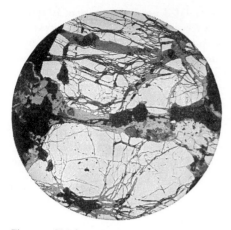

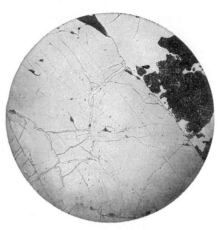

Fig. 35—Veinlets. Pyrite grains (wh'te) cut by veinlets filled with tetrahedrite, chalcopyrite, and bornite (all shades of gray). Some replacement has accompanied fracture filling. Black areas are pits in the polished surface. (×25) (*Photo by* T. G. Moore and E. B. Dane, Jr., Harvard Laboratory of M:ning Geology)

Fig. 36—Replacement veinlets. Gold (white) forming veinlets in pyrite (gray). The margins of the veinlets are noticeably corroded and rounded. Porcupine District, Ontario. (×17) (*Photo by* Harvard Laboratory of M:ning Geology)

sembles a fracture-filling. Alternatively the borders of the veinlets may be lenticular or highly irregular. Replacement may be governed by cleavage, forming a geometrical pattern.

B. *Replacement breccias.* Replacement along a network of veinlets may proceed to such a stage that only the isolated remnants of the host mineral are left. The fragments do not necessarily lose their angular

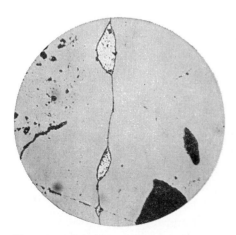

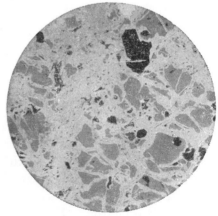

Fig. 37—Intergrain replacement. Lenticular areas of gold (white) along a boundary between two grains of pyrite (gray). Hollinger Mine, Ontario. (×425) (*Photo by* Harvard Laboratory of Mining Geology)

Fig. 38—Replacement breccia. Sphalerite (gray) partly replaced by chalcoc'te (white). Cerro de Pasco, Peru. (×150) (*Photo by* S. I. Bowditch and E. B. Dane, Jr., Harvard Laboratory of Mining Geology)

shape; [34] they may, however, become rounded until they appear as rudely circular areas, giving what is known as ice-cake or exploded bomb texture. *C. Sea-and-island texture.* The boundary between two minerals may resemble the map of a drowned coast-line, the guest mineral extending into the host in the form of bays and also surrounding remnants of it in the shape of off-shore islands. Re-entrants, convex toward the host mineral, have been called "caries" by Lindgren in allusion to dental cavities.

Although islands, especially if rounded, are usually remnants of an older mineral in a younger, it is not uncommon to see isolated areas of the younger mineral in the older. These "lakes" often lie inland from the shore-line of the sea-and-island pattern and, in some cases at least, have been shown to be connected in the third dimension with the invading mineral. Isolated bodies, in themselves, should not be accepted as criteria of sequence without supporting evidence.

D. Intergrain replacements. A favorite position of a guest mineral is along grain boundaries of earlier minerals. Sometimes the guest extends along the boundary for only a short distance. In other cases it forms complete rims around grains of the older mineral.

E. Metacrysts. Isolated grains of a guest mineral are common; cubes of pyrite in slate are especially familiar and unequivocal. The extent to which ideas of genesis can color interpretation is evident when one recalls that similar euhedral grains of magnetite or chromite in an igneous rock are interpreted by petrographers (in some cases doubtless correctly) as early-formed minerals. Euhedral grains of pyrite, arsenopyrite, and other hard minerals within gangue may lack visible channels of entry yet unquestionably be later than the surrounding material.

Caution: A somewhat similar appearance is presented by a crystal of, say, pyrite in a vug that was later filled by calcite and cut by the polished surface in such a way that the point of attachment is not exposed.

Ambiguous and Controversial Textures

In the textures just described there is not much trouble in deciding which minerals are earlier and which are later, so long as no complications are involved. There are cases, however, in which a mineral that forms veinlets is actually older than the mineral that it appears to cut.[35] To take a specific case, suppose that tennantite is veined by galena and then later stromeyerite replaces the tennantite. A casual inspection suggests that the galena is younger than the stromeyerite, whereas the opposite is really the truth. Textures of this sort have been termed "antecedent veinlets" by Graton. The deceptive relationship is not restricted to veinlets; any of the other textures that are diagnostic of sequence may be

---

[34] Bateman, Alan M., Angular inclusions and replacement deposits: *Econ. Geol.*, vol. 19, 1924, pp. 504–520.

[35] Harvey, R. D., The geometrical pattern of contacts in determinative paragenesis: *Econ. Geol.*, vol. 26, 1931, pp. 764–771, especially Prewall veins, p. 770.

complicated by the replacement of one of the earlier minerals by a younger one. This natural hoax can usually be detected by careful inspection under high-power magnification. Reverting to our previous example, places may be found where the stromeyerite replaces the edge of the galena vein or, somewhere else in the section, enough of the original tennantite will remain to reveal all the stages in the process.

Where two minerals occur together in such a way as to give no evidence as to which is the older, the tendency of the interpreter is to assume that they are contemporaneous. This assumption may happen to be correct but it is not a safe conclusion. Lack of evidence of sequence is not proof of contemporaneity. The so-called "mutual boundary texture," consisting of curved and often highly irregular boundaries between two minerals, in which the positions of the minerals might be reversed without changing the nature of the pattern, was formerly regarded as evidence that the two minerals were of the same age. It is no longer considered a sound criterion.[36] Any doubt on this score was removed by Newhouse's[37] picture of perfect mutual boundary relationship between "limonite" and pyrite, which could hardly have been contemporaneous.

There are some other types of textures which have occasioned differences of opinion among authorities. Among the most perplexing are those which resemble the patterns common in metals and alloys and consequently considered by many students to indicate either contemporaneity or origin through ex-solution. The triangular grid-work known as the *Widmanstätten texture*[38] is simulated in natural minerals. In the case of ilmenite-magnetite intergrowths, it is probably due to unmixing since the two minerals have been shown to form a solid solution above 800° C.[39] Similarly it has been shown that solid solutions form between cubanite and chalcopyrite,[40] between bornite and chalcocite,[41] and between covellite and digenite[42] ("isometric blue chalcocite").

On the other hand, very similar patterns can be formed by replace-

---

[36] Bastin, E. S., *et al.*, Criteria of age relations of minerals, etc.: *Econ. Geol.*, vol. 26, p. 605, 1931.

[37] Newhouse, Walter H., in Fairbanks: *Laboratory Investigation of Ores.* New York: McGraw-Hill, 1928, p. 159, fig. 7.

[38] Mehl, Robert F., and Barrett, Charles S., Studies upon the Widmanstätten Structure: *A.I.M.E. Tech. Pub.* no. 353, 1930.

[39] Ramdohr, P., *Beobachtungen an Magnetit, Ilmenit, Eisenglanz und Überlegungen das System FeO, Fe₂O₃, TiO₂. Festschrift zur Jahrfeier der Bergakademie Clausthal,* 1925.

[40] Schwartz, G. M., A new natural intergrowth of bornite and chalcocite: *Econ. Geol.*, vol. 24, 1929, pp. 443–444. Experiments bearing on bornite-chalcocite intergrowths: *Econ. Geol.*, vol. 23, 1928, pp. 381–397.

[41] Schwartz, G. M., Experiments bearing on bornite-chalcocite intergrowths: *Econ. Geol.*, vol. 23, 1928, pp. 381–397.

[42] Bateman, A. M., Some covellite-chalcocite relationships: *Econ. Geol.*, vol. 24, 1929, pp. 424–439.

ment along cleavage planes.   An example of anglesite traversing galena in triangular pattern, figured by Schwartz,[43] is especially convincing. In general when such textures are formed by ex-solution, the plate-like or rod-like forms have sharp boundaries with no enlargements at the places where the plates join or cross.   The included mineral often forms disconnected units rather than the networks common in replacement along cleavage, and it is usually absent outside the intergrowths.[44]

Fig. 39—Gridlike pattern formed by replacement of "blue chalcocite" by white chalcocite along cleavage directions inherited from bornite. Harper Mine, Messina, Transvaal. (×40) (*Photo by* P. G. Söhnge and E. B. Dane, Jr., Harvard Laboratory of Mining Geology)

The pseudo-eutectic or graphic pattern, resembling the pearlite of steels[45] was formerly believed to represent contemporaneous intergrowth, but it can be imitated by replacement.[46]   Lindgren finds that these textures are commonest among soft minerals and believes that they are characteristic of feeble replacement.

The so-called *emulsion texture,* consisting of tiny rounded blebs of one mineral in another, often along crystallographic directions, is very familiar in sphalerite where the included blebs consist of chalcopyrite. It is usually attributed to ex-solution, but, as Newhouse has shown, very similar if not identical textures can be formed by replacement.[47]

"Usual" Mineral Sequence

Through the range of hydrothermal deposits there is a general similarity in the order of deposition of the minerals in spite of local variations and exceptions.   Therefore the "usual" or "standard" sequence

[43] Bastin, E. S., *et al., Criteria of age relations of minerals, etc.: Econ. Geol.,* vol. 26, p. 593, fig. 19, 1931.

[44] Bastin, E. S., *et al., op. cit.,* page 570.

[45] Green, C. H., Eutectic patterns in metallic alloys: *Tr. A.I.M.E.,* vol. 71, pp. 651–665, 1925.

[46] Whitehead, W. L., The paragenesis of certain sulphide intergrowths: *Econ. Geol.,* vol. 11, pp. 1–13, 1916.

Lindgren, Waldemar, Pseudo-eutectic textures: *Econ. Geol.,* vol. 25, pp. 1–13, 1930.

Anderson, Alfred L., Some pseudo-eutectic ore textures: *Econ. Geol.,* vol. 24, pp. 577–589, 1939.

[47] Newhouse, W. H., An examination as to the intergrowth of certain minerals: *Econ. Geol.,* vol. 21, 1926, pp. 68–69.

is useful as an index and calls attention to unusual features in the sequence in any particular locality. Apparent exceptions to the usual sequence call for re-examination to make sure that they are really exceptions and not merely mistakes in interpreting the evidence. If they prove to be real exceptions, they may indicate something unusual in the conditions of deposition and thus lead to further productive inquiry.

Just what the "usual" sequence really is may be open to some difference of opinion as to detail, because minor variations are common and in many localities the simple sequence is interrupted by local repetitions or even reversals. Furthermore, since only a limited number of minerals occur in any one place, the complete list is not a matter of direct observation but must be compiled by fitting together in dovetail fashion the incomplete sequences observed in different districts, a procedure which must unavoidably entail judgment. However, the list prepared by Newhouse [48] (Table 5) and based largely on Lindgren's [49] compilation is not far from the sequence commonly observed.

Quartz is usually earlier than the metallic minerals and may continue or repeat throughout the sequence. Carbonates are usually later than quartz but earlier than sulphides, although it is not uncommon to find a late generation of calcite youngest of all.

Why minerals deposit in this order has never been fully explained. It is interesting to note a general decrease in hardness,[50, 51] increase in solubility in most reagents,[52] decrease in heat of formation,[53] and decrease in fusing point.[54] Bandy [55] shows that throughout the series of sulphides there is a decrease in percentage of anion elements and suggests that certain exceptions to this rule are due to the use of faulty criteria in interpreting textures.

[48] Newhouse, W. H., The time sequence of hypogene ore mineral deposition: *Econ. Geol.*, vol. 23, 1928, p. 651.

[49] Lindgren, Waldemar, *Mineral Deposits*, 4th Edition. New York: McGraw-Hill, 1933, p. 122.

Lindgren, Waldemar, Magmas, dikes and veins: *Trans. A.I.M.E.*, vol. 74, 1926, p. 88.

[50] Gilbert, Geoffrey, The relation of hardness to the sequence of the ore minerals: *Econ. Geol.*, vol. 19, 1924, pp. 668–673.

[51] Newhouse, W. H., The time sequence of hypogene ore mineral deposition: *Econ. Geol.*, vol. 23, 1928, pp. 647–659.

[52, 53] Newhouse, W. H., *op. cit.*, pp. 647–659.

[54] Gilbert, Geoffrey, The relation of hardness to the sequence of the ore minerals: *Econ. Geol.*, vol. 19, 1924, pp. 668–673.

[55] Bandy, Mark C., A theory of mineral sequence in hypogene ore deposits: *Econ. Geol.*, vol. 35, 1940, pp. 359–381, 546–570.

TABLE 5

"USUAL" SEQUENCE OF DEPOSITION OF ORE MINERALS

Magnetite	Enargite
Specularite	Tennantite
Pyrite	Tetrahedrite
Arsenopyrite	Chalcopyrite
Nickel-Cobalt arsenides	Bornite
Wolframite	Galena
Cassiterite	Chalcocite
Molybdenite	Argentite
Bismuth	Ruby Silver
Bismuthinite	Polybasite
Pyrrhotite	Chalcopyrite
Pentlandite	Electrum
Stannite	Lead sulphantimonides
Sphalerite	

Criteria of Supergene Enrichment

Recognizing minerals that have been deposited in the course of super-gene enrichment is one of the most practical uses of the reflecting micro-scope, for a mineral of supergene origin is likely to disappear within a few hundred feet of depth. If the relative proportion of supergene to hypogene ore minerals can be estimated, the ratio gives a basis for estimating the grade of ore that will be expected in the primary zone below the reach of enrichment.

Supergene sulphide enrichment is of paramount importance only in copper ores, although it is a matter of very considerable interest in silver deposits. In rare instances supergene gold has been deposited in the sulphide zone, particularly near its top. Some of the other metals, notably nickel (as silicate), lead, tin, aluminum, iron, and manganese, are susceptible of natural concentration by groundwater but chiefly through leaching away of less valuable elements. The resulting en-riched ore is found in the oxidized rather than the sulphide zone, and there is usually no difficulty in distinguishing its minerals from those of primary ore. Some of the metals just named have in places been noted in the form of supergene minerals in the sulphide zone but never in sufficient quantity to make the difference between ore and waste.

In Copper Ores

The chief and characteristic mineral of copper sulphide enrichment is chalcocite. Along with it there may be covellite, bornite and a little chalcopyrite, but unless a substantial part of the copper occurs as chalcocite there need be no fear that the copper values will fall off seriously as a consequence of bottoming of supergene enrichment. But where chalcocite is an important constituent, the question of its supergene or hypogene origin needs to be answered. The sooty form of chalcocite is characteristically supergene, but the converse, that compact chalcocite is necessarily hypogene, does not follow. Supergene chalcocite commonly seeks out fractures and cleavage planes in older sulphides, especially chalcopyrite, bornite, sphalerite, and galena, or forms rims around grains of the earlier minerals. This texture, although suggestive, is not in itself an infallible criterion.

The crystallographic structure of the chalcocite can sometimes be used as a guide to the temperature of deposition and therefore to the probability of supergene vs. hypogene conditions. Ideas regarding chalcocite are undergoing revision as a result of the Buergers' [56] recent

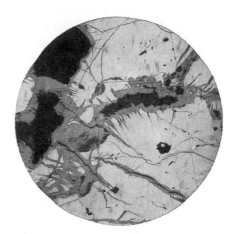

Fig. 40—Chalcopyrite (white) partly replaced by chalcocite (gray). Center of veinlet filled by "limonite" (black). Prince Leopold (Kipushi) Mine, Belgian Congo. (×70) (*Photo by* Harvard Laboratory of Mining Geology)

work which has shown that below 105° C chalcocite crystallizes in the orthorhombic system. Above 105° it inverts to a hexagonal form but reverts on cooling. N. W. Buerger has discovered (or rather re-discovered) the mineral digenite, Cu_9S_5 which is isometric and had long been miscalled "blue chalcocite" or "isometric chalcocite." Digenite can exist at room temperature, but whether it can form below 80° under natural conditions is uncertain. Above 80° it is capable of holding either copper or sulphur in solid solution and upon cooling, whichever is in excess will unmix as covellite or chalcocite (orthorhombic).

[56] Buerger, Newton W., The chalcocite problem: *Econ. Geol.*, vol. 36, 1941, pp. 19–44. X-Ray evidence of the existence of the mineral digenite: *Am. Mineralogist*, vol. 27, 1942, pp. 712–716.

Buerger, M. H., and Buerger, Newton W., Low-chalcocite and high-chalcocite: *Am. Mineralogist*, vol. 29, 1944, pp. 55–65.

Therefore, where an intergrowth of digenite ("blue chalcocite") with covellite or with chalcocite has demonstrably been formed by unmixing, one can assume that the material crystallized above 80° and is therefore presumably hypogene.[57]

Digenite ("isometric chalcocite") is isotropic in polarized light, whereas orthorhombic chalcocite shows alternate lightening and darkening in adjacent grains on rotating the stage and displays a play of colors.[58]

Certain triangular patterns are believed to be characteristic of hypogene chalcocite. In considering this, however, it is important to exclude the triangular patterns of somewhat similar appearance that are inherited from bornite which chalcocite has replaced. The following are believed by Bateman to be inherited from the high temperature modification:

(a) Octahedral partings: visible only under high magnification (500 to 2000 diameters).

(b) Lamellar microstructure. Chalcocite lamellae, somewhat resembling perthite lamellae in feldspar but occupying three directions and forming a triangular pattern. They are revealed by polarized light in which one set appears white and the others blue; the colors reverse on rotating the stage.

(c) Intergrowths with bornite consisting of blades of chalcocite in a triangular pattern enclosing interstitial areas of a pseudo-eutectic intergrowth of chalcocite and bornite. These patterns observed by Bateman in ore from Northern Rhodesia are identical with patterns artificially produced by Schwartz [59] by unmixing of a solid solution of bornite in chalcocite.

In Silver Ores

The characteristic supergene silver minerals are argentite and native silver. Argentite, since it is common both as a primary and a secondary mineral is not in itself a sign of secondary enrichment. Native silver, although it occurs as a primary mineral in certain uncommon types of deposits (notably at Cobalt, Ontario, and in the copper deposits of Michigan), is always secondary in the ordinary type of sulphide deposits. Especially when it is in the form of wire silver, it points strongly to secondary enrichment. The silver sulphantimonides and sulpharse-

---

[57] It was previously believed that above 91° chalcocite was isometric and, although it reverted to the orthorhombic form on cooling, the inversion was prevented by over 8% of CuS in solid solution. Buerger has shown that chalcocite does not dissolve over 8% of CuS and that the high temperature form dissolves only about 2%. What had been regarded as isometric chalcocite containing CuS in solution proves to be digenite.

[58] Bateman, Alan M., The ores of the Northern Rhodesian copper belt, Econ. Geol., vol. 25, p. 394.

[59] Schwartz, G. M., Experiments bearing on bornite-chalcocite intergrowths: Econ. Geol., vol. 23, 1928, page 391.

nides can certainly form under hypogene conditions; whether any of them can also be supergene is open to discussion, but Grout [60] has shown that cold silver sulphate solutions react with arsenical alkaline solutions to precipitate silver sulpharsenides; antimony compounds behave similarly. The silver sulpho-salts, especially polybasite and the ruby silvers have been described as supergene in so many localities that their mere presence cannot safely be considered a criterion either for supergene or hypogene origin. The same is true of stromeyerite,[61] although I believe that it is usually supergene.

Thus the identity of the silver-bearing mineral that is present does not in itself offer a safe guide to the presence or absence of secondary enrichment. The decision must be reached by considering field evidence together with the texture and nature of associated minerals. The quantitative aspect of enrichment may also help in pointing toward a conclusion; for example, it would be irrational to decide that *all* of the silver-bearing minerals in a deposit are supergene, for enough primary silver must have been present in the zone that has been leached (including its eroded portion) to supply the materials for the supergene minerals. Similarly, if much of the silver occurs in sulpharsenides and sulphantimonides, some or all of these minerals must be hypogene unless other primary minerals were present to supply the arsenic and antimony.

General Criteria of Enrichment

Unfortunately it is not possible to set down infallible rules for distinguishing supergene from hypogene mineralization. As Schwartz [62] says, "If one insisted on using only those facts to which there are no exceptions the criteria could be stated very briefly. They would also be of limited use." In general, several criteria have to point in the same direction before a conclusion can be accepted. Laboratory evidence should always be weighed along with field relations, and, if the two are not in accord, the reason for the discrepancy should be sought in order to learn whether one or both of the hypotheses needs to be modified.

When the primary ore is hypothermal, any supergene mineralization

[60] Grout, F. F., Behavior of cold, acid sulphate solutions of copper, silver and gold with alkaline extracts of metallic sulphides: *Econ. Geol.*, vol. 8, 1913, pp. 407 ff.

[61] Lindgren, W., The silver mine of Colquijirca, Peru: *Econ. Geol.*, vol. 30, 1935, pp. 331–346.

McKinstry, H. E., Geology of the silver deposit at Colquijirca, Peru: *Econ. Geol.*, vol. 31, 1936, pp. 625–627.

[62] Schwartz, G. M., Microscopic criteria of hypogene and supergene origin of ore minerals: *Econ. Geol.*, vol. 27, 1932, p. 533.

is usually easy to recognize because of the contrast in texture and mineralogy. But where the primary mineralization is epithermal, its later stages are hard to distinguish from secondary enrichment; the low temperatures of deposition approach those of groundwaters, and acid conditions are not uncommon, so that there may be little essential difference in the chemistry; the fundamental distinction (whether solutions have moved upward or downward) is unlikely to have recorded itself very distinctly. The ambiguity is especially pronounced in silver deposits, since so many of them are epithermal, whereas copper deposits are mainly hypothermal and mesothermal.

Enrichment is always separated from primary deposition by a period (and often a very long period) of erosion and oxidation. Therefore, there is necessarily a gap in the sequence between the hypogene and the supergene mineralization. If deposition can be shown to be continuous, enrichment is ruled out. If there is evidence of a definite gap, enrichment is possible but not proved; but if the minerals and textures of the last generation are exclusively those which are common in supergene ores the case for enrichment becomes very strong.

Schwartz [63] has prepared a very convenient list of the criteria that have been proposed for distinguishing supergene and hypogene origin. Some of the more useful of these will be discussed briefly:

Sequence of Deposition. If a characteristic high temperature mineral is recognized, all minerals which the sequence shows to be older are necessarily hypogene. The following minerals are definitely hypogene:

> pyrrhotite
> cubanite
> specular hematite (as distinguished from
>   compact and botryoidal hematite)
> ilmenite
> arsenopyrite
> cassiterite
> wolframite
> molybdenite
> electrum

In addition to the copper and silver minerals discussed in a preceding section, the following minerals are, with rare exceptions, hypogene:

> pyrite (when in hydrothermal vein matter)
> galena
> sphalerite

[63] Schwartz, G. M., *op. cit.*, pp. 533–553.

Any mineral that is definitely younger than one of supergene origin is, of course, supergene.   The number of exclusively supergene minerals is small, and most of them, aside from those already discussed, belong in the zone of oxidization rather than of supergene sulphide enrichment. Locally and occasionally they are earlier than some of the supergene sulphides.   When they are younger they point to conditions permitting enrichment.   Their absence, however, does not indicate that enrichment has not taken place, for all traces of oxidation may stop where sulphide enrichment begins.   The common minerals of the zone of oxidation are:

"limonite"	chrysacolla
anglesite	cuprite
cerussite	tenorite
malachite	smithsonite
azurite	hemimorphite
brochantite	manganese oxides
antlerite	

cerargyrite (and other silver halides)
kaolinite (as distinguished from dickite)

Habits in Replacement.   Supergene metallic minerals rarely replace solid wall rock though they may grow as flakes or dendrites in gouge or kaolin.   They do not commonly replace quartz and, although supergene carbonates often replace carbonate gangue, supergene sulphides rarely do so.

When supergene minerals replace primary sulphides they are likely to be highly selective in choosing the sulphides that they will replace. Thus covellite may replace bornite along fractures but refuse to follow the fractures into chalcopyrite or pyrite.[64]   Similarly a single grain of a supergene sulphide, instead of replacing two or more adjoining grains of different earlier minerals as a grain of hypogene sulphide might do, is likely to stop at the boundary of the earlier mineral.

In supergene replacement it is rare to find two minerals simultaneously replacing the same host.[65]   If several supergene minerals are deposited, they are likely to be in sequence, as when galena is replaced by a rim of argentite and later by native silver[66] or where pyrite is replaced by successive zones of chalcopyrite, bornite, and chalcocite.

---

[64] Bastin, E. S., *et al.*, Criteria of age relations of minerals: *Econ. Geol.*, vol. 26, 1931, p. 609.
[65] Bastin, *et al.*, *op. cit.*, p. 608.
[66] Bastin, *et al.*, *op. cit.*, p. 608.

X-RAY AND SPECTROSCOPIC STUDIES

X-rays [67] have become an indispensable tool in mineralogical investigations. They are used not only in studying the properties of new and obscure minerals but, to an increasing extent, in routine identification. Although instruments for the purpose are not available at most mines, at least one large mining company has established a well-equipped X-ray laboratory where powder-diffraction methods, supplemented to a limited extent by chemical tests for the elements, are the principal means of identification; there etch tests have been virtually abandoned.

The value of X-ray methods is clear when it is recalled that a chemical analysis alone, even a quantitative analysis, is not adequate to identify a mineral (although it does decidedly limit the possible alternatives) because a mineral species is defined by internal structure as well as chemical composition. Thus quartz and cristobalite, although distinct species, have the same chemical composition; likewise sphalerite and wurtzite. Physical properties such as hardness, color, and specific gravity may or may not serve as a practical means of distinguishing between dimorphous species in individual cases; optical properties, so useful for determining non-opaque minerals, unfortunately have only limited application among ore minerals. X-ray powder patterns, however, are diagnostic except in the case of a very few practically identical patterns which can then be distinguished by chemical tests for the elements.

Haycock [68] describes methods of isolating powder samples from small grains in polished sections, and Harcourt's determinative tables [69] present diffraction data specially arranged for use in the identification of ore minerals.

The spectroscope affords a quick and delicate method of detecting very small quantities of elements. Spectrographs can be used to detect

[67] Bunn, C. W., *Chemical Crystallography*, an introduction to optical and X-ray methods. Oxford: The Clarendon Press, 1945.

Buerger, M. J., *X-ray Crystallography*, an introduction to the investigation of crystals by their diffraction of monochromatic x-radiation. New York: John Wiley and Sons, 1942.

James, R. W., *X-ray Crystallography*, 2nd Ed., London: Methuen, 1941.

Bragg, W. L., *The Atomic Structure of Minerals*, Ithaca: Cornell University Press, 1937.

Halla, F., and Mark, H., *Leitfaden für die röntgenographische Untersuchungsmethoden von Kristallen*, Leipzig: Barth, 1937, (reprinted by J. W. Edwards, Ann Arbor, Michigan).

Some of the references listed here and elsewhere were supplied by Dr. George Tunell, who read this chapter in manuscript and made many valuable suggestions.

[68] Haycock, Maurice, A method for sampling minerals in polished sections: *Economic Geology*, vol. 26, pp. 415–420, 1931. *See also* Harcourt, G. Alan, The distinction between enargite and famatinite (luzonite): *American Mineralogist*, vol. 22, pp. 517–518, 1937.

[69] Harcourt, G. Alan, Tables for the identification of ore minerals by X-ray powder patterns: *American Mineralogist*, vol. 27, pp. 63–113, 1942.

the presence of rare elements that are sought for their own sake or for detecting variations in minor impurities [70] which may throw some light on problems of zoning.

COLLECTIONS

The shelves and window-sills of every geologist's office are adorned with pieces of ore and rock which have been brought up from underground. Some of them are odd and freakish specimens, and some are handsome crystals. Such an accumulation, however, does not constitute a working collection. To be of real value the specimens must be assembled purposefully and must be carefully labeled and conveniently arranged. Actually the resident geologist can see the rock underground whenever he likes and, by seeing a large expanse of it, can examine it there to best advantage. Therefore he is not under so much pressure to collect specimens as the teacher or survey worker who must carry portable portions of the mine along with him in order to be able to study them at leisure.

Nevertheless, a good collection serves a useful purpose. A specimen of each rock-type that is being mapped constitutes a standard for color, grain-size and appearance; in fact it is not a bad plan to carry type specimens underground for comparison with the rock in other parts of the mine. Specimens, moreover, furnish the material for thin or polished sections to be studied under the microscope.

Specimens should be selected discretely in order to be typical of the rock that they are intended to represent; unusual material is serviceable only if it illustrates some point or raises a question that needs to be answered. For solving a specific problem, a suite from a particular locality is likely to be more informative than a single specimen, and the members of such a suite should be taken at regular intervals measured from a vein or contact so as to form a progressive series.

Labeling Specimens. Specimens should be labeled underground or in the field at the time they are collected. A temporary label is written out and wrapped with the specimen. Some geologists prefer to enter the information in a notebook, identifying the specimen with a number that is either wrapped with it or written on a square of adhesive tape and stuck to the specimen. In any case the specimen should be well wrapped in newspaper or placed in an individual paper bag to prevent it from rubbing against other specimens. This is especially true of crystals. They should always be wrapped with great care in plenty

[70] Brode, Wallace R., *Chemical Spectroscopy*, 2nd Edition. New York: John Wiley & Sons, 1943. (Contains full bibliography.)

Sawyer, Ralph Alanson, *Experimental Spectroscopy*. New York: Prentice-Hall, Inc., 1944.

of paper; if they are delicate, tissue paper or even cotton should be provided; and if they are to be shipped, so much paper should be used that the corners of the specimens cannot be felt through the wrapping.

In the office the specimens are ticketed as soon as possible with permanent labels, which are typed or neatly lettered. To prevent the label from getting lost from the specimen a permanent number is placed on the specimen by painting a small square on its surface with white enamel and, when dry, marking the number in India ink which is then protected by a coat of shellac. The paper label bears a corresponding number in one corner and states the type of material, exact location where the specimen was taken, date, initials of collector and a note stating the purpose for which the specimen was collected or the point it is intended to illustrate. If the specimen is one of a series, the fact should be stated. Specimens without locality are worthless and should be thrown out.

It is convenient to have labels printed in some form such as the following:

OJALA MINING CO. Geological Department

Name .... No..............
Mine .... Level..............
Location ....
Collected by .... Date..............
Remarks ....

The best way of filing specimens is in a cabinet with drawers about 3 inches deep and deeper drawers at the bottom for large specimens. Each specimen is placed on its label in an individual cardboard tray.[71] In some collections, standard sheets of transparent celluloid, each the size of the tray, are placed on the label under the specimen to prevent the label from getting dusty or abraded.

No matter what pains are taken to avoid it, a collection tends to get cluttered with miscellaneous and freakish rather than representative material. It is well to cull it over from time to time and discard all specimens that do not illustrate any particular point.

Numbering Specimens. Specimens may, of course, be given consecutive numbers, but in a large collection the numbers run into an unwieldy number of digits. If more than one mine is represented, it is convenient to use an abbreviation for each mine or each district, thus specimens from the Happy Hit mine would be numbered Hh 1, Hh 2, etc. Decimal systems such as are used in libraries have been tried, but usually

[71] A convenient size for trays is $4\frac{1}{4}'' \times 3'' \times \frac{3}{4}''$.

prove confusing to assistants or secretaries who seem to have difficulty in arranging them in numerical order.

SAMPLES FOR CHEMICAL ANALYSIS

Rock analyses are often used for attacking petrological problems and for studying alteration. The material to be analyzed should be a sample and not a specimen, and since these two terms are sometimes confused it may be well here to explain the difference. A specimen, according to the Oxford Dictionary, is an "individual or part taken as an example of a class or whole." A specimen of rock or ore may be taken because it looks like the rest of the material around it, but it is not necessarily representative of the exact chemical composition of the mass. A sample, on the other hand, is taken according to methods designed to eliminate the personal factor in selection. It is of sufficient size and taken over an area large enough to be consistent with the mathematical probability that it is truly representative. Most of the care and precision that goes into a chemical analysis is wasted if the sampling is not consistent in accuracy with the analytical method. The practice common among petrographers of breaking off a corner of a specimen and sending it to a chemist is possibly defensible in the case of exceptionally homogeneous igneous bodies, but it cannot provide a representative sample of altered or bedded formations. Is it not an imposition to ask a chemist to determine, say, the silica content to the nearest .01% when a specimen taken a few inches away might differ by as much as 2%? Moreover, the result will be misleading since it implies that the composition has been ascertained to a decimal of a per cent. Accordingly, samples for chemical analysis should be taken with fully as much care as is devoted to taking samples for assay. However, since a complete analysis is much more expensive and time-consuming than routine assay, the number of analyses that can be made at reasonable expense is limited. Therefore if the material for analysis is intended to be representative of a large block of ground, it should be prepared by combining individual samples into a suitably weighed composite.

ROLE OF LABORATORY INVESTIGATION

Microscopic and other laboratory studies offer a fascinating field for investigation. Since many young graduates have more training in these methods than in the investigation of the structure and geometry of ore occurrence, they are often prone to approach a mining district as they would a field thesis area and undertake at the outset to solve the problems of petrogenesis, sequence of mineral deposition, and mechanics of intrusion. These problems, however, are not always the ones that yield the most immediate and tangible results. Whether the galena is earlier or later than the sphalerite may make little difference in the methods of development, and in many districts the question of whether a given rock should be designated a rhyolite or a dacite is not of first importance. Realizing this, the geologist of more "practical" turn of mind is inclined to skip laboratory investigation altogether. Yet such an extreme attitude may result in neglecting brilliant opportunities. In a particular district the recognition of late and presumably supergene argentite may change the whole course of development, and, in another, the fact that ore is present where the vein cuts andesite flows and absent where it cuts an intrusive diorite indistinguishable from the andesite without detailed petrographic study may throw new light on the problem of ore search. Laboratory methods therefore have their place, and often a very important place, among the tools available to the geologist. It does not follow that they should be a necessary part of the routine, especially in a preliminary or short investigation, but they should be invoked immediately if a problem appears which they hold promise of solving. In large mines employing a permanent geological staff, every problem, however academic it may seem, will be attacked sooner or later, for there is no certainty that it may not bring to light a new guide to ore, and the thorough inquiry into most problems leads ultimately to microscopic or other laboratory methods as means of study.

In short, whether laboratory investigations should be undertaken and at what stage in the program depends, like most other methods of geological investigation, on the question, "Just what may I hope to learn from it?"

SELECTED REFERENCES

Mineralogy

Hurlbut, Cornelius S., Jr., *Dana's Manual of Mineralogy*, 15th Edition (revised). New York: John Wiley and Sons, Incorporated, 1941.

Kraus, E. H., *Mineralogy*, 3rd Edition. New York: McGraw-Hill Book Company, Incorporated, 1936.

Lewis, J. Volney, and Hawkins, A. C., *Manual of Determinative Mineralogy*, 4th Edition. New York: John Wiley and Sons, Incorporated, 1931.

Palache, Charles, Berman, Harry, and Frondel, Clifford, (Dana's) *System of Mineralogy*, 7th Edition, vol. 1. New York: John Wiley and Sons, Incorporated, 1944.

Rogers, A. F., *Introduction to the Study of Minerals*, 3d Ed. New York: McGraw-Hill Book Co., 1937.

Microscopic Study of Non-Opaque Minerals

Johannsen, Albert, *Descriptive Petrology of the Igneous Rocks.* University of Chicago Press, 1938.

Larsen, Esper S., and Berman, Harry, *Microscopic Determination of the Non-Opaque Minerals.* U. S. Geological Survey, Bulletin 848, 1934.

Rogers, Austin F., and Kerr, Paul F., *Optical Mineralogy.* New York: McGraw-Hill Book Company, Incorporated, 1942.

Winchell, A. N., *Elements of Optical Mineralogy,* 5th Edition. New York: John Wiley and Sons, Incorporated, 1937.

Evans, J. W., *The determination of minerals under the microscope.* London: Thomas Murby and Company, 1928.

Hartshorne, N. H., and Stuart, A., *Crystals and the Polarizing Microscope.* London: Arnold, 1934.

Rosenbusch, H., and Wülfing, E. A., *Mikroskopische Physiographie der petrographisch wichtigen Mineralien Bd. 1.* Erste Hälfte, Untersuchungsmethoden, 5te Aufl., Schweitzerbart'sche Verlagsbuchhandlung, Stuttgart, 1924.

Rosenbusch, H., and Mügge, O., *Mikroskopische Physiographie der petrographisch wichtigen Mineralien Bd. 1.* Zweite Hälfte, Spezieller Teil, 5te Aufl., Schweitzerbart'sche Verlagsbuchhandlung, Stuttgart, 1927.

Microscopic Study of Opaque Minerals

Graton, L. C., Technique in mineralography at Harvard, *American Mineralogist,* vol. 22, pp. 491–516, 1937.

Short, M. N., *Microscopic Determination of the Ore Minerals.* U. S. Geological Survey, Bulletin 914, 1940.

Ore Texture and Sequence

Bastin, E. S., Graton, L. C., Lindgren, Waldemar, Newhouse, W. H., Schwartz, G. M., and Short, M. N., Criteria of age relations of minerals with especial reference to polished sections of ores, *Economic Geology,* vol. 26, pp. 561–610, 1931.

Edwards, A. B., *Textures of the Ore Minerals and their Significance.* Melbourne: Australasian Institute of Mining and Metallurgy, 1947.

Fairbanks, E. E. (Editor), *Laboratory Investigation of Ores.* New York: McGraw-Hill Book Company, Incorporated, 1928.

Schwartz, G. M., Microscopic criteria of hypogene and supergene origin of ore minerals, *Economic Geology,* vol. 27, pp. 533–553, 1932.

6

Correlating Data

To reason without data is nothing but delusion.

—Arthur Holmes [1]

Much of the information essential to ore-search is of the sort that can be shown on plans and sections. This is true not only of data from geologic mapping—rock-types, bedding, faults, etc.—but also of assays and ore tonnages, of drilling-records, of geophysical observations and even the significant results of laboratory studies, especially those which involve the distribution of alteration-phases and mineral-ratios. To show these varied types of information on a single sheet for any level would result in overcrowding and confusion of lines, and to show it on all the necessary planes, cross sections, and longitudinal sections for a large mine of many levels must inevitably require a great multiplicty of sheets. Only a thoroughly planned system makes it possible to find the proper sheets when needed, to compare and superimpose them, and to collect the particular combination of details required for the solution of a given problem.

Maps and Sections

Size of Maps

The first essential is to select a convenient standard size for map-sheets. The base for the geologic maps—the engineers' survey of the mine workings—may or may not have been plotted on sheets of manageable size, although, as Hayes says, the modern trend even for engineering maps is toward subdivision into blocks.

"An official map of twenty-five years ago was two yards wide and

---

[1] Holmes, Arthur, *The Age of the Earth*. New York: Harper & Bros., 1913.

thirteen paces long. The time consumed in plotting actual engineering features was hardly half of that spent on decorative borders and pretentious titles. Such large maps were necessarily of the 'roll' variety. It is not difficult to summarize their only advantage: a large area of ground shown on a single map. The disadvantages are many: (1) they require unusually large drafting tables; (2) the constant inconvenience of rolling and unrolling; (3) to be retained in a flat position they must be weighted down on the corners; (4) drafting instruments and ink bottles are placed on the face of the map, and even though it escapes the upset of an ink bottle a heavy coating of dirt and grease will accumulate; (5) letters and numbers are printed at all angles, and, the map being too large to pivot, the draftsman must sprawl bodily upon it after the fashion of a contortionist. The roll map was discarded by the Anaconda engineering department about twenty years ago." [2]

The disadvantages of large sheets for engineering base maps apply with even more force to geologic maps which are plotted, not on hard drawing paper, but almost invariably on tracing cloth. Farmin says: [3] "If a tracing is rolled for storage . . . its ink lines become broken and dimmed as the ink film cracks and scales off. . . . Creasing and snagging . . . break the glazed starch surface and fracture the ink film; grime works into the fabric and destroys its transparency. . . . The most important step toward prolonging the life of a map is to store and use it flat." Apart from the longer life that they are likely to enjoy, small unrolled sheets are much easier to manipulate. Making up cross sections, for example, involves tracing comparatively little data from each of a large number of level maps, a most awkward process if each map has to be detached from a roll, spread out, weighted down at the corners, used for a moment and then replaced in its curling pile.

Block Systems

In order that sheets may be small it is imperative that the plan of a large mine be subdivided into blocks of such dimensions that the plan of each block on the largest scale used will be of manageable proportions. Thirty-six × 40 inches is about the largest convenient size; 30 × 40 is recommended by Gilbert,[4] and maps as small as 18 × 24 inches are used in some offices.

[2] Hayes, J. L., Anaconda Copper Mining Company's mapping practice: *Engineering and Mining Jour.*, vol. 116, Nov. 17, 1923, p. 841.

[3] Farmin, Rollin, Longer life for mine maps: *Engineering and Mining Jour.*, vol. 138, November 1937, p. 54.

[4] Gilbert, D. C., Mine maps, their preparation, correlation and maintenance: *Engineering and Mining Jour.*, vol. 132, 1931, p. 18.

Even though the engineering base map may be a composite, showing the workings of all levels on a single sheet, as is usually the case when the lode is not too steep, the geologic plans should comprise a separate sheet for each level. An exception may possibly be made where the ore-bearing structure is so gently inclined that the workings nowhere lie one above another, but even in this case there is danger that data from crosscuts or drill holes, present or future, will be confused with those of other levels.

Laying Out Blocks. In laying out blocks it pays to devote abundant care and meditation to selecting a size of sheet and locating its boundaries in such a way that block-margins cut through as few workings as possible. However, in a mine of any complexity, some margins are sure to fall in inconvenient places. It is much better to accept this fact as inevitable than to use blocks of irregular shape or orientation in the attempt to avoid it. And at all cost, have the boundaries the same on all levels. Nothing is more exasperating than to superimpose a series of level maps of divergent orientation and non-uniform size whose coordinates are in different positions with respect to the margins. If the workings of a level run off the block, let them go and start a new block. Do not attempt to keep them in by shifting the margins. And of all things, do not seek to achieve a well-balanced and artistic effect by centering the workings in the middle of each sheet. If all the workings fall in one corner of a sheet, leave them there.

It is desirable if possible to select a size for sheets so that the margins will fall on coordinates of even hundreds of feet. In this way all blocks will have the same pattern of coordinates and can be ruled up from a single template by merely writing in the proper coordinate numbers. Sometimes, however, there are good reasons for designing blocks whose dimensions are not measured in even hundreds of feet, and, exceptionally, there are overwhelming reasons for laying out blocks oblique to the coordinates (and only when the reasons are overwhelming should this be done). It is then imperative to calculate trigonometrically the coordinates of the corners of each block and to draw up on hard paper a separate template for each block with coordinates accurately plotted. Only by using this template as a guide can the tracings be made to match accurately.

Numbering Blocks. The blocks should be named or numbered according to a definite system. In some districts the names of mines or shafts are used, as Ombla Block, Esperanza Block, etc. From this, anyone familiar with the district will know where the block is or which block he wishes to consult. Alternatively the blocks may be designated by numbering or lettering. For example the columns might be lettered and the rows numbered so that a given block would be called A-4, B-2, etc. Still another method is to number the blocks beginning in the northwest corner with 00, as shown below:

```
00 01 02 03 04 05 06 07 08 09
10 11 12 13 14 15 16 17 18 19
20 21 22 23 24 25 26 27 28 29
30 31 32 33 34 35 36 37 38 39
40 41 42 43 44 45 46 47 48 49
50 51 52 53 54 55 56 57 58 59
60 61 62 63 64 65 66 67 68 69
70 71 72 73 74 75 76 77 78 79
80 81 82 83 84 85 86 87 88 89
90 91 92 93 94 95 96 97 98 99
```

The first digit denotes the row, the second digit denotes the column. Not all the blocks need be used. For example, the numbers in the center of the square (say rows 4 to 6 and columns 4 to 6) could be used for a system of nine blocks; other blocks could be added on any side where necessary.

Scales

A uniform scale for the maps should be chosen and adhered to. The most convenient scale for ordinary mapping is either 1 inch to 40 feet, 1 inch to 50 feet, or a metric scale of 1:500. A smaller scale, such as 1 inch to 100 feet, is too small to show the usual features, since the scaled width of an average drift is only 1/20 of an inch, which does not allow room for more than a single ink line between the walls. On the other hand, a larger scale, though very convenient for detailed mapping, is unnecessarily large for ordinary features. In a mine of any considerable size it means that an inconvenient number of sheets must be used to show each level. Under special conditions, in places of critical structure or unusual complexity, a large scale such as 1 inch to 20 feet or even 1 inch to 10 feet may be necessary however.

In very small mines and prospects, one is often tempted to plot the maps on a large scale, but there is seldom good reason for this. If all the data can be placed on a map the size of a letter sheet, so much the better.

When a standard scale is chosen for the basic records, this will be the scale on which the underground mapping is done. Data are quickly transferred from the "work sheets" to the standard office maps by laying the work sheet under the standard map and tracing the lines.

In addition to the standard plans which constitute the record of the mapping, it is often convenient to have a series of smaller-scale plans on which only major features are shown. The workings of a large mine can thus be placed on a single sheet and viewed as a whole. For this purpose a scale of 100 feet to the inch or, in larger mines, 200 feet to the inch is often very convenient for purposes of study. A still smaller scale is usually used to show the surrounding district as a unit.[5]

If the scales selected are even multiples of each other, the plans on different scales can all be drawn on sheets the same size.

Common combinations of scales are:

50', 200', 500'   (Homestake)
50', 100', 200', 400' (Old Dominion)
40', 400', 1200'   (recommended by D. C. Gilbert)

Metric Scale:

1:500, 1:1000, 1:5000 (Casapalca)

Titles

Each level plan has a title plate which shows:

Name of mine
Number of level
Scale
Name of geologist
Date

All of this information is essential and should never be omitted from any individual sheet. Even temporary maps should show all of these facts, if only in pencil.

The title should be in the same position on each page and large enough to be conveniently found and read, but within this limitation it should be as small as possible. Large fancy titles are a waste of time and space and are outmoded. While titles are usually placed in a rectangle about 2 x 4 inches in the lower right-hand corner of the map, this location is in danger sooner or later of conflicting with workings. All of the necessary information can be placed in the lower margin of the map outside the block, thus:

Scale: 1" = 40'	IMPORTANT MINING COMPANY	1250' Level
Geol. by R.V.S.		Block A-3
March 3, 1948		Geologic Map

[5] But Farmin sagely advises, "Don't keep too many sets going or you won't have time to go fishing." (personal letter.)

Each sheet should bear a legend unless it is part of a set, in which case the legend should appear on the first sheet of the set.   It is often convenient to mark on each plan the elevation of the level at the shaft station; this facilitates making up cross sections or calculating differences in elevation.   If the plans are not drawn on coordinates, each must have a meridian, indicating the north point.   For accuracy of scaling bearings, this should be several inches long, preferably at least a foot except on small maps.

Cross sections should show similar data, in particular the bearing of the section, the coordinates of a point through which it passes and the direction in which the section is facing.   This information is essential for future use in bringing the section up to date.   Thus a title might read:

> Cross section on line N72°W through coord. 8,345 N   3,486 E
> Looking north.
> Scale 1″ 40′

or

> Longitudinal section on coord. 3,000 E
> Looking east.

Colors and Conventions

Maps are most graphic if different features are shown in different colors.   Thus the convention used for many years in Butte and quite generally adopted elsewhere is to show veins or mineralization in red, faults in blue and wall-rock geology in black.

Additional colors may be used for other features.   Even descriptive notes may conveniently be lettered in appropriate colors; thus, notes pertaining to mineralization may be inked in red, notes regarding wall-rock in black.   In this way, if you are studying, let us say, variations in mineralization on a series of maps, you need not be distracted by notes referring to wall-rock texture.

The only objection to the use of colored inks is that they do not always register well on blueprints or whiteprints made from the tracings.   Yellow is especially deficient in this respect, although orange prints fairly well and can usually substitute for it.   Schmitt [6] recommends adding orange ink in the proportion of 1 cc. to an ounce of ink to improve the printing qualities, especially of green, blue, purple, brown, and carmine.   Except for this purpose he discourages the use of orange and yellow in inks as they dissolve the starch in the tracing cloth and are, therefore, hard to erase.

[6] Schmitt, Harrison: On mapping underground geology, *Engineering and Mining Jour.*, vol. 137, 1936, page 561.

If it is necessary to make many prints, the geologist may find it convenient to limit conventional signs to black ink, but in most offices the working maps are inked in color.

Rock formations and rock types are usually shown in solid color. In addition an abbreviation should be used to help in identifying the color. On maps covering a large area the practice of the U. S. Geological Survey is a convenient one to follow, using a capital letter to designate the era and a small letter following it to indicate the formation; thus, "Om" for Martinsburg shale of Ordovician age. In a single mine the sedimentary formations are all likely to be of the same geologic era, and space is saved by omitting the age designation, thus "cr" for Casapalca redbeds.

While the U.S.G.S. practice uses a characteristic color for each period and varying shades or patterns for individual formations, it is desirable on mine maps to have a greater contrast and range of color than would be possible if this system were followed.

The following colors are so commonly used that they are almost conventional:

Igneous rocks:	siliceous	red to orange
	basic	green
Sedimentary rocks:		(light colors)
	limestone	blue
	sandstone	yellow
	shale	green

There is, however, nothing compulsory about a color scheme; colors should be chosen to give the best emphasis to the structure.

Tracings can be conveniently colored by blocking in evenly with crayon (Faber's Castell is very satisfactory) and then smoothing the color by rubbing with a cloth moistened with gasoline or, as Schmitt suggests, with xylol which is noninflammable. For smoothing narrow bands of color on tracing cloth, the "stumps" supplied by art dealers are useful and for colors on drawing paper or whiteprints these are better than a rag. As a makeshift, a stump can be made by rolling a piece of hard blotting paper into the shape of a pencil and sharpening it.

For recording mineralization, a conventional system adopted many years ago in Cerro de Pasco is now used in various modifications in a number of offices. A vein carrying primary sulphides is shown by crosshatching, secondary sulphides are shown by double crosshatching and oxidized ore by stippling. The metals are distinguished by using lines or dots of standard colors:

iron (pyrite)	red
copper	green
lead	purple
zinc	brown
silver	yellow

If this color scheme is followed consistently, the same colors are used for the metals on assay graphs.

On composite maps the levels are distinguished by using a different color for each level. It is convenient to use a standard sequence of colors—the easiest to remember is the sequence supplied by the rainbow. Thus the top level may be shown in red, the second in orange and so on through yellow, green, blue, to violet or purple. Black may be used for the next and then the sequence repeated. When one is accustomed to this sequence it is not necessary to refer to a legend to remember which level is below which.

This sequence may be used for graphic portrayal of a variety of data. Thus it has been used with advantage to indicate angle of dip: red for steep dips, green for medium and blue for flat dips. This helps to outline areas of steep or flat dipping beds which would not attract the eye so readily if the dips were indicated merely by numbers.

Conventions commonly used on mine maps are shown in Figure 41. Abbreviations for common geological terms are the same as those used in other branches of geology as listed in texts on field geology. For the ore minerals the set of symbols given in Table 6 is convenient.

TABLE 6

STANDARD SYMBOLS FOR ORE MINERALS

The following abbreviations are widely used for labeling minerals in photomicrographs and for field notes. Those for the commoner minerals were used by the Secondary Enrichment Investigation. Those given below are in accord with the list used in the Harvard Laboratory of Mining Geology. Note that, unlike the symbols for the chemical elements, the abbreviations for compounds (with the exception of G) begin with lower case letters.

arg argentite	cv covellite	mc marcasite	sl sphalerite
asp arsenopyrite	en enargite	nc niccolite	st stannite
bi bismuth	fm famatinite	plb polybasite	sp specularite
bn bornite	G gangue	pc pearceite	td tetrahedrite
bo bournonite	gn galena	pn pentlandite	tn tennantite
cc chalcocite	Au gold	po pyrrhotite	wf wolframite
cup cuprite	hm hematite	pu proustite	wz wurtzite
cb cobaltite	jm jamesonite	py pyrite	
cp chalcopyrite	li limonite	si stibnite	
cu copper	mo molybdenite	Ag silver	

Sections

Cross Sections. From the plans and from data collected in raises and stopes, a series of cross sections is drawn up.

Sometimes the question comes up: "Should we draw the cross sections at regular intervals or in the places where they will give the most information?" The answer is, "Both." There is no objection to drawing too many cross sections; the usual tendency is to draw too few. Cross sections should be drawn through places where there is a series of cross-cuts on successive levels or a series of raises. These, together with the plans, afford the basic data. But for purposes of study there should be a system of uniformly spaced cross sections based, where necessary, on the best available interpolation and interpretation of data. Irregularly spaced cross sections, like irregularly spaced contours, do not give a clear picture of the shape of the veins and orebodies. If there is doubt as to how the structures should be connected in sections where there are incomplete data, the fact merely emphasizes questions that will need sooner or later to be answered and may even lead to the discovery of ore.

These systematic cross sections should be so closely spaced as to leave no doubt as to how structures behave between one cross section and the next. The spacing, of course, will depend on the nature of the mine; a 200-foot interval is usually the widest permissible and 100 or even 50 feet is often necessary to give a complete picture.

If the cross sections are made on tracing cloth they can be drawn up rapidly without the use of dividers for transferring points. The routine procedure is very simple:

Draw on each plan the horizontal trace of the proposed section, marking with a dot the point on which the margin of the section-sheet will fall. Then, on the section-sheet draw a series of horizontal lines, each representing the elevation of a level. Lay the section over the level plan, trace the positions of workings and plot the apparent dips of geological features, using an apparent-dip chart (*see* Appendix) or an apparent-dip protractor. In making up a whole series of cross sections, it is convenient first to draw on hard paper a template and from this to trace a blank-sheet for each cross section showing margins and the elevation-lines for the respective levels. Then lay each section-sheet in turn upon the plan and, when information from the plan has been traced for all sections, repeat with the next plan. On sections intended for permanent use it will be necessary to make allowance for differences in elevation occasioned by the gradient of the drifts, but for sections made

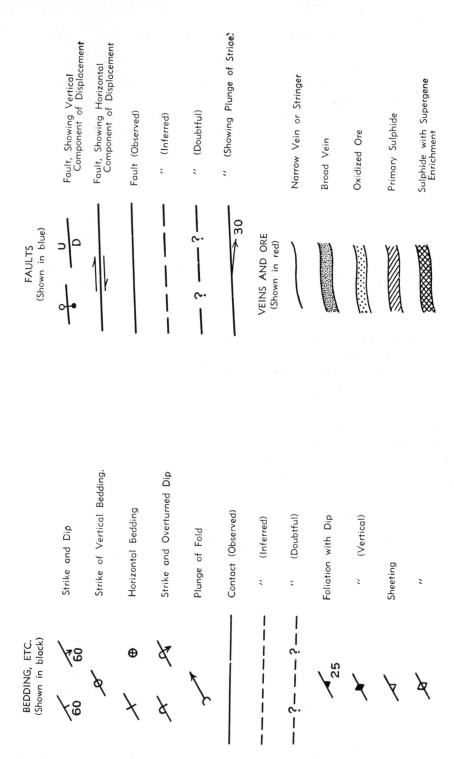

Fig. 41—Conventions commonly used on geologic maps.

for purposes of temporary study the error introduced by neglect of this factor is usually not serious, especially if all drifts have been driven from the same shaft on the same grade.

Conventionally, cross sections are drawn looking north or east rather than south or west. But in the case of a pitching structure it is convenient to draw sections looking in the direction of the pitch, so that geological features will have the same general shape on both plans and sections.

Longitudinal Sections. In addition to the plans and cross sections there should be one or more longitudinal sections. For veins these are particularly useful, since they are capable of showing drifts, raises, and stopes on the same sheet.

A longitudinal section consists of a projection of workings and geology to a vertical plane which strikes parallel to the average strike of the vein. If the strike of the vein curves or deviates sharply, this protection may introduce some distortion in that part of the vein which is not parallel to the plane of the section. In this case it may be advisable to "bend" the section so as to keep it approximately parallel to the plane of the vein, but this practice is confusing and should not be resorted to unless the vein deviates so far that it is nearly at right angles to the plane of the section.

The longitudinal section should show all workings, including drifts, raises, and crosscuts (which will appear in cross-sectional view). It should also show such geological features as can be depicted on this plane; thus it should show faults, fractures, junctions, and branch veins. Longitudinal sections are especially useful for analyzing vein structures, as explained in a later paragraph.

Assay Data

Records of the results of sampling form a highly important part of the geologist's basic data. Assay results may be shown on the geologic maps themselves, but it is usually preferable to present them on a separate set of plans and sections. These should be drawn on sheets of tracing cloth with margins corresponding exactly to the geologic maps so that the one may be superimposed on the other.

Since numerals take up considerable space the individual assays can be shown only on the maps of large scales. For scales of 100 feet to the inch or smaller it will be necessary to present assay data either in the form of averages or by some graphic method (see p. 193).

Recording Samples. In recording assay data the object is not merely to get the information written down but to present it in form that can be sized up without loss of effort. Toward the preparation of neat and convenient maps, the following rules are helpful. Although some of them may seem obvious, I have seen all of them violated, often with confusing results.

1. Omit sample numbers from the map. They take up space and serve no useful purpose once the location of the sample is fixed.

2. Enter the sample results close to the place in which the sample was cut. A map with "skyrockets" pointing in all directions to tables of results is not a sample map but merely a keyed list, and usually merits a less dignified description.

3. Tabulate the sample data in columns or rows with the same data in each column or row in order that the figures may be scanned rapidly. Do not make the eye skip figures.

ft.—% Cu	3.0–4.0	5.2–6.4	5.2–7.8		3.0/4.0	5.2/6.4	5.2/7.8	ft. / % Cu
	I	I	I		I	I	I	
		Right				Permissible		

3.0/4.0	5.2/6.4	5.2/7.8		3.0–4.0	5.2–6.4	5.2–7.8
I	I	I		I	I	I
	Wrong				Wrong	

4. Record the content in each metal separately. Do not add up the value and merely record the total in dollars.

5. Record gold values in grams, in ounces, or, if local custom decrees, in pennyweights; use units and decimals. (Nothing is more awkward than the outmoded custom of recording ounces, pennyweights, and grains.) State on the map what the unit is. Don't record gold values in dollars or in shillings but if you *do* disregard this rule, state on the map what price is used in arriving at the value.

6. If dollars *are* used, the second decimal is not significant except in placer deposits and should be dropped to save space. If hundredths of feet are obtained as a result of converting inches to decimals, the second decimal is likewise not a significant figure.

In recording samples the values should be placed on the map as reported by the assayer; high values should not be reduced unless they are out-and-out mistakes, for they may be of geological significance even though they are not entitled to full weight in calculation.

Maps and Sections Constituting a Set

Thus, the data acquired by geologic mapping and from other sources should be assembled on a systematic set of maps and sections. These records might include plans and sections on the following scales:

Large Scale (say 50 feet to the inch)
Geologic plans, a sheet for each level and a file of level-sheets for each block.
Assay plans, on sheets of identical scale and orientation, showing assays graphically and possibly also numerically.
Geologic cross sections.
Assay cross sections.
Geologic longitudinal sections, one for each vein.
Assay longitudinal sections, showing values by contours or color.
Medium Scale (100 or 200 feet to the inch)
Geologic plans (generalized geology).
Assay plans (averaged or generalized assay data shown by graph or color).
Geologic cross sections.
Assay cross sections.
Geologic longitudinal sections.
Assay longitudinal sections (showing ore distribution by color or contour).
Small Scale (500 or 1000 feet to the inch)
Surface plan of district.
Plan showing all underground workings in district (if mines are deep or if there is great surface relief, workings or veins are projected to several plans each representing a different elevation).
Cross sections showing geologic structure.

Filing Maps

The series of plans representing the successive levels of a mine within the boundaries of a single block are filed together, usually bound to a sheet of fibre board or plywood slightly larger than the maps. At the Idaho Maryland Mine [7] a convenient system of binding is provided by a series of "Cello-Clips" attached to the binding edge of the map. These "snap around the short posts which are spaced along the margin of the board and permit an individual sheet to be removed from or replaced to its position deep in the block without first removing the overlying maps." To hold the two lower corners tight against the baseboard and prevent fluttering and curling of the sheets while the maps are being carried from table to vault, Farmin uses large rubber bands (cut from

[7] Farmin, Rollin, Longer life for mine maps: *Engineering and Mining Jour.*, vol. 138, November 1937, p. 54.

old inner tubes) stretched diagonally across the corners and fitted into saw cuts in the plywood baseboard.

A simpler but usually less convenient filing system consists merely of a cabinet of broad drawers not more than two inches deep. The most satisfactory cabinets are made of steel; those with drawers of relatively small sizes are stocked by office equipment companies. Larger sizes, whether of wood or steel, have to be made to order. When of wood they must be exceptionally well constructed or the drawers will lack rigidity at the corners and tend to stick. It is well to have the rear few inches of each drawer covered to form a pocket at the back in order to prevent the maps from curling and getting torn.

Materials

Tracing cloth rather than drawing paper is invariably used for the office maps for several excellent reasons: first, tracing is the simplest method of transferring data from the work sheets; second, the series of maps, one for each level, can be superimposed in order to see relations in the vertical dimension; and third, copies can be made by blueprinting for the use of the mine foreman or other officials. These considerations outweigh the disadvantages of tracing cloth, *i.e.,* liability to shrinkage and to wear. The shrinking of tracing cloth is greatest during the first few days after it is unrolled, and Schmitt advises cutting it to size and stretching it on a wall for several weeks before drawing the coordinates.

As a protection from wear, Farmin recommends a coating of fixative to cover and protect all new ink lines or crayon colors as soon as they have thoroughly dried after their addition to the map. The fixative used is Fuller's NL 4434, a clear gloss lacquer which is thinned with lacquer-thinner for quicker drying to prevent the softening of certain colored inks. It is brushed or sprayed lightly over the strip of newly added workings and geologic symbols, dries quickly, and provides a transparent water- and wear-proof coating.

If it is expected that geologic maps will be subject to serious wear, the original should be put away and copies made for office use. The alternative, making the copies when the original map is ready to fall to pieces and repeating the process from year to year, results in cumulative inaccuracies which creep in with each successive copying, especially when the copy is made from a wrinkled and worn tracing.

If a large number of sheets are to be used, it is eonomical to have the tracing cloth cut to size and the margins and title printed on it by the manufacturer.

Tracing paper will be found very convenient for temporary studies of special features. A good grade of oiled paper such as that recommended for work sheets is advisable. It takes ink, pencil, or colored pencil well. Eggshell paper is usually too flimsy and tears easily. In using tracing paper, however, remember that even the best grades deteriorate and either tear or become brittle after a few months or at most a few years. It is therefore inadvisable to use it for any work of a permanent nature. While tracing cloth is expensive it is usually less costly than the work of drawing; if ten dollars' worth of drafting is to be put on a map it is better economy to use a two-dollar sheet of tracing linen than a ten-cent sheet of flimsy paper.

Reducing, Enlarging and Copying

Since the same data are presented on maps of different scales, the enlarging and especially the reduction of maps constitutes a laborious part of the routine work in a geological office.

Every sizable office should be equipped with a large precision pantagraph of the suspension type. But these instruments are expensive and the small mine or the temporary job may have to get along without such luxury. If so, a small pantagraph of wood or preferably light metal can be bought for three or four dollars from a dealer in artists' supplies and it is quite good enough for ordinary jobs of reducing, though a little too stiff and jerky for accurate enlargements. It is light and compact enough to go along on examination work.

For certain kinds of work, photography is even more convenient than pantagraphing. Photostating facilities will be found in only a few of the larger and better equipped mine offices, but every sizable city has a commercial establishment prepared to do the work.

Lacking mechanical equipment for enlarging or reducing there are several drafting methods that can be used.

1. Replotting by coordinates: Scale the coordinates of each point from the original map and plot the point on the new map, using the appropriate scale. A pair of proportional dividers is a great time-saver in this process.
2. Reducing or enlarging by squares: Rule off the original map and the new one in small squares and copy the details within each square by sketching.
3. Reducing and enlarging by angle and distance: Plot points for control on tracing paper. Lay the tracing over the original, carefully oriented and with one of the points coinciding. Draw lines from the control points radiating out to the points to be plotted. Measure distances to these points on the original and lay off the distances along the lines to the new scale. This process is repeated for each control point until all of the detail of the map is filled in. Here again proportional dividers speed up the work. This is a

particularly rapid method of filling in geological detail on drifts between stations; the strike of fractures, etc. can be plotted either by shifting the paper or by using a parallel ruler.

If much work is to be traced from blueprints or transferred to opaque paper it will be worth while to make a tracing table by setting a sheet of plate glass into the top of a drafting table and illuminating it from below with fluorescent light tubes. The itinerant geologist who has to do his office work in hotel rooms can make a temporary tracing box by removing a drawer from a hotel dresser, placing the ubiquitous adjustable desk lamp inside it and laying a sheet of glass across the top of the drawer. The glass, although awkward to pack in the kit of equipment, is useful also for making small blueprints.

Details may be transferred from tracings to opaque drawing paper by placing the tracing accurately over the paper, slipping a sheet of carbon paper between the two and going over the lines with a medium-soft pencil.

Block Diagrams

The eye grasps geological structures most quickly if they are presented in a three-dimensional drawing. Block diagrams and perspective drawings are very useful in illustrating reports and presenting information to anyone who is unfamiliar with a particular property. For the geologist's own use in working out structural problems they are less definitely helpful for it is difficult to construct a picture in three dimensions unless it has already been visualized. For this very reason, however, it is often worth while to prepare a block diagram of selected structural features, for in attempting to fill in the details the geologist becomes painfully aware of any gaps in his knowledge or understanding of shapes.

The construction of a block diagram is essentially a mechanical operation; all that is necessary is to follow established rules.[8] The first step is to transform the plan of each level of the mine into a distorted map plotted on oblique coordinates. The angle between coordinates may

[8] Lobeck, A. K., *Block Diagrams and Other Graphic Methods Used in Geology and Geography.* New York: John Wiley and Sons, 1924.

Johnston, W. D., Jr., and Nolan, T. B., Isometric block diagrams in mining geology: *Economic Geology*, vol. 32, No. 5, 1937, pp. 550–569.

Valois, Leon, Three dimensional drawings in mining practice: *Canadian Mining Jour.*, vol. 60, 1939, p. 397.

Wilson, W. H., Tri-dimensional mapping of extensive mine workings: *Trans. Inst. Mining and Metallurgy*, vol. 45, March, 1936, pp. 365–393.

Broderick, A. T., Useful block diagrams are easy to construct: *E. & M. J.*, vol. 147, pp. 74, 75, Oct., 1946.

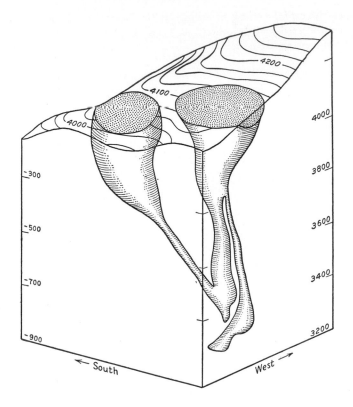

Fig. 42—Block diagram showing shape of pipelike orebodies. (*After* Kuhn, *Economic Geology*)

be translated from the true 90° to 60°, as in isometric projection, but there is no necessity to use this particular angle; any angle that serves best to bring out the features can be used. The coordinate system is first laid out on the angle decided upon; then the workings are replotted on this coordinate system. As distances measured parallel to either co-ordinate are unchanged, the transformation can be carried out by scaling distances from the coordinates and plotting the map point by point. As a time-saving alternative there are various mechanical devices, modifications of the pantagraph principle that can be used.[9] Optical methods, such as photographing each plan from a definite angle, or tracing it through a camera lucida should be feasible.

When the plan of each level has been transformed from a rectangle into a lozenge, the next step is to assemble the levels into a single block. This is done by drawing a line which is to serve as the vertical dimension

[9] Bain, George W., The perspectograph: *Econ. Geol.*, vol. 36, 1941, pp. 71–83.

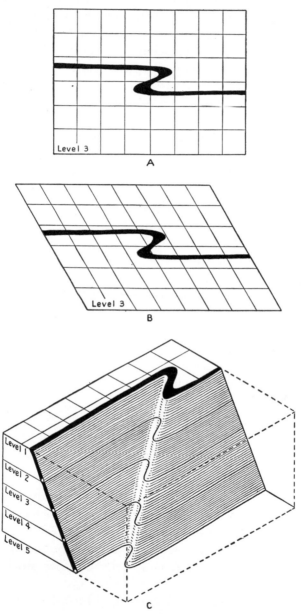

Fig. 43—Stages in the construction of a block diagram. *A:*
Plan of a level. *B:* Plan of same level transformed to acute-
angled coordinate system. *C:* Transformed plans of five levels
assembled in respective positions on vertical coordinates.

and laying off on it the vertical intervals between levels.   Each level is then placed in its proper position touching this line and traced onto the final drawing.   The surface of the ground may be converted to block diagram by transforming surface contours to the "skew" co-ordinates and tracing each contour in its appropriate position in the vertical dimension.

Needless to say, a block diagram can be constructed from cross sections instead of plans, or from a combination of the two.

In deciding the angle and the viewpoint, the choice is made in such a way that the shape of the features can be most clearly seen; for example, if veins are depicted it is best to arrange the diagram so that they dip toward the observer.

If the distance from the near to the far corner of the diagram is relatively large a more realistic effect is produced by introducing vanishing perspective; [10] this is done by laying out the plans in such a way that one or both sets of coordinates are not parallel lines but converge at a distant point.   To enhance the illusion of space, lettering and numbering should also be drawn parallel to oblique guides, i.e., the lettering should appear as though printed on the surface of the plan or on a plane parallel to one of the sides of the drawing.

Up to this point the construction of the diagram is wholly mechanical and mathematical except for the choice of angle and viewpoint.   To produce a more striking effect, however, curved surfaces such as folded beds may be shaded in order to bring out their shape; this requires some ability in free-hand drawing which is not vouchsafed to all geologists, but often an artist friend is willing to add the finishing touches.

Models

Models are scorned by some geologists as pretty gadgets to show to directors and visitors but superfluous for an engineer who is schooled in visualizing three dimensions.   This attitude is correct as regards mine workings and simpler geologic structure, but for really complex three-dimensional problems a model is most helpful if not absolutely indispensable.

A great variety of ingenious methods have been devised for portraying various kinds of data.[11]   One of the simplest, often used for assembling the results of churn drilling, consists of a baseboard fitted with holes to take rods which are erected vertically and painted in ap-

[10] Secrist, Mark H., Perspective block diagrams: *Econ. Geol.*, vol. 31, 1936, pp. 867–880.
[11] Ellertsen, N. A., Maps to models: *Canadian Mining Journal*, vol. 58, p. 773, 1937.

propriate colors to represent different grades of ore or different types of rock.

Models of mine workings are of two general types: those in which the excavations are represented by solid material and those in which the features are drawn on transparent sheets, or on opaque sheets made visible by cutting away portions of them.

Solid models are often preferred by operators. Ellertsen describes a method of making them by cutting out the successive stope-floor plans from Balsa wood and sticking them together with LePage's glue; rectangular rods can be used to represent crosscuts and raises.

For geological purposes skeleton or plate models are usually preferred. The commonest type consists of a series of glass plates, one for each level, supported in a rack at the proper vertical intervals. The mine workings and geology are drawn [12] on each plate as though on a tracing. Illumination is supplied by light globes or, preferably, fluorescent tubes at the base of the model under a ground glass plate or under an ordinary plate covered with white paper to diffuse the light.[13] Ordinarily models of this type show only plans but North [14] describes a model in which cross sections are added by inserting vertical strips of glass between the levels and holding them in place with wire clips.

Some types of structure are best revealed by a series of cross sections drawn on sheets of glass standing vertically, lighted from the back of the model. A very handsome model built on this principle was constructed at the Lake View and Star Mine in Western Australia. The construction may be compared to that of a chest of drawers standing on its side. Each drawer is mounted on ball bearings and consists of a set of five glass cross sections spaced at 50-foot intervals. If all of the drawers are pulled out the model of the mine is complete, but, since there are so many sections that it is impossible to see through them all at once, the arrangement is such that any drawer or combination of drawers can be pulled out for studying and comparing different sections of the mine.

Temporary models for study purposes can be made by drawing geological features on sheets of cardboard.[15] The sheets are cut with

---

[12] Well cleaned glass will take India ink but unfortunately it is easily rubbed or washed off; Duco enamel applied with a pen or brush may be substituted (Ellertsen). For solid colors Windsor and Newton oil colors may be mixed with Japan drier. (North)

[13] Unless fluorescent "cold" lamps are used, plenty of space and ventilation must be allowed or the plate will crack.

[14] North, E. D., Glass mine models: *Trans. Am. Inst. Mining and Metallurgical Engineers,* vol. 40, 1909, p. 755.

[15] Ellertsen recommends No. 62 cardboard which comes in sheets 30″ × 40″ obtainable from Art Metropole, Toronto.

window-like openings to see through.   Or cardboard plans or sections of the orebody can be cut out and suspended on wires.

A very convenient type of model for temporary study can be made out of celluloid sheets.[16]   Celluloid has the advantage that pieces of it can be cemented by acetone.   It takes ink better than does glass, but it is less transparent, less rigid, and tends to warp, hence it is not altogether satisfactory for permanent models.

A convenient model of this type can be made in the form of a pile of trays each shaped like a shallow box.   Detailed instructions will serve to explain the methods which can be adapted to a variety of types of celluloid models.

Cut sheets of 40-gauge celluloid to uniform size by scratching along a line with a needle and then bending the sheet until it breaks along the line of the scratch.   Lay each sheet on the map and trace the geologic features with a pen in India ink.   Such a sheet will form the bottom of each tray.   Then cut strips to form the sides of the trays, each strip corresponding in height to the vertical distance between levels.   To cement the sides to the bottom, lay the bottom flat on a table or preferably on a sheet of glass; hold the side in a vertical position against the edge of the bottom.   Apply acetone with a glass tube drawn out to a capillary point; when the point is touched to the joint between the two sheets the acetone spreads along the joint by capillary attraction.   After the pieces have been held together for a minute or so, the joint will be found to be solidly cemented.

To insert cross sections into the plan model, trace each section on a sheet of celluloid, then cut the traced section into horizontal strips by breaking along the line of each level.   Insert the strip into its proper position in each tray and cement it with acetone.   If desired, small rectangles on which drill-hole data have been plotted may be cemented in their appropriate places between levels.   To make the pile of trays rigid yet separable, each tray may be fastened to the one above it by means of a vertical celluloid pin cemented to the underlying tray and fitting into a small hole in the bottom of the overlying one.   The hole can be bored by piercing the celluloid with a red-hot needle.

A model of this sort is useful either for showing a whole mine on a small scale or for showing selected portions of the mine.   A larger model can be built up as a series of cells.   This sort of model is very convenient because it can easily be taken apart to add new features or bring it up to date.

[16] Dr. W. J. Mead introduced me to this method.

INTERPOLATION AND ANALYSIS

The foregoing discussions of mapping and recording have emphasized the portrayal of observed facts. But a systematic record of facts, although it forms the foundation for the geologist's work, has but limited practical value in itself; in order that the facts may tell their story, the geologist must correlate and analyze them. Some useful methods of analyzing structural and assay data will receive attention in the following sections.

Interpolating Contacts

If observed contacts and other structural features are to be used in solving geological problems, it is necessary first to interpolate their positions between known exposures and then to project them into unexplored ground.

The shape of a contact between exposures will be inferred from what is known of the structure, with particular attention to the local habits. For example, Fig. 44 represents a contact as mapped in two crosscuts.

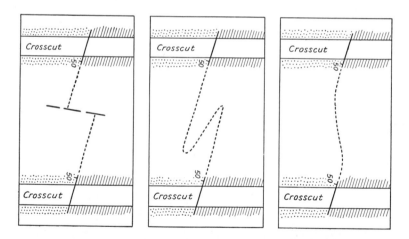

Fig. 44—Alternative interpretations of identical observations. *Left:* As faulted contact. *Center:* As folded contact. *Right:* As curving contact. (Diagrammatic)

The intervening part might be interpreted as a pitching fold if such folds are observed in the crosscut or on another level. It might be mapped as a gentle curve if neighboring contacts have this form. Or a probable fault might be drawn in, especially if the continuation of a known fault would pass through this interval. Even if no nearby fault has been observed, the contact might still be interpreted in this way if other faults of this attitude and direction of displacement are known in the district; in this case the degree of probability would be much lower than in the case of projection of a known fault.

If no definite indication of the shape of the contact is available, the geologist "will follow the analogies of his district, and run in his boundaries with the same kind of flowing lines which he sees them to possess where they can be actually examined." [17]

"We shall be wise if we make studies of the 'style' prevalent in each class [of geologic lines] where we can actually see it, and then map in accordance with that style in ground where there is lack of direct evidence. If our lines be ungraceful, we may be tolerably sure that there is something wrong, and yet, on the other hand, our lines may be graceful and still not be faithful. Regular symmetrical curves are graceful, but the grace of our lines should be that of the irregular curves of nature." [18]

The minor structures in the rocks often afford a hint as to the proper shape of interpolated lines. If there are dragfolds of hand-size exposed in a crosscut, there are likely to be folds of a larger order of magnitude; and their plunges, axial planes and general symmetry are likely to be analogous to those of the small folds. It is well to remember, though, that folds in competent rock such as quartzite are likely to be more open and regular than in such adjoining incompetent beds as slates and schists, and that igneous rocks that have been deformed along with sediments are likely to fail by faulting and lensing where the sediments respond by folding.

In completing the picture of the shape of a particular structural feature, it is often helpful to make up maps which show only this feature and omit all workings and other details which would distract the eye from the structural pattern. Suppose, for example, that you are studying the shape of the contact between two formations. Make up a blank sheet the size of the geological block and trace off from one level the contact at all points at which it is known. Then lay the blank on the map of the next level and trace off the known points on the contact, using another color. When this is done for all levels you will have, if the levels are at equal vertical intervals, a skeleton contour map of the contact. On this the inferred position of the contact between exposures may be filled in consistently for each level.

[17] Gieke, Sir Archibald, *Outlines of Field Geology*, London: Macmillan & Co., 1889, pp. 96–97.
[18] Greenly, Edward, and Williams, Howel, *Methods in Geological Surveying*: Thos. Murby and Co., London; D. Van Nostrand Co., N. Y., 1930, p. 207.

The shape of a vein may be studied in the same manner.   But veins are often steep (and so, for that matter are some rock contacts) so that,

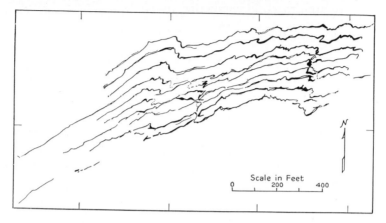

Fig. 45—Composite plan of a vein as exposed on successive levels. Pickle Crow Mine. (*After* McLaren, *Canadian Mining Journal*)

on an ordinary composite plan, the upper levels obscure the deeper ones. In this case it is a good scheme to offset each level by an amount proportional to the vertical interval between the levels.   This is done by simply moving the tracing paper a given distance perpendicular to the strike of the vein before tracing the next level.

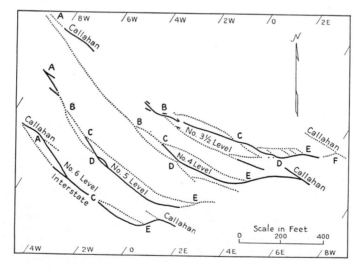

Fig. 46—Composite plan of a vein system as exposed on successive levels. In order to avoid overlapping of lines, each level has been offset by a distance proportional to the vertical distance between levels. Interstate Mine, Idaho. (*After* McKinstry and Svendsen, *Economic Geology*)

As a supplement to such a composite plan, a composite cross section may be made by tracing successive sections on a single sheet, separating them only enough to avoid conflicting lines.

Composite Plunge Plans

It is sometimes helpful, instead of moving levels apart, as just suggested, to bring them closer together. In some cases the plunge of a fold or of an intersection is uniform over long distances even though the dip and strike vary from place to place. In one mine a body of porphyry has been deformed during the folding of the enclosing rocks, and, while its outlines are irregular, it has a persistent plunge of 45 degrees. The method of interpolating the contact, as illustrated in Figure 47, is

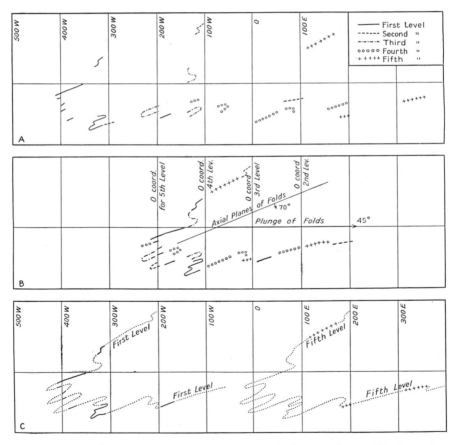

Fig. 47—Steps in interpolation of contact by composite plunge projection. *A:* Composite plan of contacts as mapped on five levels. *B:* Observed contacts projected on the direction of plunge to a common plane. *C:* Interpolation by projecting data from *B.* to individual levels. Second, third and fourth levels are omitted here to avoid confusion of lines. (Idealized diagram)

as follows: Trace the contacts to a composite plan, offsetting the contact as mapped on each level by an amount corresponding with the horizontal component of the plunge (in this case, 100 feet horizontally for each 100-foot vertical level interval). Fill in the gaps between projected observations in accordance with the local structural habits. Then place the composite in its true position on each successive level and trace the interpolated position of the contact between observations. Although the result is still an interpolation and must be recognized as such, it is likely to be more accurate and consistent than interpolations made independently level by level.

Longitudinal Sections

Longitudinal sections lend themselves especially well to interpolating and projecting the structural features of a vein and to showing the intersections of geologic features with the vein-surface; these features

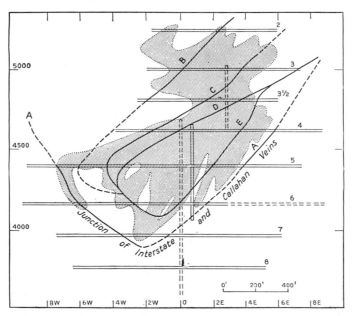

Fig. 48—Longitudinal section of a vein, showing ore-shoot and intersections of fractures. (Intersections lettered A, B, etc.). Interstate Mine, Idaho. (*After* McKinstry and Svendsen, *Economic Geol.*)

should include branch veins, faults, joints, bedding planes, and formation boundaries. It is hardly necessary to say that in plotting such features, the observed dip as shown on a plan needs to be corrected to the apparent dip by use of a dip table or dip chart.[19]

[19] See Appendix, Art. 7.

On comparing longitudinal sections of structure with similar sections showing distribution of ore, it sometimes turns out that structural features have an unexpected relation to ore localization. In one example [20] the ore in a vein is localized by zones in the folded wall rock within which bedding has a flat dip; here contouring of degree of dip of bedding in wall rock adjoining the vein showed a definite relation to the distribution of values.

Composite Longitudinal Sections. In a district in which there are many oreshoots on parallel or intersecting veins, a single longitudinal section on which all of the orebodies are projected may bring out significant relationships. It may, for example, indicate that the orebearing zone has a pitch which would not be obvious on individual sections (see Figure 103); it may also suggest a favorable elevation or a uniform depth of bottoming.

Inclined Sections

Although sections as conventionally plotted are projections to a vertical plane, a series of inclined sections dipping at some selected angle to the horizontal may be useful in bringing out special features. If a vein has a reasonably uniform dip and strike, an inclined longitudinal section drawn parallel to the average dip will show the vein in less distorted form than will a vertical section. To plot the trace of a bedding plane or a fracture on such a section, it is necessary, of course, to calculate its apparent dip by a process which is somewhat more involved than the calculation for a vertical section.

If many dips are to be plotted, a special protractor is convenient.[21] The one described here may be used also as an ordinary apparent dip protractor for use on vertical sections.

Construction of Protractor. The protractor consists of two sheets of transparent celluloid (heavy photographic films cleaned of emulsion will do), together with a pointer, all fastened together on a pivot at *a*. (An annular rivet of the type used in repairing steel tapes is convenient.)

The ruling of the lower sheet depends on the inclination of the plane of projection, *i.e.*, the dip of the inclined section. In Figure 49 it is drawn for use on a section inclined at 60 degrees with the horizontal. The distance from *A* to *A′* is the natural cotangent of this angle plotted to any convenient scale. The distance from *A* to *C* is the cosecant of

[20] McKinstry, H. E. and Svendsen, R. H., Control of ore by rock structure in a Coeur d'Alene Mine: *Economic Geology*, vol. 37, 1942, pp. 215–230.

[21] McKinstry, H. E., A protractor for plotting dips on inclined section: *Econ. Geol.*, vol 18, pp. 393–397, 1923.

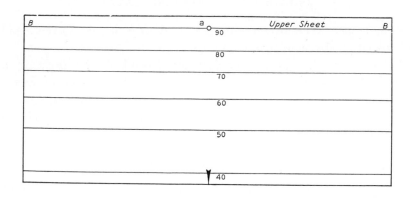

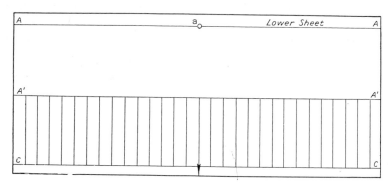

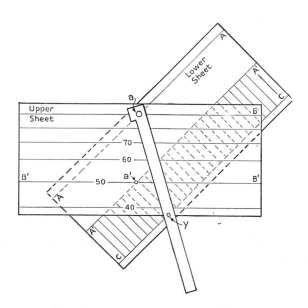

Fig. 49—Protractor for plotting apparent dips on vertical or inclined sections.
(*After* McKinstry, *Economic Geology*)

189

the same angle.   The cross lines from A'-A' to C-C are merely guide lines spaced at any convenient interval.

The ruling of the upper sheet does not depend on the angle of inclination of the section but is designed to deal with fractures of various dips.   The longitudinal lines are spaced at distances from the line B-B corresponding to the cotangents of angles from 90 degrees to (in the illustration) 40 degrees.   (The sheet can be extended to include smaller angles if desired.)

Use.   Lay the protractor on a horizontal plan (a level map) so that the line A-A of the lower sheet is parallel to the trace of the section. Rotate the upper sheet until the line B-B is parallel to the feature that you are plotting (a bed or fracture).   Select the numbered line on the upper sheet corresponding to the dip of the fracture and find the point (a') at which this line intersects the line A'-A'.   Carry this point across to the line C-C using the parallel cross lines as a guide and find the point y opposite a'.   Rotate the pointer until it passes through y.   Then the angle Aay is the apparent dip to be plotted on the inclined section.   To plot it, pick up the protractor without changing its adjustment and lay it on the inclined section with A-A parallel to a horizontal line on the section (the trace of a mine level) and a on the point where the fracture intersects the cross section.   Then the pointer is the trace of the fracture on the inclined section.   The whole operation takes about a minute.

To use as a simple apparent dip protractor for vertical sections, disregard the line A'-A' and use the line A-A instead; that is, find the intersection of A-A with the numbered line corresponding to the dip of the fracture, carry this point of intersection across to C-C to give the point y and rotate the pointer until it passes through y.   The apparent dip is the angle Aay.

Utility of Inclined Sections.   In plunging folds, sections cut normal to the plunge give a true cross section of the folded structure.   If veins intersect each other, sections normal to the line of the intersection show the true angle of intersection and may throw light on the mechanics of fracturing.   Thus a series of sections parallel to the plunge of a fold or to the intersection of two veins can be used to show progressive changes in structure.

Exaggerated Scales

It is sometimes desirable to bring out subtle variations in the dip or strike of a vein, since ore distribution is often delicately related to very minor changes in structure which are too small to be noticed on conventional maps. They may be accentuated by plotting the vein on a distorted scale. For example, the vein may be compressed longitudinally, so to speak, by using a scale in the direction of the strike, 1/5 or 1/10 the scale of the original map. Similarly curvatures in the dip may be exaggerated by making the vertical scale a fraction of the horizontal. This is a quick way of revealing irregularities in attitude, but it should be used only for purposes of analysis. Permanent working plans or sections drawn to distorted scales are misleading and should be avoided as the plague.

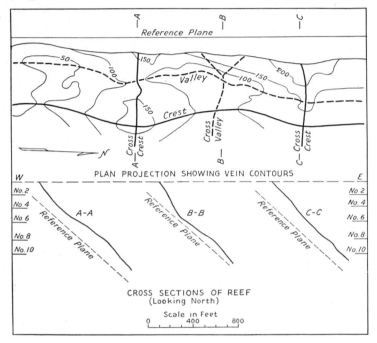

Fig. 50—Method of contouring vein structure with reference to an inclined datum plane. Contours represent distance from datum plane. (Original plan showed 10-foot contour interval. Only 50-foot contours are shown here.) Norseman, W. A. (*After* Conolly, *Economic Geology*)

Contours on Inclined Datum

A more comprehensive method of showing the curvature of a vein surface is to make a contour map of the vein using as the datum of reference some arbitrarily chosen plane, a method developed and described by H. J. C. Conolly.[22] In principle, the method consists in "laying the vein down flat." More accurately described, it consists of selecting

[22] Conolly, H. J. C., A contour method of revealing some ore structures: *Economic Geology*, vol. 31, pp. 259–271, 1936.

an inclined plane of reference and drawing contours showing the distance between the vein and this plane. The plane used may be that of the average dip and strike of the vein, though other slightly different planes may be preferable for bringing out special relationships.

Theoretically, the contours should represent distances measured at right angles to the reference plane, but the same result may be achieved more simply by plotting horizontal distances instead, since these can be measured directly on the plans. The procedure is as follows: After selecting a dip and strike for the reference plane, make up a template the size of the level map and lay off on it the strike of the plane of reference. Then calculate graphically or trigonometrically the position of the traces of this plane on each level and draw on the template a series of parallel lines one for each level. Trace the appropriate line on each level plan. Draw up a blank longitudinal section with a horizontal line representing the elevation of each level. Place this blank over the level map with the level line superimposed on the strike-line of the reference plane. Going along the level map with a scale, put down numbers recording the distance between the reference line and the center of the vein (alternatively the hanging-wall or the footwall of the vein may be used). Similarly measurements are made on cross sections between the dip line of the reference plane and the center of the vein as shown in sections of raises and stopes. From the longitudinal section, now filled out with numbers, draw contour lines to show the form of the vein.

Obviously the shape of the contours will depend on the reference plane that is chosen, hence it may be necessary to try various reference planes of varying dips and strikes in order to find the position that gives the most clean-cut correspondence between vein-structure and ore distribution. Generally speaking the best datum is a plane whose dip and strike lie somewhere between the favorable orebearing attitude and the unfavorable barren attitude. Not all veins respond to the contouring method, but it is always worth trying.

Analyzing Assay Data

The localization of orebodies is usually controlled, in some degree at least, by geologic structure. The structural control is not always obvious and sometimes is to be recognized, if at all, only by accurate and detailed analysis of both the structure and the distribution of the ore. It is best revealed by comparing the structural pattern with the distribution of metal content in the orebody. The data for metal distribution are afforded by sample records, but such figures, valuable as they are, convey no very clear picture unless they are presented in graphic form. In operating mines there is usually a sample map on which the width and assay of each sample is shown opposite the place in the drift or crosscut where the sample was taken. Either of two rather rapid methods will convert these figures into visual form. One is by coloring; the other is the preparation of an assay graph.

The coloring method may be illustrated by the procedure for a gold-bearing vein in which individual samples range from a trace to $30 or more. We may choose colors as follows: (see p. 170)

Over $25	red
$10 to $25	yellow
$5 to $10	green
$2 to $5	blue
Under $5	black

Going rapidly along the plan of the drift, place a dot of the appropriate color at the point where each sample was cut. From this color scheme, the limits of ore and the sections of low and high metal content become apparent.

The assay-graph method is slightly more laborious but yields a more precise record. In this method a line paralleling the side of a drift constitutes the abscissa, and the assay values form the ordinates in tracing the curve of values. If the graph proves to be so highly irregular that a smoother trendline is desired, the extreme fluctuations may be eliminated by drawing a new curve through the midpoints of the lines connecting each pair of assays. Sample widths may be evident from the mapping of the vein, but if not, they can be shown by a curve of still another color or by plotting a graph either on the opposite side of the zero abscissa or on the other side of the drift.

Since the values in a vein are not likely to be uniformly distributed from wall to wall, it is common practice in sampling wide veins to subdivide each channel sample into sections each representing a width of 5 feet or less (see p. 40). Thus a channel sample cut across a 20-foot vein might consist of six samples, each representing a width of from two to five feet. If these samples are plotted on a plan of the vein and their respective assays indicated by their appropriate colors, the correlation of the colors often reveals a distribution of metal content in consistent streaks or bands.

The assembled sample records from different levels on a vein are best studied in a longitudinal section on which the data from drifts, raises, and stopes may be shown simultaneously. Here assay values can be

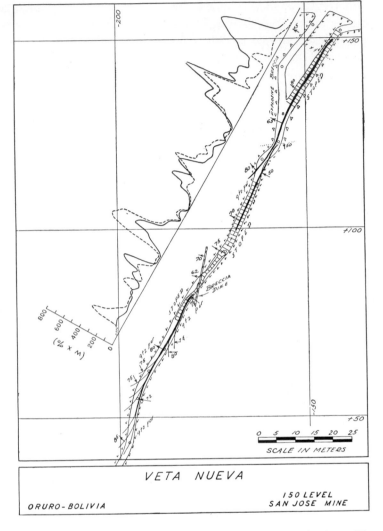

Fig. 51—Geologic map with assay graphs showing content in tin (solid
line) and silver (dashed line) as related to geological features. The ordinate for tin shows percent of tin multiplied by vein-width in centimeters.
The ordinate for silver shows hundredths of a percent of silver times vein-
width in centimeters. Oruro, Bolivia. (*Courtesy* of F. M. Chace)

indicated in color but are more clearly depicted by contours (*i.e.*, equal-
value curves). For this purpose, data from stopes are most helpful,
since they indicate the correct courses of curves through the intervals
between levels and raises. If the values of stope assays are too "spotty"
to show recognizable trends, it may be necessary to average them in
groups, say, by ruling the stope into a grid and averaging all of the

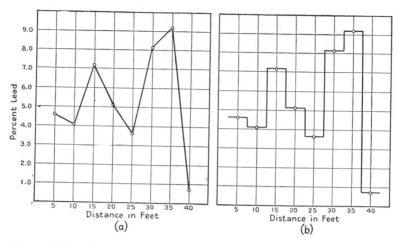

Fig. 52—Types of assay graphs. (*a*) is probably more realistic; (*b*) is sometimes better suited to visual estimate of average grade.

assays in each square. Unfortunately, stope-assay data are not always readily available in usable form. Even where samples are taken regularly in the routine control of stoping, the engineers do not, as a rule, plot them on a longitudinal section and in fact do not always preserve sufficiently accurate records to permit the geologist to do so. Hence it may be possible to plot only their approximate position, using as a guide the date of sampling as compared with the dates of stope surveys. Alternatively, the only available information may be the average of assays or the average grade of production from a stope during a given period. But even this may be of some help when plotted on the section in an appropriate color. In the complete absence of sample data, one may have to resort to indicating the high-, medium-, and low-grade portions of the stope from the mine foreman's verbal description. This information may be only mildly accurate and should not be accepted too literally, but it may nevertheless serve as a valuable clue to the distribution of values.

In mines where assays for more than one metal are recorded, the contouring of metal ratios, *e.g.*, gold:copper, silver:copper, or lead:zinc may give a key to secondary enrichment, to zoning, to the identification of distinct ore channels or to the approach to the roots of an orebody.

Résumé

All of these methods of analysis are for the purpose of bringing out geometrical relationships. When plans or sections showing the form of the structural features are superimposed on corresponding plans or

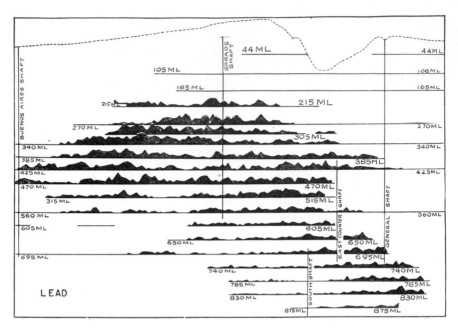

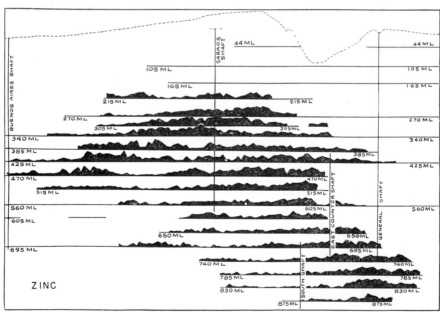

Fig. 53—A graphic method of showing assay-values on a longitudinal section. Cueva Santa Vein, Fresnillo, Mexico. (*After* Stone and McCarthy, *A.I.M.E.*)

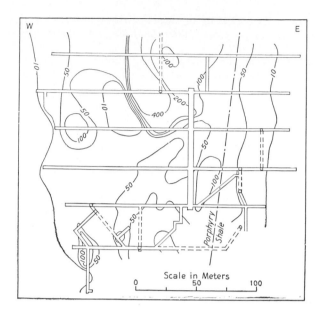

Fig. 54—Longitudinal section showing metal content by contours. Figures and contour lines represent tin in kilos per square meter of vein-surface. Note relation of values to contact. Itos Mine, Oruro, Bolivia. Data from G. Weissing and E. Kittl. (*After* Lindgren and Abbott, *Economic Geology*)

sections showing distribution of the ore, significant relationships often appear. The ore may be associated with a favored vein-attitude or a favored stratigraphic horizon. Indeed the orebodies may be arranged *en echelon* or according to some pattern which at once suggests places for further exploration even without reference to the geology. One should not, however, be content with the geometrical pattern in itself. If it is real and not imaginary there is a geological reason for it. This reason should be sought, not only because it induces more confidence in the geometrical theory, but because it is likely to lead to other useful deductions which the geometry itself does not suggest.

SELECTED REFERENCES

Conolly, H. J. C., A contour method of revealing some ore structures, *Economic Geology*, vol. 31, pp. 259–271, 1936.

Forrester, James Donald, *Principles of Field and Mining Geology*, pp. 448–482. New York: John Wiley and Sons, Incorporated, 1946.

Sales, Reno H., Mine maps and models, in Peele's *Mining Engineers' Handbook*, Section 19, pp. 2–11, New York: John Wiley and Sons, Incorporated, 1941.

Schmitt, Harrison, Extension of oreshoots with comments on the art of ore finding, Transactions, *American Institute Mining and Metallurgical Engineers*, vol. 85, pp. 318–329, 1929.

Wilson, Philip D., Report on the collection, recording and economic application of geological data, *American Mining Congress*, 25th Annual Convention, 1924.

PART TWO

GEOLOGICAL PRINCIPLES OF
ORE-SEARCH AND ORE APPRAISAL

The Use of Fact and Theory

Finding that the world would not accommodate itself to the theory, he very wisely determined to accommodate the theory to the world.
— Washington Irving
Knickerbocker's History of New York

Gathering facts in a routine manner and even analyzing them in terms of structure are not ends in themselves. As Wilson [1] puts it: "It is the careful thoughtful study of the material gathered underground and the flashes of revelation coming with it which make geological work valuable. Without them a set of underground geological maps may be likened, as far as practical value is concerned, to a collection of postage stamps."

The recorded facts assume significance only when you begin to "understand" them. A theory is an attempt to fit the observations together into a rational, consistent story and, in particular, to account for the relationship between the geological features and the occurrence of ore.

Any inquisitive mind derives satisfaction, of course, from "explaining" the facts, but the utility of a theory is not mere mental satisfaction. Without the development of theory the art of orefinding can advance but slowly. Theory is the stimulus that guides and inspires its progress. First, the struggle to achieve a satisfactory theory cannot fail to stimulate accurate observation; second, a consistent explanation inspires confidence that the existence of ore under the observed conditions is more than a coincidence, and, third, the growth and perfection of genetic theory opens the way to new techniques and methods of search.

[1] Wilson, Philip D., *Report on the Collecting, Recording and Economic Application of Geological Data:* American Mining Congress, 25th Annual Convention, 1924.

Good and Bad Theories

Nearly all exploration for ore is founded on a theory of some sort. Even the program laid out by the most "practical" miner is usually based on a theory, whether correct or mistaken. Some of the most elaborate and fantastic of theories are proposed by the very prospectors who (often with pardonable pride) disclaim all knowledge of geology. One may wonder that they ever find ore. Yet ore has been found again and again by exploration based on a wholly mistaken theory. Pure good luck? Sometimes. But often there is an underlying reason for it. The man who has lived with orebodies and watched them develop acquires what is known to the profession as a "nose for ore." This is not, as some people suppose, a sort of sixth sense. It is a sub-conscious feeling for the signs of ore and the behavior of orebodies, usually those of a particular district. It is like the weather eye of a Gloucester fisherman whose theories of meteorology may be based on the phases of the moon but whose predictions have a sound basis in the appearance of the sky and sea, viewed in the light of long experience.

Some of the miners in Wisconsin believe that the zinc ore there has, by its weight, caused the limestone beds to sag so they look for places where this weighing-down appears to have taken place. Their theory would hardly find acceptance in a sophisticated philosophy of ore genesis; yet it gives satisfactory results in certain mines where the beds have been dropped (relatively) on the footwall of a reverse fault. The miners have observed a condition that is favorable to ore occurrence and have looked for a repetition of this condition. Similarly not a few successful geologists have on many occasions found ore by following incorrect theories. They have succeeded because their predictions are based on what they can see; their theories are concocted to rationalize their subconscious empirical deductions. The incorrect theory has not interfered with successful results, since its implications were not followed beyond the facts which it attempted to rationalize.

Growth of a "Correct" Theory

But since a bad theory cannot survive indefinitely in the face of repeated observations, the geologist who is candid and imaginative will be alert to kill an incorrect theory and modify an imperfect one. He will greet each new fact with the questions "How come?" and "So what?" (or their equivalents in more technical language). To him, every observation confirms an old idea or suggests a new one. He will welcome facts that agree with his ideas but he will look even more diligently for observations that disprove them.   He will develop theories, sometimes two or more conflicting ones side by side, and watch them grow or die, depending on whether the successive facts that he finds are nourishment or poison to them.   He will cultivate such theories as seem healthy and will fight for them against enemies from without, but he will never develop such a sentimental attachment to them that he will be unable to part with them if better ones appear.   As Joralemon [2] says, "the geologist must not devote himself to any one theory or to the facts that support it long enough to fall hopelessly in love with it. He must make each theory the object of a summer flirtation and not a wife—and he must be ready to throw each one over the moment a more attractive mental maiden comes along."

The mining geologist has a better opportunity than some of his more academic colleagues to test his theories.   "The opportunity in mines for actual three-dimensional investigation and in high detail inevitably sets a more exacting standard of what is plausible than ordinarily obtains in conventional surface studies" [3] and as Graton further remarks: "A complicated structural puzzle at a critical place cannot be disposed of by the happy thought of putting in a fault just here on the map, or by assuming an unconformity at the base of so and so.   The mining geologist must not mistake plausibility for proof."

So, in stimulating the search for confirming testimony and in forcing the re-examination of any evidence that seems at variance, the theory imposes a discipline on observation.   If the observations stand up under verification but still seem inconsistent, we must modify the theory or think up a better one which, in turn, we put to the test by determining whether or not its consequences are found to be facts.   Thus theories, like organisms evolve by survival of the fittest and by adaptation to environment.

General vs. Local Theory

It is reasonable to assume that all ore deposits which are similar in their essential features have had a similar origin.   Therefore any theory of origin that is satisfactory must apply to all deposits of a given class. But since no two deposits even of the same class are exactly alike, the process that created them must have varied in its local details.   In order to allow for local variations in conditions, any general theory must be broad and adaptable in its nature and for this very reason must remain non-committal in regard to precise details.   Lacking quantitative exact-

[2] Joralemon, Ira B., *Mining Congress Journal*, pp. 35, 36, 1940.
[3] Graton, L. C., Ore deposits, in *50th Anniversary Volume*, G.S.A., pp. 480, 504, 1941.

ness, it is of limited practical use so long as it remains generalized. It is like an algebraic equation involving several unknowns or like a sketch map drawn to no particular scale. But when the theory is applied to a specific deposit we can begin to substitute numbers for the x's and y's; we can affix a scale to the map.

Under general theory we can say, for example, that an epithermal silver vein is likely to change in depth to lead-zinc mineralization, but we cannot predict on theoretical grounds the depth at which this change will take place nor can we be sure that the quantity of base metal will be greater or less than the amount required to meet mining costs. In a particular district, however, experience may teach that the change habitually takes place at an elevation of about 4000 feet, that the base-metal ores in the strong veins are commercial and that the best shoots are within a certain andesite flow. We are then in a position to particularize the general theory, to express it in terms of local geological structure.

For this reason, geology succeeds best in districts where there has been enough development to establish the local habits of ore occurrence, districts where it has been possible to fill in some of the variables in the general equation, calibrate the theory against local conditions and give it a definite, quantitative aspect. It might follow from this that the general theory is superfluous; that if we see the ore occurring under certain conditions, we need only look for a repetition of the same conditions. Or to revert to our example, the only requirement is to find a place where a strong vein is in the andesite flow at the proper elevation. Certainly there is much to be said for this mode of approach.

But the difficulty is that the same conditions are never duplicated in all particulars. Some details will be similar; others will be different. Yet all ore occurrences of common origin have some feature in common besides the ore itself. They may, in fact have many features in common, some of which are essential to ore occurrence and some of which are associated with ore only by coincidence. Which are the indispensable features and which are supernumerary? A sound and tested theory should point to the answer. For example, if the initial gold discoveries in a district have been on throughgoing shears near porphyry intrusions, we naturally explore shears near other porphyry intrusions. But if investigation leads to a theory that the ore did not come from the porphyry we need no longer confine our search to the vicinity of porphyry but may look for ore wherever the throughgoing shears intersect any rock-mass that is of such nature as to localize fracturing.

When the geologist moves from one district to another the process of adapting the general theory to local conditions has to be reversed. The guides that are purely local must be abandoned while retaining the principles that are fundamental and susceptible to general application. A man from Leadville who looked for ore under porphyry sills would be helpless in the Coeur d'Alenes. In his new location he could cling to throughgoing fractures, but he would have to adopt a new theory of local control. The geologist of broad experience and sound theoretical grounding develops a feeling for the distinction between those features which apply to whole classes of ore deposits and those which are purely local. He avoids making serious blunders in an unfamiliar district because he knows which of his accustomed rules he may safely use and which he will do well to forget.

Limitations of Theory

Although theories of genesis and of ore occurrence provide the background for geological thinking, they are not infallible guides, for it is unlikely that even the best theory is correct in all of its details. After all, it has to be based on circumstantial evidence. Since none of us were on hand when an ore deposit was formed we can never know exactly what the conditions were. We have to base our conclusions on inference from the facts that we have—and we never have quite all of the facts. Some of the details must always be in doubt and we must never overlook the element of doubt. In short a theory must never to taken too seriously. As Locke [4] says, ". . . no amount of reasoning that ore ought to occur at a given kind of intersection will take the place of the fact that, in that district, or in that mine, it habitually does so."

Above all, a prediction that ore will *not* be found in a given place should be made only on the most conclusive evidence. As McLaughlin and Sales [5] put it, "Negative theories . . . in general, are far more dangerous than positive ones. Loss from unsuccessful attempts to find ore will rarely exceed the cost of development to test the ground (plus possibly initial payments on options if a new property is being investigated), but negative ideas blindly followed might lead to the unforgivable sin of missing a great opportunity to find or acquire an important orebody."

Exploration based on pure theory and exploration based wholly on empirical observation are both permissible under the appropriate circumstances. If a vein is due to intersect a competent bed at greater

---

[4] Locke, Augustus, Ore finding: *Mining and Met.*, December, p. 523, 1926.
[5] McLaughlin, D. H., and Sales, Reno H., Utilization of geology by mining companies: *Ore Deposits of the Western States*, A.I.M.E., Lindgren Volume, p. 689, 1933.

depth, there is no harm in putting down a drill hole to see if it makes ore, banking merely on the theory that the competent rock should provide conditions favorable to ore deposition.

On the other hand, if ore has been found consistently in a certain conglomerate, known, let us say, as the Main Reef Leader, the fact that authorities disagree as to why it occurs there is certainly no deterrent to exploring that horizon. So no matter whether a proposed exploratory project is based on pure theory or on observed but unexplained habits, the only question that one need ask is whether the expense of development is consistent with the probability of finding ore.

Beyond the use of theories in their present status there is the hope that as the science grows we may gain a better insight into the laws of ore deposition and may progress toward general theories that are more strictly quantitative. Indeed we shall have to do this if we expect to better the technique of ore search.[6] For it is embarassing to admit that we cannot yet hunt with confidence in regions that are not already known to be mineralized. Even in mineralized regions we usually cannot search scientifically unless enough ore has already been found to serve as an index to local habits. Sooner or later we shall have to remedy this situation. In many parts of the world the time has already arrived when the prospector finds fewer and fewer signs of ore at the surface. We must prepare to search for new districts in regions where no outcrop discloses the existence of ore.

The potential number of such districts is great. A large proportion of the earth's surface is blanketed by young sedimentary formations and by recent lava flows. How many Guanajuatos lie concealed beneath the rhyolitic capping of the Sierra Madre of Mexico? How many Kirkland Lake Districts are under the drift-cover of the Canadian Shield? How many Wilunas are still hidden by the alluvium of the desert of Western Australia? How many ore deposits lurk underneath the basalt-covered plateaus of the Columbia River region? If erosion at Goldfield, Nevada, had stopped 100 feet higher, probably no ore would have been exposed.[7] How many Goldfields are still awaiting discovery? Yet the search for such deposits by present methods is like looking for the proverbial needle in the haystack. We need sharper and more precise tools, not only improved geophysical techniques and cheaper and longer-range drilling but more quantitative and better-calibrated theory. If we are looking for ore deposits of magmatic affiliation, it is not suffi-

---

[6] Cf. Locke, Augustus, Present tendencies in exploration for new mines: Tr. A.I.M.E., No. 1260-M, August, pp. 9 ff., 1932.

[7] Schmitt, Harrison, Outcrops of ore shoots: Economic Geology, vol. 34, p. 663, 1939.

cient to know that such ores are likely to be associated with igneous rocks; we must know with what kind of igneous rocks and how far from an intrusive of given size, shape, and depth. We should know what structural conditions are the ones to look for, and we should have better methods of projecting and following structure beneath a concealing cover.

In the direction of regional exploration, the petroleum industry has made spectacular progress.[8] True, the structures are simpler and the targets are larger; on a map of scale convenient to show an oil-pool, the space occupied by a lucrative orebody would be a mere dot. But an additional reason for the success of geology in petroleum exploration is the substantial reward for discovery which has served as an incentive to taking long risks, sharpening exploratory tools, and conducting expensive researches and experiments.

Although mining geology has not felt the full impact of this incentive, it is beginning to make long-range projections of structure and to undertake wild-cat development on the basis of structural theory. The recently discovered westward extension of the Rand is the direct result of structural projections aided by geophysical (mainly magnetic) methods. The rapid development of the great copper-bearing region of Northern Rhodesia was accomplished by tracing the orebearing horizons by areal and structural geology. Nevertheless, it is no disparagement of the courage and genius behind these developments to note that both are in regions of relatively simple structure in which the stratigraphic locus of the ore was known through existence of previously discovered deposits.

Better practice must grow along with better theories, which in turn must evolve through an alternation of imaginative proposals and rigid tests. Meanwhile, in striving to improve our theories we must recognize their weaknesses and limitations.

[8] DeGolyer, E., *The Development of the Art of Prospecting, with Special Reference to the American Petroleum Industry*, Brackett Lecture, Princeton University Press, 1940. An excellent and interesting review of the development of methods of oil-search.

$\mathcal{8}$

GUIDES TO ORE—TARGETS AND LOCI

*For this reason men penetrate with eyes of appraisal and judgment within
the mountains and see almost exactly the places where there is ore and the
quantity of it. They direct the excavation toward these, for otherwise
they would go by chance. . . .*

—VANNOCCIO BIRINGUCCIO, 1540 [1]

IT GOES without saying that you can find ore most simply and cheaply
if you know where to look for it. Therefore, one of the mining geologist's first aims in any district is to discern guides to ore—that is, structural or other features and conditions which serve as clues to the location
of orebodies. The most definite and practical types of guides are those
which are capable of representation on maps, sections, or models. These
are of two general types which we may term ringed targets and intersecting loci.

Ringed Targets

If we may compare the search for ore to the pastime of shooting at a
target, we find the geological marksman performing under a peculiar
handicap. His bull's-eye, the orebody, is concealed and its position is
betrayed only by the rings that surround it. The handicap is all the
more severe because the rings are not truly circular but are likely to
be elliptical or irregular. Worse still, instead of being concentric they
are usually so lopsided that they deserve the name of rings only by
courtesy. Instead of a series of rings there may be only one. But far
from complaining of deficiency in the shape or number of rings, the
geologist may consider himself fortunate if he can discern rings at all.

[1] Biringuccio, Vannoccio, *The Pirotechnia*, Venice, 1540. Translation by Smith, C. S., and
Gnudi, M. T., New York: A.I.M.E., p. 14, 1942.

The rings may express themselves geologically in a variety of ways. Perhaps the simplest and commonest is a halo of altered rock around the orebody, but there are other types: for example, the limits of a particular mineral or group of minerals in a vein, the ratio of metals within the vein-matter, the thickness of the vein, or the intensity of fracturing.

Rings on a district scale may delimit all of the orebearing ground. Blanchard [2] says that at Pilares the belt within 75 feet of the outer edges of a fractured oval 1600 × 2000 feet contains 75% of the mine's

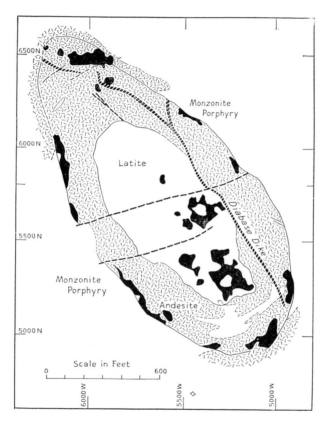

Fig. 55.—Relation of ore to pipe-like "oval" of fracturing. Ore shown in black. Pilares Mine, Sonora, Mexico. (*After* Leland, U.S. Bureau of Mines)

production and that at Christmas (Arizona) and San Pedro (New Mexico), prospecting the "marble line" (the boundary between the garnet zone and the marmorized limestone lying beyond it) would have found most of the commercial ore produced at the mines to date.

[2] Blanchard, Roland, Use of ore guides: *E. & M. J.*, vol. 131, p. 173, 1931.

To be useful a ring must be neither too large nor too small in comparison to the size of the bull's-eye. It is evident that if an orebody is 100 feet in diameter, an irregular target ring two miles across would not be of great help. On the other hand, a ring only ten feet larger than the orebody would be at least as hard to find as the orebody itself.

Now an ordinary rifle target is a two-dimensional surface and so, in effect, is an oreshoot in a vein. So also is a plan of a pipe of ore viewed from above. But some orebodies are like big lumps or fat lenses within a mass of rock. If they have rings, the rings are three dimensional affairs like the shells of an onion.

Target rings which the geologist discovers will not be obvious, otherwise they will already have been recognized by the miners in the district. In order to recognize them it may be necessary to do a great deal of detailed observing and plotting. Since it is often impossible to tell in advance what the rings will consist of, the search may require repeated trial and error. It may be necessary to collect hundreds of rock specimens and examine them microscopically in order to recognize variations in rock alteration or mineralization. Special chemical analyses or assays may be required to bring out the distribution of metals or other elements. Yet to be of the most practical use, the criteria derived by laboratory methods must be reduced to features that can be recognized by the unaided eye or distinguished in routine assays.

Intersecting Loci

If you were looking for the Hotel Waldorf-Astoria and knew only that it was somewhere in New York, you would have a long search through the city before you found it. At least your search would be confined to two dimensions because the Waldorf, like most hotels, is built on the earth's surface and not underground or suspended in the sky. But if you knew furthermore that it was on Park Avenue your search would be still further simplified, and if you knew that it was on Park Avenue at 50th Street, you would have no trouble in going directly to it.

Similarly, if you were looking for an orebody which might, so far as you knew, be anywhere within a whole district you would have to cut up the ground with an entire grid of exploratory workings on level after level if you wished to be sure to find it. But if you know that it is likely to be at some definite depth (say within a horizontal stratum), you will have only two dimensions to explore. If the orebody is localized within the stratum by a line (say the trace of a vertical vein) you need explore only one dimension and if the orebody is localized within

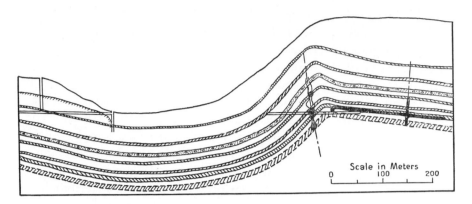

Fig. 56—Intersecting loci. Ore (shown in black) is in dolomitic limestone beds where crossed by steep fractures. Buena Vista Area, Minas Viejas, N.L., Mexico. (*After* Hayward and Triplett, *Trans. A.I.M.E.*)

the stratum by two intersecting lines you will know exactly where to look for it.   This is the principle of intersecting loci.   One ore locus is helpful, two loci that intersect are better, and three intersecting loci present ideal conditions.

Loci are not always simple planes.   In the Homestake Mine, one locus consists of a sedimentary formation which is very tightly and complexly folded, yet orebodies consistently occur within it and not elsewhere. The second locus in the control is structural—orebodies within the Homestake Formation are found on the noses of plunging anticlines. These controls were not known from the start, however.   It was only after many years of mining operations and more recent years of highly detailed geological study that the "intersecting loci" were clearly recognized and utilized.

A striking example of the successful use of intersecting loci is the discovery of an orebody in the Tintic District, Utah, as described by Billingsley.[3]   The factors that are favorable to ore occurrence in the district were known from many years of detailed underground study, and it was found by surface mapping and by drilling that on a property known as the North Lilly, half a mile from the highly productive Tintic Standard, there was an intersection of three favorable loci: a fault fissure, a "pebble dike," and the favorable bed of Ophir limestone.   In addition, the rhyolite which covered and concealed the limestone, was altered in the same manner as in the Tintic Standard.   Although no ore had been found by the drilling, the decision was made to test the

[3] Billingsley, Paul, North Lily development in East Tintic: *Mining and Metallurgy*, vol. 8, pp. 182–183, 1927.

favorable intersection underground by a crosscut 2400 feet long on the 700 level. As a result the ore bed was found to be completely mineralized by high-grade silver-lead ore.

In order to be of the most use, loci must be features which are recognizable in the field and be capable of projection into unexplored ground. In Park City, Utah, the principal orebodies are found where the limestone underlying the Weber Quartzite is intersected by fissures. The position of the Weber Quartzite in any part of the field is well known from mapping of the district and from knowledge of the stratigraphic section. When a fissure is recognized, either on the surface or underground, it is merely a matter of descriptive geometry to determine the place where the fissure and the favorable formation will intersect. Beyond this, other considerations may determine the relative favorability of different intersections.

Evidence from Outlying Areas

Whether guides to ore, should they exist within a district, will have the form of target rings, intersecting loci, or combinations of the two will rarely be known in advance but can be determined only by careful studies of known ore occurrences and their geological associations. Such studies may extend far afield. Ore controls are usually more readily recognizable on the margins of a mining district than in the center, for where mineralization is so intense that even "unfavorable" rocks and structure contain ore it may be difficult to recognize one rock as more favorable than another. But in the outskirts, where ore forms only under conducive conditions, the distinctions are strongly emphasized. Add to this that the rocks are more easily recognized where the alteration is less intense, and it is evident that the outer edges of a district repay study out of proportion to their economic importance.

REGIONAL GUIDES

Some guides to ore are broad and general in their nature. Most guides of this sort, while helpful in selecting regions in which to explore for ore deposits of some particular sort, are not capable of sufficiently sharp focusing for direct use in development within a given district. The more important of these guides may be listed:

1. Igneous rocks
   a. Batholiths and other major bodies with which ore is known to be associated.
   Note: Most of the orebodies are in the margins of the batholithic areas,

both inside and outside the igneous rock.[4] In particular, ore in certain regions is associated with truncated stocks.[5]

Examples:

The Coast Range Batholith of British Columbia.[6]

The Sierra Nevada Batholith of California.

The Boulder Batholith of Montana.[7]

The Nipissing Diabase sill in the Cobalt region.

b. Volcanic rocks of specific types and ages (whether because they are evidence of igneous activity at certain favored times or because they were present at certain periods of mineralization and served as suitable hosts).

Examples:

The Keewatin Greenstones of the Canadian Shield.

The Kalgoorlie Series (greenstones) of Western Australia.

Tertiary andesites in the Mexican Sierra.

c. Igneous rocks of those petrologic types with which certain ores are characteristically associated.[8] (Ores are not necessarily within the intrusive bodies.)

Examples:

Acid intrusives: tin, tungsten and molybdenum ores.

Basic intrusives (especially norites): nickel.

Ultrabasic intrusives: chromium, nickel and platinum.

2. Age-relations with respect to metallogenetic epochs.[9, 10]

Examples:

Laramide (late Cretaceous and early Tertiary) in Western U. S.

Hercynian [11] (between Carboniferous and Triassic) in Europe (the ores of Freiberg, Cornwall, Saxony, etc.).

Killarnean Revolution in the Canadian Shield: nickel-copper at Sudbury, cobalt-silver at Cobalt; copper in Northern Michigan.

3. Major zones of faulting with which ore is known to be associated. (Orebodies are mostly adjacent to the fault zones rather than within them.)

Examples:

The Mother Lode of California (120 miles long).

The Kirkland Lake—Malartic "break" (156 miles long).

[4] Emmons, W. H., Relations of metalliferous lode systems to igneous intrusives: *A.I.M.E. Tech. Pub.* 1571–I, pp. 1–42, 1926; *Tr. A.I.M.E.*, vol. 74, pp. 29–70, 1926.

[5] Butler, B. S., Relations of ore deposits to different types of intrusive bodies in Utah: *Econ. Geol.*, vol. 10, p. 101, 1915.

[6] Wilson, P. D., British Columbia batholith and related ore deposits, *Tr. A.I.M.E.*, vol. 68, p. 536, 1923.

[7] Billingsley, P., and Grimes, J. A., The ore deposits of the Boulder batholith, *Tr. A.I.M.E.*, vol. 58, pp. 284–368, 1918.

[8] Buddington, A. F., Correlation of kinds of igneous rocks with kinds of mineralization, *Ore Deposits of the Western States*, A.I.M.E. (Lindgren Volume), pp. 350–385, 1933.

[9] Lindgren, Waldemar, *Mineral Deposits* (Chapter 33, Metallogenetic Epochs, pp. 878–894). New York: McGraw-Hill, 1933.

[10] Emmons, W. H., *Principles of Economic Geology*, table, p. 200. New York: McGraw-Hill, 1940.

[11] DeLaunée, L., *Gîtes Minéraux et Métallifères*, p. 246. Paris: Ch. Beranger, 1913.

The Pinchi Fault Zone in British Columbia,[12] (150 miles long). Since discovery in 1937, a score of mercury deposits have been found by systematic prospecting along the zone and have produced 4,000,000 lb. of mercury between 1940 and 1944.

4. Sedimentary rocks of specific ages.

Examples:

General occurrence of iron formations in the Huronian rocks of the Lake Superior region.

Specific iron formations at definite horizons:

Biwabic Iron Formation on the Mesabi Range.

Ironwood Iron Formation on the Gogebic Range.

Vulcan Iron Formation on the Menominee Range.

Clinton iron ores at a definite horizon from New York to Alabama.

Minette Ores in the Jurassic of France and Luxemburg.

Applications:

Areas occupied at the surface by rocks older than the ore-bearing formations are hopeless for ore of the particular type sought.

Areas underlain by rocks younger than orebearing formations are possible provided the ore horizon is above minable depth.

5. Climatic and topographic conditions (past and present) conducive to formation of certain types of deposits.

a. Tropical climates, favoring lateritic weathering especially in plateau regions.

Examples:

British and Dutch Guiana: bauxite.

Cuba: lateritic iron ores; manganese ores.

India: manganese ores.

b. Arid and semi-arid climates and deep water level, favoring formation and preservation of zones of supergene enrichment.

Examples:

Southwestern United States: "porphyry coppers."

Northern Chile: "porphyry copper" deposits.

c. Long period of deep weathering followed by vigorous erosion conducive to accumulation of placer gold.

Examples:

West slope of the Sierra Nevada, California.[13]

Central and Southern Victoria, Australia.

CLASSIFICATION OF GUIDES

Guides, though of great variety, have in common the fact that they are associated with ore in one way or another. Genetically they may be grouped in three categories:

1. Features that were in existence before the ore was deposited and served to localize it. Examples: fractures, beds subject to replacement, breccia pipes.

2. Features which came into existence with the ore. Examples: alteration

---

[12] Armstrong, J. E., and Thurber, J. B., Prospecting possibilities in part of the Omineca Mining Division, B. C.: *Can. Mining Journal*, pp. 217–222, April, 1945.

[13] Lindgren, W., Tertiary gravels of the Sierra Nevada: *U.S.G.S., Prof. Paper* 73, 1911.

haloes, barren parts of veins, areas of subsidence due to mineralization stoping. 3. Features resulting from the presence of ore or from presence of mineralization. Examples: gossans, iron or manganese stain below an oxidized orebody, oxidation subsidence, ancient workings.

A classification on this basis, although philosophically satisfying, is not so well suited to practical discussion as one based on the geological nature of the guiding features. Accordingly the discussion in succeeding chapters will follow the headings:

Physiographic Guides

Mineralogical Guides (alteration, mineralization, oxidation products)

Stratigraphic and Lithologic Guides

Structural Guides (fracture patterns, contacts, folds).

Before proceeding to these topics, however, it may be well to consider certain types of guides which do not fit neatly into any of the major geological pigeonholes.

GEOCHEMICAL GUIDES

Proximity to an orebody is indicated in some instances by the presence of metallic ions in rocks, soil, or groundwater. Even though the element in question may be present in traces so small as to be detectable only by delicate chemical tests, a map showing its distribution may disclose target rings surrounding an orebody.

The small amounts of metal may represent primary minerals disseminated in the rocks—leakages or wanderings which occurred during the original mineralization—or they may result from migration of metal in solution during oxidation of the ore; their presence may be disclosed by direct analysis or by the nature or mineral content of plants growing in the soil. This method of ore search has been called geochemical prospecting, a designation which is unfortunate because it threatens to narrow and particularize the wide field of geochemistry. I have used "geochemical" in the present sense only for want of a better word.

Groundwater as a Guide

Groundwater in a mineralized region, especially where sulphides are undergoing oxidation, contains metals and sulphates in amounts ranging from traces to so much that the water is undrinkable. Thus copper-bearing springs were among the signs which led to the early discoveries of copper in Northern Rhodesia. In studying the metal content of groundwater Th. Vogt[14] determined sulphates and copper in springs

[14] Vogt, Th. (Series of articles with abstracts in English). *Konisl. Norske Vidensk. Selskabs. Forhandlinger,* 1939–1944. Rankama, Kalervo, Some recent trends in prospecting: *Mining and Metallurgy.* vol. 28, pp. 282–284, June, 1947.

and creeks issuing from the neighborhood of copper-bearing sulphide deposits in the Roros district, Norway.   Limonite deposited as bog ore and as brown coatings on pebbles and on water plants indicates that the water probably came from a source in which ferrous sulphate was available.   If other metals are present in the water they are likely to be adsorbed by the limonite or by the manganese dioxide associated with it and show up as traces on analysis.   Such metals may include Cu, Zn, Pb, Ni, Co, Mo, W, Sb, and Bi.   In particular, cobalt, if available, is likely to precipitate along with manganese.   Thus in the Skoger area, where cobalt minerals are known to occur, Vogt found that the manganiferous bog ore contained significant amounts of cobalt.

The U. S. Geological Survey is working on a program of research including the sampling of natural groundwaters in the vicinity of copper lead or zinc mineralization, meanwhile developing simple methods of analysis to measure the vanishingly small quantities of metallic elements.[15]

Geobotanical and Biochemical Guides

The possibility of using vegetation as a guide to ore depends first (and probably least in importance), on the suggestion that metals and other elements may modify the appearance of foliage; second, on the fact that certain elements play a role in determining what species of plants are able or unable to grow in a given place; and third, on the well-established observation that certain plants can take up and concentrate elements selectively from soil solutions.

Agricola [16] said nearly 400 years ago: "There are trees whose foliage in springtime has a bluish or leaden tint, the upper branches especially being tinged with black or other unnatural color," and Barba [17] wrote in 1729: "Trees, bush and plants are frequently signs of presence of a vein.   In such cases they appear as if planted in a line giving signs of the Vein running beneath them.   They do not grow so well nor is their color so bright as that of other plants when they grow over metallic Veins, for the exhalations of the Veins diminish their vitality and they become thin."   Since Barba's time, no one has done much either to substantiate or discredit this generalization.

There is evidence, however, that some species of plants are poisoned

[15] Fleischer, Michael F., Mimeographed memorandum, U.S.G.S., 1946.

[16] *Agricola de re Metallica*, 1555, Hoover translation.   London: The Mining Magazine, 1912.

[17] Reprinted by permission from *El Arte de los Metales* by Barba, Alvaro Alonzo (1729), translated by Douglass, R. E. and Mathewson, E. P., and published by John Wiley & Sons Co., 1923, p. 60.

by certain elements in the soil, while others, if they do not actually thrive on the same substances, are at least able to tolerate them and thus grow more abundantly where competition is lacking. According to Rankama [18] *Polycarpaea spirostylis* in Australia indicates copper deposits and *amorpha canescens* in Missouri grows near galena deposits. Studies by Th. Vogt in Norway indicate that *Viscaria alpina* and *Melandrium dioecum* will endure soils high in copper. Dorn [19] states that *viola caliminaria*, the "zinc pansy," grows only on soils overlying deposits of zinc. It flourishes on waste dumps of zinc mines in Central Europe and its ashes sometimes contain several percent of ZnO. Most of the investigation of this problem has been carried out in Europe, and there is need for more study before the method can be used with confidence on other continents. Investigation should be critical and statistical, and should include a plant census not only near orebearing ground but on ground known or firmly believed *not* to be orebearing.

Although "picking flowers" might seem an extraordinary method of ore hunting, it has been shown that collecting and analyzing selected parts from growing plants discloses measurable amounts of chemical elements whose quantity in the soil is too small for direct detection. The greatest accumulations are in the parts of the plants where evaporation is strongest, especially the leaves and young shoots. Since different species have varying selectivity for elements, it has been recommended that sampling for comparative purposes in any one district be limited to a single species, and since the content of foliage changes with the seasons, all samples should be collected at the same time of the year. The foliage constituting each sample is incinerated and the ashes are analyzed, usually by spectographic methods.[20] By this means, Rankama [21] found that ashes of beech leaves near a nickel deposit in Finland contained from 0.006% to 0.2% of Ni, and the values when plotted showed a striking arrangement centering on the nickel orebody.

[18] Rankama, Kalervo, Some recent trends in prospecting: *Mining and Metallurgy*, vol. 28, pp. 282–284, June, 1947.

[19] Dorn, Paul, Pflantzen als Anzeichen für Erzlagerstätten, *Der Biologe (Deut. Biol.—Verb., Msch.)*, vol. 6, No. 1, pp. 11–13, January, 1937, through *Annotated Bibliography of Economic Geology*, vol. 15, No. 1, title 24, 1942.

See also two interesting papers which appeared after the present manuscript was completed: Warren, H. V., and Howatson, C. H., Biogeochemical prospecting for copper and zinc: *Bull. G.S.A.*, vol. 58, pp. 803–820. Sept., 1947. (Contains a summary of the literature and results of new sampling) and Robinson, W. O., Lakin, H. W., and Reichen, Laura E., The zinc content of plants of the Friedensville zinc slime ponds in relation to biochemical prospecting: *Econ. Geol.*, vol. 42, pp. 572–582, 1947.

[20] Scribner, Bourdon F., Detection of rare elements in plants: *Proc. Sixth Summer Conf. Spectroscopy*, p. 10, New York, 1939.

[21] Rankama, Kalervo, On the use of trace elements in some problems of practical geology: *Comptes Rendus de la Société Geologique de Finlande*, No. 14, Helsinki, 1940.

Certain elements accumulate in the topmost layers of forest soils. Goldschmidt's [22] work showed that when leaves accumulate on the ground and decay, the more soluble elements (alkalis, alkaline earths, iron and manganese) are leached out leaving the products of leaf-decay correspondingly enriched in the less soluble elements: Ag, Au, Be, Zn, Cd, Sc, Tl, Ge, Sn, Pb, As, Mn, Co and Ni. Rankama states that new tin and tungsten deposits were discovered by using this method in Cornwall, Devonshire, and Wales, and that it was found useful in locating chromite deposits in Greece. For obvious reasons the testing of soil and plants is best suited to regions that have not been glaciated, yet encouraging results have been obtained in glaciated regions, provided the drift is thin enough to allow the roots of trees to reach down nearly to the bedrock surface. This fact is shown by investigations in Scandinavia. Likewise Hans Lundberg reports favorable results in Canada and Newfoundland on glacial drift as thick as 30 to 40 feet.

These methods require and deserve much further investigation. But to emphasize the need for circumspection in interpreting the results it may not be amiss to recall a program in Michigan where a very painstaking sampling of vegetation pointed to a distinct grouping of copper values around a certain center. The center, however, was not an orebody but a smelting plant!

SELECTED REFERENCES

Bateman, Alan M., *Economic Mineral Deposits*, Chapter 6, pp. 304–327, Controls of mineral localization. New York: John Wiley and Sons, Incorporated, 1942.

Blanchard, Roland, Use of ore guides, *Engineering and Mining Journal*, vol. 131, pp. 173–175, 1931.

Locke, Augustus, The profession of orehunting, *Economic Geology*, vol. 16, pp. 243–278, 1921.

Locke, Augustus, and Billingsley, Paul, Trend of orehunting in the United States, *Engineering and Mining Journal*, vol. 130, pp. 565–566, 609–612, 1930.

McLaughlin, Donald H., and Sales, Reno H., Utilization of geology by mining companies, in *Ore Deposits of the Western States* (Lindgren Volume), A.I.M.E., pp. 683–695, 1933.

Rankama, Kalervo, Some recent trends in prospecting, *Mining and Metallurgy*, vol. 28, pp. 282–284, June, 1947.

[22] Goldschmidt, V. M., Drei Vorträge über Geochemie: *Geol. For.*, Stockholm Förh. Bd. 56, p. 385, 1934.

9

PHYSIOGRAPHIC GUIDES

According to the famous geologist Heim, the people in certain parts of Switzerland say of a weak-minded and morally unreliable person that he is as undependable as a cliff. And this is said by people who spend their lives among rocky mountains and observe the disintegration with their own eyes.

—B. B. POLYNOV [1]

PHYSIOGRAPHIC features may serve either as direct or as indirect evidence of the presence of ore. Direct indications, such as the surface expression of an orebody, are, of course the most immediately useful. But indirect evidence may also be of value. Such features as fault scarps, hogbacks, and cuestas serve as clues to the geologic structure. Evidence bearing on the physiographic history of the region may indicate the conditions under which ore was accumulated or enriched and so point to the places in which it may now exist. These historical considerations find their widest use in guiding the selection of broad regions for exploration, but even in problems of ore-search within a restricted district they contribute to the background for constructive geological thinking.

TOPOGRAPHIC EXPRESSIONS OF OREBODIES

Eminences and Depressions

The outcrop of the Broken Hill lode is a ridge visible for miles across the plains and so conspicuous that it perforce attracted the attention of Captain Charles Sturt, the first white man to penetrate this part of

[1] Polynov, B. B., *The Cycle of Weathering*, translation by Alexander Muir. London: Thomas Murby & Co., 1937, p. 11.

Australia. The outcrop consisted of iron-rich gossan, reinforced by walls of hard metamorphic schist. Beneath it were some of the largest lead-zinc orebodies in the world. Ore-outcrops, almost as conspicuous, are to be seen in many other mining regions. At Parral, Chihuahua, the Cerro Negro towers above the town as a precipitous knob. At Santa Barbara, not many miles away, the massive quartz veins make ridges while the unsilicified rock between them weathers into arroyos.[2] In the Oatman district, Arizona,[3] and on the California Mother Lode, as well as in many other districts, quartz veins stand out in relief.

But not all outcrops are marked by eminences. In contrast to the quartz veins at Oatman, calcite veins in the same district have no conspicuous outcrops and, where they go over ridges, form well-defined depressions.[4] At Beaverdell, British Columbia, the veins have a calcite gangue and carry pyrite with other sulphides. Their outcrops are very inconspicuous and trenches show only a streak of limonitic clay where the vein should be. Not until depths of ten feet or more does any semblance of a well-formed vein appear. Similarly, some of the best veins in the Coeur d'Alene district, where the gangue is siderite, have no visible outcrops.

As these examples suggest, veins lacking much quartz and, in particular, veins with carbonate gangue, or orebodies which consist of sulphide impregnations without much silica or silicates, do not give rise to conspicuous outcrops (unless conditions of oxidation have been favorable to the development of jasperoid gossans). Depressions formed by the weathering of such veins are usually not conspicuous because soil and debris fill them up. Special kinds of debris, however, may serve as guides. In the Little Florida Mountains, near Deming, New Mexico,[5] a prospector noticed that minor fractures in the bedrock disappeared under a strip of talus. Finding manganese-bearing float nearby, he became inquisitive and sank a prospect hole through the talus. At a depth of ten feet he found solid manganese ore. Here between resistant walls of volcanic agglomerate, the soft, steeply dipping fault-veins had weathered out to form resting places for talus and mantle rock. Other depressed outcrops, especially in arid regions, are capped with *caliche* (surface crust of fine-grained calcium carbonate). As described by Schmitt,[6] the Cordero vein in the San Juan district, Chihuahua, is

[2] Schmitt, Harrison, Outcrops of ore shoots: *Econ. Geol.*, vol. 34, 1939, p. 666.

[3] Lausen, Carl, Geology and ore deposits of the Oatman and Katherine Districts: *Arizona Bureau Mines Bull. 131*, p. 85. Undated, c. 1931.

[4] Lausen, Carl, *op. cit.*, p. 87.

[5] Schmitt, Harrison, *op. cit.*, p. 664.

[6] Schmitt, Harrison, *op. cit.*, p. 667.

capped by a ribbon-like scab of caliche up to five feet thick. The Manto oreshoot at Erupcion-Ahumada was discovered by breaking through a surface scab of similar caliche.

Deceptive Outcrops

In veins which are more resistant than the enclosing rocks, one might expect that the broadest parts would form the most prominent outcrops, but this does not always happen. The broad parts may consist of networks of stringers rather than solid quartz and so lack strength and chemical stability. Nor are the richest parts likely to be the most prominent; they often consist of sheared and shattered vein matter which is easily eroded while the barren, massive quartz is resistant. Then too, the sulphides characteristic of the richer portions promote decomposition of any rock-minerals other than quartz. So covered ground along the strike of a prominent outcrop is often worth trenching even though the material that crops out is not rich.

The width of projecting vein matter at the surface may give an erroneous impression of the width of the underlying orebody; masses of quartz and other resistant material are likely to accumulate on the erosion surface and creep downhill, thus occupying a larger area at the surface than does the parent orebody at depth. Also, sulphate solutions from pyritic ore may soak into the surrounding rocks, converting them into limonite or jasperoid and giving rise to a wide body of gossan.[7] Veins with carbonate gangue, on the other hand, may give deceptively narrow outcrops like those already described.

Oxidational Subsidence

Depressions may result not only from erosion of soft material but from subsidence due to removal of support through shrinkage of orebodies during oxidation. This process has received careful attention at Bisbee,[8] where the effects are somewhat similar to those of mine subsidence.[9] The origin of the surface features at Bisbee is made clear by a description of the conditions that were observed in the mine workings beneath them. Crosscuts above the orebodies found a jumble of rock fragments resembling old fill, extending as much as 100 feet above an orebody and terminating upward in an irregular dome-like roof. Above

---

[7] Locke, Augustus, *Leached Outcrops as Guides to Copper Ore*, p. 139. Baltimore: Williams and Wilkins Company, 1926.

[8] Ransome, F. L., Geology and ore deposits of the Bisbee Quadrangle, Arizona, *U.S.G.S. Prof. Paper 21*, 1904, p. 159.

[9] Wisser, Edward, Oxidation subsidence at Bisbee, Ariz.: *Econ. Geol.*, vol. 22, pp. 761–790, 1927.

the roof, marginal cracks reach to the surface and outline an irregular cracked body of ground.   In limestone "they are cemented with calcite and serve to indicate at the surface the position of oxidized ore below, even where it lies at a depth as great as 700 feet." [10]

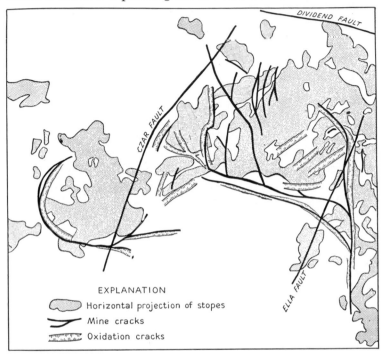

Fig. 57—Cracks due to pre-mine oxidation and cracks due to mine subsidence. Bisbee, Arizona. (*After* Wisser, *Economic Geology*)

"Indeed had this effect been recognized early in the Bisbee history and had the surface cracks and small surface subsidences been carefully mapped, an area which later yielded three thousand million pounds of copper could have been marked out, even to include ore 1000 feet below the surface." [11]

PHYSIOGRAPHIC ENVIRONMENT OF ORE DEPOSITS

Not only may topographic features result directly from the presence of veins or mineralized bodies, but in a broader way they may reflect general conditions favorable to the presence of ore.   These conditions

[10] Locke, Augustus, *Leached Outcrops as Guides to Copper Ore*, p. 78.   Baltimore: Williams and Wilkins Company, 1926.
[11] Locke, Augustus, and Billingsley, Paul, Trend of ore-hunting in the United States, *E. & M. J.* vol. 130, 1930, p. 609.

vary so widely, depending on the type of deposit and its associated rocks, and express themselves in such a variety of land-forms, depending on the climate and geomorphic history, that it is impossible to formulate any general proposition to the effect that hills, valleys, peneplanes, monadnocks, or any other geomorphic features are either favorable or unfavorable. But in a given region a study of the relations of specific deposits to their geomorphic setting can often lead to the recognition of useful guides.

Thus, in the Sierra Madre of Western Mexico, where the high plateaus are capped by young volcanic rocks (rhyolite and dacite), the silver ores are found chiefly if not solely in the canyons which cut through the siliceous lavas and expose the productive rocks beneath them.

In the arid basin-and-range country of the southwestern United States, pediments are specially favorable situations for vein deposits. A mountain pediment, as defined by Bryan [12] is a rock-floored plain "of combined erosion and transportation at the foot of a desert mountain range. . . . The normal pediment has a smoothly sloping surface more or less covered by alluvium and broken only by scattered hills which rise abruptly from its surface." Whereas the mountains represent in general the more massive and resistant rocks, the pediments develop on those parts of the rock-mass which faulting, fracturing, and chemical decay have rendered vulnerable to erosion. It is in just these places that hydrothermal ore deposits are to be expected, not only because zones of structural disturbance are hospitable, but because hydrothermal solutions soften the rocks and because pyrite, by furnishing sulphuric acid, promotes weathering. Thus in southern Yuma County, Arizona, Wilson [13] finds that "with few exceptions the commercially important veins . . . have been found on pediments rather than on mountain sides or high ridges." For similar reasons most of the gold placers throughout Arizona [14] are related to pediments; they occur in gulches and old channels which traverse or issue from pediments or as mantle on the pediment itself; it is on pediments that chemical decay has freed the gold whereas on steep mountain slopes, gold-bearing rock, if it occurs at all, is broken down into coarse fragments without releasing the particles of metal.

[12] Bryan, Kirk, The Papago country, Arizona: *U.S.G.S. Water Supply Paper 499*, p. 93, p. 94, 1925.

[13] Wilson, Eldred D., Geology and mineral resources of Southern Yuma County, Arizona: *Ariz. Bur. Mines, Geol. Ser. No. 7*, Bull. 134, 1933, p. 46.

[14] Wilson, Eldred D., in Arizona Gold Placers and Placering: *Arizona Bur. Mines, Tech. Series No. 35*, Bull. 135, 1933, p. 12.

Topography as a Guide to Iron Ore

Topographic expressions can be helpful in prospecting for almost any metal, but they are especially useful in the search for iron ore,[15] because iron deposits, to be of commercial value, have to be large; consequently, whatever topographic features they occasion are likely to be major ones. Iron ore in the Lake Superior region is so characteristically associated with hills and ridges that the various producing districts are known as "ranges." The relation of the ore to the hills is not the same in all of the districts, however. The hard and resistant ore of the Vermilion Range occurs on hills. The soft ores of the Mesabi Range occur on the middle slopes. The soft ores of the Gogebic, Marquette, and Menominee districts occur in low swampy ground adjacent to hills formed by the harder adjoining formations.

Comparable topographic expressions are found in other regions as well. In the eastern United States many of the magnetite orebodies, because of their resistance to erosion, are found on hilltops or hill slopes. In the state of Minas Geraes, Brazil, the iron formation generally outcrops in well-marked foothills along the main quartzite ridges, and, locally, where it is especially resistant, it forms the main ridges with the associated quartzite occupying the slopes.

The use of topography in locating iron orebodies, must, like most other geologic tools, be tempered with caution, for topography is dependent not only upon the resistance of a rock (both intrinsic and relative) but upon many other factors such as faulting, folding, location of stream divides and other features which are relics from the geologic past.

PHYSIOGRAPHIC RELATIONS OF PLACER DEPOSITS

Physiographic events play a critical role in the accumulation of placer deposits of gold and of other durable heavy minerals. The most favorable conditions are those in which the sequence of events has been conducive to (1) preparation, (2) concentration, and (3) preservation. The best preparation is a long period of deep weathering on a surface of mature or sub-mature topography. This releases the individual particles of metal or heavy mineral from their enclosing material and prepares a deep layer of residual soil for concentration by the action of sorting agents when later uplift, accompanied and followed by vigorous erosion, causes streams to cut channels into the old surface, transporting debris and depositing the heavy minerals in favored places.

---

[15] This section on topography in relation to iron ores was prepared for this book by Dr. Stanley A. Tyler.

Placers formed in this stage are valuable, but they may be short-lived because continued or accelerated erosion will destroy them if it goes on for a long period. Destruction is prevented, however, if the placers are covered by younger deposits, as by aggradation of the stream channels or by outpouring of lava which fills the valleys either partly or completely. If a second rejuvenation takes place and new streams exhume the old placers, re-sorting and reconcentrating them, the resulting deposits can be extremely rich.

Guides to Channels

The position of a buried channel may not be obvious, especially if new drainage has assumed a different pattern. In outlining the channel, both geology and geomorphology may be of assistance. In Calaveras County, California, the Eocene channels, cut in pre-Cretaceous granitic rocks and schists, were later filled with Miocene to Pliocene sediments and volcanics. Thus, mapping the contact between the pre-Cretaceous and the Tertiary formations serves to outline the old valleys and indicate their general form. To this end aerial photographs are most helpful.

When the position of the old valley is established, geophysical methods may be used to determine the depth to bedrock and indicate the probable position of the deepest parts of the channel.[16] A magnetic survey may outline the position of the magnetite-bearing "black sands" which usually accumulate along with the gold; this method is most effective where the cover is not too deep and the bedrock is siliceous. Where bedrock is mafic and has a higher magnetic intensity than the gravel, the position of magnetic "lows" indicates the position of the channel. Electrical methods sometimes follow the preliminary magnetic survey in order to confirm and supplement its results. Their effectiveness depends on the contrast in conductivity between the dense bedrock and the damp alluvial material.

Whether or not the aid of geophysics has been invoked, the shape of the valley is ascertained by drilling transverse rows of scout holes. Contouring the bedrock, using as guides the results of drill holes and the habitual shapes of valleys, may give a still sharper indication as to the parts of the channel which should be tested by holes more closely spaced.

Somewhat similar methods have been used in exploring the "deep leads" of Victoria.[17] These are placers deposited by Pliocene streams

---

[16] Jenkins, Olaf P., and Wright, W. Quinby, California's goldbearing Tertiary channels: E. & M. J., vol. 135, pp. 497–502, Nov., 1934.

[17] Hunter, Stanley, The deep leads of Victoria: Geol. Surv. Victoria, Memoir No. 7, pp. 4–9, 1909.

in valleys cut into Paleozoic sediments and preserved by basalt which filled some of the valleys completely and some only partially. As the basalt was more resistant to erosion than the Paleozoic slates that underlie and flank it, the old valleys are now marked by sinuous plateaus; the modern streams are typically in pairs, one on each side of the strip of basalt, though some streams cross and dissect the basalt. As the floors of the old valleys, except near their heads, are still below the level of the modern drainage system, the placers have been mined by underground methods to depths of as much as 400 feet beneath the present surface.

In prospecting the deep leads, a map showing the location of the basalt and of the adjoining slate establishes the position of the old valley. Further testing is by churn drill holes which, of necessity, are relatively deep and therefore cannot economically be numerous enough to allow close spacing. Their purpose is to determine the position of the channel and not to test the tenor of the gravel, although any free gold in the drill samples is, of course, an encouraging indication. The actual gold content is not known until the gravel has been opened by underground workings.

Location of Pay Streaks

In placer deposits the major ore-locus is the stream channel, but subsidiary loci determine the position of pay streaks within the channel. As gold tends to accumulate in places of slackened stream velocity, the portions of the profile in which the gradient flattens are more favorable than those where it is steep. However, the *present* gradient is not always indicative. The Tertiary channels of the Sierra Nevada have experienced tilting by movements connected with major block faulting so that some of the channels now "run up hill."

Places in which the stream emerged from rapids into quiet water are favorable because of reduced velocity and increased opportunity for deposition. A broader valley below a narrow gorge presents an opportunity for shifting of channels with consequent re-sorting of earlier gravels. The resulting multiplicity of channels affords more potential sites for pay streaks. The broader valley permits meandering with development of curving channels and oxbow loops, and it is well known that the inner sides of curves are especially favorable. Mouths of side streams are points of enrichment if the tributaries flowed over gold-bearing terrain.

The efficiency of bedrock in catching heavy particles is an important determining factor. Some of the richest California stream placers are on limestone whose pitted and pinnacled surface has provided ideal settling places. In contrast, diorite, which wears to a smooth streambed is inferior to either limestone or schist, although rich local accumulations have been found in potholes and among nests of boulders on diorite. Schists and other formations that erode into miniature ridges and grooves form natural riffles, but surprisingly, bedrock riffles parallel to the direction of stream-flow are more effective than riffles crossing it at a large angle; therefore, portions of channels roughly paralleling the strike of schistose rocks are favored.

In placer deposits of relatively low gold content, the nature of the bedrock may determine the feasibility of mining. Bucket-line or drag-line dredges, since they are unable to get all of the gold from hard, rough bedrock surfaces, succeed best where the underlying material is clay, tuff, or partly decomposed rock.

A productive placer may not consist of a single simple channel; in fact some of the richest placers have a complex history of sedimentation. Younger channels cross and cut through older ones, leaving them as bench-gravels at a higher elevation and reconcentrating the gold in the younger channel. Alternatively, younger channels may occur at higher elevations than older, thus representing accumulation after partial filling has taken place. Inter-volcanic channels in California have been productive, although they are usually leaner than bedrock channels.

In interpreting this history, the nature of the alluvial material may be of assistance. The size and shape of the gold particles, whether coarse or fine and whether rough or water-worn, is an index to the distance of travel; the shape, arrangement, and petrologic nature of the accompanying pebbles give a clue to the source and, in some cases, to the age of the gravel in respective channels.

Thus, reconstruction of the history of erosion and deposition, using principles of geomorphology and sedimentation gives an insight into the arrangement of channels and the probable position of pay streaks.

PHYSIOGRAPHY IN RELATION TO OXIDATION AND ENRICHMENT

Residual Ores

Since rock weathering is controlled partly by topography, those types of ore which owe their value to the removal of undesirable elements through processes of weathering occupy definite positions with respect to erosion surfaces, past or present. This is true of nickel silicate, bauxite, some manganese ores, and lateritic iron ores, all of which form best through weathering under tropical conditions. It is also true of gossans, such as those minable for their content in gold, silver, lead, or iron, although lateritic weathering or tropical climates are not essential in these cases.

The processes of weathering which produce ores of these types proceed slowly and reach completion to worth-while depths only where the water-table has been relatively deep and where time has been available for a long period of weathering. This, in general, calls for topographic surfaces in a state of maturity or old age. Raised peneplains and plateau surfaces which have not yet been too seriously dissected offer the appropriate combination of conditions.

Examples. The bauxite [18] deposits of the southern Appalachian states were formed during the Eocene when the climate was favorable to lateritic weathering as attested by remains of tropical plants in the Gulf Coast sediments of this age. At this time, the margins of the Appalachian Mountains, as well as valleys within the mountain uplift, had been reduced to a base level known as the Highland Rim peneplain. Where the floor of the peneplain was of limestone or dolomite, karst topography developed and bauxite accumulated in sinkholes; it was deposited also as beds among the sediments that were being laid down to seaward. With subsequent erosion the Highland Rim peneplain was dissected, leaving remnants now known as the Intermediate Ridges within the old Appalachian Valley. Most of the bauxite deposits are on the remnants of the peneplain or in the Eocene sediments at the base of the Wilcox formation on what is now the Coastal Plain.

Manganese ores in Maryland and Virginia are likewise related to an early Tertiary peneplain developed on relatively soft rocks below the summit-level of the Blue Ridge. According to Hewett [19] the deposits are replacements of residual clays in stream channels and in structural troughs and fault zones. They were formed through the agency of groundwater which leached sparsely distributed manganese from Cambrian limestones and shales and redeposited it at greater depth. This process operated most effectively after peneplanation had been perfected, for then physical erosion was no longer vigorous and chemical decay had ample time to function. Subsequent uplift of the peneplain stimulated groundwater circulation and thus favored continued leach-

---

[18] Adams, George I., Bauxite deposits of the Southern States: *Econ. Geol.*, vol. 22, pp. 615–620, 1927.

[19] Hewett, D. F., Some manganese mines in Virginia and Maryland: *U.S.G.S. Bull.* 640, pp. 43–46, 1917.

ing, but after the rejuvenated streams had dissected the tableland the enriched deposits were stranded in their elevated positions.   As a result, most of the deposits are now to be found either at the peneplain surface or not more than 50 feet below it.   But the correspondence is by no means perfect,[20] probably because the physiographic history was not ideally simple; there are a few exceptional deposits as much as 500 feet above or below the peneplain.   Hence this physiographic guide, while pointing to the most productive elevation, cannot safely be applied in a negative way to the extent of definitely condemning other parts of the region.

In the nickel silicate deposits of São Jose do Tocantíns, Brazil, Pecora [21] finds a very pronounced relationship of ore to topography. The nickel enrichment occurred in two stages: (1) deep weathering of peridotite to clay on an old erosion surface (the Goiáz Upland Surface), which is now preserved only on the crests of a series of long narrow ridges, (2) supergene enrichment of the deep clay layer and deposition of garnierite (nickel silicate) in joints and fractures in the peridotite to depths on the order of 20 meters below the present surface.   This latter phase took place during the latest erosion stage when the old surface was dissected by deep canyons; probably it is still going on. Consequently, the nickel deposits occur only at elevations just below the Goiáz Upland Surface, at 900 meters and above, particularly under sites which were occupied by shallow valleys in the old high surface. The canyons, with bottoms at 500 to 900 meters, expose unweathered or little-weathered peridotite without ore.

In addition to this topographic locus there is at Tocantíns a lithologic ore guide: hydrothermal alteration has converted the peridotite into serpentine along strip-like zones.   Here hydrothermal alteration has been detrimental to ore-formation because the clay overlying serpentinized rocks weathers ultimately to jasperoidal chalcedony and not to nickel ore.   The ore is thus restricted to material overlying strips of unserpentinized peridotite and these occupy only about one third of the area.   By outlining areas in which unserpentinized peridotite occurs at the favorable topographic horizon, Pecora was able to delimit the ground in which ore may occur and thus estimate the potentialities of the deposits.

The residual iron ore deposits of Mayarí, Cuba, also occur on an

[20] Hewett, D. F., Stose, G. W., Katz, F. J., and Miser, H. D., Possibilities for manganese ore on certain undeveloped tracts in the Shenandoah Valley, Va.: U.S.G.S. Bull. 660-J, pp. 280, 281, 1918.

[21] Pecora, William T., Nickel silicate and associated nickel-cobalt-manganese-oxide deposits near São Jose do Tocantins, Goiáz, Brazil: U.S.G.S. Bull. 935-E, 1944.

uplifted peneplain.   The plateau has an elevation of 1700 to 2000 feet;[22] peaks which rise above it to altitudes of 2600 to 3000 feet are without ore and little or no ore occurs on the steep slopes where the plateau falls off to the sea nor in the sides of ravines which dissect the old surface.[23] The ore, which was formed by lateritic weathering of the serpentine bedrock, varies in thickness from a few inches to 80 feet and occurs within an area fifteen miles long and up to 5 miles wide.

Supergene Sulphide Zones

Favorable and Unfavorable Physiographic Conditions.   Physiographic conditions favorable to supergene sulphide enrichment of copper and silver ores are rather similar to those which produce the residual deposits just described.   Concentration of sufficient metal to form a thick and high-grade zone of enrichment requires the extraction of metal from a correspondingly thick overlying zone of leaching.   If enrichment were carried to completion under static conditions, this would mean an extremely deep water-table, but more probably the zone of leaching and the zone of enrichment below it descend progressively as erosion lowers the surface, thus keeping pace with enrichment without overtaking it. Such a balance between erosion and enrichment is typical of a physiographic surface in the state of post-maturity or of old age.   With greater relief, as in youthful or merely mature topography, ground-water circulates more actively and the oxidized zone descends more rapidly, but the process proceeds too fast for complete leaching of the copper.   Thus, to borrow a phrase from the technology of ore-treatment, extraction is poor.

An example of conditions favorable to enrichment is to be seen in the Peruvian Andes, where long continued erosion during the early Tertiary produced the Puna[24] surface of post-mature topography, now at an elevation of 13,000 to 15,000 feet between the Eastern and Western Cordilleras.   It was ideal for deep oxidation and secondary enrichment as at Cerro de Pasco and elsewhere.   In contrast, erosion on the steep western slopes of the Andes has been so rapid that supergene zones, if they ever had a chance to form, have been removed.   In Casapalca and many other districts on the western drainage area, primary sulphides

[22] Little, James E., The Mayari iron-mines, Oriente Province, Island of Cuba, as developed by the Spanish-American Iron Company, *Tr. A.I.M.E.*, vol. 42, p. 155, 1911.

[23] Leith, C. K., and Mead, W. J., Origin of the iron ores of central and northeastern Cuba, *Tr. A.I.M.E.*, vol. 42, p. 91, 1911.

[24] McLaughlin, D. H., Geology and physiography of the Peruvian Cordillera, Departments of Junin and Lima: *Bull. G.S.A.*, vol. 35, pp. 591–632, 1924.

occur a very few feet below the outcrops and supergene enrichment is negligible.

Glacial erosion is even more effective in outstripping oxidation and enrichment. Glaciated surfaces, especially where protected by impervious clay in regions of low relief, have undergone remarkably little oxidation since the Pleistocene, as was well shown at Noranda, Quebec, when one of the orebodies, which was first discovered underground, had just been stripped of its surface cover of glacial clay. On the bedrock there was a crust of iron oxide, but as this "oxidized zone" was less than a quarter of an inch thick, a blow with a pick readily exposed a mass of shining yellow chalcopyrite.

Relation to Former Erosion Cycles. Even though the presently existing stage of erosion may not be conducive to enrichment, this fact does not preclude the existence of enriched ore, for enrichment may have taken place beneath an old surface which, although now undergoing dissection, has not been destroyed. While recent oxidation usually tends to eat downward into an enriched zone, it does not always leach copper out of the zone. Where chalcocite has replaced pyrite and chalcopyrite to such an extent that not enough excess sulphur remains to make abundant sulphuric acid, the copper may remain in place in the form of cuprite, chrysacolla, and carbonate, as in the upper part of the ore-bearing zone at Braden, Chile. Where water is too scant to carry away the copper salts, copper may remain in the form of sulphate as in the oxidized zone at Chuquicamata.

The relation of physiographic history to supergene enrichment at Butte, Montana, has been described in a well-known paper by Atwood [25] who recognizes four physiographic cycles and concludes that enrichment was accomplished during the second and third of these. Erosion during the second cycle, in Oligocene time, carved broad intermountain troughs and developed mature topography beneath whose surface enrichment reached an advanced stage. During the third cycle, in late Oligocene time, enrichment was interrupted by lava flows which covered the orebearing area, but when this capping had been removed from the outcrops, enrichment was resumed and continued during the fourth cycle, though interrupted again by rise of the water level during several succeeding glacial stages. As a result of these events, the bottom of enrichment, though irregular in detail, is regular in its broader aspects,

[25] Atwood, Wallace W., The physiographic conditions at Butte, Montana, and Bingham Canyon, Utah, when copper ores in these districts were enriched: *Econ. Geol.*, vol. 11, pp. 697–732, 1916.

in fact considerably more so than the present topography.   It stands at a depth of at least 1100 feet below the surface of Anaconda Hill and at an elevation of about 4600 feet.

SELECTED REFERENCES

Outcrops

Schmitt, Harrison, Outcrops of ore shoots, *Economic Geology*, vol. 34, pp. 654–673, 1939.

Geomorphology

Cotton, C. A., *Landscape as Developed by the Processes of Normal Erosion.* Cambridge: Cambridge University Press, 1941.

Cotton, C. A., *Climatic Accidents in Landscape-making; A Sequel to Landscape as Developed by the Processes of Normal Erosion.*   Christchurch, N.Z.: Whitcomb and Tombs, 1942.

Hinds, Norman E. A., *Geomorphology.* New York: Prentice-Hall, Incorporated, 1943.

Lobeck, A. K., *Geomorphology.* New York: McGraw-Hill Book Company, Incorporated, 1939.

von Engeln, O. D., *Geomorphology.* New York: Macmillan Company, 1942.

Sedimentation

Twenhofel, W. H., *Principles of Sedimentation.* New York: McGraw-Hill Book Company, Incorporated, 1939.

Hydrology

Meinzer, Oscar E. (Editor), *Hydrology* (Physics of the Earth No. 9).   New York: McGraw-Hill Book Company, Incorporated, 1942.

Tolman, C. F., *Ground Water.* New York: McGraw-Hill Book Company, Incorporated, 1937.

Rock Weathering

Leith, C. K., and Mead, W. J., *Metamorphic Geology.* New York: Henry Holt and Company, 1915.

Oxidation and Enrichment

Emmons, William Harvey, *Enrichment of Ore Deposits*, U. S. Geological Survey, Bulletin 625, 1917.

Lindgren, Waldemar, *Mineral Deposits*, Chapter 32, pp. 813–877, Oxidation of metallic ores. New York: McGraw-Hill Book Company, Incorporated, 1933.

10

Mineralogical Guides

*Of these the truest and most certain sign that can be given is when the
ore shows itself clearly to the sight on the surface of the ground . . .*
—Vannoccio Biringuccio, 1540 [1]

The minerals that are present and their relative abundance serve as
very practical guides in ore-search. Variations in the proportions of
minerals, whether in the wall rock or the vein matter,[2] and whether
apparent in plan or in vertical sections, may constitute target rings.
Oxidized minerals at the surface serve as an indication of what lies
beneath.

Mineralogical variations in wall rock, unless inherent in the original
rock-mass, are usually the result of alteration of the rock by mineral-
bringing solutions; variations within the vein matter may reflect local
variations in conditions of ore deposition or the subsequent influence of
descending solutions.

ROCK ALTERATION

Nature of Alteration

The mineralogical changes that are so common in rocks surrounding
epigenetic ore deposits usually involve the introduction of certain chemical elements and the removal of others, but occasionally the chemical

---

[1] *De la Pirotechnia,* Venice, 1540, translation by Smith, Cyril Stanley, and Gnudi, Martha
Teach. New York: A.I.M.E., 1942.

[2] Again I am using "vein matter" without wishing to restrict it to material that occurs in
vein-like form. Unfortunately, there is no satisfactory general term. "Junore" has been suggested for material that would be ore were it not too lean to extract at a profit, but the term
would not be generally understood. "Protore" has somewhat the same significance, but it is
restricted to the primary counterpart of material that has been secondarily enriched.

change is negligible and the elements that were present originally merely rearrange themselves into new assemblages of minerals.   In monomineralic rocks, such as pure limestones and sandstones, the few elements present do not provide the makings of new minerals, and, in the absence of introduced material, alteration is recognizable only by difference in texture or color.   Gray limestone at Hanover, New Mexico,[3] is coarsened by alteration and also whitened, probably by expulsion of the small amount of carbonaceous matter that it contains.   In most rocks, however, both chemical and mineralogical changes take place.

One of the commonest minerals of hydrothermal alteration is pyrite, representing introduced sulphur which combines with iron already present in the rock and usually also with iron brought in along with the sulphur.   Common alteration minerals [4] characteristic of various types of mineralization are:

> With hypothermal mineralization: garnet, amphiboles, pyroxenes, tourmaline, biotite.
> With mesothermal mineralization (and also in many deposits classed as hypothermal and epithermal): sericite, chlorite, carbonates, and silica.
> With epithermal mineralization: some sericite, often much chlorite and carbonate, adularia or alunite.

Replacement of rock minerals by any of these alteration products, jointly or severally, and especially by pyrite, may produce an altered rock so conspicuous that the miners themselves recognize it as a guide to ore.   Alternatively, the altered rock may be scarcely distinguishable by naked eye from its fresh equivalent although it can always be recognized readily in thin sections under the microscope.

Like other guides to ore, rock alteration is most serviceable if it is neither too restricted nor too widespread.   "A very extensive phase of alteration, such as propylitization associated with gold-silver veins in certain western districts, may be so widespread that it merely serves to call attention to the possibility of ore in the district in general.   At the other extreme, alteration confined to a few feet from the walls of a deposit is not apt to be of much value in exploration except possibly where it may serve to locate outcrops." [5]

[3] Schmitt, Harrison, Outcrops of ore shoots: *Econ. Geol.*, vol. 34, p. 660, 1939.

[4] For an excellent summary of types of alteration in igneous rocks see Schwartz, G. M., Hydrothermal alteration of igneous rocks: *Bull. G.S.A.*, vol. 50, p. 181, 1939.

[5] McLaughlin, D. H., and Sales, R. H., *Ore Deposits of the Western States*, p. 690.

Target Rings of Alteration

The outer limits of a zone of alteration form the outer rings of a target for exploration. Within the outer ring, internal rings may be drawn by outlining different types of altered rock or by plotting successive degrees of intensity. Thus at Casapalca, Peru, the outer limit of alteration in andesite is a fairly abrupt gradation from the surrounding purplish or grayish porphyry to a greenish altered rock consisting of epidote, chlorite, and carbonate. This zone is rudely spindle-shaped in plan, surrounding the system of roughly parallel veins. Near the middle of the vein-system it extends as much as 150 feet from the vein-walls; toward the extremities of the veins it closes in to within a very few feet of them. Within this outer zone of propylitization, there is an inner zone of white to pinkish altered rock consisting of sericite and fine-grained quartz with carbonates and disseminated pyrite. This zone begins at a maximum of 30 feet from the vein-zone and narrows to zero toward the ends of the veins. Similarly, at the Ground Hog [6] mine in New Mexico an outer zone of epidote-bearing alteration gives way about eighty feet from the vein to a sheath of quartz and sericite. Examples could be multiplied *ad infinitum*.

Where veins are closely spaced, their altered zones merge to form a general halo surrounding the system. An inner zone of more intense alteration may be more closely identified with an individual vein, merging with that of a neighboring vein where the two are close together and fingering apart where the veins diverge.

Systematic mapping of altered zones as exposed on the surface and in underground workings serves to delimit the orebearing area, discouraging too extensive a program of exploration outside it and calling attention to parts of it that have not been explored and to places where its limits have not been reached.

Locke [7] says that at either Bingham or Miami an outcrop map based on evidence of alteration would have indicated the location of all the better-grade orebodies. In both these camps the original texture of the rock is obliterated by a "fine-grained mosaic of quartz, sericite, and adularia carrying abundant micro-vugs and following tiny irregular cracks or flooding the rock." Destruction of the original texture (porphyritic at Bingham and schistose at Miami) affords a readily mappable criterion which is recognizable in the field.

---

[6] Schmitt, Harrison, Outcrops of ore shoots, *Econ. Geol.*, vol. 34, p. 661, 1939.
[7] Locke, Augustus, *Leached Outcrops as Guides to Copper Ore*, p. 69. Baltimore: Williams and Wilkins, 1926.

Alteration of a type which habitually sheathes individual orebodies and veins has a number of practical uses. For example, if a crosscut passes through an altered zone without finding ore, the possibility that the altered zone is part of an outer halo surrounding an orebody may

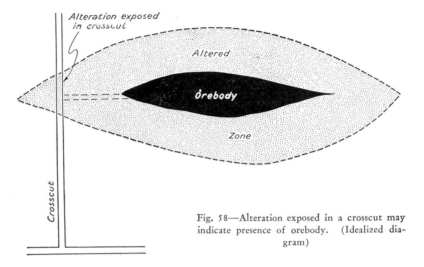

Fig. 58—Alteration exposed in a crosscut may indicate presence of orebody. (Idealized diagram)

suggest exploration on one side or the other of the crosscut. In a drill hole, altered rock may be the first sign of the approach to an orebody and may serve as a signal for redoubled care in supervising the ensuing drilling. Such a hole, whether or not it encounters ore, should be continued until it has passed completely through the altered rock. An example of bad practice through failure to follow this rule is pointed out by Clarke and Ellis [8] in a graphic log of a drill hole in Western Australia, which passed through two veins, each bordered by biotitic alteration, and stopped in another band of biotite without continuing through it to see if it enclosed a new vein.

Rock alteration as one of the guides to the discovery of the North Lily orebody in East Tintic, Utah, has already received brief mention (page 211). Subsequent detailed mapping in this district by Lovering and his associates [9] shows the manner in which altered zones, discernible at the surface, reflect blind limestone replacement orebodies at depth. In all, four stages of hydrothermal alteration are recognized, only one of which (the last) directly accompanied productive mineralization. The minerals formed during the three barren stages were: (1) hydro-

[8] Clarke, E. de C., and Ellis, H. A., Metasomatism of country near ore-bodies and its possible economic significance: Econ. Geol., vol. 34, p. 779, 1939.

[9] Lovering, T. S., Stoll, W. M., Wadsworth, A. H., Wagner, H. C., Stringham, B. F., Hilpert, L. S., Smith, J. F., and Terrones, Alberto, Alteration and structure in the East Tintic District, Utah: Geol. Soc. of America Bull., vol. 56, p. 1178, 1945 (Abstract).

thermal dolomite and minor amounts of chlorite, (2) (accompanying the first intrusion of quartz monzonite porphyry) dickite, kaolinite, halloysite, beidellite, and rutile with local quartz and alunite, (3) (immediately preceding ore deposition and restricted to channels of mineralization) allophane, quartz, and barite. The fourth stage, which accompanied the ore deposition, was marked chiefly by sericite and "hydromica." From the standpoint of ore-search it is significant that the carbonate which was replaced by ore and silica during the fourth stage made its way upward and was deposited as calcite in the overlying lavas. Lovering states that the relative bulk of rock affected by the different types of alteration gives an approximate index to the probable size and location of ore targets.[10] He and his co-workers believe that the methods have a field of application beyond this particular district, as the character of altering solutions and the sequence of alterations is general in western mining camps, though the mineralogy may vary with the character of rock and with the physical conditions that prevailed during ore deposition.

Despite the impressive degree of similarity in the nature of rock altera- tion associated with similar ore deposits throughout a region, the pres- ence of alteration of a given type is not in itself a guarantee that commercial ore is to be found, although the more consistent the associa- tion has proved to be in a given district the more confidence it inspires. Conversely, the absence of strong alteration, although by and large a discouraging sign, is not necessarily a sufficient reason for condemning a vein. This is illustrated by Wisser's example of a district (locality not stated, though one might hazard a guess that it is Pachuca) where strong alteration haloes encase veins with an east-west strike, whereas only weak alteration, showing little relation to oreshoots, accompanies the north-south veins which are nevertheless productive. Wisser concludes that the two sets of veins have been mineralized at separate times and under different conditions, whose nature he infers from other geological evidence. He cites this as a warning against the blind use of empirical criteria without understanding their causes in terms of ore genesis.[11]

PRIMARY MINERALIZATION

Target Rings of Mineral Distribution

That the quartz or other gangue in a vein constitutes an ore-guide is axiomatic to all miners and prospectors. Almost invariably the gangue extends far beyond the limits of minable ore, both along the vein and

---

[10] Lovering, T. S., personal communication.
[11] Wisser, Edward, Environment of ore bodies: A.I.M.E. Tech. Pub. No. 1206, p. 5, 1939.

downward.   The mineral matter as a whole may constitute a very large target, but distribution of certain vein minerals may provide inner rings surrounding the oreshoot in the plane of the vein.   The index mineral may be the valuable mineral of the ore itself if it occurs in decreasing amounts outside the minable shoot, or it may be a sulphide or a gangue mineral which accompanies the valuable mineralization though having a wider distribution.   Thus, in many districts, chalcopyrite, sphalerite, and galena are hailed as an indication of the approach to gold.

In a swarm of closely spaced veins, mapping types of mineralization and plotting them on coordinated plans and cross sections may serve to outline the favorable area.   At the Hollinger Mine,[12] chiefly as a result of Gustafson's work, it was found that in the quartz veins in the central orebearing portion of the area the accompanying carbonate mineral was ankerite, whereas in veins outside this area the carbonate was calcite.   Mapping the distribution of the carbonate minerals made it possible to define the limits of the most productive zone.

Composition of garnet serves as a reliable index of proximity to magnetite bodies in the Jumbo Basin, Alaska.[13]   According to Kennedy this garnet is an isomorphous mixture of andradite and grossularite "molecules" in proportions which vary systematically from place to place within the skarn zone.   Measurement of refractive indices shows that the andradite content of the garnet in magnetite-free skarn varies from 45% to 85%, increasing toward the magnetite bodies and reaching 96% to 100% within the magnetite bodies themselves.

In addition to target rings consisting of mineralogical variations, it is often fruitful to test the usefulness of rings expressed by varying metal content.   They have the advantage that their basis is quantitative —data supplied by the assay returns.   Where the samples have been assayed for more than one metal, a variety of methods of plotting the information can be used:

1. *Plotting each metal separately.*   This permits a comparison and shows which metals tend to occur together.   Sometimes one of the metals gives a more definite oreshoot pattern than the others.

2. *Plotting the sum of the metals.*   The data may take the form of a combined percentage, *e.g.*, lead plus zinc, but where precious metals are present their weights are so small that they will have little influence on the base-metal pattern.   In this case the total dollar value is the most convenient common denominator.

[12] Graton, L. C., McKinstry, H. E., and others, Outstanding features of Hollinger geology: *Can. Inst. Mining & Met.*, April, 1933.

[13] Kennedy, George C., Geology, contact metamorphism and mineral deposits of Jumbo Basin, Prince of Wales Island, Southeastern Alaska: Unpublished *Thesis*, Harvard University, p. 63, 1947.

3. *Plotting metal ratios.* The ratio of any metal to any other may be plotted, *e.g.,* Pb:Zn or Au:Ag, or the ratio of one metal to the sum of certain others, as copper: (lead plus zinc).

Thus, in brief, target rings within a vein or vein system may express themselves in the arrangement of gangue minerals or of ore minerals. The proportion of ore minerals may be mapped by visual inspection or by plotting assay data.

Mineralogical Guides to Solution-Paths

There is another type of locus which may express itself mineralogically, yet has a shape which cannot be described in terms of either a ring-like or X-like target, or indeed very readily as a target at all. This is the orebearing system of a mine or a district, viewed as a whole—the anatomy or morphology of the labyrinth of channelways which the ore solutions have followed. For every hydrothermal orebody must have had an inlet [14] and an outlet—conceivably several of each. The necessity of an outlet is sometimes overlooked, and, in fact, its existence is not always demonstrable, for in many instances it has been removed by erosion. Its absence, however, is not proved even by reported descriptions of orebodies which have been followed to their tops and found to end upward against solid unaltered rock, for solutions, although their ultimate goal is the surface, need not travel vertically upward; in fact, in some districts, they must have travelled thousands of feet horizontally, as through the manto-pipes of Santa Eulalia (Mexico) [15] and the horizontal and gently pitching saddle reefs of Bendigo. Locally, and for at least short distances, they appear to have moved downward. Whatever the course, it is difficult to visualize deposition without an avenue of disposal for the spent solutions, to say nothing of the great bulk of material that has been replaced.

It is profitable, then, to think of the "plumbing system" by which the solutions moved from depth toward the surface through intricate and perhaps changing channelways, taking advantage of devious openings and permeable horizons. Not all of the path, by any means, will be orebearing; most of it will be marked by barren gangue or altered wall rock. But there should be some trace. That mineralizing solutions can move through fractures or even through solid rock without leaving any trace of their passage is possible in the sense that it has not been disproved, but it seems highly improbable.

---

[14] Locke, Augustus, Billingsley, Paul, and Schmitt, Harrison, Some ideas on the occurrence of ore in the Western United States: *Econ. Geol.,* vol. 29, pp. 561 *ff.,* 1934.

[15] Prescott, Basil, The underlying principles of limestone replacement deposits of the Mexican Province: *E. & M. J.,* vol. 122, pp. 246–253, 289–296, 1925.

Recognition of connected orebearing conduits has probably achieved most success in replacement deposits in limestone, many of which, despite their notorious irregularity and their great variation in structural detail, have certain broad aspects of similarity. The general shape of such a conduit-system may be compared to one's hand and wrist, the wrist representing the inlet, the palm the main productive zone, and the fingers the outlet or outlets. The "wrist" is usually very small in proportion and may be either flattened or pipe-like. In some cases it makes out from a shattered intrusive. The palm may be tubular and horizontal like the Chihuahua mantos, or may be upright as at Morococha or blanket-like as at Leadville. It may alternate between a tabular and a tubular form as in some of the more complex Mexican deposits. At Tintic, Utah,[16] the "wrists" are hardly wrist-like at all, but are feeding fissures through beds underlying the "creases" of synclines; the palms are synclinal troughs. The outlet of the system may be portrayed either by holding one's fingers close together to form a thin plane or by spreading them apart to simulate pipes, depending on whether the upward escape was through isolated openings in a flat roof or along a steep bed or fracture. The position and shape of the wrists and the fingers determine the shape of the palm, for the palm is merely the connection between the two as modified by the path of least resistance through favorable beds and guided, partly at least, by fractures.

In vein deposits it is even more difficult to trace the pathways of solutions, yet, unless generally accepted concepts of ore deposition are completely mistaken, no hydrothermal oreshoot is an isolated phenomenon. The utility of the concept is this: the possibilities of a deposit are not necessarily exhausted so long as a "missing" part of the channelway remains unexplored, especially if it could pass through "favorable" structure. Thus, if ore has been stoped down to the 500 level at the north end of a mine and new ore has been found on the 1000 level at the south end, one must inquire what path the solutions followed between the two. Or if the two shoots are clearly not connected even by alteration or barren vein matter, the presumption is that the shallow orebody has a separate inlet and the deep orebody a separate outlet, a concept which in itself stimulates further search.

In veins, as well as in some other types of deposits, plotting metal or mineral ratios may help to trace the pathways of most active circulation within the more widespread locus of mineralization, as these pathways may be marked by a change from the center outward toward the

[16] Billingsley, Paul, in *Ore Deposits of the Western States* (Lindgren Volume), A.I.M.E., 1933, p. 716.

margins of the stream of flow, with low-grade ore or barren gangue in the stagnant back waters.

Hypogene Zoning as a Guide

All of the foregoing mineralogical variations might be regarded as aspects of hypogene zoning, but zoning in the stricter sense—the progressive change in mineralization along channelways from source to surface, or outward from a central axis—is serviceable in a somewhat different way. It finds its chief usefulness in the epithermal and the shallower of the mesothermal deposits, where noticeable changes may take place either laterally within the limits of a single company's holding or in depth within the limits accessible to mining. Wisser [17] presents a generalized description of an epithermal vein typical of Tertiary deposits in Western United States and Mexico:

"At horizons above the top of the ore zone the vein fracture is often a mere slip. . . . Sparse quartz starts to come in with depth, usually as a narrow stringer along the slip. The quartz increases rapidly with depth and the top of the ore zone lies not far below the top of the quartz. Base sulphides are sparse here. . . . Base sulphides increase with depth and reach a maximum at the heart of [the precious-ore] zone. Fragments of wall rock cemented by vein matter become abundant at this horizon; many are completely replaced by silica and sulphides. Here the vein attains its maximum width and this width usually continues to the lowest explored horizon."

Such a vein may be productive either in the precious-metal zone or in the base-metal zone, or both. But,

"A vein that carries base metals in commercial quantity at the heart of its precious-metal horizon may be expected to continue to do so to considerable depth below the bottom of precious metal ore. But there appears no reason, judging by actual results of deep exploration, to suppose that a precious metal vein carrying but small amounts of base metals at the heart of its ore zone shall turn into a base-metal mine at depth."

Changes of the sort which Wisser describes take place within depths of a few hundred or a very few thousand feet. What of zoning in deeper-seated deposits like those of Cornwall, Butte, or Bingham? In general it is likely to be of less direct use as a guide to ore though it may point to parts of a district which are relatively favorable or unfavorable. On the basis of theory, one might reasonably hope to find ore by sink-

[17] Wisser, Edward, in symposium, Some observations in ore-search: A.I.M.E. Tech. Pub. 1209, p. 31 and p. 34. Same paper in Transactions, A.I.M.E., vol. 144, p. 141 and p. 144, 1941.

ing from an unfavorable to a favorable zone; if surface mineralization consists of non-commercial lead-zinc minerals, why not go deeper for the copper or the silver-copper zone?   Such successions are not uncommon, but the difficulty is that at present we are too ignorant of the quantitative aspects of zoning to know how deep we would have to go or what grade of copper mineralization to expect.   For in some districts the copper zone, if it exists, is merely a "token" zone of pyrite with a little chalcopyrite and sphalerite, but not enough to pay.   But if, in a given district, a highly payable zone like the enargite zone at Butte, or the silver-bearing tetrahedrite zone in the Silver Belt of the Coeur d'Alene, is known to exist, the expectation is on a different and, of course, much more favorable basis of probability.

Primary mineralization may serve as a guide to richer supergene ore. If primary copper or silver mineralization is first discovered at depth, there is a possibility that higher workings may find a zone of enrichment, especially under the remnant of an old erosion surface.   The supergene ore may be richest where precipitating minerals were present in the primary ore.   Thus in the pyrite body at Cerro de Pasco (Peru),[18] sphalerite and galena were especially active precipitants of secondary copper.   Here prospecting was carried out from below by raising on bunches of sphalerite and galena into the enriched ore in the secondary zone.

OXIDATION PRODUCTS

The oxidation products of an orebody constitute a type of guide that has been used effectively by miners and prospectors since time immemorial, but modern understanding of the chemistry and geology of oxidation have made it even more effective.   For obvious reasons, oxidation products are to be seen most commonly in outcrops and shallow workings, though in some mines they are found in, around, and even below orebodies to depths of several hundred feet.

Oxidation Products at Depth

Downward or lateral leakage of the waste products of oxidation or enrichment may serve as a guide in underground development.   Below oxidized lead-silver mantos at Santa Eulalia, Chihuahua, iron-stain along fractures in limestone leads upward to the ore.   Below the copper orebodies at Bisbee,[19] descending solutions that have passed through and

---

[18] McLaughlin, Donald H., and Bowditch, Samuel I., The Cerro de Pasco District in *Copper Resources of the World*, International Geological Congress, Washington, p. 516, 1935.

[19] Trischka, C., Rove, O. N., and Barringer, D. M., Boxwork siderite: *Econ. Geol.*, vol. 24, pp. 677–686, 1929.

reacted with the ore are rich in ferrous sulphate. They attack the underlying limestone to form bodies of siderite, which serve as guides to the copper orebodies above. The siderite does not necessarily lie vertically below the copper ore, however, as the solutions are frequently carried laterally by bedding planes or fractures. The relationship is similar to that of zinc carbonate bodies to oxidized lead ore, and the discovery of a mass of smithsonite at depth should at once arouse curiosity as to the location of the former sulphide body from which its zinc was derived.

Unoxidized Ore in Outcrops

Not all outcropping material is oxidized, of course. Glaciation and other agents of rapid erosion can remove any oxidized zone that may have formed and so expose primary ore at the surface. Then too, some ores are so resistant to oxidation that grains of metallic minerals ("relict sulphides") are still visible in the outcrops. Occasionally massive sulphides crop out, even in regions of deep oxidation. Thus, at Hanover, New Mexico,[20] though most of the outcrops are oxidized and leached, there is one place in which a body of massive sphalerite outcrops. Oddly enough this was overlooked until 1927, as the sphalerite was coated with manganese dioxide, and was discovered only through a program of large scale mapping (1 inch to 30 feet) which included the systematic cracking open of all outcropping material.

Where unoxidized vein matter has been well exposed, either naturally or artificially, and does not show interesting values, there is little incentive to explore at slightly greater depth unless there are definite reasons to expect some change that is not dependent on the distance below the present erosion surface. I have seen more than one prospect in which a system of quartz veins with low gold content was exposed on a perfectly fresh glaciated surface, yet expensive development had been undertaken at a level 100 feet or less below the outcrop only to find conditions identical with those on the surface, as might have been expected at the start.

Minable Oxidized Ore

A body of oxidized ore may be rich enough to make a mine in its own right. In fact some orebodies are minable only in the oxidized zone, either because oxidation, by softening the material, has made it cheaper to mine or, by releasing metallic minerals, has simplified metallurgical treatment or, by removing undesirable or harmful elements, has improved the

[20] Schmitt, Harrison, Outcrops of ore shoots: *Econ. Geol.*, vol. 34, p. 656, 1939.

grade. This is true of many minable gossans and of eluvial deposits of gold, silver, tin, and other metals; also of residual ores of aluminum, manganese, nickel, cobalt, and iron.

Surface Oxidation Products as Indicators

Whether or not the oxidized material is of commercial interest for its own sake, it always prompts the question: What is underneath? What primary (or secondary) minerals were the parents of the oxidized gossan or capping? Will the unoxidized material in depth be richer or leaner and what minerals will it contain? These questions apply to oxidized ores of all sorts but particularly to those derived from sulphides.

In the oxidized zone, sulphides have been decomposed, their sulphur converted to sulphate, and their metal content carried away in solution or else fixed, wholly or in part, as stable compounds, chiefly oxides, carbonates, and silicates. Most of the gangue minerals succumb to weather-

TABLE 7

STABILITY OF COMPOUNDS IN THE ZONE OF OXIDATION

	Native	Silicate	Carbonate	Oxide	Sulphate
Au	X	—	—	—	—
Ag	X	—	—	—	S
Cu	X	X	X *	X	S
Zn	—	X	X	—	S
Fe	—	X	X	X	S
Pb	—	—	X	X	X

X = stable; S = soluble in water; — = unknown as a mineral or rare in zone of oxidation; * = basic carbonate.

ing; carbonates dissolve readily and ultimately the silicates break down. Of the original gangue minerals, quartz is the sole survivor; others are represented, if at all, only by their decomposition products: iron and manganese oxides, clay minerals, and some of the most stable of the other metallic compounds. But not everywhere have the chemical changes reached completion; varying amounts of the original minerals and transition products may remain. The nature of such material and the textures preserved in silica and "limonite" are the chief clues to the composition of the original ore.

In a few districts the mineral matter at the immediate outcrop is not a simple residual gossan, but a capping or crust formed by chemical deposition. Cappings of caliche are described on page 220. Jasperoidal silica caps the ore at Ground Hog, New Mexico, and prongs downward, terminating in supergene chalcocite,[21] usually at depths of ten feet or less, although minor quantities of jasperoid have been found as deep as 600 feet. The jasperoid capping here is confusing because a similar material covers the outcrop of drag ore in a fault zone and is distinguishable only by a greater proportion of fragments of kaolinized porphyry than the vein cappings carry.

Behavior during oxidation varies so much among different types of ore that each of the common metals merits separate discussion.

Metals in the Oxidized Zone

GOLD

Of the familiar metals, gold is the most resistant to weathering. Particles of native gold accumulate in fractures and voids in the rock and often produce spectacularly high assays at the immediate surface. In addition, chemical leaching of associated material tends to concentrate the gold. For these reasons, high gold values in the top few feet of the oxidized zone are not to be taken too seriously. They demand attention, of course, but there is little fear that they will fail to receive it.

Gold is not completely insoluble; it is converted into soluble chloride by nascent chlorine for whose generation the requisite chemicals are present in many oxidizing deposits: sulphuric acid is always available, manganese dioxide is common, especially in leptothermal deposits, and salt is at hand, particularly in arid climates. Accordingly, many instances of migration of gold in the presence of manganese have been described. But as a rule the migration is local and produces small rich seams and pockets rather than a well-defined zone of enrichment. However, there are a few well-authenticated cases of a thin supergene gold zone at the top of a massive pyrite or pyrrhotite body.

But most enriched gold ores occur within the oxidized zone where they owe their value to the removal of other elements and where any leaching of gold has been more than compensated by "residual enrichment." Where this has happened, it is to be expected that the sulphides will be leaner than the oxidized zone, perhaps so lean as to be, for practical purposes, barren. This does not mean that all gold ores will show loss of values when followed from the oxidized to the sulphide zone. Some do and some don't. How can you tell what will happen? It is probably true in a general way that quartz veins whose content in sulphides and soluble gangue is small will show little change in gold con-

---

[21] Schmitt, Harrison, Outcrops of ore shoots: *Econ. Geol.*, vol. 34, p. 661, 1939.

TABLE 8

METAL-BEARING MINERALS OF THE OXIDIZED ZONE

Metal	Native	Oxide	Carbonate	Silicate	Sulphate	Halide	Other Compounds
Gold	GOLD	—	—	—	—	—	—
Silver	SILVER	—	—	—	Argentojarosite	CERARGYRITE	
Copper	COPPER	CUPRITE Tenorite	MALACHITE Azurite	CHRYSACOLLA	(Chalcanthite) (Antlerite) (Brochantite) (Krohnkite) Linarite	(Atacamite) (Nantokite)	Olivenite Turquois
Lead	—	Minium Massicot Platnerite	CERUSSITE	—	ANGLESITE Plumbojarosite	(Cotunite)	Pyromorphite Vanadinite Wulfenite Mimetite Crococite Stolzite
Zinc	—	—	SMITHSONITE Monheimite Hydrozincite	HEMIMORPHITE Willemite	(Goslarite)		Hopeite
Cobalt	—	Cobaltian Wad	Spaerocobaltite Remingtonite				ERYTHRITE
Nickel	—	Bunsenite	Zaratite	GARNIERITE Genthite	(Bieberite)	—	Annabergite
Iron	—	"LIMONITE" GOETHITE HEMATITE Lepidocrocite	Siderite	NONTRONITE Beidellite(?) Montmorillonite	JAROSITE (Melanterite) (Copiapite) "Borgstromite"	—	Vivianite

246

Element						
Manganese	"WAD" / "PSILOMELANE" / CRYPTOMELANE / PYROLUSITE		Braunite		—	
Arsenic	Arsenolite / Claudetite				—	Scorodite / Mimetite
Antimony	Senarmontite / Cervantite / Valentinite / Stibiconite				—	Arsenobismite
Bismuth	BISMUTH	Bismutite	Bismite		—	
Tin	Cassiterite				—	
Mercury	Quicksilver		Montroydite	Kleinite? / Mosesite?	Calomel / Terlinguaite / Eglestonite / —	
Aluminum	"BAUXITE" / Gibbsite / Diaspore		Kaolinite / Other clay minerals	ALUNITE / (Alum)		Wavellite / Turquois
Tungsten	Tungstite				—	Stolzite / Scheelite(?) / Wulfenite / Powellite
Molybdenum	MOLYBDIC OCHRE / Ilsemannite				—	
Vanadium	Vanoxite			(Soluble)		Vanadinite / Descloisite
Uranium	Many yellow, orange and green radioactive minerals.	Uranothallite(?)	Uranophane	(Soluble)		Autunite / Torbernite

Names in CAPITALS are relatively common or conspicuous minerals.
Names in Parentheses are soluble or unstable.
(Supergene and relict sulphides are omitted.)

tent, whereas highly porous gossans and quartz skeletons indicate loss
of soluble material and consequent residual enrichment. Earthy oxidized ores may be the result of compaction; hence, one may suspect
loss of volume and a higher gold content per cubic foot than in the parent
ore. But all these considerations are merely suggestive and are not infallible guides. Unfortunately there has not been enough investigation
of the general problem to afford dependable criteria; here is a fertile
field for research. Meanwhile, the best index is the behavior of similar
ores in any particular district. In the absence of local precedent, one
cannot be sure that commercial values in the oxidized zone will continue
into the sulphides, but the chance is usually worth testing. But, if
gold-values in outcrops and gossans are low or absent, there is no reason
to expect that the underlying sulphides will be commercially gold-bearing.

The stability of gold—its tendency to "stay put"—aids greatly in the
search for primary gold deposits. Most of the world's lode-gold districts
(outside glaciated terrain) have been discovered after a region was first
worked for placer gold; many individual lodes have been found by following placer gold upstream to its source. In fact, the distribution of
gold in streams and soil can constitute the outer ring of a target—
usually an unsymmetrical target whose rings spread widest on the downhill or down-stream side of the deposit.

In Western Australia many orebodies have been found by panning
the desert soil, a process locally known as "loaming," or, in the vernacular,
"looming." In its systematic form the technique consists of taking
samples of soil at intervals on a regular gridwork, panning each sample,
and recording the number of flakes ("colors") of gold recovered at each
point. When these results are plotted and contoured, the location of
their source is indicated. A similar process in Kenya Colony is carried
out amid corn and banana plantations, where the soil is as much as forty
feet thick, by putting down holes with a post-hole digger. Where concentrations of "colors" appear, the evidence is followed up by deep
trenching.

Some types of gold deposits, however, do not respond to this method
of prospecting. Gold tellurides, when they oxidize, yield gold in very
finely divided form. Also some of the epithermal ores, even though not
high in tellurides, have primary gold in very minute particles. Gold
of this sort does not accumulate in placers and is very hard to detect
by panning. In districts in which gold is associated with particular
sulphides, the characteristic limonites derived from the sulphides may
serve as a guide. The derivatives of arsenopyrite, which very commonly

carries gold, may be recognized from residual scorodite and by characteristic textures (see page 269).

Tin

Cassiterite, the only tin ore mineral of great commercial importance, is highly stable and survives in alluvial deposits and placers. It is, therefore, similar to gold in serving as a guide to covered deposits. Like gold, it is susceptible to residual enrichment in the oxidized zone. The possibility of supergene enrichment in the sulphide zone has been the subject of much discussion, but most geologists familiar with the Bolivian and other deposits dismiss the process as unimportant commercially if it takes place at all.[22]

Stannite, a much less abundant ore mineral, is quite stable, but it is said to break down on oxidation to yield cassiterite.

Lead

Of the base metals, lead is the most resistant to leaching because its sulphate and carbonate are "insoluble." Although galena oxidizes rather easily to sulphate, its complete oxidation is retarded by the oxidized sheath which forms when solutions attack the periphery of a grain or nodule. But ultimately galena is converted to anglesite ($PbSO_4$) which, in turn is likely to alter into cerussite ($PbCO_3$), a mineral that is even more stable. Despite their "insolubility," the lead minerals are eventually leached away,[23] and the space that they leave is partially occupied by porous and friable "limonite." Only with extreme oxidation, however, does the removal of lead approach completion, so that, although the lead minerals may not appear at the immediate outcrop, they usually can be found at a depth of a few feet if much galena was present before oxidation. Therefore, if reasonably deep trenching fails to disclose increasing amounts of lead minerals or of the "limonite" products resulting from them, one may conclude that the primary ore was not rich in lead. Although the commonest lead minerals of the oxidized zone are cerussite and anglesite, some of the rarer ones, especially pyromorphite, vanadinite, and wulfenite, are more conspicuous when present.

[22] Lindgren, Waldemar, *Mineral Deposits*, 4th Edition, p. 872. New York: McGraw-Hill, 1933.

Singewald, Joseph T., Jr., The problem of supergene cassiterite in Bolivian tin veins: *Econ. Geol.*, vol. 24, pp. 343–367, 1929.

[23] Boswell, P. F., and Blanchard, Roland, Oxidation products derived from sphalerite and galena: *Econ. Geol.*, vol. 22, pp. 419–453, 1927.

Garretty, M. D., and Blanchard, Roland, Post-mine leaching of galena and marmatite at Broken Hill: *Econ. Geol.*, vol. 37, pp. 365–407, 1942. The authors describe a condition that is extraordinary in that galena is being leached faster than marmatite (iron-bearing sphalerite)

ZINC

Zinc is one of the most soluble of the common metals. Even though its carbonate and silicate are quite stable, its sulphate is so soluble that oxidized zinc minerals rarely if ever appear at the surface; only in carbonate rocks do they form in any quantity and then usually at considerable depth in the zone of oxidation or even below it. Therefore, absence of zinc in the gossan does not indicate its absence in the sulphide ore; in fact, if lead is present in the gossan, zinc may normally be expected at depth.

In some districts the lead-zinc-silver ratio in the sulphide ore is reasonably constant from one orebody to another, so that composition of the gossan can serve as the basis for a rough estimate of the metal content of the sulphides. Such a calculation is based on the assumption that the quantity of lead and also of silica in a cubic foot of sulphide ore is the same as in a cubic foot of leached ore. The lead is recalculated as galena, sphalerite is added in accordance with the lead-zinc ratio of the district, iron is calculated as pyrite, and soluble components (characteristically calcite or dolomite) added to make up the necessary volume. It is necessary of course to make appropriate allowance for migration of iron and for compaction of the gossan and slumping of walls in accordance with local conditions. Naturally, no great precision can be claimed for such an estimate, but it may be helpful in arriving at a decision as to whether or not a lead-bearing outcrop is worth developing.

The former presence of lead and zinc sulphides is often attested by residual types of "limonite," [24] in spite of the fact that galena and sphalerite (if in its pure form) contain no iron and therefore do not in themselves produce "limonite," and that in inert gangue (e.g., quartz) sphalerite leaves clean voids and galena leaves cavities containing cerussite and other oxidized lead minerals. But when the gangue is moderately reactive, iron derived from pyrite, which is usually present, deposits as limonite in the spaces formerly occupied by the sulphides. Boswell and Blanchard [25] believe that the limonite is not deposited until the sulphides have been completely oxidized and that it therefore replaces metallic carbonates (and lead sulphate) rather than the sulphides themselves. Nevertheless, enough of the original texture of the sulphide is often inherited to influence the texture of the limonite. Characteristics

---

[24] For the connotation of limonite see footnote 55, p. 261.

[25] Boswell, P. F., and Blanchard, Roland, Oxidation products derived from sphalerite and galena: *Econ. Geol.*, vol. 22, 1927, p. 419.

Boswell, P. F., and Blanchard, Roland, Cellular structure in limonite: *Econ. Geol.*, vol. 24, 1929, p. 791–796.

of the boxworks derived from each of the sulphides will be found in a later section.

COPPER

Copper is readily leached. Where pyrite is available to furnish abundant sulphuric acid, and where the gangue or wall-rock is not too strong a neutralizer, most of the copper is removed. Nevertheless, traces usually remain. Locke [26] finds that in croppings overlying disseminated copper bodies "if [no copper] occurs in the capping, experience suggests that none existed in the sulphide from which it was derived." This does not mean that copper occurs in every hand specimen, but that out of several specimens there is usually one that shows at least a trace. Where the rock contains a mineral that can neutralize sulphuric acid, as, for example, a carbonate gangue or a limestone wall-rock, copper may survive at shallow depth in the form of malachite with subordinate azurite and chrysacolla. It is well known that spectacular copper showings in limestone may give an exaggerated impression of the amount of copper below, and that limestone wall-rocks and carbonate gangue are not favorable to supergene sulphide enrichment.

For judging the outcrops of copper deposits of the "porphyry" type, Locke and his associates have worked out a technique based on their study of thousands of samples from oxidized croppings derived from ore of known composition. The technique, as originally developed, was not intended to apply to aggregated ores (massive sulphides) since they oxidize with widespread migration of iron and usually with important change of volume, forming a gossan that may bear little textural relation to the original sulphides. But disseminated ores, defined as those which contain not more than 20% of sulphide, oxidize with little change of aggregate volume and their textures retain evidence which is helpful in reconstructing the mineralogy of the now-departed sulphides.

The aim of the croppings technique is to distinguish between croppings derived from the oxidation of copper ore and croppings derived from the oxidation of pyritic waste, thereby outlining the most promising areas for later exploration by drilling or other means. Such a distinction calls for an estimate of the approximate percentage of copper that the material contained before it experienced oxidation, an estimate which involves (1) the percentage of total sulphides and (2) the ratio of copper-bearing sulphide to total sulphide—usually, in practice, the relative quantities of pyrite and chalcocite.

[26] Locke, Augustus, *Leached Outcrops as Guides to Copper Ore*, p. 87. Baltimore: Williams and Wilkins Co., 1926, p. 87.

The total percentage of sulphides is estimated from the relative volume of former sulphide grains, as indicated by the voids or by oxidation products that now occupy the sites of the grains.   In judging the former ratio of pyrite to chalcocite (or other copper-bearing minerals), grains of relict sulphide, which a painstaking search usually reveals, may be very helpful, although one must remember that some sulphides disappear before others and that pyrite is likely to survive longest.   Of still greater usefulness are the nature and distribution of the products of oxidation, particularly the texture [27] and identity of the limonitic minerals and the degree to which iron has migrated out of the sites of the original sulphide grains, *i.e.*, the ratio of "indigenous" to "transported" limonite.

Chemical Principles.   The reasons why iron and copper compounds are, under some conditions, deposited chiefly *in situ* and, under other conditions, carried away in solution to varying distances by groundwater have been clarified to a large degree by careful investigations of the chemical systems involved.[28]   Further investigation is still needed, both in the laboratory and in the field, particularly of systems containing other components besides Fe_2O_3, CuO, SO_3 and H_2O.

A full discussion of the phase relations in the explored systems would be impracticable here, but some pertinent inferences based largely on Tunell's [29] study of the systems and on his field work will be in order.

When pyrite is oxidized gradually and thoroughly [30] by oxygen from the air in the presence of a given quantity of water but in the absence of any other substances except inert gangue minerals (such as quartz), the products formed and their proportions are determined by the stability fields in the system Fe_2O_3–SO_3–H_2O.   At first (that is, when the proportion of water is high and the proportion of the products of oxidation is minute) a little goethite precipitates but re-dissolves at an early stage (provided equilibrium is maintained), and there is no further precipitation of goethite; all of the products remain in solution until the concentration becomes so high that basic ferric sulphates precipitate.   Thus

[27] Types of limonite are described in the last section of this chapter.

[28] Posnjak, Eugen, and Merwin, H. E., The system Fe_2O_3–SO_3–H_2O: *Jour. Am. Chem. Soc.*, vol. 44, p. 1965, 1922.

Posnjak, E., and Tunell, George, The system CuO–SO_3–H_2O: *Am. Jour. Sci.*, vol. 18, p. 1, 1929.

Tunell, George, and Posnjak, E., A portion of the system Fe_2O_3–CuO–SO_3–H_2O: *Jour. Phys. Chem.*, vol. 35, p. 939, 1931.

[29] Tunell, George, The oxidation of disseminated copper ores in altered porphyry, *Doctorate Thesis*, Harvard University, 1930.

[30] In *thorough* oxidation, as the term is used by Tunell, "oxidation of ferrous sulphate keeps pace with its production and the oxidation of the small amount of free sulphur produced, if any, also keeps pace with its production." Tunell, George, *Doctorate Thesis, op. cit.*, p. 41.

in the presence of sufficient water (about 46% of the total weight of the system) to keep basic sulphates from precipitating, pyrite can be completely dissolved without deposition of any limonitic minerals.

But when chalcocite is present together with the pyrite, it modifies the course of solution and precipitation in a manner that has paramount practical interest. Since chalcocite contains less than half as much sulphur as does an equal weight of pyrite, the oxidation of a mixture of chalcocite and pyrite produces less SO_3 than does the oxidization of the same weight of pure pyrite. To describe the condition in somewhat loose terms, the product is less acid and has less power to keep ferric oxide in solution. Moreover, presence of copper favors precipitation of ferric oxide minerals. Thus if CuO is added to a solution just saturated in goethite, goethite precipitates; [31] similarly, borgströmite [32] precipitates from a solution just saturated in $3CuO.4SO_3.9H_2O$.

Since chalcocite carries only one atom of sulphur to two of copper, it must, if it is to be converted to copper sulphate, acquire additional sulphur from pyrite, which has more than enough to convert its own iron into ferrous and even into ferric sulphate. Accordingly, one might expect that mixtures of pyrite and chalcocite lying between the extremes of 100% chalcocite and 100% pyrite could be divided into three significant ranges marked off by two critical ratios of pyrite to chalcocite: (1) low pyrite-chalcocite ratios furnishing insufficient sulphur to convert all of the copper to normal sulphate and thus yielding precipitates containing both copper and iron; (2) intermediate ratios furnishing sufficient sulphur to convert all of the copper but not all of the iron into sulphate and thus yielding precipitates consisting solely of ferric minerals; (3) high ratios furnishing sufficient sulphur to convert all of both copper and iron into sulphate and thus yielding no precipitates.

Investigation of the quaternary system has shown that the chemical behavior is not quite as simple as this, yet the concept of critical ratios, suggested originally as a hypothesis [33] finds considerable support in physical chemistry.

As to the dividing point between the ranges (1) and (2), an ex-

[31] This behavior, suggested as probable by Posnjak (Locke, p. 42) was confirmed by further investigation of the quaternary system. Tunell, *op. cit.*, p. 84.

[32] "Borgströmite" is used here, as by Locke, to designate the compound $3Fe_2O_3.4SO_3.9H_2O$, which has a well-defined stability field and has been identified repeatedly in laboratory preparations. Borgströmite, originally described by Saxén, is classed as a "doubtful species" (*American Mineralogist*, vol. 10, p. 180, 1925) because of discrepancy between analysis and formula, but Posnjak and Merwin (*Jour. Am. Chem. Soc.*, vol. 44, p. 1977, 1922) suggest that Saxén's material "may be the 3:4:9 compound slightly contaminated with limonite."

[33] Morse, H. W., and Locke, Augustus, Recent progress with leached ore capping, *Econ. Geol.*, vol. 19, p. 250, 1924.

amination of stability fields shows that in oxidation of pyrite and chalcocite, present together in the molecular ratio 1:2, nearly all of the copper is in solution and nearly all of the iron is in precipitate. This is so, at any rate, when the concentration of water is 96.06%; data for less dilute compositions are not available.

As to the limit between ranges (2) and (3), simple equations might suggest that two parts pyrite with one part chalcocite would supply enough sulphur to convert both the iron and the copper into sulphate. The stability relations indicate, however, that with this ratio a considerable amount of goethite is precipitated while an excess of sulphur trioxide remains in the solution together with all of the copper. If all of the iron as well as all of the copper is to dissolve, the ratio of pyrite to chalcocite must be at least 5.3 to 1.[34]   (This is the ratio in a system containing 96.06% of water. With a higher percentage of water the proportion of pyrite would have to be still higher; with a lower percentage of water the required percentage of pyrite would be somewhat less.)

While chalcocite has been considered throughout this section as the typical copper sulphide, similar general principles apply if the copper-bearing sulphide is covellite, bornite, or chalcopyrite. Different numerical ratios are involved, of course, because these minerals do not supply components to the system in the same proportions as does chalcocite.

Non-thorough Oxidation. The foregoing considerations assume thorough oxidation. If oxidation is not thorough, some of the iron may remain in the ferrous state, in which case the ratio of SO_3 to Fe_2O_3 in the system is higher than it would be if the iron were thoroughly oxidized, and, accordingly, the tendency to precipitate ferric minerals is retarded. But cupric sulphate, if present, acts as a powerful catalytic [35] in promoting the oxidation of ferrous to ferric sulphate. Hence even with non-thorough oxidation (or perhaps one should say: *especially* with non-thorough oxidation) the presence of copper favors precipitation of ferric minerals.

Influence of Gangue. If the gangue is reactive instead of inert, its products enter into the reactions and modify the course of oxidation. Alkalis and alkaline earths, by reacting with sulphuric acid and reducing the concentration of SO_3, have a general tendency to favor precipitation of limonitic minerals and oppose the removal of iron in solution.

[34] Tunell, *op. cit.*, p. 85.

[35] Posnjak, E. W., Acceleration of rate of oxidation of ferrous iron in presence of copper, and its application to 'heap leaching' process, *A.I.M.E. Paper No. 1615-D*, pp. 1–10, 1926.

In this respect the influence of reactive gangue operates in the same direction as that of copper sulphide, and the results of the two influences are not readily distinguishable.

The presence of reactive compounds in gangue can influence the mineralogical form as well as the quantity of the precipitate. Thus, whereas hematite does not precipitate during oxidation in inert gangue (since it has no stability field in the quaternary system Fe_2O_3–CuO–SO_3–H_2O below at least 50 degrees), it deposits readily instead of goethite (or along with it), if potash is present. Jarosite, which cannot form in the absence of potash (an essential constituent of the mineral) tends to deposit in place of borgströmite if potash is available.

The effectiveness of a limited concentration of potash in inducing the precipitation of hematite varies not only with the proportion of total sulphides but also with the proportion of iron to copper among the sulphides. With a given ratio of iron disulphide to copper-bearing sulphides, precipitation of hematite is favored by low total sulphide content; with a given total sulphide content, precipitation of hematite is favored by a low ratio of iron disulphide to copper-bearing sulphide.

Accordingly, Tunell,[36] as a result of detailed field and microscopic studies, recognizes three types of sericitic capping distinguished by the mineralogical form in which limonitic minerals occur and characterized by distinct colors:

1. Capping containing goethite and some jarosite occurring as replacements of gangue. "The ferric minerals precipitate as minute spherules and discs and euhedral and anhedral crystals finely distributed in gangue and thus color the rock brown or yellowish brown." Capping of this type is correlated with a moderate to high percentage of sulphides and a high proportion of iron disulphide to copper-bearing sulphide.
2. Capping containing hematite and goethite as botryoidal coatings in the cavities left by sulphides. The capping is maroon to seal brown in color. It is correlated with ores containing a moderate total percentage of sulphides in which the ratio of pyrite to chalcocite is low, i.e., copper ore of fair to good grade.
3. Capping containing hematite deposited in the gangue rather than in cavities. The hematite "tends to crystallize in extremely thin, rounded, fibrous plates in the sericite cleavage spaces and thus, owing to its wide distribution

[36] Tunell, George, Studies of weathering and sedimentation: Field aspects of the problem, *Carnegie Institution of Washington Yearbook No. 27*, 1928, pp. 74–75.

Others had previously pointed out somewhat similar relationships between color of capping and nature of parent disseminated sulphides but with some disagreement between the conclusions of different individuals. Tunell, by correlating colors with mineral content and reexamining a number of localities, showed that the discrepancies were attributable to difference in the use of descriptive terms and in particular to the recognition of only two color designations instead of three.

and fine subdivision, to impart a brick red color to the capping." This type of material is correlated with a small percentage of total sulphides, high in iron-copper ratio, *i.e.*, with waste.

Examples. The effect of a low pyrite-chalcocite ratio is illustrated by conditions at Miami, Arizona, where the molecular ratio of pyrite to chalcocite is less than 1:2, and oxidized copper minerals are found generally throughout the capping.[37] In fact, large tonnages of capping are now being mined in this district and treated by leaching.

In contrast, capping at Bingham over ore in which the pyrite-chalcocite ratio is greater than 1:2 is marked by general absence of oxidized copper compounds.[38]

In capping at Bingham over pyritic waste in which the ratio of pyrite to combined covellite and chalcopyrite is about 10.8:1 oxidized copper is virtually absent, as might be expected but, in addition, an appreciable part of the iron remains in most of the sulphide cavities. This is explained by presence of potash in the groundwater. The amount of potash is small, however, for otherwise the capping over ore would contain oxidized copper minerals.

Conclusions. While few general statements can be made which are accurate for all conditions, the following broad conclusions emerge. Other factors being equal in each case:

1. The higher the ratio of pyrite to chalcocite, the greater the tendency of iron to migrate in solution and in consequence the higher the proportion of transported to indigenous limonite.

2. Reactive gangue, such as carbonate or sericitized rock, tends to prevent or limit migration of iron.

3. In the presence of potash (available from sericitic gangue), hematite and/or jarosite can deposit. The influence in this respect of a given small amount of potash is greater where sulphides are sparse than where they are abundant. With the same amount of total sulphide, the influence of potash is greater when the proportion of pyrite to chalcocite is low than when it is high.

Since solution and precipitation are governed by the composition of the natural chemical system that exists during the oxidation of a particular deposit or part of a deposit, including the system's concentration in water and in extraneous metallic and non-metallic compounds, a number of variables are involved besides the total sulphide content and

---

[37] Ransome, F. L., The copper deposits of Ray and Miami, Arizona: *U.S.G.S. Professional Paper 115*, p. 144 and p. 159, 1919.

Tunell, *op. cit.*, p. 87.

[38] Tunell, *op. cit.*, p. 87.

the pyrite-chalcocite ratio of the ore or protore. Conspicuous among the variables are the mineralogical nature of the gangue, the condition of the rock with respect to permeability and porosity, the climate, and the topography. In view of these variables, any attempt at a quantitative estimate in a given district calls for calibration of the general technique in terms of the local environment. The results which inspire the most confidence are those derived from croppings which can be compared with others known to overlie ore in the same district.

SILVER

Silver, like copper and zinc, forms a soluble sulphate, but unlike them forms no stable carbonate. However, its chloride and other halides are highly insoluble and even native silver is relatively resistant in the absence of sulphate radical. In addition to the halides and the native metal, silver in the outcrop may occur as argentojarosite and perhaps in other inconspicuous minerals. The predominant form in which it exists in the "pacos" (gossan) at Cerro de Pasco [39] has defied identification for years.

The mobility of silver varies greatly under different conditions. Silver which occurs in galena is likely to be protected from solution and retained in the resulting anglesite or cerussite, whereas silver in tetrahedrite and other copper minerals is released with their breakdown and carried away unless a precipitant such as chlorine is present. Green copper stain may record the former presence of argentiferous tetrahedrite. In oxidized ores, silver, like gold, is apt to be spotty. But in contrast to gold, a lack of appreciable silver in the gossan does not necessarily mean absence of silver at depth. The significance of the presence of traces of silver or absence of them in the outcrop is a topic that requires further investigation.

NICKEL

Sulphide ores of nickel oxidize in much the same manner as copper sulphides and form soluble sulphates.[40] Nickel that occurs in pyrrhotite deposits normally leaches from the oxidized outcrop but may leave traces in the form of apple-green stain consisting chiefly of the silicate gar-

---

[39] McLaughlin, D. H., Bowditch, Samuel I., and others, The Cerro de Pasco district: *Copper Resources of the World*. 16th Int. Geol. Cong., Washington, 1935, p. 526.

[40] Intermediate products that form when pentlandite, $(Fe,Ni)S$, oxidizes in association with pyrrhotite are violarite, (Ni_2FeS_4), nickel-bearing pyrite and marcasite, and more rarely, millerite, (NiS). Michener, C. E., and Yates, A. B., Oxidation of primary nickel sulphides: *Econ. Geol.*, vol. 39, pp. 506–514, 1944.

nierite. Where arsenic is present in the primary ore the outcrop may retain traces of annabergite, also an apple-green mineral.

Redeposition of supergene nickel sulphide is known to take place [41] but supergene sulphide enrichment is not of commercial importance. This may be because nickel sulphides, unlike the corresponding copper compounds, do not precipitate from acid solutions.

The silicate ores of nickel, found overlying peridotite or serpentine, are the product of residual enrichment of a sparse content of nickel which is believed to have been present in silicate minerals of the rock. Such ores are restricted to the zone of oxidation and to joints in the upper few feet of fresher rock.

COBALT

The primary cobalt minerals, chiefly arsenides, sulpharsenides, and sulphides, break down in the zone of oxidation. The sulphate is soluble, but the pink arsenate, erythrite $(Co_3As_2O_8.8H_2O)$ is stable and constitutes "cobalt bloom," a conspicuous guide to cobalt. A good share of the world's supply of the metal comes from oxidized ores in the Belgian Congo, in which the cobalt is said to occur as heterogenite, a black hydrous oxide, and in asbolite, a cobalt-manganese oxide, both of indefinite composition.

The oxidation and migration of cobalt needs further investigation. Judging from occurrences in the state of Goiaz (Brazil),[42] it would appear that cobalt is less mobile than nickel, at least in the presence of manganese, since oxidized cobalt ore forms cappings a fraction of a meter thick with veinlets extending down one, two, or at most ten meters, over supergene nickel deposits. Likewise, in New Caledonia, asbolite ores associated with serpentine rest on the bedrock and are capped by iron oxides, whereas the nickel occurs in stringers in the upper part of the serpentine rock-mass.

MOLYBDENUM

The only primary ore mineral, molybdenite (MoS_2), is relatively resistant to oxidation. Associated pyrite, instead of promoting oxidation, probably has a protective effect on molybdenite, which stands above pyrite in the electromotive series.[43] In the Hall deposit in Nevada,

[41] Lindgren, Waldemar, and Davy, W. Myron, Nickel ores from Key West Mine, Nevada: *Econ. Geol.,* vol. 19, pp. 309–319, 1924.

[42] Pecora, William T., Nickel silicate and associated nickel-cobalt-manganese-oxide deposits near São José do Tocantins, Goiaz, Brazil: *U.S.G.S. Bull.* 935-E, pp. 272–275, 1944.

[43] Gottschalk, V. H., and Buehler, H. A., Oxidation of sulphides: *Econ. Geol.,* vol. 7, p. 31, 1912.

where oxidation was unusually thorough, 30% to 40% of the total molybdenum in the oxidized zone is still present as sulphide. At the Climax mine (Colorado) the proportion is 80% to 90%.[44] Molybdenum is not susceptible to supergene sulphide enrichment and migrates little, if at all, in the oxidized zone. Michell finds that at the Hall property there is no change in total molybdenum content on passing from the oxide to the sulphide zone, and he states that at the Climax mine there is no evidence of significant transportation of molybdenum.

Although molybdenite is comparatively stable, it does oxidize to form secondary minerals. The blue oxide, ilsemannite ($Mo_3O_8.nH_2O$),[45] forms as a tarnish on molybdenite but does not long survive its parent. Molybdite (MoO_3), the yellow oxide, is fairly soluble in water, but the yellowish to greenish buff ferrimolybdite or molybdic ochre ($Fe_2O_3.-3MoO_3.7\frac{1}{2}H_2O$)[46] is more stable and serves as a guide to underlying molybdenite. In the presence of pyrite or other source of iron, the final product of oxidation of disseminated molybdenite is a "limonite"[47] which may have a maroon color resembling the product derived from chalcocite, but distinguishable from it under the hand lens (see page 274). Powellite ($CaMoO_4$), an oxidation product of molybdenite, is inconspicuous in daylight but fluorescent in ultraviolet light. Lead, if present in the ore, is such an effective precipitant of molybdenum that wulfenite ($PbMoO_4$) is formed during the oxidation, even in some lead ores which contain too little molybdenum to be recognizable in the primary ore. Molybdenum is recovered from oxidized lead ore at Mammoth-St. Anthony in Arizona but practically nowhere else.

CHROMIUM

The only ore mineral, chromite, is relatively stable under oxidizing conditions. Quite commonly it survives unaltered in the outcrop and even in placer deposits. Under conditions of extreme weathering, however, it does leach out, leaving a "limonite" boxwork (see page 274). Blanchard[48] states that in New Caledonia leaching of chromite extends to more than 30 feet below the surface in some areas.

[44] Michell, Wilson D., Oxidation in a molybdenite deposit, Nye County, Nevada: *Econ. Geol.,* vol. 40, pp. 99–114, 1945. This paper is an excellent description of oxidation at the Hall property, and, in addition, gives a good summary and bibliography of oxidation of molybdenum deposits in general.

[45] Formula as given by Palache, Charles, Berman, Harry, and Frondel, Clifford, *Dana's System of Mineralogy,* vol. 1, p. 603. New York: Wiley, 1944.

[46] Michell, *op. cit.,* p. 102.

[47] Blanchard, Roland, Limonite of molybdenite derivation: *Econ. Geol.,* vol. 30, pp. 313–319, 1935.

[48] Blanchard, Roland, Leached derivatives of arsenopyrite and chromite: *Econ. Geol.,* vol. 37, pp. 615–626, 1942.

ACCESSORY ELEMENTS

Some of the minor elements may survive in the oxidized capping after their associated metals have been removed.   Arsenic, which might be expected to leach readily, is in some places preserved as scorodite and other arsenates.   Locke [49] has suggested that quantitative tests for it might serve as a guide to enargite-bearing copper ores.   Similarly, antimony, which is considerably less mobile than arsenic, might indicate tetrahedrite or one of the silver sulphantimonides.

The possibility of sampling for molybdenum in the outcrops of molybdenite-bearing copper ores and for fluorine have been suggested. [50]

Systematic sampling and analysis for these and other elements present a phase of orehunting which deserves further research.

Significance of Gangue

Ore minerals, or else evidence of their former presence, are of course the most direct guides to ore that the outcrops have to offer.   But gangue minerals may afford indirect evidence.   The quartz that was present in the original ore suffers very little attack during weathering, but the other gangue minerals are decomposed and either leached out completely or broken down into minerals of the clay group, more or less stained with iron oxide.   Despite the radical changes in mineralogy, traces of the texture of the original ore and wall rock may still be recognizable.

Where quartz is abundant it may enclose sulphides and protect them.   Yet oxidation can penetrate seemingly impervious quartz masses to an amazing degree.   The texture of the quartz and the nature of the voids in it become significant.   In any particular district the type of quartz typically associated with ore can often be distinguished from the barren gangue.   No general rules can be given, but masses of coarse, uniform, white quartz, devoid of sulphides or iron-stain and called by miners "bull quartz" or "buck quartz," are likely to represent barren vein-matter.   In some parts of the world—one of them is Western Australia—large masses of barren quartz, locally known as "blow-outs" or "blows," are characteristic of mineralized districts, and although they neither overlie ore nor occur very close to it, they do serve as broadscale guides to mineralization.   Calcite and the other carbonates suffer badly in the zone of oxidation, but there are two reasons why it is desirable to recognize whatever evidence there may be as to their former presence: first,

[49] Locke, Augustus, *Leached Outcrops as Guides to Copper Ore*, p. 85.   Baltimore: Williams and Wilkins Co., 1923.

[50] Locke, Augustus, and Billingsley, Paul, Trend of orehunting in the United States: *E. & M. J.*, vol. 130, p. 611, 1930.

there is danger of mistaking the cavities left by carbonates for those left by sulphides, and, second, carbonates in some districts are guides to ore.

In some cases the former presence of carbonates may be recognized by the rhombohedral shape of their cavities or by preservation of their cleavage by replacing material. The iron-bearing carbonates, e.g., ankerite and siderite, leave residual "limonite," but even calcite, which is free from iron, and dolomite, which contains very little, are often replaced by "limonite" since they are strong neutralizers of acid iron-bearing groundwaters. The "limonite" is characterized by certain textural peculiarities (see page 275), one of the most distinctive of which is the pulverulent, dull, yellow, "fluffy limonite."

Rhodochrosite, a characteristic gangue of certain silver ores, leaves manganese dioxide in the gossan. The latter often retains silver in a little-understood form which is difficult to treat metallurgically. There are many outcrops of this type in Mexico; some of them are quite rich in silver but unmined because the material is refractory; below oxidation the silver ores may be minable, although in some cases they are no richer than the outcrops.

Fluorite is a characteristic gangue mineral of certain orebodies, especially those of zinc and lead. It is relatively resistant to chemical attack, considerably more so than the alkaline earth carbonates, and in some districts it can be used to indicate the location of oreshoots.[51]

Barite is comparatively resistant to weathering, although it is not as stable as laboratory reactions would lead one to expect, for it can be completely removed in the oxidized zone.[52] In some cases, however, it survives at the surface. In the Urals Kingsbury "used fragments of barite found in swamps to indicate gold ores immediately below."[53]

Types of Limonite Derived from Sulphides and Other Minerals [54]

"Limonite," [55] as we have seen, is one of the few products that remain

[51] Schmitt, Harrison, Application of geology to mining: E. & M. J., vol. 133, pp. 509 ff., October, 1932.

[52] McKinstry, H. E., Geology of the silver deposit at Colquijirca, Peru: Econ. Geol., vol. 31, p. 630, 1936.

[53] Locke, Augustus, Leached Outcrops as Guides to Copper Ore, p. 69. Baltimore: Williams and Wilkins Co., 1926.

[54] Dr. Roland Blanchard has very generously cooperated in correlating the data presented in this section and in bringing the information up to date. A substantial portion of the discussion is based on notes which he supplied.

[55] Limonite, a name formerly given to hydrous iron oxide with a supposed formula $2Fe_2O_3.3H_2O$, is no longer considered a mineral species of definite chemical composition. It is a convenient field term for hydrous iron oxides whose real identity has not been determined. The term includes lepidocrocite ($Fe_2O_3.H_2O$), goethite (also $Fe_2O_3.H_2O$), and hematite (Fe_2O_3), all with more or less adsorbed water—Palache, Charles, Berman, Harry, and Frondel, Clifford, Dana's System of Mineralogy, p. 685. New York: John Wiley and Sons, Inc., 1944. For purposes of present description, limonite may also include jarosite ($K_2O.3Fe_2O_3.4SO_3.6H_2O$).

in gossans and oxidized outcrops, but since it is nearly always present, its characteristics can serve as very helpful clues in reconstructing the mineralogical composition of the material from which the outcropping remnants were derived. Under favorable conditions, the form and quantity of the limonite may even afford the basis for an approximate estimate of the original percentage of copper, lead, or zinc.

The technique of leached outcrop interpretation rests upon the observed fact that limonite products derived from any given mineral, such as chalcopyrite, usually differ in minute physical characteristics from corresponding products derived from other minerals, such as molybdenite or galena. The differences involve cellular structure, texture, pulverulency, size and arrangement of the limonite grains, and a host of other factors. Of these the *cellular structure* is the most outstanding and is the easiest to recognize and identify. It derives its shape or pattern from the cleavage, crystal form, fracture pattern, or grain boundary of the sulphide or other mineral undergoing oxidation, and results from a webwork of limonite or limonitic jasper "eating" its way during oxidation along the cleavage, fracture, or other boundary plane. Thus, galena often yields a cubic boxwork, patterned after the cubic cleavage of galena.[56]

All of the familiar base metal sulphides, and various non-sulphide minerals, yield cellular pseudomorphs under favorable conditions, but not in proportional amounts. Chalcopyrite, for example, yields them prolifically; sphalerite yields them freely; chalcocite, bornite, pyrrhotite, and galena yield them more sparingly; pyrite and arsenopyrite, because of the high acidity accompanying their oxidation, yield them only rarely and under special conditions.

The cellular pseudomorphs, however, constitute only one group of the various limonite derivatives yielded by these minerals during oxidation; some of the other products are found in positions more or less remote from the site of the original sulphide grain. A fundamental consideration underlying the leached outcrop technique, and one of especial importance where limonite products other than the cellular pseudomorphs are involved, is that solutions of high acidity tend to export the iron from its place of origin and deposit it at a distant point; whereas those of lowered acidity tend more generally to deposit it either indigenously, or immediately adjacent to the place of origin. Since pyrite, upon oxidation, yields highly acid solutions, and since most of the copper, lead, and zinc minerals yield less acid ones, it follows that indigenous limonite more commonly is associated with decomposition of the latter minerals.

---

[56] Blanchard, Roland, Interpretation of leached outcrops: *Journal Chem. Met. and Min. Soc. of South Africa*, May, 1939.

Similarly, because the concentration of iron in solution normally varies with the acidity, limonite derived solely from pyrite commonly is precipitated as porous granules or particles, which impart to the product distinct body and relief, with a resultant "live" appearance.

To illustrate: Where a pyrite grain has been replaced by chalcocite of the sooty type, and the replacement is moderately complete, the copper provides sufficient base to neutralize most of the acidity generated by the pyrite's oxidation. A large part or all of the iron accordingly is precipitated to form a tiny porous limonite granule at that place. Since oxidation of each chalcocite-pyrite grain proceeds largely independently of the oxidation going on within surrounding grains of similar composition, there tends to be built up, in place of the chalcocite-pyrite bleb, nodule, or mass involved, an indigenous aggregation of tiny porous, craggy, lightly coalesced granules of limonite possessing distinct relief for the mass. This is one origin of so-called "relief" limonite.

Many other limonite types, besides the cellular pseudomorphs, "relief" limonite, and the smeary crusts named above, occur in nature. Although they may be meaningless to the uninitiated, the trained observer usually is able to relate an unidentified one back to its parent mineral or minerals by noting in the field the various gradations from the fully oxidized and leached product to its unoxidized parent.

Locke, Blanchard, Tunell, Boswell and their associates have made careful studies of a large number of the more common varieties of such limonitic products and have published many of their results, with accompanying sketches, photographs, and discussions of the chemistry involved. My endeavor to condense much of this information has benefited from many suggestions from Dr. Blanchard, but this summary is of necessity relatively brief. For more detailed and graphic descriptions, as well as for fuller criteria to be used in distinguishing the products of different sulphides, the reader should consult the original publications listed in the footnotes.[57] Very detailed field, microscopic and

[57] Locke, Augustus, *Leached Outcrops as Guides to Copper Ore*, pp. 134–137. Baltimore: Williams and Wilkins Co., 1926.

Blanchard, Roland, Interpretation of leached outcrops: *Journal Chem. Met. and Mining Soc. of South Africa*, May, 1939.

Blanchard, Roland, Leached derivatives of arsenopyrite and chromite: *Econ. Geol.*, vol. 37, pp. 596–615, 1942.

Blanchard, Roland, and Boswell, P. F., Notes on the oxidation products derived from chalcopyrite: *Econ. Geol.*, vol. 20, pp. 613–638, 1925.

Blanchard, Roland, and Boswell, P. F., Limonite types derived from bornite and tetrahedrite: *Econ. Geol.*, vol. 25, pp. 557–580, 1930.

Boswell, P. F., and Blanchard, Roland, Oxidation products derived from sphalerite and galena: *Econ. Geol.*, vol. 22, pp. 419–453, 1927. Additional limonite types of galena and sphalerite derivation: *Econ. Geol.*, vol. 29, pp. 671–690, 1934.

Blanchard, Roland, and Boswell, P. F., Limonite of molybdenite derivation: *Econ. Geol.*, vol. 30, pp. 313–319, 1935.

physio-chemical studies of porphyry ores and their contained minerals have been made by Tunell,[58] and major portions of his results have been published. For practical application, especially where quantitative deductions are desired, a thorough field and laboratory study of material of known derivation is an indispensable preparation. The observer needs to become familiar with the various limonite derivatives of the different iron-yielding minerals and to understand the physics and chemistry of the processes involved in producing them. He can attain real proficiency in his interpretation only after experience with many individual leached deposits extending over a broad geographic and climatic range and involving varied types or limonitic derivatives.

I. LIMONITE IN COPPER DEPOSITS OF THE PORPHYRY TYPE

Locke describes five types of indigenous limonite which constitute a series or scale of increasing proportion of pyrite to copper minerals. Inasmuch as the types are not all derived from the same original copper minerals, the series is shown here spread into three columns.

Order of increasing proportion of pyrite	Original copper mineral		
	Chalcocite or covellite	Bornite (or chalcopyrite)	Chalcopyrite (or bornite)
1	a. Relief limonite		
2		a′. Limonite pitch	
3	gradation	b′. Fine limonite boxwork	
4			c. Coarse limonite boxwork
5	b. Nodular void-linings		

[58] Tunell, George, The oxidation of disseminated copper ores in altered porphyry, *Doctorate Thesis*, Harvard University, 1930. See also footnote 28, p. 252.

Locke, Augustus, *Leached Outcrops as Guides to Copper Ore*. Baltimore: Williams and Wilkins Co., 1926. Some of Tunell's results and conclusions are quoted on pp. 105–107 and pp. 114–115. A series of photomicrographs by Tunell is reproduced as plates 19–24.

These types of limonite are described under *A* (below). Transported limonites resulting from still higher proportions of pyrite to copper sulphides are described under B.

A. *Indigenous Limonite*

a. Relief limonite, so-called because its surface is one of high relief, minutely craggy and cavernous with tiny sponges rising above the general level. Locke concludes that in disseminated copper deposits relief limonite represents chalcocite and covellite accompanied by minor amounts of pyrite.[59]

b. Nodular or botryoidal crusts lining minute cavities. Minutely nodular crusts compacted to the wall of a void left by disappearance of sulphides. Dark brown to black; surface submetallic; streak reddish to orange. Gradational into (*a*) (see above). So far as observed, type *b* is likewise derived from chalcocite and represents an increased proportion of pyrite to chalcocite. Another series of types roughly corresponding in copper-iron ratio to the a-b series is derived not from chalcocite but from bornite and chalcopyrite with varying amounts of pyrite:

a'. Limonite pitch. Very dark brown to black with pitch lustre. Derived from chalcopyrite or bornite, having iron-copper ratio about the same as in those sulphides which weather to "relief limonite." A transitory phase, rarely surviving at the outcrop. Usually relatively sparse and not one of the important products.

b'. Fine limonite boxwork, composed of thin-walled cells giving a porosity of 75% to 90%.

c. Coarse limonite boxwork. Angular cells between thin walls a millimeter to a centimeter apart of limonite or jaspery limonite. Derived directly from sulphides; usually chalcopyrite or chalcopyrite with pyrite.

B. *Transported Limonite*

d. As halos and borders contiguous to voids left by sulphide. The voids themselves are empty or merely painted on the inside with iron oxide. Derived from pyrite.

e. As halos and borders attached to voids left by sulphide but separated from

---

[59] Blanchard and Boswell state relief limonite is not peculiar to any sulphide, nor is it necessarily derived from sulphides. Originally they included "fluffy" limonite in this classification because its relief is so marked; but because the fluffy type usually signifies nothing more than that an iron-bearing solution of indefinite source has come in contact with strong neutralizer they have deleted it from the "relief" group, and now restrict the latter term to the indigenous and closely transported varieties of porous, craggy limonite formed under the general conditions discussed in the introductory remarks. They do not restrict the term to chalcocite-pyrite or covellite-pyrite mixtures, because they state that (a) an identical product, indistinguishable as to origin unless traced gradationally through a series of specimens directly to the parent mineral, may be derived from chalcopyrite-bornite or bornite-pyrite mixtures, or other sulphide combinations possessing the proper sulphur-iron ratios, and (b) because the product is known to have been derived indigenously through the leaching of both cerussite and smithsonite by ferric sulphate solutions. Where only chalcocite-pyrite or covellite-pyrite mixtures are involved, the term relief limonite, according to them, has the precise significance attached to it by Locke.

Fig. 59—Oxidation of pyrite in monzonite. *Left:* In slightly kaolinized monzonite. Incompletely kaolinized feldspars tend to neutralize acid and precipitate a strong limonite halo. Niagara Gulch, Bagdad, Arizona. *Right:* In well-kaolinized monzonite. Less effective neutralizer permits migration of iron outward through inner bleached zone. Alum Creek, Bagdad, Arizona. (*After* Blanchard and Boswell, *Economic Geology*)

them by unstained zones.   Derived from pyrite.   The iron has migrated away from the cavity leaving an iron-free ring around it but has been precipitated in the rock just beyond.

f. In various forms flooding the matrix.   The iron has traveled so far that its relation to its sulphide source is obscured.   Its nature is determined rather by the nature of the gangue than by the original sulphide.   It is found in gossans from massive sulphides, from disseminated ores rich in pyrite, and in small quantity from copper-rich, disseminated ore, but in this case associated with specimens showing indigenous limonite.

II. LIMONITE IN GOSSANS OF THE SEMI-MASSIVE AND MASSIVE TYPE

In outcrops derived from the leaching of semi-massive and massive sulphides, as contrasted with the disseminated porphyry type, a greater variety of limonite products usually is in evidence; particular varieties, such as the cellular pseudomorphs, are developed upon a larger scale and generally stand out more conspicuously to the unaided eye, and there is greater tendency for the merging of one variety with another, owing to the interplay of solutions of different origin during the oxidation.

The cellular pseudomorphs find their most extensive and persistent development in outcrops of this type.   Where the structure is guided in its formation by cleavage or through-going fracture planes, *cellular boxwork,* of sharply angular pattern and with cell walls frequently continuous in a straight line past several cells, is the usual development. Where the structure is guided in its formation by the boundaries of coarse and irregularly shaped grains, *cellular sponge* is the usual development, with the cell walls more rounded, more irregular and heterogeneous in pattern, and with no defined cell orientation or formal structure.

In these deposits, too, where semi-massive or massive pyrite is involved in association with other sulphides, the tendency exists for the smeary crusts, as exotic limonite, to occur in masses, often upward of several inches across, as coatings which in part obscure the indigenous derivatives of the more useful sulphides. This is due to the fact (1) that such crusts are the most characteristic variety of limonite yielded by semi-massive or massive pyrite, (2) that with high acidity of the solutions the iron tends to travel from its place of origin before precipitation, and (3) that pyrite is a resistant sulphide, and its oxidation tends to lag behind that of most other sulphides. It thus is not uncommon to find these smeary crusts of exotic limonite precipitated upon and partly obscuring even cellular limonite. Except locally, they rarely submerge the cellular structure completely, however, and the experienced observer seldom has difficulty in diagnosing the relationships correctly.

Although in semi-massive and massive sulphides of the mixed type, the solutions derived from the oxidation of adjacent sulphides tend to mix to some extent, especially where the sulphides are fine-grained and intimately intergrown, it remains a fact, backed by much field evidence, that when the individual sulphide nodules are upward of 6 cm. (often upward of 2 cm.) in diameter, oxidation within a given nodule commonly proceeds more or less independently of oxidation within surrounding nodules of different composition; and if the entire limonite mass be broken into and examined, portions of it often will be found to contain, in place, the limonite products characteristic of the particular sulphide nodules that have been leached.

All limonite derivatives diagnostic of particular minerals may be modified and, in extreme cases, largely prevented from forming, if the solutions derived from their oxidation come in contact with strong neutralizer, such as limestone, either as enclosing gangue or as a bicarbonate groundwater constituent. The reason is that strong neutralization induces rapid precipitation of the iron, which expresses itself in various ways but most often is reflected in the formation of a distinctly fluffy limonite that under the hand lens resembles powdered sugar sprinkled over a surface. The source of the iron in such material often is difficult to trace, and, as previously noted, fluffy limonite frequently signifies nothing more than that an iron-bearing solution of indefinite source has come in contact with strong neutralizer. But in many cases the effects of strong neutralization are local, and often the cellular structure or other limonite type characteristic of a particular mineral emerges with varying degree of clarity through the fluffy mass to serve as a clue in appraising whatever indigenous limonite may be present.

III. LIMONITE DERIVED FROM SPECIFIC MINERALS

Below are listed the principal limonite derivatives of specific minerals as re-corded in the published literature, supplemented by certain unpublished data made available for this chapter by Dr. Roland Blanchard. For each mineral the derivatives are listed in the order of dominance in the field, based upon occur-rences in many districts. Unless otherwise noted, the products are indigenous.

Granular and pulverulent limonite, derived under varying conditions from all iron-yielding minerals, are usually not identifiable as to the parent in a par-ticular case, except through direct field association and correlation with a more distinctive and diagnostic derivative of that mineral. These types are listed only when they possess some uncommon feature such as resinous luster, etc.

Pyrite: Pyrite normally is leached away unless the sulphuric acid produced by its oxidation is neutralized, whether by a reactive gangue such as limestone, by alkali-bearing water, or by other base. The indigenous product or a pyrite derivation always calls for a neutralizing environment.

a. Smeary crusts, flat or finely nodular, usually dark to blackish in color, sometimes iridescent. Mostly exotic, but may be indigenous where enough admixed base is present to reduce the high acidity, as in the disseminated chal-cocite-pyrite specks or blebs of the porphyry coppers.

b. Columnar limonite, representing stalactite-stalagmite precipitates through evaporation of dripping acid solutions with high iron content. Closely related to (*a*). Always exotic.

c. Thick-walled cellular sponge. Cells highly irregular in size and shape, mostly rounded. Cell wall thickness varies abruptly, usually exceeds diameter of the cavity. Often coated in part with the smeary crusts. Formed where sufficient neutralizer is present in the groundwater to overcome acidity of the iron-bearing solutions slowly, not rapidly enough to yield fluffy limonite. May be exotic, or may be indigenous to a volume of somewhat greater size of semi-massive or massive pyrite, but without grain-for-grain replacement by limonite, and with at least partial collapse and usually much local transfer of iron during oxidation within the pyritic mass involved.

d. Thin-walled cellular boxwork or sponge, representing webwork of li-monitic jasper "eating" its way into massive pyrite during incipient oxidation. Usually highly siliceous, as acidity precludes much iron being retained. Cubic boxwork sometimes preserved but usually it is a sponge of heterogeneous pattern.

e. Hard pseudomorphs. Mostly cubic, hard and compact, with shape of the original pyrite faithfully preserved. Found largely in impure limy rocks.

Pyrrhotite: Thus far only the cellular product has been isolated as a diagnostic derivative, although several varieties of finely granular-relief limonite have been correlated with pyrrhotite in certain districts. Frequent intimate pyrite admixture may tend to obscure the features of strictly pyrrhotite origin.

a. The cellular structure is intermediate between boxwork and sponge. Characteristic pattern is oval, with an underlying hexagonal shape usually detectable. In some cases long, slender, trough-like boxwork emerges erratically from the matrix of oval pattern. Cell walls generally coated sparsely with thin shriveled limonitic crusts for pyrite-free pyrrhotite, with finely nodular crusts where slight pyrite admixture was present. With increase in pyrite the structure grades insensibly into the pyrite derivatives.

Fig. 60—Botryoidal limonite from massive pyrite in limestone gangue. Gardiner Mine, Bisbee, Arizona. (*After* Blanchard and Boswell, *Engineering and Mining Journal*)

Arsenopyrite: In absence of neutralizer arsenopyrite is mostly leached away, often leaving only faint greenish ferric arsenate or acid or basic ferric sulphate stains; but a small amount of neutralizer appears to yield a disproportionate amount of indigenous precipitate.

All such known derivatives are mixtures of scorodite and limonite granules. Scorodite often predominates in fresh material, undergoes progressive replacement by limonite through weathering, but the scorodite is rarely if ever wholly effaced.

a. Arborescent pattern of high relief, built up of small branching clusters of scorodite-limonite granules forming projections whose height (2–3 mm) is several times their thickness. Luster resinous to submetallic. Mass bound together by minute intergrowths of limonitic jasper, forming porous clinkery mass of loosely aggregated but firmly joined granules. Through encroachment by limonitic replacement of the scorodite, arborescent granules become more globular, some of the limonitic matter usually weathers away, and the arborescent projections begin to resemble stubby stalagmites.

b. Granular fretwork. Closely related to the arborescent type in origin and appearance, but projections more slender and fragile, lightly joined to resemble a fretwork. Has been most commonly observed where galena was an admixed primary sulphide, in which case mimetite may be intergrown to a limited extent with the scorodite and limonite. With weathering it tends to become limonitized and more stalactitic.

c. Cellular boxwork has characteristic obtuse angle. Main ribs are limonitic jasper with scorodite increasing toward edges, often merging with surrounding granular material. Poorly developed cross webs, predominantly of scorodite, at obtuse angles with main ribs.

d. Fluffy limonite. From disseminated or thinly dispersed sulphide (sulphide grains in contact with a large surface of neutralizing rock). Former presence of arsenopyrite indicated by acicular shape of cavities as contrasted with granular to cubic casts of pyrite.

Chalcopyrite: a. Cellular boxwork. Whether it is coarse (cell diameter in general 1 to 5 mm) or fine (cell diameter in general less than 2 mm) depends primarily in a given case on whether the inherent fracture pattern in the chalcopyrite from which it was derived was coarse or fine. With increased admixture of pyrite, the probability of cross webs developing within the cells decreases. Coarse cells free of limonite cell filling of any sort thus point to a greater proportion of admixed pyrite than do cells with cross webs or granular cell filling. The characteristic angle in chalcopyrite boxwork is obtuse, commonly approximating 110°. Limonitic webwork inside the cells generally is discontinuous and fragile, but compact pulverulent limonite may coat cell walls and also partly fill cell space if little or no pyrite was present.

b. Cellular sponge, less abundant than the boxwork, nevertheless is common, and is characteristic where for some reason the parent sulphide lacked an inherent formal fracture pattern. More likely to occur where chalcopyrite contained a fine uniformly dispersed pyrite intermixture. Cells thus more often empty than with the boxwork.

c. In some districts relief limonite has been traced gradationally back to a chalcopyrite parent containing an intimately intergrown lean bornite admixture. Ghosts of fine cellular boxwork of characteristic chalcopyrite pattern sometimes emerge dimly through the porous, craggy "relief" granules.

d. Brown limonite varnish and brownish-black to black limonite pitch are comparatively rare transitional phases in the decomposition of chalcopyrite to limonite.

Bornite: a. Cellular boxwork characteristically triangular or trapezoidal in shape, with the larger cells often containing smaller ones, or fine friable webwork of similar shape. Cells usually filled in part and often fully with partially sintered crusts (*c*) or caked limonite crusts (*d*).

b. Cellular sponge. Cells rounded rather than angular, with marked disparity in cell size, large cells commonly 20 to 30 times as large as adjoining small ones. Grades indefinitely into (*a*) which nearly always emerges sporadically through the sponge mass.

c. Partially sintered crusts: Made up of small aggregates or dabs of limonitic granules, coalesced to resemble in appearance the surface of dead-burned magnesia brick but slightly rougher. Color of fresh material usually prominent orange to orange-yellow. Discontinuous fine triangular boxwork almost invariably discernible through it if carefully searched for.

(*c*) probably is more abundant than (*a*) or (*b*), but is placed third because (*a*) or (*b*) usually are present in (*c*) and are more diagnostic.

d. Caked limonite crusts. Kaolinic mass thoroughly impregnated with limonite. Usually polygonal shrinkage cracks separate masses with curled up, semi-flaky edges. Nearly always reveal individual superimposed layers of clayey limonite .05 to 0.3 mm thick. Color usually orange red to Indian red. A common cell filling, especially in the triangular boxwork, but less abundant than (*c*).

e. Relief limonite. Ranges from "hit and miss" aggregates of partially sintered crusts (*c*), to the typical porous craggy relief product. Frequently embedded in pulverulent limonite, giving to the whole mass a velvety appearance. Discontinuous remnants of triangular boxwork usually discernible.

Chalcocite: a. Relief limonite is the most abundant limonitic derivative of chalcocite and covellite.

b. Cellular boxwork of chalcocite derivation has been observed only as a derivative of seams or nodules of massive, metallic chalcocite, never of the sooty type. Its pattern is less formal than that of chalcopyrite or bornite boxwork, its lines more wavering and discontinuous, and its structure more fragile; but it is boxwork, not sponge. Only in a few districts has it been observed well developed as a continuous structure (Morenci, Miami, Chino and Bagdad furnish good examples), but numerous districts exhibit it as fragile wisps of limonitic jasper embedded in the relief product (*a*). Cellular boxwork after covellite has not been observed to date.

Tetrahedrite: a. Contour boxwork. In cross section resembles superficially a contour map of a steeply mountainous region (see Fig. 6 A and B, p. 571, *Econ. Geol.*, 1930). Cell length (0.2 to 10 mm), two to ten times width. Cells relatively deeper than in most limonite boxwork. Cell walls coated with a thin continuous mat of fine-grained, sandy, dully resinous granules, faintly glistening in sunlight. Frequently encrusted in part by antimony oxides which occur as colorless, yellow or white scabs like barnacles.

b. Coagulated limonite (chiefly from tetrahedrite accompanied by pyrite). Highly coagulated aggregate of dully resinous granules (*a*, above). Where pyrite predominates, contour boxwork largely obliterated and limonite is semi-vitreous with metallic luster.

Sphalerite: a. Coarse and fine cellular boxwork. Boxwork forms with varying angles, but scattered through the mass is usually detectable the diagnostic

Fig. 61—"Contour boxwork" derived from tetrahedrite. Hachita, New Mexico. (*After* Blanchard, *Economic Geology*)

acute one ranging from 30° to 55°. Cell walls more flaky and shriveled than for chalcopyrite, but cell wall structure, especially of the finer cell, usually more firmly joined. Cell walls coated with scattered minute sandy grains and occasional aggregates of small limonite rosettes projecting from cell wall surfaces. Rosettes related in origin to the caked limonite crusts of bornite derivation, but never completely fill an individual cell, and usually are only of sporadic occurrence through the cellular mass.

b. Cellular sponge. In appearance resembles rubber bath sponge. Cell walls rigid and thicker, relatively, to cell size, than in (*a*); otherwise exhibit same flaky cell wall with sparse coating of minute sandy grains and scattered rosettes. Cell walls often coated locally with minute crystals of smithsonite or calamine. Usually discernible within the sponge mass are occurrences of the acute angular boxwork. Limonitic jasper of both boxwork and sponge from sphalerite is characteristically strongly siliceous.

c. Limonite moss (rare). Long, loosely interconnected flakes and shreds somewhat resembling shredded-wheat biscuit but darker and more slender. Locally fills and overruns cellular limonite much as Spanish moss overruns and locally masks the limbs and foliage of a tree. Shriveled appearance characteristic.

Galena and Cerussite: a. Partially sintered crusts. In pattern not readily distinguishable from similar crusts of bornite derivation, but under microscope may be observed to represent pseudomorphic limonitic replacement of finely globular aggregates of cerussite, with usually some further coalescence after formation of the limonite granules. Often carries grains of unleached cerussite. Color more distinctly brownish than in the bornite derivative, though fresh material often is orange-yellow. Constitutes 50 to 90 per cent of the lead-derived limonite of most outcrops.

b. Cleavage boxwork. Straight and strikingly parallel walls of very thin (.005 to .05 mm) limonitic jasper. Sometimes, though not very commonly, crossed at right angles by a second set forming a cubical boxwork correspond-

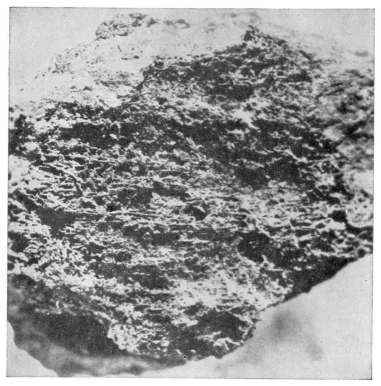

Fig. 62—Boxwork derived from oxidation of galena. Laun Hill, Queensland. (*After* Blanchard, *Economic Geology*)

ing to the cleavage planes of galena. Cell walls nearly always coated with partially sintered crusts to fill from ¼ to ½ of cell space. All gradations are known from such product to partially sintered crusts in which only occasional wisps of the fragile boxwork are detectable.

c. Diamond mesh boxwork. Boxwork of unsystematic diamond mesh pattern. The major ribs, which have an apparent thickness of 0.2 to 0.5 mm., are not solid but consist of two or more closely spaced, rigidly parallel, minutely thin webs, not readily visible except under a hand lens. Originally was correlated with "steel" galena, with suggestion that it may have represented pseudomorphs after imperfect crystalline cerussite. Now known to represent the latter.

d. Relief limonite. Limonitic derivative of cerussite which represents an intermixture of the globular variety intimately intergrown with very finely crystalline cerussite. The relief product is the derivative of the crystalline cerussite whose crystals are too minute to permit limonitic preservation of the diamond mesh pattern. Grades into the partially sintered crusts, and decreases with increase of globular material in the parent cerussite mass. Occasional cleavage or diamond mesh boxwork detectable.

e. Cellular sponge (derived from granular galena that had replaced schist or sedimentary beds other than limestone). Confused sponge-like structure partially obscured by partially sintered crusts (*d* above). Under high magnification it consists of small, poorly developed interlocking limonite boxes irregularly patterned after galena's cubic cleavage.

f. Pyramidal boxwork. Slender boxwork structure of step-pyramidal pattern. Limonite plates rigidly parallel but with shrinkage spaces between. More or less coated with partially sintered crusts.

g. Ragged cellular type. Derived from galena carrying abundant pyrite. Less regular honeycomb grading with increase of pyrite into pyrite-derived types with darkening of color from ocherous orange through seal brown to dark chocolate.

Molybdenite. Molybdenite generally decomposes to molybdic ocher without limonitization, especially where massive. In some districts disseminations and blebs up to $\frac{1}{4}$ inch or more across have been observed to form:

a. Foliated boxwork, which represents limonitic jasper deposited between foliations of the molybdenite during incipient decomposition. Cell flakes extremely thin: .005 to 0.03 mm. Smooth and rounded. Molybdenite residuals usually leach out cleanly.

b. Granular limonite with slightly greasy luster has been observed as replicas after decomposing molybdic ocher, but is not diagnostic except when traced gradationally into such parent in a particular district.

Chromite: Well preserved limonitic jasper cellular derivatives after chromite have been observed only in gossans from Tiebaghi, New Caledonia. Similar structures formed by limonite essentially free of silica, and thus crumbling readily into granular material, have been observed "eating" into decomposing chromite at two deposits in Queensland and two in California.

a. Honeycomb boxwork (Tiebaghi). Coarse boxwork, representing irregular highly siliceous honeycomb with cells up to 5 mm, pseudomorphic after irregularly octahedral structure of massive chromite. Rigid coherent boxwork with ribs well joined.

b. Minute cellular sponge. Indigenous drab-colored sponge filling the boxwork, but with much lower silica content. Sometimes also constituting the sole derivative of small chromite disseminations in serpentine. Cell diameter as small as .005 mm but averaging 0.02 mm, hence so fine it looks pulverulent without magnification. Wall thickness $\frac{1}{3}$ to $\frac{1}{5}$ cell diameter characteristically crinkled, like cornflakes. Sponge contains no through-going ribs and is therefore not miniature boxwork. Much of sponge whipped out by weathering, but thin coatings always remain lining cell or cavity walls.

Gangue Carbonate: a. Fluffy limonite. Relief and incoherence resemble that of powdered sugar. Fluffiness due to rapid precipitation, resulting in extremely fine, porous grains. Relics of rhombohed.al structure, consisting of grains parallel to crystal direction, sometimes preserved. Usually exotic, but may be indigenous where groundwater containing strong neutralizer flows over decomposing iron-yielding mineral. (Fluffy limonite is not difficult to distinguish under hand lens from fine cellular chalcopyrite or bornite boxwork, despite Locke's early statement.) Jarosite precipitates from solutions of limited concentration in K_2O and rather high concentration in Fe_2O_3 and SO_3; it is in no way inherent in fluffy limonite.

b. Fine brown limonitic sponge. Cells rounded rather than angular. Streak dark orange. Consists of a fabric made up of strings and clusters of (usually botryoidal) goethite, hematite, and quartz granules enclosing minute openings. Difference from fluffy limonite: coherent and rigid though it may be brittle.

c. Rhombohedral boxwork. Rare relative to the fluffy and sponge products, but conspicuous in numerous districts. That pseudomorphic after calcite cleavage or grain orientation in limestone has firmly knit grid, is clean-cut in appearance, and always is highly siliceous. That pseudomorphic after siderite usually has more discontinuity of structure, and higher Fe_2O_3 content. Boxwork after dolomite observed only infrequently, always with abnormally thick cell walls, as if soft mud had oozed over the boxwork and much of it had adhered to the cell walls.

Fluorite: a. Cleavage boxwork. At Broken Hill, crystalline fluorite yields an angular boxwork of siliceous jasper with cell walls 0.1 to 0.25 mm, exceptionally 0.5 mm. Incrusted with minute crystals of supergene carbonate gangue growing at right angles to the center web and closely packed, like stacked cordwood. Granular fluorite yields a coarser boxwork with cell-wall diameter up to 1 cm or more. In this type the cordwood type of carbonate crystals is less abundant. More common are loose coatings of stubby crystals or shapeless grains.

Resembles the cleavage boxwork from galena. Distinguished by fact that the longitudinal ribs are never strictly parallel and the cross ribs make obtuse angles with them.

From or in Kaolin (All forms exotic): *a.* Massive jasper. Formed in various ways, but most often through alteration and leaching, following strong acid attack, of aluminous rock silicates or impure shaly limestone to kaolinic-alumina residual. Therefore usually associated with semi-massive or massive pyrite occurrences in such rocks. As leaching proceeds the interstices are filled with fine chalcedony, opal, or both; forming the prospector's white or ivory-colored kaolinic "soap." The introduced quartz, as also the kaolinic residual, slowly undergoes replacement by hematite or goethite up to 50% or more of Fe_2O_3, resulting in massive jasper. Can be confused with oxidized hypogene jasperoid.

b. Coarse limonite sponge. Clusters and jumbles of cubic or irregular cells up to 5 mm diameter with walls of hard dark rigid limonite, rich in impurities of quartz and kaolin. Sometimes the cells are sprinkled on the inside with jarosite crystals. (The cells represent pyrite cubes from which the iron has been totally transported into the surrounding kaolin.) Often grades into massive jasper.

c. Sponge. Similar to (*a*) but finer with curved crusts surrounding residual cores of pyrite. (May survive after the pyrite is gone.)

d. Limonite clay. Clay soaked with iron and containing admixture of water, kaolin, and colloidal silica. Cracks on drying. Not found in cappings but only in gossan and then not in immediate outcrop; apparently a temporary form.

SELECTED REFERENCES

Rock Alteration

Schwartz, G. M., Hydrothermal alteration of igneous rocks, *Bulletin Geological Society of America,* vol. 50, p. 181, 1939.

Leached Croppings

Boswell, P. F., and Blanchard, Roland, Notes on the oxidation products derived from chalcopyrite, *Economic Geology,* vol. 20, pp. 613–638, 1925.

Boswell, P. F., and Blanchard, Roland, Oxidation products derived from sphalerite and galena, *Economic Geology,* vol. 22, pp. 419–453, 1927.

Boswell, P. F., and Blanchard, Roland, Cellular structure in limonite, *Economic Geology,* vol. 24, pp. 791–796, 1929.

Blanchard, Roland, and Boswell, P. F., Additional limonite types of galena and sphalerite derivation, *Economic Geology,* vol. 29, pp. 671–690, 1934.

Locke, Augustus, *Leached Outcrops as Guides to Copper Ore.* Baltimore: Williams and Wilkins Company, 1926.

Tunell, George, and Posnjak, E. W., Studies of Weathering and Sedimentation, *Carnegie Institution of Washington,* Yearbook No. 27, pp. 71–76, 1928.

11

Stratigraphic and Lithologic Guides

. . . the earth does not conceal metals in her depths because she does not wish that men should dig them out, but because provident and sagacious Nature has appointed for each thing its place.
—Agricola de re Metallica, 1556 [1]

If ORE occurs exclusively in a given sedimentary bed, the bed constitutes an ideal *stratigraphic guide*. Less perfect, but still serviceable as a guide, is a bed or group of beds which contains most of the orebodies even though other stratigraphic horizons may not be entirely barren. If the containing rock is not a sedimentary formation but an intrusive body or a volcanic flow, the same principles are applicable so far as ore search is concerned, but, since in such cases the guide cannot properly be called stratigraphic, the term *lithologic* is more appropriate.

The ore may be *syngenetic* (an original part of the body of rock) or it may be *epigenetic* (introduced into the rock). The distinction might be dismissed as academic if our only concern were to seek the productive formation among its enclosing rocks, but naturally there are other problems to consider. Often we are obliged to judge the degree of confidence that a given stratigraphic guide inspires and (still more important) to predict what places within the favorable formation are most likely to be ore-bearing. The answers to such questions depend on the mode of emplacement of the ore and the factors which have determined its present position. In this respect the syngenetic and epigenetic classes are in sharp contrast with each other and consequently require separate consideration.

---

[1] Translation by Herbert Clark Hoover and Lou Henry Hoover. London: The Mining Magazine, 1912.

In Syngenetic Deposits

If the ore is an original part of a body of rock, the rock itself will serve as a guide; that is, the ore will be found within the particular rock-formation and will be absent outside it.   The localization is most precise in layered rocks, especially sediments, but it is definite enough to be useful even in homogeneous igneous rocks.

If the ore consists of a bed in a sedimentary formation, one need only know the stratigraphic sequence and the structure of the beds in order to predict where the outcrop will be found or at what depth the ore will be at any given place.   For this purpose a structure-contour map is the most convenient device for depicting the shape of the ore bed and projecting its position.   The problem is simplicity itself in beds that have suffered little folding, as in the "minette" iron ores of Central Europe, which dip uniformly eastward at angles of only one to two degrees.   The intricacy increases when the structure becomes more complex, so that ore-search may require the solution of difficult problems in post-ore folding and faulting.

Except where the ore has been interrupted or thickened as a result of structural accidents, the localization of oreshoots in one part of a favorable bed rather than another is not controlled by such intersecting loci as shear zones, breccia zones, and folds (which are so important in epigenetic deposits) but is determined by the conditions of sedimentation that prevailed while the beds were being deposited—conditions which include not only the shape and extent of basins of accumulation but also the position of unconformities.

Syngenetic deposits of igneous origin are usually less regular than sedimentary beds.   However, in some thick sills and lopoliths, the rock constituents have a very regular stratiform arrangement.   Thus the chromite of the Bushveld Complex occurs within a zone 500 feet thick and traceable for scores of miles underlying a layer of diallage norite. Individual seams of chromite are one inch or less up to 6 feet thick and conform closely to the pseudo-stratification.   Some have proved to be continuous for several miles, although others do not persist.[1a]   The chromite in the Stillwater Complex, Montana, has similar structural re-

[1a] DuToit, Alexander, *Geology of South Africa*, 2nd Ed., p. 454.   Edinburgh: Oliver and Boyd, 1939.

Wagner, Percy A., Magmatic nickel deposits of the Bushveld Complex: *Union of So. Africa Geol. Survey*, Mem. 21, p. 66, 1924.

Wagner, Percy A., and Reinecke, Leopold, *Mineral Deposits of The Union of So. Africa*, Third Empire Mining and Metallurgical Congress, p. 214, 1930.

lations except that the layered igneous rocks have been tilted to a nearly vertical position. In less regularly shaped intrusives, syngenetic ore deposits may be so highly erratic in their distribution that the most one can say is that they are somewhere within the igneous body. Yet even this fact is useful in delimiting the field of search. For example, chromite orebodies are confined to bodies of highly mafic rock or to serpentines derived from them. They are not to be sought in other rocks, nor in serpentine of other origin. Serpentine derived from peridotite or dunite is usually recognized by the presence of veinlets of asbestos, crisscrossed magnesite veinlets and commonly by abundant talc.[2]

In pegmatites the metallic minerals (if they can be truly described as syngenetic) are proverbially erratic in distribution. However, in many pegmatites the constituent minerals form rude zones[3] from a micaceous selvage adjoining the host rock through graphic granite and/or perthitic feldspar to a central core of quartz. The tantalite and beryl in the pegmatites of northeastern Brazil are usually found next to the quartz core.[4]

In Epigenetic Deposits

Ore that has been introduced into rocks may show strong partiality to certain formations, whether the ore follows fractures or replaces formations bodily. Replacement orebodies differ from most sedimentary (syngenetic) deposits in that not all of the favorable stratum is ore; replacement within the bed is often controlled by some additional loci which may consist of fold axes, as in the Homestake Mine, fractures as at Park City, or veins as at Leadville. The orebody, if localized by a vein that cuts the favorable horizon, may range in shape from a mere enlargement or enrichment of the vein to a blanket-like replacement extending a long distance from the vein itself; that is, there are all variations, from the case in which the bed localizes ore within the vein to the case in which the vein localizes ore within the bed. Accordingly there are two general modes of search—exploring the vein in search of favorable beds and exploring the beds in search of localizing veins.

The favorable formation need not be sedimentary in origin; volcanic

---

[2] McLaren, D. C., Notes on chromite: *Mining Magazine*, p. 203, Apr. 1944.

[3] Cameron, E. N., Larrabee, D. M., McNair, A. H., Page, J. J., Shainin, V. E., and Stewart, G. W., Structural and economic characteristics of New England mica deposits: *Econ. Geol.*, vol. 40, p. 372, 1945.

[4] de Almeida, S. C., Johnston, W. D., Jr., Leonardos, O. H., and Scorza, E. P., The beryl-tantalite-cassiterite pegmatites of Paraiba and Rio Grande do Norte, Northeastern Brazil: *Econ. Geol.*, vol. 39, pp. 206–223. 1944.

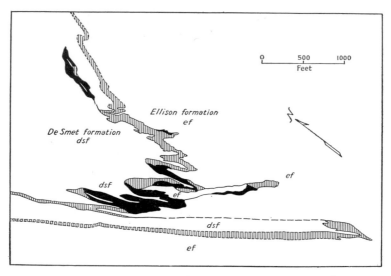

Fig. 63—Ore (shown in black) localized in favorable portions of folds in the Homestake formation (cross-hatched). Homestake Mine. (*After* McLaughlin, *Engineering and Mining Journal*)

flows or their brecciated tops may play the same role as water-laid strata. Nor need the formation be stratiform at all. Igneous dikes or sills or, in fact, intrusives of any shape may constitute favorable formations.

Reasons for Favorability

The reason why one rock is more receptive to ore than another is not always evident. On theoretical grounds, two conditions would be expected to be favorable: (a) permeability, in order to allow passage of solutions, and (b) chemical reactivity, in order to induce precipitation of ore-minerals. The two conditions may be combined in the case of a soluble rock through which solutions can eat their own way by chemical reaction. Permeability may be either a primary property of the rock, as in sandstones, conglomerates, or vesicular lava-tops, or it may be imposed by fracturing or shearing. Whether physical properties (especially permeability) or chemical properties (especially reactivity) will be the predominating influence is rarely predictable in advance of exploration. Thus, if a porphyry and a limestone occur together, the ore may favor the porphyry, because of more open fractures in it, or it may favor the limestone, which it finds more hospitable chemically. Although limestones are normally very receptive to ore, there are cases in which the ore shuns them and deposits in rocks which might ordinarily be considered as poor hosts. Thus at Mount Isa (Queensland), the great lead-zinc deposits occur in shale while limestones in the region have not been mineralized.[5]

There is some indication that certain host-rocks show a preference for specific metals. Limestone is especially hospitable to lead and zinc but relatively unreceptive to gold.

Quartzite is also a good carrier of lead-zinc ores in some districts. In the Coeur d'Alene district, the Burke and Revette quartzites account for the bulk of the lead production, whereas the slates of the underlying Pritchard formation and the overlying Wallace formation are, in comparison, very poor lead producers. The Pritchard slate, however, carries rich zinc deposits. That there may be a chemical reason for this preference of lead for the more siliceous rocks in this district is suggested by the observation that, within the zinc deposits, sphalerite replaces slate but any galena present seems by preference to replace vein-quartz which was left untouched by the sphalerite.

The rocks most receptive to gold seem to be those which contain chlorite or other minerals of similar composition, although chlorite in the immediate vicinity of the ore is often altered to sericite. There are more gold deposits in chloritic slates and phyllites and in basic to intermediate igneous rocks than in quartzites,[6] rhyolites, or limestones.

Susceptibility to replacement is often a matter of delicate if not obscure control. Why replacement should, for example, single out certain beds within apparently uniform limestones is a question that has aroused much inquiry but has received no conclusive answer, at least none that is applicable to the general case.[7] In some camps dolomites[8] are more favorable than calcareous limestones, but this relationship is not universal. J. S. Brown[9] concludes that in silicated limestones a proportion of silicate to carbonate of 1:1 is more favorable than either pure carbonate on the one hand or highly silicated rock, on the other. He suggests, following Bain,[10] that an optimum size of pore space, neither too large nor too small is a determining factor.

It is probable, however, that the mineralogy and texture of the rock,

[5] Blanchard, Roland, Use of ore guides: E. & M. J., vol. 131, p. 174, 1931.

[6] There are always exceptions to such generalizations. The greatest of all gold deposits, those of the Rand, are in siliceous conglomerates.

[7] Cf. Symposium, Some observations in ore search, A.I.M.E. Tech. Pub. 1209, pp. 16–22, 1940.

[8] Hayward, M. W., and Triplett, W. H., Occurrence of lead-zinc ores in dolomitic limestones in Northern Mexico, A.I.M.E. Tech. Pub. 442, 1932. Cf. Hewett, D. F., Dolomitization and ore deposition, Econ. Geol., vol. 23, pp. 821–863, 1928.

[9] Brown, J. S., Factors of composition and porosity in lead-zinc replacements in metamorphosed limestone, A.I.M.E. Tech. Pub. 1194, p. 13, 1940.

[10] Bain, G. W., in Symposium, Some observations in ore search, p. 17; also Mechanics of metasomatism, Econ. Geol., vol. 31, pp. 505–526, 1936.

though important, do not tell the whole story, and that the manner in which individual beds behaved during folding may hold part of the secret. Delicate differences in relative competency could control the manner in which individual beds are prepared to receive ore solutions.[10a]

Competent vs. Incompetent Formations

In some districts, at least, competent rocks are more hospitable hosts to ore than incompetent ones,[11] and surely this is what would be expected from their mode of failure in fracturing. "Competent" as the term is used here, refers to rocks that are relatively strong but, when they do fail, break as though they were brittle material. "Incompetent" refers to rocks which are weak and have a tendency to deform plastically or by flow. Under most conditions, quartzites, conglomerates, and fresh igneous rocks are competent. Incompetent are shales, slates, schists, and limestones; also igneous rocks that have been altered to sericite, chlorite or serpentine. These generalizations, however, are subject to some modifications with varying circumstances. In the first place, competence is a relative matter. A limestone between shale beds is likely to behave as a competent rock; an identical limestone between beds of quartzite is likely to behave incompetently. Furthermore, the manner of failure depends in some degree on the manner in which the rocks were deformed.

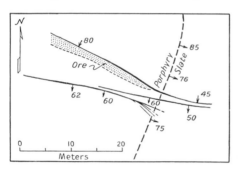

Fig. 64—Influence of competency on fracturing. Flattish vein in slate splits, steepens, and makes ore on entering porphyry. San Luis Vein, Itos Mine, Oruro, Bolivia. (*Courtesy of F. M. Chace*)

A limestone under light load may behave as a competent rock, but under high confining pressure, especially in the presence of solvent and with the rate of deformation slow enough to give time for recrystallization, it may behave as very incompetent material.

Competent rocks, in addition to their tendency to fail by fracture rather than by shear, have an advantage in that they yield to fracture in such a way as to provide permeable channelways.[12] Their strength

[10a] A recent paper not only confirms this suggestion but adds excellent experimental data. See Rove, Olaf N., Some physical characteristics of certain favorable and unfavorable ore horizons, *Econ. Geol.*, vol. 42, pp. 57–77, pp. 161–193, 1947.

[11] Wisser, Edward, Discussion, *Tr. A.I.M.E.*, vol. 114, p. 89, 1942.

[12] Newhouse, W. H., *Ore Deposits as Related to Structural Features*, p. 14. Princeton: Princeton University Press, 1942.

tends to prevent fractures from squeezing shut, and, if they do succumb to failure adjacent to fracture-walls, it is by spalling to produce a jumble of fragments which presents large surfaces to ore depositing solutions.   When competent rocks shatter, they produce either a network of interconnected cracks or a permeable breccia free from gouge. Furthermore, since the shearing angle (see p. 295) decreases with increasing brittleness, a shear-fracture passing from semi-plastic into brittle rock is deflected toward the plane of maximum normal stress and therefore toward an attitude more favorable to opening by the movement that initiated the shear.   An example of the contrast in mode of failure between competent and incompetent material is to be seen at Woods Point in Victoria (Figure 65), where two complementary sets of reverse faults form gold-bearing veins within a broad dike but disappear in the adjoining incompetent slates.

In spite of the superior mode of failure of competent rocks, it is not everywhere true that they are the most hospitable to ore deposition. At Bendigo (Victoria), incompetent slate beds have localized slipping: On the limbs of the anticlines where they overlie competent quartzite beds, they form the sites of quartz veins, locally known as "backs," some of which carry much visible gold.   Similarly in the Porcupine District [13] (Ontario) highly incompetent beds of carbonaceous slate have been replaced by gold-bearing quartz to form exceptionally rich veins, apparently because they became localized zones of intense shearing.   In contrast, some of the thickest and most massive flows of dacite are poor ore-carriers because they were too strong to break.   However, among the formations in this district that conform to neither of these extremes, the usual rules of competency hold fairly well; the most consistent ore-bearing zone is a series of competent greenstone flows, each thin enough to fail, but brittle enough to form good fractures.   The poorest horizons are thick incompetent pillow lavas that yielded along myriads of tight minor shears but afforded no continuous localized open channelways.

Of the districts listed in *Ore Deposits as Related to Structural Features* [14] there are 21 in which rocks more competent than their neighbors are the favored ore-carriers, as against seven in which weak or incompetent rocks are the favorable ones.   (In 17 other districts listed, it is not clear whether the favored rock, if any, was more competent or less so than the adjoining formations.)   If this is a fair sampling it would

[13] Graton, L. C., McKinstry, H. E., and others, *Outstanding Features of Hollinger Geology* (20 pp.), Toronto: Canadian Institute of Mining and Metallurgy, April, 1933.

[14] Newhouse, W. H., Ed., *Ore Deposits as Related to Structural Features*, pp. 45–48. Princeton, N. J.: Princeton Univ. Press, 1942.

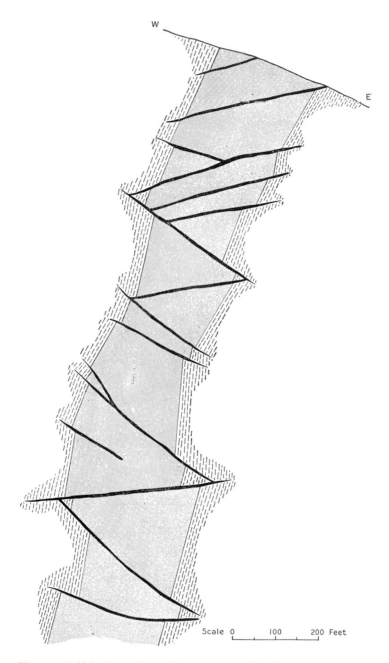

Fig. 65—Gold-bearing veins in fractures in a dike of massive monzonite.
Veins die out in adjoining slate. Cross-section through Morning Star Mine,
Woods Point, Victoria. (*Chem. Eng. and Mining Rev.*, Melbourne)

indicate that the odds are 3 to 1 in favor of competent rocks. But the exceptions are so numerous that the generalization is not of much help in predicting in advance which rocks are likely to be ore-carriers.

Examples of Favorable Formations

In Limestones. The use of a stratigraphic guide is neatly illustrated at Santa Eulalia (Chihuahua, Mexico).[15] Here the silver-lead "mantos" occur almost exclusively in two favored horizons within a series of limestone beds 5000 feet thick. As the orebodies are oxidized, fractures that extend down from them are stained with iron oxide. One method of exploration is to drift on a level below the "manto horizon" and raise on the iron-stained fractures.

In the Mascot-Jefferson City district in Eastern Tennessee, although the zinc sulphide mineralization occurs in various parts of the Knox Dolomite, 3000 feet thick, the only commercial ore is in the formation known as the Kingsport, which is only 350 to 400 feet thick. Within this formation the greater part of the ore occurs at a particular horizon marked by an underlying bed of light gray fine-grained dolomite.[16]

Many other examples of preferential replacement in limestone might be described. Among the most familiar are the lead-zinc ores of the Mississippi Valley region, the silver-lead-zinc deposits of Leadville (Colorado), of Park City and Tintic (Utah), and of many deposits in Mexico, and the copper deposits of Morococha (Peru) and of Bisbee (Arizona).

In Other Sedimentary Rocks. Argillite between a footwall of conglomerate and a hanging wall of quartzite is the host-rock of the enormous lead-zinc orebodies of the Sullivan Mine [17] (Kimberly, B. C.). In the "world's other greatest" silver-lead-zinc deposit, Broken Hill (N.S.W.), the orebodies follow faithfully two or perhaps three very complexly folded beds within a series of schists and gneisses. In Northern Rhodesia the copper ore is limited to the Lower Roan formation and in each individual deposit it conforms to the folded structure of a particular group of sandy shale or feldspathic quartzite beds (Fig. 66).

A very thin seam of pyrite-bearing carbonaceous slate interbedded with thicker slate beds and sandstones localizes the richest portions of

[15] Prescott, Basil, Limestone replacement deposits of the Mexican Province, *E. & M. J.*, vol. 122, p. 246, 1926.

[16] Oder, Charles R. L., and Miller, H. W., Stratigraphy of the Mascot-Jefferson City district: *A.I.M.E. Tech. Pub. 1818*, 1945.

[17] Swanson, C. O., and Gunning, H. C., Geology of the Sullivan Mine: *Canadian Inst. M. and M. Tr.*, vol. 48, p. 657, 1945.

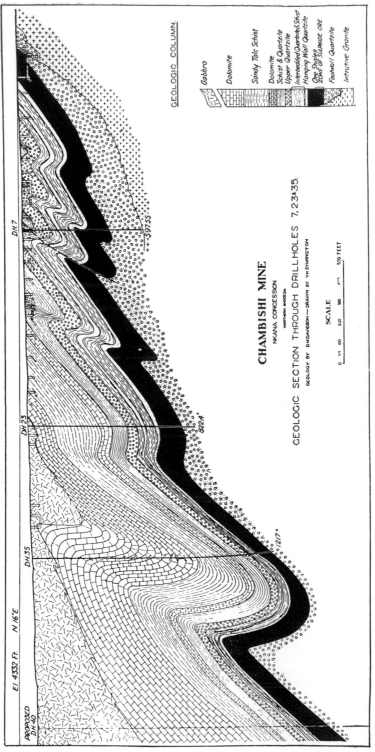

GEOLOGIC COLUMN.

Gabbro
Dolomite
Sandy Talc Schist
Dolomite
Schist & Quartzite
Upper Quartzite
Interbedded Quartzites & Schist
Hanging Wall Quartzite
Ore Shales ZONE OF SULPHIDE ORE
Footwall Quartzite
Intrusive Granite

CHAMBISHI MINE

NKANA CONCESSION
NORTHERN RHODESIA

GEOLOGIC SECTION THROUGH DRILLHOLES 7, 23 & 35

GEOLOGY BY D.M.DAVIDSON ~ DRAWN BY V.H.SYMINGTON

SCALE

0   50   100   200   300   400   500 FEET

Fig. 66—Localization of ore in a favorable stratigraphic horizon. The Ore Shale (carrying copper ore) is shown in black. Cnambishi Mine, Northern Rhodesia. (*After Davidson, Economic Geology*)

the gold-quartz bodies at Ballarat, Victoria, although the orebodies themselves are gash-veins which do not conform to bedding. Locally this seam or "indicator" is replaced by an exceptionally rich slab of gold.[18]

In Volcanic Rocks. Rhyolite flows, closely folded and brecciated, have been converted into rich copper-gold bodies at Noranda, Quebec, while pre-ore basic dikes that cut the rhyolites have almost completely escaped replacement. *Andesite* is the favorable rock for silver deposits in many camps in Western Mexico. Throughout this region the andesite is capped by several thousand feet of rhyolitic and dacitic tuffs and is underlain by one of a variety of rocks: rhyolite, schist, or plutonic intrusives. The veins, which fill fissures that were formed during a

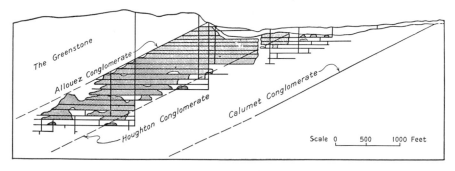

Fig. 67—Ore-shoot on a fissure vein. Shoot localized in a series of basic lava flows between two conglomerate beds. Keweenaw Peninsula, Mich. (*After* Broderick, *Economic Geology*)

period of normal block-faulting, carry oreshoots chiefly, if not exclusively, in the andesite. Extrusive *breccias* and *amygdaloids* are the hosts of the ore in the Michigan "copper country" (the largest deposit, however, is in conglomerate).

In Intrusive Rocks. Plutonic igneous rocks have been used with great success as ore guides in the Kirkland Lake District, Ontario, where the favorable quality of the "porphyry" has long been known. In that district the Macassa Mine was operating on ore of only moderately good grade in syenite until deeper development, recommended by J. E. Todd and W. F. James, followed the vein into the porphyry at the 3000 level where the grade improved phenomenally and the mine became highly profitable.

Intrusive breccias, as in the Cresson pipe at Cripple Creek, Colorado, are especially hospitable rocks.

[18] Baragwanath, W., The Ballarat goldfield: *Geol. Survey of Victoria*, Memoir No. 15, Melbourne, 1923.

Application

The examples that have been given and many more that could be cited indicate that the ore in district after district shows a preference for some particular sedimentary formation or igneous mass. Even in

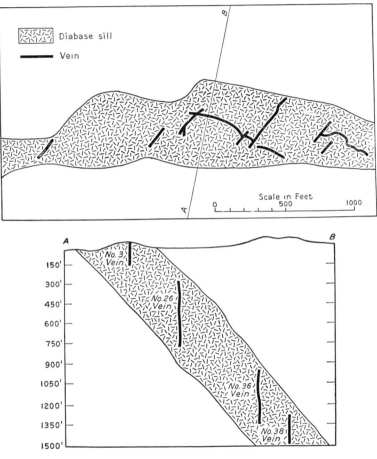

Fig. 68—Veins localized within a diabase sill. San Antonio Mine, Rice Lake, Manitoba. (*After* Stockwell, *Can. Mining and Metallurgical Bulletin*)

districts where such a preference is not now recognized, it may exist nevertheless, for if the rocks are difficult to distinguish or if the structure is complex, the boundaries of the individual formations may not have been traced out in detail. Painstaking mapping and a correct interpretation of faulted or folded structure may show that individual beds or rock-bodies have shapes which correspond more closely with the distribution of ore than had been even suspected before. Once it is definitely established that ore is partial to a particular formation or rock-type, the next step is to predict the location of this rock-type in unexplored or incompletely explored ground. This is done by structural analysis, confirmed where necessary by drilling or other investigation. Where ore within the favorable formation is controlled by additional guides, you are in a position to make use of the principle of intersecting loci.

If you can show on statistical grounds that some particular formation is favorable, you are warranted in using the formation as a guide even though you are unable to explain why it is favorable. But if you can discover the *why* you are on still safer ground and in a position to broaden the principles on which your search is founded. If, for example, you can be sure that a certain andesite flow is favorable because it is a competent rock and yielded to fracture, you will center your attention on parts of it that are so situated as to have experienced fracturing. Furthermore you will become interested in other competent rocks, say well-cemented conglomerates, which might fracture equally well.

Although you can use a stratigraphic guide to excellent advantage, once it is established, you will rarely be safe in assuming that no other horizon will be ore-bearing. A formation that has been shown by experience or by statistics to be unfavorable sometimes springs surprises, especially where it is located on a main channelway. Although such a rock is obviously a relatively poor bet, it should be tested, just as a precaution, provided a test can be made without an expenditure that is out of proportion to the probable risk involved.

Although stratigraphic and lithologic controls are very common, there is no reason to expect that they will always be present; in some districts the ore seems supremely indifferent to stratigraphy or petrology.

SELECTED REFERENCES

Fletcher, A. R., Mexico's lead-silver manto deposits and their origin, *Engineering and Mining Journal*, vol. 127, pp. 509–513, 1929.

Newhouse, W. H., (Editor), *Ore Deposits as Related to Structural Features.* Princeton, N. J.: Princeton University Press, 1942.

Symposium, Some observations in ore search, *American Institute of Mining and Metallurgical Engineers, Technical Publication 1209,* 1940.

12

FRACTURE PATTERNS AS GUIDES

A further result attending to the Disturbances of the surface of the Earth has been to produce Rents or Fissures in the Rocks which have been subject to their violent movements, and to convert them into receptacles of metallic ores accessible by the labors of men.
—REVEREND WILLIAM BUCKLAND,[1] 1835

THERE are those who maintain that no ore deposits can form in solid rock without the aid of fractures. While this statement is much too sweeping to be accurate, it does carry a good deal of truth. Fractures form the channelways for entry of solutions, the receptacles for ore deposition, and the starting-places for replacement. True, there are other forms of permeable channelways, and true also, metallic and other elements can pass through massive rock by diffusion,[2] utilizing capillary and sub-capillary openings, but diffusion is a slow process suited to local transportation inward from the highways of main travel that fractures provide. In vein deposits, fractures are the dominant control; but even in most disseminated and replacement deposits, fractures have exerted a noticeable influence on the forms of orebodies. The shapes of fractures and of fracture-systems therefore provide the key to the structure of many types of ore deposits.

Fractures are not purely accidental. They are the result of failure in a rock-mass that has experienced stress; therefore, they are formed in response to physical laws. Unfortunately there is much that we have yet to learn about the operation of these laws, and we are still unable to

[1] Buckland, William, *Geology and Mineralogy with reference to Natural Theology.* London: William Pickering, 1836.
[2] Duffel, Stanley, Diffusion and its relation to ore deposition: *Economic Geology,* vol. 32, pp. 494–510, 1937.

explain why, under apparently identical stress conditions, some materials fail in one way and some in another. That is to say, we do not yet have a satisfactory theory of rupture. Nevertheless, we do know both from experiment and from observation that the surfaces along which materials fail have at least a qualitative relation to the orientation of the stress. If we had all of the numerical data regarding the stress that was active and knew everything about the strength distribution in the rock, we might be able to predict the general shape and in some instances the detailed shape of the pattern of fractures. Unfortunately, we rarely have this full information, yet some of the data can be deduced from observation. Interpreted with a knowledge of how rocks are known to fail, it often permits the completion of a partly concealed pattern and a prediction as to which portions of the pattern will be most productive.

MECHANICAL PRINCIPLES OF FRACTURING

STRESS

If a body of material is deformed within the elastic limit, each part of it exerts force on the adjoining part. This internal force, called *stress*, can be resolved into components. If we select any point within the body and pass through this point an imaginary plane, there will, in the general case, be a component of the force which tends to make the material on one side of the plane slide over the material on the other side, *i.e.*, a *shearing* component. There is also a component which tends either to press the sides of the plane together or to pull them apart, *i.e.*, a *normal* component. If the tendency is to pull apart, the normal component is *tensile* and, according to the convention of physicists and engineers, is given a positive sign. If the tendency is to squeeze together, the normal stress is *compressive* and has a negative sign.

PLANES OF PRINCIPAL STRESS

Both shearing and normal components act on any given plane except in the case of certain special planes called planes of principal stress. To illustrate this, we might consider a block lying on a table with a weight on top of it, two of its sides confined as in a box and the other pair of sides free. If the block were cut along an inclined plane dipping toward the free side, the upper part of the block would slide down and would at the same time be pressed against the lower part. This shows that in this plane there was both shearing and normal stress (in this case the normal stress is compressive, *i.e.*, negative in sign). But on

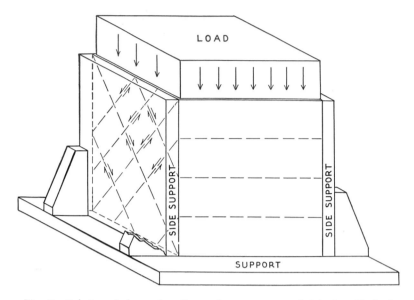

Fig. 69—Relation of planes of maximum shear stress to applied load. (Idealized diagram)

a horizontal plane there is no tendency to slide. There is only compressive stress. And on two other special planes there is also no tendency to slide. On one of these, the one parallel to the supported side, there is compressive stress due to the reaction of the side supports. On the other, parallel to the free side, there is no stress of any sort. (Odd as it may seem at first thought, this is the plane of maximum normal stress even though the intensity of that stress is zero, since zero is larger than any negative quantity. To illustrate this by analogy, a thermometer can reach a maximum reading of zero on a cold day if the other observations during the day read minus 10 or minus 20 and none are above zero.)

To turn from the illustration to the general case, there are, passing through each point in the body, three planes in which shearing stress is zero and these three planes are at right angles to each other. One has the greatest normal stress of the three, one has the least of the three, and the third has a value intermediate between the other two.

In all planes other than these three, there is shearing stress (and, in the most general case, normal stress as well), but in two of these many planes, the shearing stress reaches its maximum value. These two planes are at right angles to each other and they bisect the angle between the two planes of maximum and minimum normal stress. That is, the planes of maximum shearing stress stand at 45 degrees with the plane of maximum normal stress (and also, of course, at 45 degrees to the plane of minimum normal stress). In our example they are planes dipping at 45 degrees and striking parallel to the free sides of the block, and in them the normal stress is negative (compressional). In the more general case, they experience both shearing and normal stress, and the normal stress may be either positive or negative. In one special case (pure shear) the normal stress on the planes of maximum shear is zero.

THE PATTERN OF PRINCIPAL STRESS PLANES

Every point in a stressed body has these four critical planes: two of maximum shear, one of maximum normal stress, and one of minimum normal stress (Figure 70). The four planes all intersect in a common line and stand at 45 degrees to each other. This is true regardless of the manner in which the body is loaded (whether it is acted on by compression, by tension, or by a shearing couple). It is also true regardless of whether the material is homogeneous or inhomogeneous and regardless of whether the stress is uniform or non-uniform. This statement is made em-

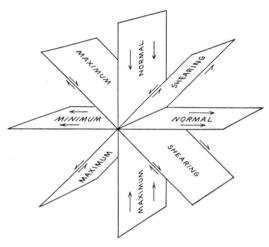

Fig. 70—Planes of principal stress. (Idealized diagram)

phatically here because the matter is confusingly treated in some geological texts.

In Uniform Stress

If the stress is uniform, the critical planes have the same orientation at all points within the body; therefore the state of stress for the body as a whole can be represented by a single diagram. If the stress is not uniform, the orientation of the assemblage of stress planes varies from point to point. Yet, at any one point they are always at 45 degrees to each other. This can be compared to the dial of a compass in a magnetic field. The direction of the north point varies from place to place within the field, but the east point always remains at right angles to it and the northeast point is always at 45 degrees to both.

In Non-Uniform Stress

Of non-uniform stress, there are infinite modifications. Two familiar varieties whose distribution is systematic are those known as bending and torsion. These are not, in effect, different *kinds* of stress, but merely different types of variation of the stress orientation, for at any one point the stress can be resolved into its normal and shearing components. But since the orientation of the critical planes varies from point to point within the body, the infinitesimal plane about each point integrates with its neighbors to form a curved surface. In a bent beam these curves do not vary in the third dimension, *i.e.*, any section cut normal to the axis of bending shows the same sort of curves.

Torsion is a special type of loading which is best described by the simple example of a rod held in a vise at one end and twisted by a pipe wrench attached to the other end. Loading analogous to this can hardly be very common under geological conditions, although it must be involved in some large-scale warpings of the earth's crust and in the kind of deformation that causes scissors-fault movements. Even so, the stress at any point in a rock-mass that is subjected to torsion can be analyzed into shear and normal stress. I am emphasizing this point because "torsional stress" (whatever such a term may mean) has repeatedly been invoked by geologists. Although it is possible that certain systems of fractures may correctly be explained by torsional loading, there is a tendency to ascribe any and all sets of intersecting fractures to torsional forces. Apparently Daubree's famous experiment in applying torsion to a strip of glass has made a graphic and lasting impression despite repeated proofs that it has no geological analogy except in special cases. Then, too, some geologists say "torsional forces" when what they have in mind is a shearing couple. Others, recognizing that the fracture systems resulting from torsion are complex, are inclined to relegate to this class any system that is difficult to analyze. This recourse, besides employing a doubtful criterion, fails to provide a satisfying solution unless the shape and arrangement of the fractures are such that the axis of torsion can be identified and the direction of movement at its opposite ends established.

Another overworked term, *"rotational stress,"* is, strictly speaking, a misnomer. What geologists usually mean by it is loading which produces the type of strain known to physicists as simple shear. Loading of this type accomplishes two results: (1) it sets up a state of stress within the body, (2) it rotates the body during distortion. Thus it is not a special breed of stress, for, at any point and at any one instant it

can be resolved into its normal and shearing components.   Its peculiarity
is that the body occupies from one instant to the next a changing position
with respect to the stress orientation; it thus has significance only when
the time element is considered.   But since the amount of rotation within
the elastic limit is negligible for geological purposes, the effects differ but
little from those of pure shear.   Once the elastic limit is exceeded,
brittle materials fail almost immediately by fracture and then we are no
longer dealing with stress in a homogeneous body but with forces that
resolve themselves into components along and across discontinuities.

Relation of Fractures to Stress

With this background of mechanical principles, we may return to
our rocks and see what relation the fractures bear to the stresses that
cause them.   There are two typical modes of failure by fracture: tension

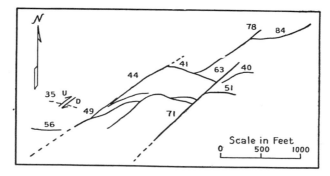

Fig. 71—Shears curving toward the tension direction. Part
of plan of Bagio District, P. I. (*After* Livingston, *Engineering
and Mining Journal*)

and shear.   Whether a rock fails by one or the other or by a combination
of the two depends on the nature of the rock and the conditions of
deformation, although not enough is known about the governing laws
to permit exact predictions.

Shear Fractures

Some materials fail by shear, *i.e.*, by slipping on surfaces which are approximately, but by no means exactly, parallel to the planes of maximum shearing stress.   If the parallelism were exact, the surfaces of
failure would make angles of 45 degrees with the planes of maximum
normal stress; but actually the angle, known as the "shearing angle," is
always less than 45 degrees, although it varies with different materials.
In metals it is but little less than 45 degrees; in limestone, sandstone, and

cement, the angles produced by experiment are as small as 15 to 30 degrees. The surfaces along which brittle materials fail are seen, when examined in detail, to consist of alternate shears and tension cracks.[3] Griggs suggests that, since high confining pressures tend to inhibit tension cracks, the shearing angle should increase with pressure.

Statements in some of the texts to the effect that the shearing angle in plastic materials is greater than 45 degrees have no rational mathematical basis,[4] and the experimental results which seem to support such statements are probably to be explained by rotation of the surfaces of shear after they are formed and, in some cases, by the modifying influence of friction on the ends of test-blocks.

According to the Mohr theory [5] the material fails along a plane in which there is an optimum combination of shearing *and* normal stress, *i.e.*, along a plane on which normal stress is greater (algebraically) than on the plane of maximum shear stress.

Although theory would call for two sets of shear planes, one of them is likely to develop before the other and may serve to relieve the stress, so that the second does not develop at all or else develops late and in "antithetic" [6] relation to the major shears.

"Tension" Fractures

When a rod of brittle material is pulled at both ends, it breaks approximately at right angles to the direction of pull. In granular materials, the broken surface is rough and sometimes jagged because the strength in different grains is not uniform and the break goes out of its course to take advantage of weakness; yet, despite irregularities, it is essentially parallel to the plane of maximum normal stress.

Similar fractures are developed when brittle materials are deformed by a shearing couple. Here again they are parallel to the plane of maximum normal stress, which in pure shear has a positive value.

Theoretically, "tension" fractures ought not to develop in materials loaded in compression, for in such cases no tensile stress is present (*i.e.*, maximum normal stress is zero). Why they should form under such conditions still lacks full and satisfactory explanation. Nevertheless, they do form; they have repeatedly been made under experimental con-

[3] Griggs, David T., Deformation of rocks under high confining pressures: *Journal of Geology*, vol. 44, p. 555, 1936.

[4] The "maximum strain" theory of shear failure has been shown to be mathematically unsound. See Nadai, A., *Plasticity*, p. 59. New York: McGraw-Hill Book Co., 1931.

[5] Nadai, A., *Plasticity*, p. 62. New York: McGraw-Hill Book Co., 1931.

[6] Cloos, H., Zur experimentellen Tektonik: *Die Naturwissenschaften*, 18 Jahrg., Heft 34, 1930.

ditions. For example, Griggs [7] finds that when cylinders and prisms of limestone are axially compressed, they fail along "tension fractures" that are approximately parallel to the axis of compression. He states that confining pressure lessens the tendency to form tension cracks but that they develop to some extent even at 10,000 atmospheres confining pressure, which corresponds to a terrestrial depth of about 20 miles. Fractures having the characteristics of tension cracks can be seen at depths of over 3000 feet in the Porcupine district and at a depth of over 6000 feet on the Rand. At the time they were formed, they must have been thousands of feet deeper still.

Tension fractures are, therefore, perhaps misnamed, unless it is true that they are caused by tensile strain, which can be present even though tensile stress is absent.[8] "Extension fractures" is probably a more appropriate term.[9]

CHARACTERISTICS OF SHEARS AND TENSION FRACTURES

To distinguish confidently between shears and tension cracks is not always possible, especially when the shapes are blurred by replacement or when the history of movements has been complex. Not uncommonly, however, the two types of fracture betray their distinguishing characteristics.

Shears. In the elementary sense of the word, a shear is a plane (or curved) surface on which one wall has moved past the other. Shears, when closely spaced, constitute a "shear zone," which consists of slabs or slivers of rock. Zones of this type are so common that geologists often use the term "shear" instead of "shear zone." If the material of a shear zone is partly or largely replaced by quartz or other vein matter, it becomes a streaked or sheeted vein. The finer fragments and gouge particles may be entirely converted to quartz, with only the larger ones remaining. The residuals may be so thin as to look like streaks. Sometimes slickensided surfaces are more resistant to replacement, either

[7] Griggs, D. T., Deformation of rocks under high confining pressures: *Journal of Geology*, vol. 44, p. 552, 1936.

[8] With compressive stress acting in the X and Y axes and no stress acting in the Z axis, the formula for strain in the Z axis is

$$\varepsilon_z = \frac{s_z - \lambda\,(s_x + s_y)}{E}$$

where E = modulus of elasticity
λ = Poisson's ratio
s_x, s_y, s_z = stresses in the principal axes
ε_z = strain on Z axis

From this it is seen that if s_x and s_y are negative and s_z zero, ε_z is finite and positive.

[9] Bridgman, P. W., Reflections on rupture: *Journal of Applied Physics*, vol. 9, pp. 517–528, 1938.

because of their compaction or because of mineralogical change, and are preserved as lines or sutures within the vein matter. Slivers of rock may be partly to completely replaced by sulphide or by quartz and sulphide; the result is a banded (but not crustified) texture, which is one of the forms of "laminated quartz" or "ribbon structure." If its origin is not recognized, it is easily misinterpreted as either the result of repeated reopening or quartz which has suffered later shearing. In replaced shear zones, however, there is no evidence of more than one generation of quartz, or, if there is, the later generation is superimposed on the original laminated structure. Differences in color of quartz do not necessarily represent different ages. Clear white quartz may represent open-space filling, and inclusion-loaded green or gray quartz may represent replaced rock-material. Nor do local vugs always rule out the possibility of replacement: openings formed during shearing may be incompletely filled; also, cavities can be produced by solution locally exceeding deposition.

Tension Fractures. Ideally, tension fractures are cracks whose walls have been opened by separation in a direction normal to the plane of the crack. Actually, they may have opened by movement oblique to the plane of the fracture; that is, a shearing component as well as a normal component has been active in opening them. In fact, fractures vary in attitude from the true tension position to a shear position with corresponding increase in the ratio of parallel to normal components of movement so that it is difficult to draw a definite line between tension openings and shears. Indeed, a single fracture may change along its course from a shear to a tension crack in accordance with minor changes in its attitude.

The direction of the movement that caused the opening can often be deduced by visualizing the walls and the inclusions fitted back into place. The inclusions in tension fractures are commonly angular and often slab-like with squarish ends forming a structure which Graton has aptly termed "domino breccia." Inclusions may be partly attached to one vein-wall, and not uncommonly they are attached to both walls, forming bridging inclusions or, as Farmin [10] calls them, "straps." Since the relative movement of the walls is the same as it would be if the walls had been pushed apart by hydrostatic pressure of the solution, this alternative mode of origin cannot be distinguished by shapes of walls or inclusions alone. I believe, however, that even though pressure of solutions may be an active agent in separating the walls of a vein, the

[10] Farmin, Rollin, Host-rock inflation by veins and dikes at Grass Valley, California: *Economic Geology*, vol. 36, p. 161, 1941.

separation takes place along planes approximately normal to the direction of easiest yielding and therefore accords with the tectonic stress-pattern.

Very often tension cracks are gash-like and fat, ending in sharp points. Characteristically they are short, though exceptionally some are of great length. Closely spaced parallel tension fractures can form a sheeted zone which is easily mistaken for a shear zone. Tension fractures are very commonly arranged along a shear in herring-bone fashion. Adjoining a normal fault, they are steep, as at El Oro, Mexico, or on the Comstock Lode in Nevada.[11] Adjoining reverse faults, they are less common, but where they do occur, they are flatter than the fault. The shear itself may be mineralized or it may be an unreplaced gouge seam which can easily be mistaken for a post-mineral fault, since tension veins end against it.

Another characteristic arrangement of tension openings is beyond the

Fig. 72—Tension fractures *en echelon* beyond the ends of a shear-fracture. Plan of 605 Stope, Canadian Malartic Mine. (*After* Derry, *Economic Geology*)

end of a shear, forming an *en-echelon* set whose axis continues in the direction of the shear. This type grades into typical "horsetail structure."

[11] Flores, Teodoro, Estudio geologico-minero de los distritos de El Oro y Tlalpujahua: *Inst. Geol. de Mexico Bol. No. 37*, 1920.

Becker, G. F., Geology of the Comstock Lode and the Washoe District. Atlas: *U.S.G.S. Monograph 3*, 1882.

The published sections suggest this origin, though Locke and Billingsley interpreted them as due to mineralization collapse. Locke, Augustus, and Billingsley, Paul, Trend of ore-hunting in the United States: *Engineering and Mining Journal*, vol. 130, p. 609, 1930.

Idealized Fracture Pattern

In homogeneous rocks subjected to uniform stress, one would expect that the pattern of fractures would consist of two sets of complementary shears plus a set of tension cracks standing parallel to the plane that bisects the angle between the shears. But rocks are never homogeneous and stresses are never uniform; hence, actual veins depart widely from the ideal. Nevertheless, the patterns of some districts bear a remarkable resemblance to the theoretical pattern. Significantly, most of these are in intrusive rocks, which are more nearly homogeneous than sediments.

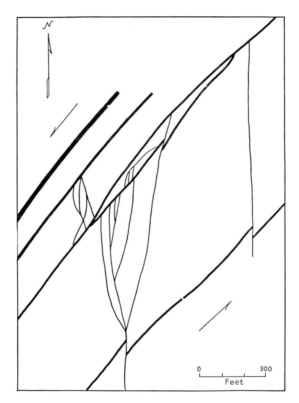

Fig. 73—Pattern of major shears with complementary minor fractures. Randsburg, California. (*After* Hulin, *Economic Geology*)

In analyzing a fracture pattern, one must, of course, remember that the true angle between fractures is to be seen only in a section drawn normal to the intersection; either a plan or a vertical section gives a distorted picture except in special cases. The great variation in the ap-

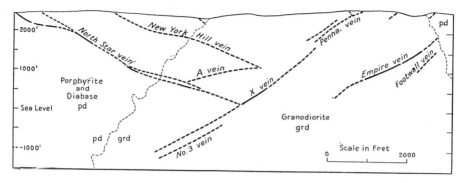

Fig. 74—Conjugate vein system. Cross section, looking north. Grass Valley, California. (*After* Johnston, *U.S.G.S.*)

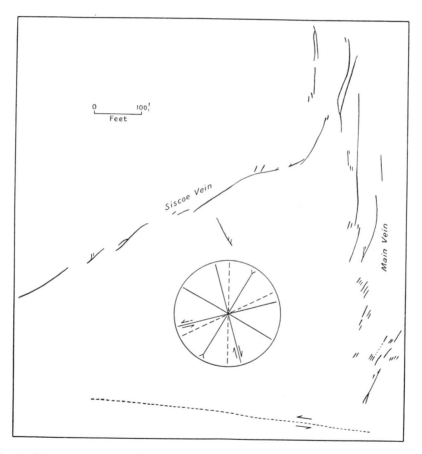

Fig. 75—Vein pattern in Siscoe Mine, Quebec. Data from mine maps by James, Gillanders, and others, projected to a plane dipping N 67 W at 35 degrees. The Main and Siscoe veins occupy the conjugate shear directions, changing along strike to zones of tension fractures. Dashed line near south edge of plan marks zone of slipping and mineralization at south contact of intrusive body. (*After* McKinstry, *Trans. A.I.M.E.*)

301

parent angle of intersection corresponding to variation in the plunge of the line of intersection is shown in Figure 76.[12] In the extreme case, where the line of intersection is horizontal, the traces of the fractures on a horizontal plane form a pair of parallel lines.

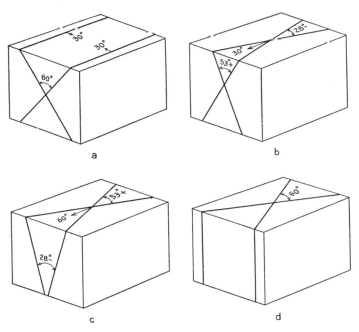

Fig. 76—Variation in apparent angle of intersection depending on plunge of intersection. True angle of intersection is 60 degrees in all figures. *a:* Plunge horizontal. *b:* Plunge 30 degrees. *c:* Plunge 60 degrees. *d:* Plunge vertical.

When fractures occur in complementary sets, the relationship usually shows up best on a scale which portrays the district as a whole. Any restricted portion of the district is likely to show fractures belonging to only one of the sets. In detail, fractures that follow the tension direction may be associated with the shear-fractures. Where both shear directions are developed, there may be evidence that one formed earlier than the other, or one may occupy an antithetical [13] relationship to the other. But even where this is true, the attitudes are those which would be called for by the orientation of stresses.

[12] The problem has been analyzed by Edward Wisser (personal communication). Sketches illustrating the same conception have been published by C. W. Livingston, Mechanics of vein formation in the northern half of the Baguio District: *Engineering and Mining Journal*, vol. 140, p. 41, September, 1939.

[13] Cloos, H., Hebung, Spaltung, Vulkanismus: *Geologische Rundschau*, Band 30, Zwischenheft 4A, p. 416, 1939.

VARIATIONS FROM THE IDEAL PATTERN

From the theoretical pattern, never fully attained in nature, there are all degrees of departure in actual cases. Any one or even any two of the hypothetical sets of fractures may fail to form, and additional fractures, either irregular or in sets, may appear in positions which the stress pattern alone does not provide for.

The idealized attitudes can be compared to the edges of a triangle on a drafting table. The draftsman does not necessarily draw lines parallel to all three of the edges, but any line that he draws with the triangle is parallel to one of the edges—parallel, that is, if the paper is smooth. If there is a groove in the paper, the pen may leave the triangle and follow the groove. The grooves are analogous to irregularities, such as planes of weakness in the rock, and in extreme cases they may be so pronounced as to dominate the fracture pattern.

Causes of Variation

Since fractures can be expected to correspond to the pattern of stress only if the material is homogeneous, it follows that any inhomogeneity in the rock will cause irregularities in the fracture pattern or add new elements to it. Of course, no rocks are truly homogeneous in the physical sense; the nearest approach that we can expect is "statistical homogeneity," in which irregularities such as grains or crystals are small in proportion to the dimensions under observation and are oriented at random so that the directional properties of individual grains tend to cancel each other out. It is significant that the closest resemblances to ideal fracture patterns are found in large masses of igneous rocks, as these come nearer to being statistically homogeneous than do bedded sediments or metamorphics.

The most conspicuous features which interrupt homogeneity are (*a*) surfaces of weakness (pre-existing fractures, bedding planes, and igneous contacts), (*b*) members of a rockmass having contrasting strength-characteristics (beds, dikes, sills), and (*c*) anisotropic rocks (slates, schists, gneisses).

Surfaces of Weakness

A rock will fail along any plane in which the stress exceeds the strength. Planes of weakness being, by definition, loci of low strength, very little stress is required to cause failure along them. Unless such a plane happens to coincide with the plane of maximum or minimum normal stress. it will experience shearing stress and become a plane of slip.   It may be opened or kept closed depending on whether the normal stress on it is compressional or tensional.   If the over-all deforming force is tensional, all planes of weakness are likely to be opened except perhaps those parallel to the axis of tension, but the planes closest in attitude to the plane of maximum normal stress tend to open first and widest.

It does not necessarily follow, however, that a rock will fail along its weakest plane, for this plane may occupy such an attitude that the stress on it, whether tensile or shearing, is small or nil.   Stress along other directions may reach an intensity sufficient to rupture the massive rock before the plane of weakness is overpowered.   Thus the pattern of fractures becomes a compromise between the ideal fracture pattern and the pattern of planes of weakness.

Pre-existing Fractures.   Where a rock containing old fractures experiences new stress, the orientation of the new stress is likely to be different from that which caused the old fractures.   The new stress, in taking advantage of the pre-existing fractures, resolves itself into components normal and parallel to them and may also create new fractures of its own.   The problem of interpretation becomes one of separating the effects of the two periods of deformation.

Compromise between old and new fracture planes is probably the explanation of a very common type of vein pattern in which a vein follows, in turn, one after another of a series of parallel shears, crossing from each to the next by a series of connecting links.

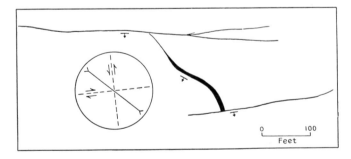

Fig. 77—Tension fracture forming link between two shears. Viking Mine, Norseman, Western Australia. Data from mapping by Conolly and Campbell. (*After* McKinstry, *Trans. A.I.M.E.*)

Some of the veins of the Coeur d'Alene district may illustrate the re-opening of a fracture system by stresses with changed orientation.   In the Burke-Mullan portion of the district there are two sets of fractures: the productive veins, which strike N70W, and faults, which strike N25W. Although the faults offset the veins slightly, it is evident that they were in existence before the veins were mineralized,[14] because in repeated instances an oreshoot is found to extend up to a fault and end there, the displaced part of the vein continuing but without ore. It has been suggested [15] that the vein and the fault constitute a complementary shear system, but that by the time mineralization occurred, the forces had assumed such an orientation that they opened the vein near the intersection and kept the fault closed. Still-later (postmineral) movement caused just enough displacement on the faults to give them the appearance of younger structures.

Bedding Planes.[16] As most stratified rocks are weaker along their bedding planes than in any other direction, these planes behave in much the same way as pre-existing fractures. The essential difference is that if not folded they all belong to a single set and that, if folded, they are curved surfaces, often of small radius. The result is that part of the surface may lie in such a position as to be favorable to opening while the rest does not. As with parallel pre-existing fractures, veins often assume a step-like shape, following one bedding plane for a distance, then "linking" over to another. Vein systems *en echelon* are common and saddle reefs occur occasionally. The relations of veins to folds will be discussed in a later section (page 333).

Igneous Contacts. Contacts between igneous rocks and their hosts are likely to be surfaces of weakness, although occasionally they are "frozen" and strong. Relations between contacts and veins are discussed in the next chapter.

Contrast in Rock-Types. A fracture, and especially a shear-fracture, on passing from one type of rock into another, very commonly changes its direction by a few degrees. In most cases the change is evidently due to contrast in strength-characteristics of the two types of rock. Each type of material has its characteristic shearing angle (p. 295), so that even though the plane of maximum shearing *stress* may be the same throughout the rock-mass, the angle between that plane and the actual surface of shear-failure differs with the type of rock. Knopf,[17] in noting this effect in the rocks of the Mother Lode (California), suggests

[14] Ransome, F. L., and Calkins, F. C., Geology and ore deposits of the Coeur d'Alene district, Idaho: *U. S. Geological Survey Professional Paper 62*, 1908.

[15] McKinstry, H. E., and Svendsen, R. H., Control of ore by rock structure in a Coeur d'Alene mine: *Economic Geology*, vol. 37, p. 228, 1942.

[16] Behre, C. H., Jr., Bedding plane faults and their economic importance: *Transactions of the American Institute of Mining and Metallurgical Engineers*, vol. 126, p. 512, 1937.

[17] Knopf, A., The Mother Lode system of California: *U. S. Geological Survey Professional Paper 157*, 1929.

the analogy to the refraction of a beam of light and estimates the "index of refraction" for different types of rock.

The refraction or deflection may be caused by a contrasting sedimentary formation or by a mass of igneous rock such as a dike or sill. The position of greatest opening will vary with the direction of deflection and with the sense of the movement on the fault.

Anisotropism.   Some rocks, such as uniform slates and schists, are homogeneous in the sense that they lack contrasting layers, yet they are weaker in some directions than in others.   In such materials, which may be described as anisotropic, a uniform stress produces a non-uniform strain.   Although further study of the mode of failure of anisotropic material is needed, everyone knows that failure tends to take advantage of slaty cleavage and schistosity.   The surprising thing is that some veins in schist, instead of following cleavage or alternating between directions parallel to it and across it, actually cut the cleavage at small angles without taking advantage of it.

FORCES CAUSING FRACTURING

If it is not always easy to deduce the orientation of the stress that caused fracturing, it is even more difficult to be sure of the type of loading that set up the stress.[18]   Whether loading of a rock-mass consists of compression, tension, or a shearing couple, the fracture pattern within the limits of a mine might be virtually the same, although study of the pattern throughout a wider region might indicate the correct interpretation.

The motivating forces that cause fracturing may be either local or regional.   Of local forces, the source most commonly invoked is movement related to igneous intrusion.   Cracks in an intrusive can result from contraction on cooling or from collapse on withdrawal of the magma.   Fractures in the adjoining rocks may also result from these causes, as well as from forceful entry of the magma.   Thus, up-punching of overlying rocks can be caused by rise of the magma in the form of stocks and necks.

Local fracturing and shattering can also result from removal of material by solution (mineralization stoping).[19]   By the latter process, Locke explains the down-dropped plugs that form the copper-bearing "ovals" of Sonora, though some other observers have attributed them to

---

[18] "Loading" is used in the engineering sense and is not restricted to the effects of the force of gravity.

[19] Locke, Augustus, The formation of certain orebodies by mineralization stoping: *Economic Geology*, vol. 21, pp. 431–453, 1926.

magma movement. It is interesting and perhaps puzzling to recall that rather similar though smaller down-dropped plugs are found in the Tri-State zinc mines in the complete absence of igneous rocks.

Local forces, especially those depending on the energy of igneous intrusion, have a seductive appeal for the economic geologist. The concept of a magma entering and supplying the solutions to traverse the cracks that its own entry and cooling have created is disarmingly plausible, but it is usually too simple to fit all of the facts. Its uncritical acceptance is likely to obscure not only the origin of the fractures but also the source of the ore-solutions, thus throwing the ore-hunter off the scent and tricking him into looking for ore in just the wrong places.

For the mere fact that fractures are localized in and around an intrusive does not prove that the emplacement or its aftereffects caused the fracturing. Bodies of igneous rock and their margins are just the places where failure would be likely during regional deformation, a fact that is too often overlooked. The quartz-filled fractures in the dike at Woods Point, Victoria, (see Figure 65) have been cited repeatedly in the texts as examples of shrinkage cracks, but an analysis of the pattern of fractures shows clearly that they are shears and testifies to failure under regional compression. The fractures in the Cripple Creek crater had long been attributed to volcanic forces or to settling, but the more careful analysis by Loughlin and Koschmann [20] indicates that they are due to regional compression.

In short, I believe that in more instances than are generally recognized, the fracturing forces have been regional rather than local. An off-hand statement that "the veins occupy fractures probably formed during cooling of the intrusive" or "the intrusion has fractured the surrounding rocks" does more harm than good unless it is supported by evidence that the pattern of fractures actually corresponds with this mode of origin rather than with another.

VEIN-PATTERNS AS GUIDES

Analyzing the Vein-Pattern

The first step in analyzing a pattern of veins is, of course, to see the pattern in its true form. This is not possible from a surface map alone unless the veins are very steep or the surface is flat. Only a projection to a uniform level will give an undistorted horizontal view of the sys-

---

[20] Loughlin, G. F., and Koschmann, A. H., Geology and ore deposits of the Cripple Creek district, Colorado: *Colorado Scientific Society*, vol. 13, no. 6, pp. 217 *ff*., 1935.

Loughlin, G. F., Cripple Creek today: *Engineering and Mining Journal*, vol. 136, no. 8, p. 372, August, 1935.

tem. But even this may not reveal the three-dimensional picture, as veins of parallel strike may be of two sets with opposite or highly divergent dips, forming a grid-pattern which is revealed only by cross sections.

When the shape of the vein-pattern is clearly evident from plans and sections, the next step is to see whether it can be analyzed in terms of a stress pattern, using not only the space-relations of the veins but indications of any pre-ore displacement, however small, that may have taken place along them and any details of vein-structure indicating shear or tension phenomena. Most important of all is to correlate the pattern with geological features: rock formations that have been particularly hospitable or inhospitable to fracturing, surfaces of weakness that have deflected veins from their general course, and attitude of fractures with relation to bedding and folds. An understanding of the origin and mechanics of the vein-pattern not only inspires greater confidence in the conclusions but permits more intelligent predictions. If you know *why* a vein makes ore under certain conditions, you are in a better position to predict *where* it will make ore again.

But understanding a vein-pattern is easier to advocate than to accomplish. Persistent striving toward the correct interpretation should never be relaxed, yet recommendations need not wait upon its completion. Exploration based purely on the geometry of a vein-pattern has repeatedly led to new veins.

Typical Vein-Patterns

Although every district has its own habits and peculiarities, there are characteristic patterns which repeat themselves with minor variations from district to district and are most readily recognized by geologists familiar with a wide variety of vein-structures. The simplest pattern consists of parallel or nearly parallel veins as exemplified in the eastern portion of the Coeur d'Alene District, Idaho, or in the Hog Mountain District, Alabama.[21] Parallel veins may be arranged *en echelon* or otherwise. More common than parallel patterns, however, are patterns in which there are two sets of veins, each with a characteristic strike. Both sets may be equally strong or the veins of one set may be wide and rich while those of the other are narrow and barren. Besides contrast in width or grade, there may be a contrast in mineralogy.

Where two sets are present, each set may dominate in a particular part of the district. Alternatively, the veins of the two sets may intersect

[21] Park, C. F., Jr., Hog Mountain Gold District, Alabama: *Transactions of the American Institute of Mining and Metallurgical Engineers,* vol. 115, pp. 209–228, 1935.

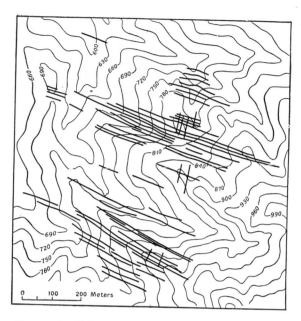

Fig. 78—Parallel vein pattern. Tachishan District, China.
(*After* Ke-Chin Hsu, *Economic Geology*)

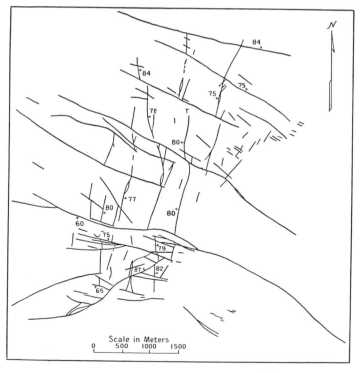

Fig. 79—Sub-rectangular grid pattern. Real del Monte, Mexico. (*After*
Wisser, *A.I.M.E.*)

309

Fig. 80—Acute grid-pattern. Zacatecas, Mexico. (*After* C. W. Botsford, *E. & M. J.*)

each other in the form of a grid, which may be rudely rectangular as at Real del Monte, Mexico (Fig. 79), or oblique as at Parral (Fig. 81). Instead of crossing each other, grid-fashion, the veins may form a Y-shaped pattern as at Fresnillo, Mexico, or they may form a linked system consisting of a set of parallel veins joined by diagonal branches which make off obliquely from one vein and join the next. Somewhat similar are braided systems in which two veins run parallel for a space, then join, then separate and become parallel again after the design of a chicken-wire mesh (Fig. 83).

Somewhat less common than patterns marked by two dominant trends are patterns of three or more, as at Butte, where the system is highly complex yet has strong aspects of symmetry. In some patterns the veins are curving rather than even approximately straight, swinging from one direction into another (Fig. 85). From these patterns, in which some semblance of orderly arrangement is discernible, there are all gradations into patterns in which the veins seem to lie helter-skelter with no recognizable scheme.

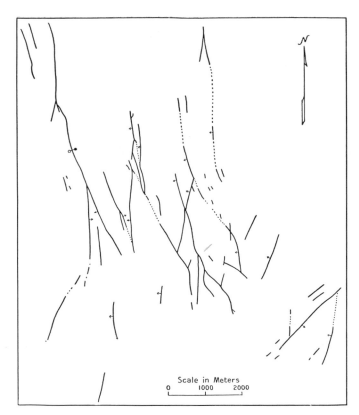

Fig. 81—Acute grid-pattern, Parral, Chihuahua, Mexico. Data for western part of district is from map by H. Schmitt. (*Modified after* Schmitt, *A.I.M.E.*)

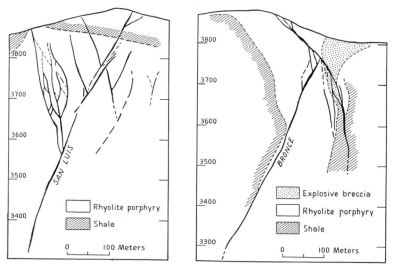

Fig. 82—Branching vein pattern. Oruro, Bolivia. (*After* Campbell, *Economic Geology*)

311

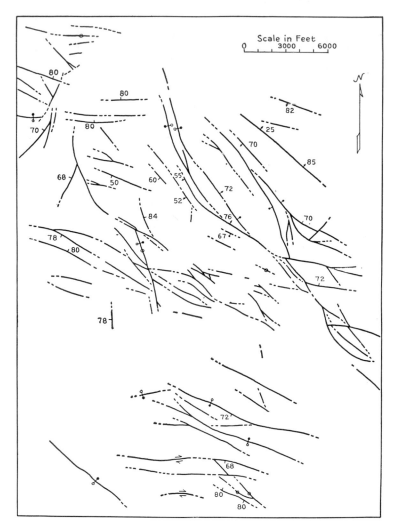

Fig. 83—Mesh-like vein pattern. Oatman, Arizona. (*After* Lausen, *Ariz.
Bur. Mines*)

Applications

Unless a district is completely developed, the map shows only part of
the vein-pattern; the rest of it consists of veins that are incompletely
explored or still undiscovered. What would the pattern look like if we
could see it all? One of the geologists' jobs is to postulate undeveloped
elements and explore for them. In this, the guiding assumption is that
the concealed part is likely to have the same general shape as the visible
part.

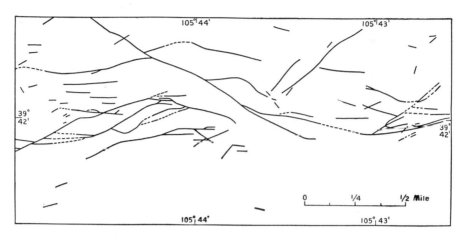

Fig. 84—Acute vein-pattern approaching mesh-like pattern. Silver Plume, Colorado. (*After* Spurr and Garrey, *U.S.G.S.*)

Close spacing of known veins will suggest development of new areas by crosscutting, whereas wide spacing will suggest that a crosscut may have to go a long way before it finds the next vein and thus will point to drilling or to search at the surface. Whatever the method of exploratory traversing, the strikes of veins as disclosed by the pattern will show what direction of traverse will cross them most nearly at right angles. Habitual dips will tell whether to explore by steep holes (for

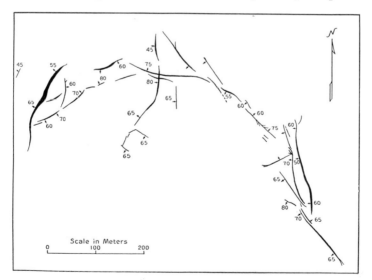

Fig. 85—Curving vein-system. Irregularity due partly to control by rock-distribution (not shown on map). Generalized map of veins on 100 level. San Jose Mine, Oruro, Bolivia. (*Courtesy of* F. M. Chace)

flattish veins) or by gently inclined holes (for steep veins). If ore occurs at vein-intersections, known veins will be projected to the points where they will intersect. Above all, any geological features, whether beds, faults, contacts, or intrusive bodies, which influence the location of veins, will be considered in projecting the vein-pattern and in laying out development.

Vein-Structure within the Pattern

Within the broad framework of the pattern of a district, the individual veins or vein-groups have their own characteristic shapes. Like the major patterns, they vary from one district to another, but a few typical structures are familiar through repetition.

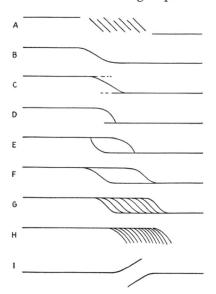

Fig. 86—Types of change in strike (or dip) of veins. (All figures are diagrammatic and idealized.) A: Gashes en echelon. B: Cymoid curve. C: Diagonal link. D: Chatter-like link. E: Double-chatter link. F: Cymoid loop. G: Multiple cymoid loops. H: Horsetail. I: Curved shingles.

Fractures arranged *en echelon* are very common. Tension fractures, especially, are likely to form zones of overlapping gashes; the axis of the group may or may not be along the prolongation of a shear. In planning development to find new members of the set, the position of the axis of the pattern should first be determined. When there is a large overlap, *i.e.*, when the axis is at a fairly large angle to the strike of the individual veins, the best plan of development is to crosscut along the axis. When there is not much overlap, the best practice is usually to drift to the end of one fracture and then crosscut (Figure 87). In any one neighborhood the axes of all sets are likely to have a common attitude, and this situation may give rise to local rules of thumb such as that employed in the Hollinger Mine: "When a vein pinches out, crosscut to the left for the next one." In developing *en echelon* veins, it is well to remember that the axis of the set is not necessarily horizontal; it may be vertical or inclined. That is to say, the next vein may not be found on the same level as the previous one but is to be sought by raising or winzing.

There is probably a relationship between the arrangement of *en eche-*

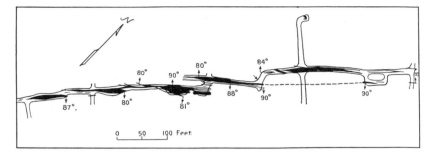

Fig. 87—En echelon arrangement of lenses. Plan of 200-foot level. Vaucluse Mine, Orange County, Va. (*After* Bass, *Economic Geology*)

lon fractures and the direction of movement which originated them, but it is difficult to formulate a useful rule of thumb unless shear-fractures can be clearly distinguished from tension openings. Normal faults are usually arranged like shingles on a roof as at Casapalca, Peru,[22] so that when one is bottomed, the next is to be found in the footwall.[23] But tension fractures in zones of normal fault movement stand steeper than the zone of shearing, so that the next lower vein is to be found in the hanging wall. For reverse faults, the relationships are opposite to those in zones of normal fault-movement. For strike-slip movement, analogous relations hold—one need only view the cross section illustrating dip-slip movement as though it were a plan.

Cymoid Structure. Characteristic of certain veins is a shape that may conveniently be termed a *cymoid* [24] curve. This is a reverse curve in which a line swerves from its course and then swings back again resuming a direction parallel to its former course but not in line with it. Such structures commonly occur in pairs, forming what might be called a *cymoid loop.* That is, a vein splits, one branch swerving aside to execute a reverse curve while the other branch continues straight for a short distance and then executes a similar curve to rejoin the first branch (see Figures 88 and 89). The two branches thus enclose a lens of wall-rock shaped somewhat like the cam of a stamp mill—a *cymoid lens.* The relation of ore to the vein structure may conform to any of the following conditions:

[22] McKinstry, H. E., and Noble, J. A., The veins of Casapalca, Peru: *Economic Geology,* vol. 27, p. 507, 1932.

[23] Lovering, T. S., Physical factors in the localization of ore: *Ore Deposits as Related to Structural Features.* W. H. Newhouse, Editor. Princeton: Princeton University Press, 1942.

[24] From the terms *cyma recta* and *cyma reversa* used in architecture to describe certain shapes of molding. Adding -oid avoids confusion with the geolog'cal term *sima,* which has an entirely different connotation. Dr. Kirk Bryan suggested the analogy of the curve to the architectural form.

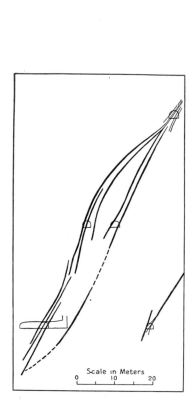

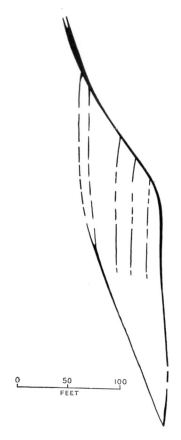

Fig. 88—Cymoid loop. Part of Bronce vein, Oruro, Bolivia. Cross section looking west. (*Courtesy of* F. M. Chace)

Fig. 89—Cymoid loop. Pachuca, Mexico. (*After* Thornburg, *Economic Geology*)

1. One or both branches may be of more than average richness.
2. The two junctions at the points of the cam are ore loci.
3. The immediate junctions are barren, but the branch-veins between them are orebearing.
4. The whole cam-shaped lens is brecciated and partly or wholly replaced by ore, forming in the third dimension a pipe-like oreshoot.

Upward or downward the included lens is likely to pinch, with disappearance of the cymoid loop and straightening of the vein into one continuous fracture. The cymoid structure is so common that it should be suspected wherever a vein swings perceptibly. One of the pair of veins bounding the lens may be inconspicuous, but it is worth looking for as it may make ore after it has swung to the oblique direction. Instead of only two veins as described here, there may be three or even multiple veins crossing over from one main track to the other.

Johnston [25] describes examples in Grass Valley in which a main vein weakens progressively as one split after another leaves it and crosses over to a parallel vein, which in turn gains strength progressively as the successive splits join it. He notes that a crosscut to find the new parallel vein should not be driven too soon; otherwise the new vein will not have gained sufficient strength to be recognizable.

Although the cymoid structure has been described here in terms of strike, it may equally well consist of a swing in dip or in both dip and strike.

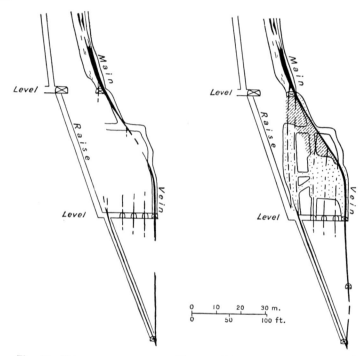

Fig. 90—Vein-pattern serves as guide to orebody in cymoid loop. *Left:* Early stage of development. *Right:* After more advanced development and beginning of stoping. (*After* Thornburg, *Economic Geology*)

Thornburg [26] describes interesting examples of discovery of ore by applying structural principles to patterns of this type. Figure 90 illustrates a case in which restoration of the structure indicated the possibility of an orebody at the point of a lens and subsequent development found the ore.

Somewhat similar to the cymoid loop is "horsetail structure," in which

[25] Johnston, W. D., Jr., The gold quartz veins of Grass Valley, California: *U. S. Geological Survey Professional Paper 194*, 1940, p. 29.

[26] Thornburg, C. L., Some applications of structural geology to mining in the Pachuca-Real del Monte Area, Pachuca silver district, Mexico: *Economic Geology*, vol. 40, pp. 283–297, 1945.

a series of branches curve off from one side of a vein and form a broad zone of closely spaced stringers. Such zones at Butte (Montana) and

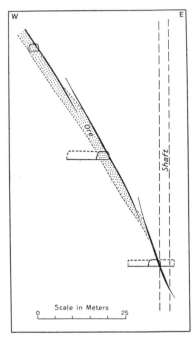

at Siscoe (Quebec) make very wide ore-bodies. Typical horsetail veins die out away from the main vein after the fashion of their zoological prototype. A modification of the structure, in which the veins curve and join again to form a new main vein, is identical in pattern with the multiple cymoid. In still another modification, the branch veins, instead of curving into the new main vein, meet it at a large angle.

An overlap or offset contrasting in shape with the cymoid loop is found in some districts, notably Oruro, Bolivia,[27] where a typical fracture swings from its course and soon pinches out. The new overlapping fracture is found not on the side toward which the vein swings but on the opposite side.[28] Thus if a fracture curves into the footwall and pinches, the new fracture is found in the hanging-wall. This structure may be distinguished from the cymoid in that

Fig. 91—Shingle structure ("inverted"). Cross section of Grande vein, La Colorada Mine, Oruro, Bolivia. (*Courtesy of* F. M. Chace)

there is no fracture carrying ahead in the main direction of the dip or strike and that the curving and pinching is rather abrupt.

Localization of Oreshoots within the Fracture Pattern

The position that ore occupies within a fracture system is determined by a wide variety of geological influences. Some of them are related to the geometry of veins, and these aspects alone will receive attention at the moment.

The shapes of veins may influence deposition by determining (1) width of openings, (2) surface area presented to solutions for reaction. A third consideration, influence on the path of ore solutions, is really largely a matter of the arrangement of continuous openings. This repeated emphasis on openings does not imply that all veins were formed by simple filling; indeed, many, and perhaps most, veins are formed by

[27] Chace, F. M., *Doctorate Thesis*, Harvard University, 1946.

[28] Lovering, T. S., Physical factors in the localization of ore: *Ore Deposits as Related to Structural Features*, p. 7. W. H. Newhouse, Editor. Princeton: Princeton University Press, 1942.

replacement of material in and adjoining the vein-fissure. But wide openings provide access for a plentiful supply of ore-bringing solution. Moreover, they tend to fill themselves by slabbing and caving of their walls and thus become zones of permeable breccia with a large area of rock-surface available for attack by solutions. Therefore, openings are potent localizing influences, whether the ore was deposited by filling or by replacement.

Position of Openings

Failure of rock along fractures may or may not in itself provide open spaces of appreciable size. Since open space implies net increase in volume, the question depends partly on whether the requisite space can be made available. It depends also on whether or not deformation is continued (or repeated) after initial failure. The positions of openings are determined by the shapes of the fractures, taken in conjunction with the orientation of the forces that tend to open them. In the simplest case, the forces that originate the fractures are also the ones that open them. In other cases the history is more complex; an early fracture system is opened or reopened by forces having a new orientation.

Favorable Attitude. Considering the simplest case in its ideally simplest form, shear fractures should really not be opened at all, since movement along them is parallel to the plane of the fracture. Indeed, they probably would not be opened if the fracture were an optically plane surface, but in nature all shear surfaces are more or less curved or irregular, so that movement along them produces an alternation of open and closed intervals. Whereas shear fractures are, ideally speaking, openings only by virtue of their irregularities, tension fractures are openings by their very nature, since they represent movement normal to their walls. It does not follow, though, that they have in all cases been opened to great width (the openings along some tension joints have probably been microscopic) nor that they were still open when solutions were seeking paths of travel. But in general the widest open spaces would be expected on tension fractures, and the wide spaces along shears would be in intervals where they curve toward the tension direction.

When the history is more complex, that is, when an old fracture system has been reopened by new forces, the original shears may find themselves in a position to be opened throughout, regardless of irregularities; original tension fractures may be in such positions that they are opened or held shut as the case may be, but the principle holds that fractures most nearly parallel to the new plane of maximum normal stress are in the most favorable position for reopening.

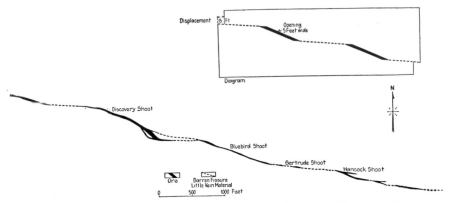

Fig. 92—Variation in width of vein with changes in strike.   Camp Bird Vein, Colorado.
(*After* Spurr, *Economic Geology*)

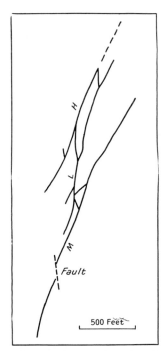

Fig. 93—Cross section through H-M vein system, Casapalca, Peru. Looking north. (*After* McKinstry and Noble, *Economic Geology*)

At Casapalca, Peru, there is a series of veins that vary in dip from vertical to fifty degrees or less.   The steeply-dipping parts of the system are the widest and richest.   The flatter parts are narrow and lean, and where the dip is flatter than 50 degrees, the veins are too narrow to mine.[29]   In contrast, the veins at Norseman, W. A., are poor where they are steep and make oreshoots where they flatten.   These observations are explainable in terms of mechanics; the vein fissures at Casapalca probably constitute a fault system of normal displacement whereas the Norseman fissures apparently are reverse faults.   In some districts the oreshoots, instead of showing relationship to dip, coincide with deflections in strike.   In a part of the Coeur d'Alene district, for example, the veins make ore where they curve to the left.

A great many other examples have been observed [30] in which those parts of vein systems which are so located as to be opened by the movement that caused the fractur-

[29] McKinstry, H. E., and Noble, J. A., The veins of Casapalca, Peru: *Economic Geology*, vol. 27, p. 508, 1932.

[30] Emmons, W. H., Certain ore shoots on warped fault planes: *American Institute of Mining and Metallurgical Engineers Technical Publication 1545*, 24 pp., 1943. (Gives extended bibliography.)

ing have received the greatest thickness of vein filling.

Openings of an Irregular Fault Fissure. If a fracture becomes a plane of fault movement, the amount of opening at places where the fault-surface diverges from its average attitude is determined by the change in direction and the amount of displacement along the fault. The relationship is expressed by the equation:

$$w = d \sin \theta$$

where: w is the width of the opening, d the displacement along the fault, and θ the angle of deflection.[31] This means, for example, that an opening one inch wide would result from a movement of 57.5 feet if the deflection angle is 1 degree, 5.5 feet if the deflection angle is 10 degrees, and only 2.9 feet if the angle is 20 degrees.

Deflection may be occasioned by intersection with bedding-planes, by change in competency of formation, or by pre-existing fractures or other loci of weakness. Whether such surfaces will produce a deflection and, if so, whether in a favorable or an unfavorable direction will depend on their attitude with respect to the fracturing forces. If the direction of displacement during fracturing is known, the change in attitude, which

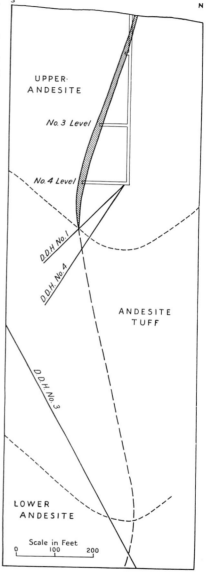

Fig. 94—Pinching of vein with change in dip, coinciding with change in wall-rock.

should bring the vein into the favorable rather than the unfavorable position, may be expressed by a simple rule: Draw a pair of arrows

[31] McKinstry, H. E., Structural control of ore deposition in fissure veins: *American Institute of Mining and Metallurgical Engineers Technical Publication 1267*, 1941; and *Transactions*, vol. 144, pp. 65–95, 1941.

Emmons, W. H., Certain ore shoots on warped fault planes: *American Institute of Mining and Metallurgical Engineers Technical Publication 1545*, 24 pp., 1942.

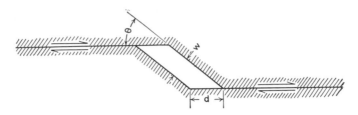

Fig. 95—Opening localized by change in attitude of a fault-fissure. (Idealized diagram)

indicating the relative direction of movement of the two walls and draw a diagonal line connecting the tails of the arrows. A swing of direction of the fracture toward parallelism with this line is favorable.

Fig. 96—Position of open or closed portion of a fault fissure with respect to direction of movement on fault. *a-a* favorable to opening; *b-b* unfavorable to opening. (Idealized diagram)

A swing away from it (*i.e.*, toward a line connecting the heads of the arrows) is unfavorable.[32] The application of this rule to dip-slip and strike-slip fault-fissures is shown in Table 9.

TABLE 9

	Direction of Movement			
	Dip-slip faults		Strike-slip faults	
	Normal *	Reverse	Right hand *	Left hand
Location of Opening	On steeper parts	On flatter parts	On deflections to the right	On deflections to the left

* Normal and reverse refer here to the true displacement, not the apparent displacement in cross section. The displacement on a fault is designated as right-hand if, as one stands facing the fault plane, the farther wall of the fault has experienced a relative movement to the right. Conversely for left-hand displacement.

[32] *Cf.* Hulin, Carlton D., Structural control of ore deposition: *Economic Geology*, vol. 24, p. 40, 1929.

In all but special cases the displacement has components in both the dip and the strike. It is important to visualize all three dimensions and consider the resultant direction of movement rather than either the vertical or horizontal component alone.[33]

Deductions based on the direction of the movement of the walls are likely to be well worth testing, but a safer guide, if it is available, is the observed relation of width and grade to vein-attitude on parts of the vein-system that are already explored. These relationships may be very

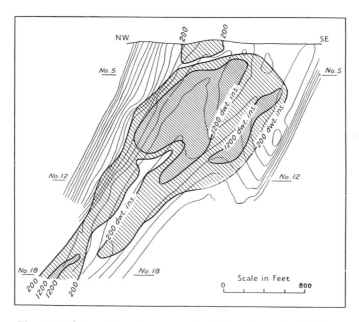

Fig. 97—Relation of ore-shoot to vein-attitude. Great Fingall Mine, Western Australia. Structure contours (light lines) indicate distance from an arbitrary inclined plane. Heavy lines and hatching indicate gold content. (*After* Conolly, *Economic Geology*)

delicate and subtle. Variations in the thickness of the ore may be related to changes in attitude which are so gentle that they will not be conspicuous on ordinary maps or sections but are recognizable only after special geometrical analysis. Since the favorable attitude may not be a matter of dip or of strike alone, but a combination of dip *and* strike, the critical attitudes are best revealed not by a plan or section but by a contouring of the surface of the vein with reference to an inclined

[33] Newhouse, Walter H., Openings due to movement along a curved or irregular fault plane: *Economic Geology*, vol. 35, pp. 445–464, 1940; republished in *Ore Deposits as Related to Structural Features*, edited by Newhouse, W. H., pp. 15–23. Princeton: Princeton University Press, 1942.

datum plane [34] (see p. 191).   For determining the relation of ore-grade to the structure, the operating stope-map does not always afford information that is sufficiently detailed.   It is preferable to prepare an assay-contour section in the form of a tracing that can be superimposed on the structure-contour sheet.

Once the fact of interrelation between values and structure is established, the next step is to predict where a favorable structural attitude will be repeated.   This prediction does not always follow automatically. I once worked out a very neat case of "zig-zag" control in a vein in uniform granite but, to my chagrin, could find nothing to give me a clue as to where the next change in strike would occur.   However, if the change has been found to take place at intervals of, say, 500 or 1000 feet, a repetition at the same distance is worth exploring on purely empirical grounds.

Sometimes data derived from mapping or obtainable by drilling will indicate that a change of attitude must take place somewhere within an unexplored interval.   For instance, a cross section prepared by mapping a series of levels and plotting the data from a deeper drill-hole may show that the vein has to steepen; otherwise it could not pass through the point where it was found in the drill-hole.   If steepening is known to be favorable, the evidence points to a good prospect between the workings and the drill-hole.   But if steepening is known to be unfavorable, the evidence is inconclusive, for there is still a possibility that the average dip may be made up of abnormally steep and abnormally flat segments.   In this case more data are called for.

A probable change of attitude is sometimes predictable on structural evidence.   Since deflections may be caused by planes of weakness or by a change in wall rock, a projection of such features may indicate that the vein will intersect them.   Whether the influence will be favorable or unfavorable will have to be inferred from an understanding of the mechanics of fracturing and preferably from local experience.

Vein Intersections

Localization of ore at vein intersections is very common.   A classic example, the Neue Hoffnung Mine at Freiberg, is familiar to all students from the figures in the texts.[35]   A common type of oreshoot at

[34] Conolly, H. J. C., A contour method of revealing some ore structures: *Economic Geology*, vol. 31, pp. 259–271, 1936.

[35] Lindgren, W., *Mineral Deposits*, fig. 86, p. 201.   New York: McGraw-Hill Book Co., 1933.
Emmons, W. H., *Principles of Economic Geology*, fig. 154B, p. 213.   New York: McGraw-Hill Book Co., 1940.

an intersection is shown in Figure 98, and many other examples have been described.   In some districts, though, intersections appear to have no ore-localizing effect whatever.   This is the case at Oatman, Arizona.[36]   It is also the case at Oruro, Bolivia,[37] where it is the local habit that one fracture either crosses and slightly offsets another, or else swings

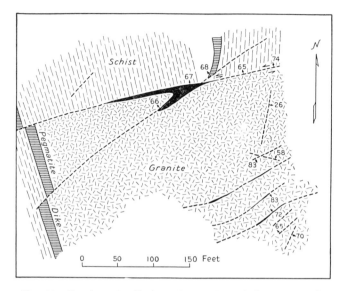

Fig. 98—Ore-shoot localized at intersection of fractures. Lilly tunnel level of the Rakeoff mine, Nederland, Colorado. (*After* Lovering, Princeton University Press)

abruptly toward parallelism with it, without making an orebody in either case.

In some districts where an oreshoot is localized by an intersection, the immediate junction is barren but the oreshoot occurs at some distance from it.   This is true at Parral, Chihuahua, where the intersection of the Tajo and Prieta veins is not orebearing, but away from the split, the two veins are mineralized for a width of 30 meters or more and for a stope-length of some 90 meters.   In one mine in Western Mexico there are two veins, both of which carry oreshoots.   The shoot in No. 1 vein has a position and pitch that corresponds exactly to the place where No. 2 vein would intersect it if projected, although No. 2 vein ceases to be a definite structure before it reaches No. 1.

The term intersection really includes two geometrical shapes: an X

[36] Lausen, Carl, Geology and ore deposits of the Oatman and Katherine Districts: *Arizona Bureau of Mines Bulletin* 131, undated, c. 1931.
[37] Chace, F. M., *Doctorate Thesis*, Harvard University, 1946.

in which both veins continue beyond the intersection, and a Y which, approached in the opposite direction, is identical with a split. The angle of intersection may vary from acute to 90 degrees. The fissures which localized the two veins may have formed at the same or in two successive periods, and regardless of whether or not the original fissures were contemporaneous, the vein-matter in the two may be of the same or of contrasting ages. In the latter case, the younger mineralization usually cuts the older. Because of these differences in shape, mechanical origin, and mode of ore deposition, it is hardly surprising that no general rules apply to all types and that intersections *per se* cannot be considered as either favorable or unfavorable. Blanchard [38] has tabulated 137 examples of vein intersections. In 74% of these the veins were richer at the intersections than elsewhere. In 12% there was no change and in 14% they were poorer (including 5% in which the junction was barren), although ore was mined from each vein nearby. These figures indicate that although intersections are not infallible guides, the odds are decidedly in their favor, and this conclusion certainly accords with the general experience of miners.

Penrose [39] has observed that shoots are more likely to occur where the intersection is acute, forming wedge-shaped blocks that are easily broken along their edges. Other writers have suggested that where veins intersect upward, A-fashion, to form a pitching, inverted trough, the conditions are more favorable to deposition by ascending solutions than when the veins intersect downward in the form of a V. Both of these suggestions are very plausible but have not been tested by statistical data.

Although there is no positive assurance that vein intersections will always be favorable, they are well worth testing except in districts where experience is overwhelmingly against them. In districts in which they have repeatedly been shown to be favorable, they constitute the simplest and most useful of ore guides.

SELECTED REFERENCES

Anderson, E. M., *The Dynamics of Faulting*, Edinburgh and London: Oliver and Boyd, 1942.

Newhouse, W. H., *Ore Deposits as Related to Structural Features*, pp. 9–53. Structural features associated with ore deposits. Princeton, N. J.: Princeton University Press, 1942.

[38] Blanchard, Roland, Use of ore guides: *Engineering and Mining Journal*, vol. 131, p. 174, 1931. (Blanchard's exact figures are 74.45%, 11.68%, 13.87%, and 5.11%.)

[39] Penrose, R. A. F., Cited by Lindgren, W., *Mineral Deposits*, p. 201. New York: McGraw-Hill, 1933.

Seidl, Eric, *Bruch und Fliess-Formen der Technischen Mechanik and ihre An-wendung auf Geologie und Bergbau,* Berlin: VDI Verlag I and II, 1930, IV, 1934.

Southwell, R. V., *Introduction to the Theory of Elasticity,* 2nd Edition. Oxford University Press, 1941.

Timoshenko, S., *Theory of Elasticity.* New York: McGraw-Hill Book Company, Incorporated, 1934.

13

Contacts and Folds as Guides

> *. . . the most favorable places for formation of ore bodies are those where rocks of different competence are in contact. The kind of rock, whether igneous or sedimentary, seems to be less important than the quality of the rock and the heterogeneity of its association.*
> —E. L. Bruce [1]

CONTACTS

CONTACTS are favored places for ore deposition because they are apt to be surfaces of weakness—but not for this reason alone. Bruce's remark regarding a Canadian district is capable of wider application. Thus contacts are of interest both as broad loci of regional proportions and as short-range guides to the positions of veins.

A vein may follow a contact for a long distance or may merely take advantage of it for part of its course. A change in direction in order to follow a contact is most common when the angle of intersection is small; a vein which meets a contact at a large angle is more likely to continue through it with little or no deviation or stop at the boundary, especially if it is a boundary between strong and weak rocks.

The place in which a vein crosses a contact is quite likely to be the site of an oreshoot, and such a condition provides a very simple X-like target for ore-search. Where the contact is flat, the ore may widen mushroom-fashion beneath it as in the limestone beneath porphyry sills at Leadville, Colorado.[2]

Contacts between igneous masses and intruded host-rocks are especially favorable to ore occurrence even when the ore is not genetically

---

[1] Bruce, E. L., Structural relations of some gold deposits between Lake Nipigon and Long Lake, Ontario: *Econ. Geol.*, vol. 34, p. 368, 1939.

[2] Emmons, S. F., Irving, J. D., and Loughlin, G. F., Leadville mining district, Colo.: *U.S.G.S. Prof. Paper 184*, p. 189, 1927.

related to the intrusive. The contrast in strength between a massive intrusive body and weaker sediments makes the contact a vulnerable place for fracturing not only during regional deformation but during adjustments accompanying and following the emplacement of the intrusive. In such cases, chemical as well as physical influences may be

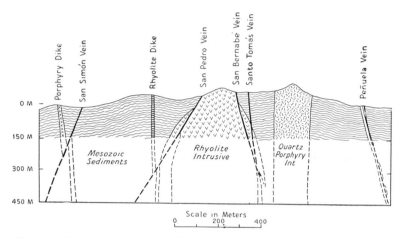

Fig. 99—Veins localized structurally by intrusive contacts. Cross section of district looking north. Tepezala, Aguas Calientes, Mexico. (*After* Wandke and Moore, *Economic Geology*)

potent. When solutions ascend through fractures in the intrusive, the contact may be the first place where they encounter limestone or other hospitable rock. Thus the contact and the fracture may constitute intersecting loci.

Deposits of the class known as "pyrometasomatic" are commonly found in the general vicinity of igneous contacts (as the older term "contact metamorphic" suggests), although they are not restricted to such positions. A short generation ago it was generally believed that contact-metamorphic ore was deposited from solutions or emanations that came from the magma during its intrusion,[3] but recent study is pointing more and more to the conclusion that "the ore-forming emanations have not come from the igneous magma adjacent to the ore deposits."[4] This is in accordance with the observation that the ore in pyrometasomatic deposits is not uniformly distributed around the con-

[3] Lindgren, Waldemar, *Mineral Deposits*, p. 704. New York: McGraw-Hill, 1933.

[4] Knopf, Adolph, Ore deposition in the metasomatic deposits, *Ore Deposits as Related to Structural Features*, p. 65. Princeton: Princeton University Press, 1942.

Cf. Spurr, J. E., *The Ore Magmas*, pp. 99, 588. New York: McGraw-Hill, 1922. Newhouse, W. H., Mineral zoning in the New Jersey-Pennsylvania-Virginia Triassic area: *Econ. Geol.*, vol. 28, p. 624, 1933.

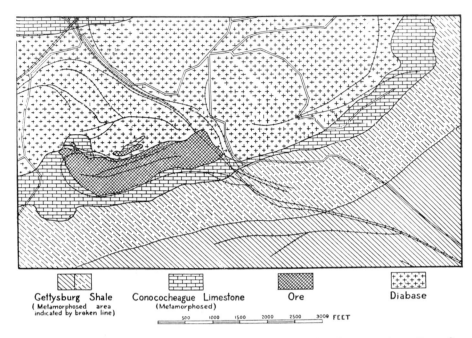

Gettysburg Shale
(Metamorphosed   area
indicated by broken line)

Conococheague Limestone
(Metamorphosed)

Ore

Diabase

500   1000   1500   2000   2500   3000 FEET

Fig. 100—Body of magnetite ore in limestone on contact of diabase intrusion. Cornwall,
Pennsylvania. (*After* Hickock, *Economic Geology*)

tact and, in fact, is usually less abundant in the immediate vicinity of
the intrusive than farther away, on the limestone side of the silicated
zone.[5]   Furthermore, the ore minerals, particularly those of copper, lead
and zinc, are later than silicate minerals and appear to belong to a
younger hydrothermal stage.

Most pyrometasomatic deposits are localized by faults, fractures, or
breccia zones, although some preserve no evidence of fracturing of the
wall rock.[6]   Selective replacement of beds is very common.   Thus contact deposits, although they are associated with a special group of earlier
silicate minerals (their only distinctive characteristic), are not different
morphologically from other types of replacement deposits.   As they
may occur anywhere within several hundred or even a few thousand
feet of a contact, the contact itself is not necessarily a useful ore guide
except on a regional scale.   Although some are found along a contact
or making outward from it, they are subject to the same types of structural control as other replacement deposits.

[5] Umpleby, J. B., The occurrence of ore on the limestone side of garnet zones: *Univ. Calif.
Dept. Geol. Bull.*, vol. 10, pp. 25–37, 1916.
[6] Knopf, Adolph, Ore deposition in the pyrometasomatic deposits, *Ore Deposits as Related to
Structural Features*, p. 67.   Princeton: Princeton University Press, 1942.

In short, contacts in some districts are useful ore guides; in others, they are not. Although an understanding of the origin of the ore may yield some hint as to what may be expected, the only reliable criterion is local experience.

FOLDS

In some areas of folded rocks the ore is found in characteristic parts of the folds: on the crests of anticlines, in the troughs of synclines, or on the intervening limbs. Which, if any, of these positions is the favorable one depends on a variety of circumstances; one determining factor is the date of the folding with respect to ore deposition, that is, whether the object of search is a folded ore deposit or ore that has been deposited in folded rocks.

Folds Younger than the Ore

Ore that was present before the folding will naturally have been deformed along with the enclosing rocks. If the ore is itself a sedimentary bed, it will have the same general shape as the beds above and below it. So long as the folding is gentle, the ore will be uniform in thickness throughout all portions of the folds, or, if there are variations in thickness, they will reflect differences that existed before folding and will bear no relation to the shapes of the folds. Events that took place after the folding may, of course, modify the distribution of the ore; obviously sufficient erosion may plane off the anticlinal part of the ore bed and leave ore only in the synclines.

But if the folds are so tight that their shapes approach those of isoclines, the ore bed is likely to be thinned on the limbs and thickened by flowage or drag-folding on the flexures. Hence the shoots of thicker ore will follow the plunge of the folds. This is the condition in some of the iron formations among the schistose rocks of the Canadian Shield. Finding and following ore structures of this type is simplified by the use of structural criteria familiar to students of pre-Cambrian geology: the relations of cleavage and drag folds to the major folds and indications of the "facing" of beds (i.e., which side was "up" before folding), as disclosed in sediments by graded bedding, cross bedding, ripple marks, and mud-cracks, and in volcanics by bun-structure, chilled bottoms, and ropy or amygdaloidal tops.

Most orebodies that have suffered folding belong to the syngenetic class just discussed, but there ought also to be examples of folded epigenetic deposits, as there is no compelling reason why a region already containing veins and replacement bodies might not undergo subsequent folding. Actually, clear-cut examples are scarce. Franklin Furnace, N. J., may be one, but authorities differ so much regarding its genesis that Bateman's terse summary, "the origin is puzzling," [7] is the one conclusion that meets universal acceptance. Some copper deposits in schist have been considered pre-folding in age, partly because the texture of the ore is banded or schistose, but Newhouse and Flaherty [8] conclude probably correctly that the flow-textures at Blue Hill, Me., Milan, N. H., and Mandy, Manitoba, are inherited from the schists that the sulphides have replaced. However, the texture of the copper-lead-zinc ore at Rammelsberg, Germany, shows evidence of strong post-mineral deformation and may represent a replacement band that has been folded along with the enclosing slates.[9] One reason for the scarcity of folded epigenetic deposits may be that ore deposition normally follows rather than precedes folding; hence such deposits would be expected only in twice-folded regions. The later folding and its accompanying faulting would tend to tear the orebodies apart and scatter them so that few would retain their identity. Their chances of survival would be much less than those of sedimentary bodies which started out with much greater extent and continuity.

Since epigenetic orebodies, unlike sedimentary deposits, do not necessarily conform to the bedding of the enclosing rocks, they are not always confined to consistent stratigraphic horizons. However, they should in large measure reflect the shapes of the folds, as folding tends to reduce the angle between the bedding and any structure that intersects it, thus bringing the orebody into an attitude more nearly parallel to the bedding than it occupied before deformation.

FOLDS OLDER THAN THE ORE

Ore that has been introduced into rocks which are already folded may disclose no relationship to the folding, but more often it reflects folded structure in one way or another. The rock-structure may impose its effects on ore deposition through (a) influence of folded beds on fracturing, (b) determining the shapes of replaced beds, (c) influence of the folds on the flow of ore solutions.

---

[7] Bateman, Alan M., *Economic Mineral Deposits*, p. 535. New York: John Wiley & Son, 1942.
[8] Newhouse, W. H., and Flaherty, G. F., Texture and origin of some banded and schistose sulphide ores: *Econ. Geol.*, vol. 25, pp. 600–626, 1930.
[9] Lindgren, Waldemar, *Mineral Deposits*, p. 628. New York: McGraw-Hill, 1933.

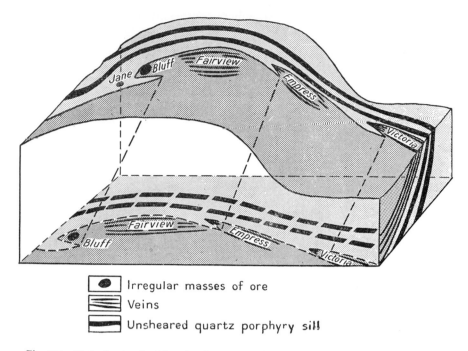

Irregular masses of ore

Veins

Unsheared quartz porphyry sill

Fig. 101—Orebodies localized by plunging minor folds in a contact. Block diagram. Britannia Mines, B. C. (*After* Schofield, *Economic Geology*)

Influence of Folding on Fracturing

Obviously the time at which fractures were formed may be either earlier than folding, during folding, or after folding.

Fractures that were in existence *before folding* are deformed along with the rock but are likely to be healed or obliterated by recrystallization, although they may retain enough of their identity to influence replacement or to serve as loci of weakness and thus influence later fracturing. Some of the gold-bearing veins in the Porcupine District have shapes that are identical with those of drag-folded structures, yet it is clear that the quartz and gold were deposited after the folding. Although many of these veins follow folded sedimentary horizons and flow-contacts, a few trend diagonally across uniform lava flows. They must have been guided by some feature that suffered folding, and the only plausible feature is a folded fracture or possibly a folded carbonate vein. Like some folded epigenetic orebodies, veins of this type reflect the shapes of folds without conforming to stratigraphic horizons.

Fractures developed *during folding* occupy characteristic positions on the folds. It is in the flexures, both synclinal and anticlinal, that the rock has been most sharply bent; where competent beds are on the out-side of a bend they experience tensile stress during folding and are sub-ject to breaking by tensile rupture. At Chañarcillo, Chile,[10] the ma-jority of the productive veins occupy axial positions on gentle anticlines. At Kennecott, Alaska,[11] minor synclinal cross-warps contain fractures

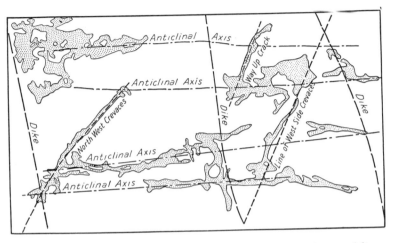

Fig. 102—Replacement orebodies in limestone localized on minor anticlines. Tombstone, Arizona. (*After* Church, A.I.M.E.)

that have localized some of the orebodies. Even very gentle warping may produce fracturing that is inconspicuous and yet capable of localiz-ing orebodies, especially in districts of limestone replacement.

Brittle beds broken by folding can be converted into breccia on the flexures of folds, particularly on drag-folds, since these are more re-stricted and confining than are major crests and troughs. If the folds plunge, the resulting orebodies have a pipe-like form. The shattered acid volcanics that have been replaced by ore at Noranda, Quebec,[12] have been interpreted as breccias on the noses of vertically plunging flexures.

But crests and troughs are not in all districts the favored parts of folds. In regions of tight folding the limbs of folds are likely to be the loci of the through-going shears. The Cadillac group of mines in Quebec lies in a shear zone as much as 200 feet wide and probably 16 miles long

[10] Whitehead, W. L., The Chañarcillo Silver District, Chile, *Ore Deposits as Related to Structural Features*, p. 218. Princeton: Princeton University Press, 1942 .

[11] Bateman, A. M., The Ore Deposits of Kennecott, Alaska, *Ore Deposits as Related to Structural Features*, p. 192. Princeton: Princeton University Press, 1943.

[12] Conolly, H. J. C. and Hart, R. C., Structural geology of the Osisko Lake Area, Quebec: *Can. Min. & Met. Bull.*, No. 285, p. 10, 1936.

on the limb of a major fold.[13] Although this ore-locus approaches regional dimensions, there are shears similar in character but smaller which serve as ore guides in individual properties.

Fractures developed during folding usually strike parallel to the bedding or to the axes; orebodies on them are apt to pitch with the folding. This is true both of tensional fractures in the flexures and of shears on the limbs. In addition, fractures of the tensional type may develop normal to the axes of folding, especially in competent beds.

Folded rocks subjected to a new period of folding on different axes develop highly complex structures which localize shearing and brecciation during or following the second disturbance. The smaller of the two sets of folds, usually termed "cross folds," may be either older or younger than the main set; in fact it is sometimes difficult to be sure of the relative ages but this need not detract from the usefulness of the structures as intersecting loci. The Hollinger Mine appears to be localized where early cross folds are crumpled and corrugated during the main period of folding.[14] Somewhat similar relations exist at Kalgoorlie.[15] At Broken Hill and at the Homestake, fold axes are themselves drag-folded; whether this occurred during a distinctly younger deformation or at a late stage in the main folding may be open to controversy. At Bendigo cross folding is present, although again the age relations are not clear. Here, dome-like undulations in the pitch of the main fold axes, arranged in zones crossing the district diagonally to the general strike have been the most productive parts of the district.

Fractures Later than Folding. When rocks already folded are subjected to stress, the surfaces on which they break are influenced by the shape of the folded beds. (See Chapter 12.) If the late forces have essentially the same orientation as those which caused the folding, the fracturing may be difficult to distinguish from fracturing developed during folding, and for practical purposes the distinction is of no great consequence. But if the later forces have a different orientation, failure will take advantage of bedding planes so far as mechanical economy permits, but stress which is not relieved in this way will cause failure in other directions.

In strongly folded rocks, shear-fractures often take advantage of

[13] Gunning, H. C., Gold deposits of Cadillac Township, Quebec, *Ore Deposits as Related to Structural Features*, p. 163. Princeton: Princeton University Press, 1943.

[14] Graton, L. C., McKinstry, H. E., and others, Outstanding features of Hollinger geology: *Can. Inst. Min. & Met. Trans.*, 1933; also *Bull.* No. 249, p. 8, 1933.

[15] Gustafson, J. K., and Miller, F. S., Kalgoorlie geology re-interpreted: *Econ. Geol.*, vol. 32, p. 305, 1937.

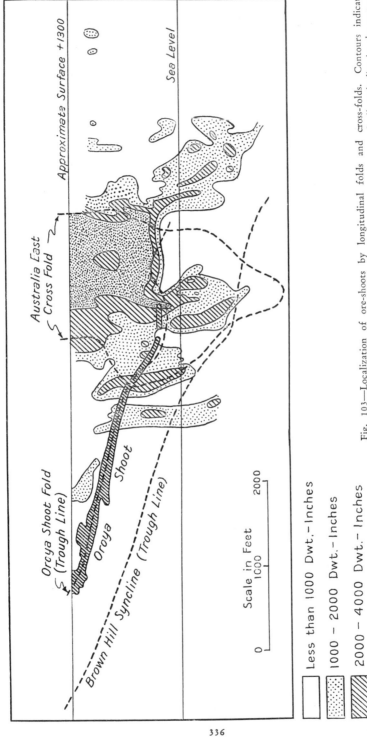

Fig. 103—Localization of ore-shoots by longitudinal folds and cross-folds. Contours indicate aggregate values in inch-pennyweights resulting from projection of all orebodies in the eastern lode-system to a longitudinal vertical plane. Note preponderance of ore within Australia East cross fold. Kalgoorlie District, W. A. (*After Gustafson and Miller, Austr. Inst. Min. and Met.*, also in *Economic Geology*)

Less than 1000 Dwt.-Inches

1000 – 2000 Dwt.-Inches

2000 – 4000 Dwt.- Inches

More than 4000 Dwt.- Inches

Oroya Shoot

bedding planes through part of their course but leave them when the attitude of bedding changes. This is well illustrated by the famous saddle reefs of Bendigo.[16, 17, 18] There a series of slates and quartzites folded with nearly vertical axial planes, has suffered further deformation by forces so oriented that the plane of maximum normal stress is approximately horizontal. With this orientation the planes of maximum shearing stress would dip at 45 degrees, but since the dip of bedding on the limbs of the folds is not too far from that angle, reverse fault-

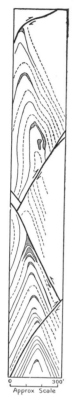

ing takes advantage of the bedding planes. Each fault follows a bedding plane up the limb of a fold to the crest. Since it can no longer follow the bedding beyond the crest it flattens somewhat and crosses the beds with a dip more nearly approximating the theoretical 45 degrees. (See Figure 105.) The saddle reefs occupy openings (or potential openings) formed by the dragging apart of beds underneath the faults or by separation of the beds on the crests where the bedding is roughly parallel to the plane of maximum normal stress (*i.e.*, horizontal). The faults con-

Fig. 104—Cross section through a Bendigo saddle reef. Garden Gulley anticline, looking north. (Slightly simplified *after* Pabst, *Chem. Eng. and Mining Rev.*)

stitute a complementary system, one set guided by each of the two limbs of an anticline.

Forces similarly oriented to those at Bendigo have produced a some-

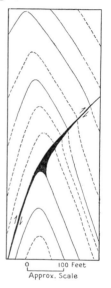

Fig. 105—Cross section through Garden Gulley anticline at Victoria Shaft. Bendigo, Vic. (*After* Pabst, *Chem. Eng. and Mining Review*)

what different result in the neighboring district of Ballarat because the folds, instead of being symmetrical, are slightly overturned, with one limb vertical and the other inclined at 60 or 70 degrees. On the vertical bedding planes, stress has no shearing component, hence the tendency

[16] McKinstry, H. E., Use of the fracture pattern in the search for orebodies: *Austr. New Zealand Assn. Adv. Sci. Report,* Melbourne Meeting, p. 132, Jan. 1935.

[17] Stone, J. B., The structural environment of the Bendigo Goldfield: *Econ. Geol.,* vol. 32, p. 874, p. 885, 1937.

[18] McKinstry, H. E., Bendigo, Victoria, Australia, *Ore Deposits as Related to Structural Features* (W. H. Newhouse, ed.) p. 161. Princeton: Princeton University Press, 1942.

to slip on the bedding is confined to the inclined limbs. Faults therefore pass from one inclined limb to the next by shearing through the
vertical limbs (Figure 106). The gold-bearing quartz bodies are horizontal tension gashes adjoining the reverse faults within the steep limbs.

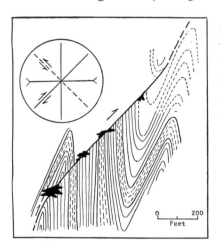

Fig. 106—Quartz bodies (shown in black) in tension openings on reverse fault. Ballarat, Vic. Cross section through Britannia United Mine, Ballarat East goldfield, looking north. (*After* Baragwanath, Vic. Dept. of Mines)

Folded beds subjected to strike faulting may fracture in contrasting ways depending on the attitude of bedding with respect to the fault movement. In the Interstate mine, Idaho,[19] a steep zone of shearing with horizontal movement intersects slates folded into a monocline. Where the bedding was steep the beds have yielded by bending; where the bedding was flat, the beds had to break. (This principle is illustrated in Figure 107.) Therefore the part of the monocline in which the beds are flat constitutes one of the ore loci. The conditions are somewhat different in the Sunshine mine (also in the Coeur d'Alene District). There the main direction of shearing strikes approximately parallel to the axis of a major fold. Thus the beds strike parallel
to the shear so long as they are on the straight limb of the fold but cross it
where they swing around on pitching drag folds. On the straight limbs
the fracture is straight, clean-cut, and richly mineralized, but where it
encounters the drag folds it frays out into lean stringers. Beyond the
zone of drag folding which limits the Sunshine oreshoot at one end,
development found a new orebody in Polaris ground approximately
where a projection of the strike of the shear enters straight beds again.

In both of these Coeur d'Alene examples it appears that attitude of
beds rather than nature of the rock imposes the detailed ore-control,
although it is true that rock formations exert an influence of a broader
nature.

A fracture that cuts folded rocks must necessarily pass from one
formation into another, and when it enters an unfavorable formation it
is likely to die out or at least cease to be orebearing. At the Little Long
Lac Mine in Ontario, the main lode strikes east-west parallel to the axis

[19] McKinstry, H. E., and Svendsen, R. H., Control of ore by rock structure in a Coeur d'Alene Mine: *Economic Geology,* vol. 37, p. 215, 1942.

of a west-plunging fold and the orebodies are confined to a series of arkose beds. Where the lode encounters an overlying graywacke on the west and another, underlying, graywacke on the east, the lode loses its identity. Thus the vein and the arkose bed constitute intersecting loci and the pitch of the orebody is determined by the plunge of the fold.

Shape of Replaced Beds as Determined by Folding

Ore that replaces a particular bed within a folded series inherits the shape of the bed, hence the folding predetermines the shape of the ore-body. If the bed is re-placed uniformly throughout its length and breadth, the condition, so far as ore-search is concerned, is the same as though the ore deposit were sedimentary. The copper-bearing beds of Northern Rhodesia have continuity and uniformity quite comparable to those of sedimentary de-posits. More often, though, the replacement is limited in extent and varies from place to place in its intensity. At Colquijirca, Peru,[20] a group of beds of shaly limestone, folded into a complete anti-cline and syncline, has been replaced by chert and sul-phides to form a series of mantos of very rich silver ore. The ore shows no obvious preference for crest, trough, or limbs, so far as primary

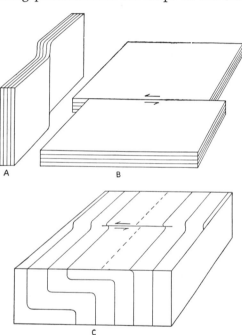

Fig. 107—Mode of failure determined by attitude of beds. A: Horizontal displacement taken up by flex-ing in steep beds. B: by fracturing in flat beds. C: Localization of fracturing in flat beds in mono-cline. Idealized diagram but simulating conditions in Interstate mine, Idaho. (After McKinstry and Svendsen, *Economic Geology*)

mineralization is concerned, although these features have had an impor-tant influence on supergene enrichment. The point of interest in the present connection is that the richest stopes are on two gentle zones of warping which cross the main fold-axes. Nor does the mineralization

[20] McKinstry, H. E., Geology of the silver deposit at Colquijirca, Peru: *Econ. Geol.*, vol. 31, pp. 618–635, 1936.

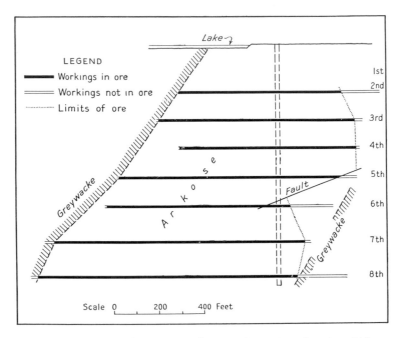

Fig. 108—Longitudinal section, Little Long Lac Mine, Ontario. (*After* Bruce, *Economic Geology*)

extend indefinitely; for reasons that are not entirely clear, it is limited to a length of about 600 meters along the strike of the structure.

In most districts the replacement is even less uniform than at Colquijirca and, within the replaced bed, is controlled by loci which may or may not bear a geometrical relationship to the shape of the fold.

Where the beds destined to future replacement have been strongly deformed by folding of the "similar" type, with thinning on the limbs and thickening and doubling up in crests and in drag-folds, the structural problems of ore finding are similar to those in tightly folded syngenetic deposits, but with the added complication that the ore is not always coextensive with the orebearing formation since some parts, or even most parts, may have escaped replacement. At Broken Hill (N.S.W.) the ore follows two (possibly three) horizons with great consistency, although the bodies have extraordinary shapes due to doubling up in complex drag-folds and to thinning to a matter of inches where the beds have been stretched and pinched. Despite great irregularity in plan or cross section, the folds maintain remarkable constancy when followed in the direction of the plunge.

Ore replacing beds which are tightly and complexly folded in this manner usually follows the plunge of the folds. The largest and, usually, the richest orebodies are likely to be found on the noses of anticlines and on drag-folds along the flanks. Synclinal flexures also carry ore in some districts, but in others they are less favorable than anticlines. The reason for greater size of orebodies occupying these positions is obvious—the thickening of the replaced bed and bunching by drag-folds as contrasted with extreme thinning of flanks. The greater richness may be due partly to greater crushing and brecciation, but in some districts it seems attributable to channelizing of solutions.

Influence of Folded Structure on Flow of Solutions

On theoretical grounds one might expect that folds would have a channelizing effect on ore depositing solutions,[21] since some beds are more impervious than others. If the solutions are ascending, anticlines, particularly pitching anticlines, should collect them and synclines should disperse them. Conversely, if the solutions are descending they should be diverted from the anticlines into the synclines. Actually these effects are not as prevalent as one might expect. Perhaps it is because fractures afford channelways of leakage and thus reduce the confining effect of otherwise impermeable troughs; perhaps it is because we do not really know enough about the factors influencing ore deposition to be sure what "ought" to happen. Nevertheless there are examples which appear to illustrate the principle. Probably the Homestake mine is the best-known. Here the orebodies, which are replacements of a favorable carbonate bed, are localized in the anticlinal portions of the system of plunging folds.

In Bendigo, the saddle reefs in anticlines have been far more productive than the corresponding "trough reefs" in the synclines, nor does this appear to be due merely to lack of development work in the synclines. Statistical studies indicate, furthermore, that the plunging portions of these anticlines are more favorable than the flat intervals at the crests of domes or between domes. Channelizing of descending solutions is well illustrated in the Menominee district of Michigan, where an important orebody follows a gently plunging drag-syncline which has acted as a trough to guide the descending solutions.[22]

In all deposits in folded rocks, it is worth while to make critical studies of the relation of ore to the folds. Rocks so nearly flat that the folds are only gentle warps may demand accurate determination of elevations

[21] Newhouse, W. H., Some relations of ore deposits to folded rocks: *Tr. A.I.M.E.*, vol. 96, pp. 224–246, 1931.

[22] Royce, Stephen, Iron ranges of the Lake Superior district, *Ore Deposits as Related to Structural Features*. Princeton: Princeton University Press, p. 58, 1942.

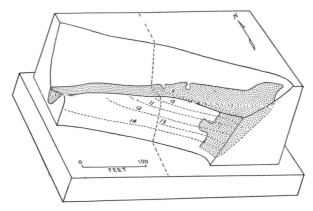

Fig. 109—Localization of iron ore in a plunging fold. Aragon
Mine, Eastern Menominee Range, Norway, Mich. (*After* Royce,
Ore Deposits as Related to Structural Features)

and the use of stratigraphy following methods similar to those used in
oilfield geology.   Where the folding is very complex, especially in monotonous rocks, it may be necessary to map minor folds in great detail,
since they serve as clues to the location of the major fold-axes.   Structure-contour maps and multiple cross-sections are especially useful in
revealing folded structure.

SELECTED REFERENCES

See references at ends of Chapters 10 and 12.

14

Dislocated Orebodies

*In the many and great upheavals of the earth's crust, resulting in conti-
nents rising above the sea, and on those continents still greater and
sharper upheavals forming mountain ranges, rocks have been much broken
and fractured, from great fissures miles in length and depth down to little
cracks of but a few inches.*

—Arthur Lakes [1]

Orebodies after they have been deposited are not safe from further
disturbance; they may suffer disruption and displacement by folding,
faulting, and igneous intrusion. All of these after-effects make the
search more complicated and pose problems that the geologists has to
solve. The effects of folding are discussed in Chapter 13. The effects
of faulting and intrusion are the subject of the present chapter.

OREBODIES DISPLACED BY FAULTS

Faulting that has occurred after the ore is in existence is at best a
nuisance and at worst a catastrophe. Even when the problems of dislocation solve themselves without serious difficulty, an over-abundance
of faults inevitably adds to the expense of finding, developing and mining ore. If the ore is of only mediocre grade the presence of too many
faults may be a sound reason for turning a property down. But where
there is a possibility of finding really good ore, the existence of faults
that have baffled former operators may offer the discerning geologist a
ready-made opportunity for real achievement. About 1928 the management of the Wright-Hargreaves mine in the Kirkland Lake district
considered the ore to be nearly worked out; it appeared to terminate in
a downward wedge between two faults. A new management under
Maurice W. Summerhayes took over the operations, drove through the
faults, found ore beyond them and made the mine one of Canada's
largest and most profitable gold producers.

Probably the most famous discovery of faulted ore is that of the

[1] *Prospecting for Gold and Silver*, p. 72. Scranton: The Colliery Engineer Co., 1895.

United Verde Extension in Arizona.[2]   The top of the pipelike group of orebodies in the old United Verde mine had been sliced off and dropped on a normal fault.   It was found 1500 feet away beyond the outcrop of the fault plane and under cover of 1100 feet of leached capping, younger sediments and basalt.   It paid over $40,000,000 in dividends.   A recent discovery of ore by solving a fault problem at Eureka, Nevada [2a] (in this case a pre-mineral fault) is an example of the success of sound geological reasoning followed by bold development.   The orebodies that were worked in the 1880's to yield $42,000,000 in silver-lead-zinc ore occurred in the Eldorado dolomite which terminated downward in a wedge between two faults (see Figure 110).   Mapping of the structure

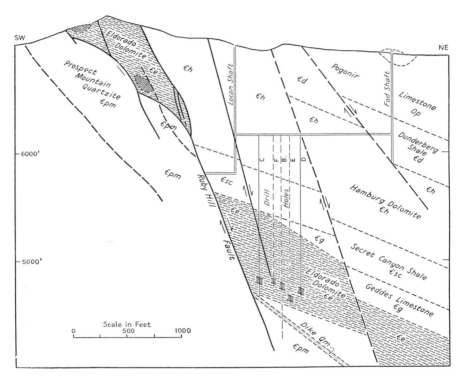

Fig. 110—Discovery of an orebody by drilling after solving a fault-problem, Eureka, Nevada. Ore indicated by cross-hatching.   (*Courtesy of* William Sharp)

and stratigraphy indicated that the favorable formation had been dropped about 1500 feet east of the Ruby Hill fault and drilling, started in 1940, discovered a new body of solid sulphides 30 to 40 feet thick

[2] Tenny, J. B., The copper deposits of Arizona, in *Copper Deposits of the World,* p. 196. 16th International Geological Congress, Washington, D. C., 1935.
[2a] Sharp, Wm., The story of Eureka: *A.I.M.E. Tech. Pub. No. 2196,* 1947.

about 2300 feet below the surface. Less happy was the experience at the Minnie Moore mine [3] in Idaho, where the vein which had produced well over $7,000,000 to a depth of 1100 feet was cut off by a fault. Exploratory workings, driven in almost every direction, failed to find a continuation of the vein beyond the fault.

The most exhaustive three-dimensional studies of faulting have been those at Butte, Montana, where the intricate system of faults rendered geological skill indispensable and was the primary reason for establishing the first permanent geological department in an American mine. The Butte technique of mapping and interpreting faults has set a standard for the profession.

GEOMETRICAL ASPECTS

When a drift encounters a fault, the geologist is called on to tell where to find the ore again. In a mine that has already been well opened up and mapped, any fault that is encountered is likely to be an old friend whose position had already been forecast by projection. In this case the geologist will be well prepared to deal with it, for he will already know the direction and amount of the displacement along it. In Butte, where staff men have been studying the faults for half a century, every fault with any continuity is known by name and can be recognized either by its position and attitude or by the nature of the gouge or mineralization that it bears.

If the amount and direction of the displacement on a fault are known, the position of the lost segment of a vein or orebody can be determined by graphic or trigonometrical methods. There is a voluminous literature on fault problems and the methods of solving them, all of which is helpful to the beginner. But as all of the solutions are applications of descriptive geometry, the geologist with a good mathematical training and adequate practice in visualizing three dimensions will not need to memorize rules but will have no serious trouble in solving his geometrical problems as they arise. One who is not proficient in this respect will do well to consort with a good text on structural geology [4] and entertain himself with block models until such matters are second nature, for so long as he is baffled by geometrical problems in faulting he can hardly expect to be successful in any form of orefinding.

---

[3] Hewett, D. F., Umpleby, J. B., Westgate, L. G., and Ross, C. P., Geology and ore deposits of the Wood River region, *U.S.G.S. Bulletin 814*, pp. 219–222, 1939.

[4] Haddock, M. H., *Disrupted Strata.* London: Technical Press, Ltd., 1938. (An exhaustive treatise on the geometry of faults). See also Billings, Marland P., Laboratory Exercises in *Structural Geology*, pp. 401–456. New York: Prentice-Hall, 1942.

An elaborate nomenclature has been proposed for classifying faults and their components of displacement [5] but any fault for which adequate data are available can be solved without the slightest acquaintance with the terminology. In fact, faults can be described accurately without employing specialized terms like "heave" and "throw"; the general term "displacement" is the only one that is really essential, since the components of displacement can always be specified in familiar geometrical language. Dip-slip and strike-slip are convenient auxiliary terms which are self-explanatory.

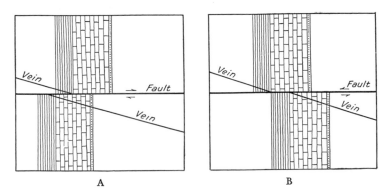

Fig. 111—Horizontal components of displacement as seen in plan. *A:* Right-hand fault. *B:* Left-hand fault.

Most of the so-called "fault rules" such as the old miner's guide: "the dip is toward the downthrow" are intended for solving normal faults. But of course there is nothing normal about a normal fault except its name. Reverse faults are probably almost as common and, unless the habits of the district are well established, there is no telling whether any particular fault is normal, reverse, or strike-slip. Steep faults are perhaps more likely to be normal than reverse, but there are so many exceptions to this rule that it is far from reliable.

Components of Displacement

The position of the vein beyond a fault on any level depends not merely on the amount and direction of displacement but on the attitude of the vein. All geologists know, although some occasionally forget, that the apparent displacement, as observed in plan or cross section, is not the true displacement, except in special cases. In other words, one cannot assume that motion along the fault has been either in the direction of

[5] Reid, H. F., and others, Report of the Committee on the Nomenclature of Faults: *Bulletin Geological Society of America*, vol. 24, pp. 163–186, 1913.

its strike or in the direction of its dip. In the general case the displacement has had components in both of these directions. Therefore the true displacement cannot be determined by comparing the positions of the severed portions of a *plane*. It can be determined only by measuring the displacement of a *line*, such as the intersection of two planes. Thus two intersecting veins of opposite dip, or a vein together with a recognizable bedding plane, are ideal for determining the magnitude and direction of faulting. The simplest solution is to draw up on tracing paper a section on each wall of the fault, superimpose one section on the other, and shift them until the corresponding features coincide.

This method has been used very effectively by Hopkins [6] in the Kirkland Lake district. In the Wright-Hargreaves mine, major veins had been developed on both sides of a transverse fault, but there were smaller minor veins in which oreshoots ended against the fault. As some of these, where found beyond the fault, did not show ore, and others had not been found at all, it was essential to determine both the horizontal and vertical components of displacement. The wall-rock being igneous, there were no stratigraphic horizons to serve as data, but there were, in addition to the known veins, strike faults dipping in the opposite direction from the veins. By preparing sections on the hanging wall and footwall of the fault and shifting them until they matched up, Hopkins restored the pre-fault structure and discovered that in addition to horizontal and vertical components there had been a rotational movement. As a result of the restoration of this and other similar transverse faults, much new ore was found, some on one side and some on the other side of each fault. Figure 112 shows the structure before and after faulting, but as this figure was prepared after several new extensions had been discovered, it includes many more data than were originally available for the solution.

This example not only illustrates a useful technique but emphasizes the importance of determining both the horizontal and vertical components of displacement. If displacement has had a strong component in the direction of the dip, the severed part of the oreshoot may have been moved to a position above or below the level, so that although the vein is found by a crosscut the ore is lacking. Determining the dip-component of displacement will indicate that the search should be undertaken on a higher or a lower level, as the case may be (Figure 113). It goes without saying that an analogous case exists if a raise or winze

---

[6] Hopkins, Harold, Faulting at the Wright-Hargreaves Mine with notes on ground movements: *Canadian Min. & Met. Bulletin No. 343*, 1940. *Transactions*, vol. 43, pp. 685–707, 1940.

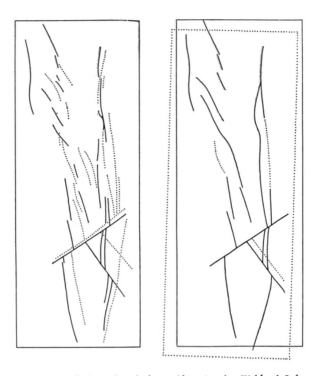

Fig. 112—Solution of a fault problem in the Kirkland Lake District. Composite section in plane of Sylvanite Fault. *Left:* After faulting (veins in hanging wall of fault shown in full lines; veins in footwall in dotted lines). *Right:* Inferred position of veins before faulting. (*After* Hopkins, *Can. Inst. M. and M.,* somewhat simplified)

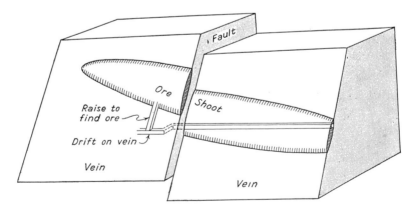

Fig. 113—Crosscut finds vein beyond fault but, because of vertical component of displacement, a raise is necessary in order to find the ore-shoot. (Idealized diagram)

encounters a fault on which the displacement has had a strong horizontal component.

The importance of establishing the amount and direction of displacement on a fault is further emphasized by a number of examples in which a vein was found beyond a fault, but when the dislocation was better understood, the segment that had been found proved to be a different vein from the one that was sought. Continued search not only resulted in finding the faulted part of the original vein but led to the discovery of the new vein on the hither side of the fault plane thus disclosing two veins where only one was known before (see Figure 114).

GEOLOGICAL ASPECTS

Guides to Direction of Displacement

Turning from the purely geometrical to the more truly geological aspects of faulting, we may consider some of the physical features of fault zones. Let us assume that a drift has broken into a fault which the geologist cannot correlate with any structure that he has seen elsewhere in the mine. How is he to decide which way the walls have moved? There are several well-known criteria that he can apply, some of them reliable, others merely suggestive.

Contrasting Wall Rock. One method is thoroughly dependable, although it applies only to special cases. That is to identify the wall rock on the opposite side of the fault-zone. For instance if a vein has a hanging-wall of shale and a footwall of porphyry and the drift goes through the fault into porphyry it is obvious that the vein is to be found by crosscutting in the direction of the hanging-wall of the vein—so obvious, in fact, that the miners will probably have solved the problem before the geologist visits the face. But if the rocks are difficult to identify, the geologist's technique is needed. He may identify the rock formation by any one of a number of methods, such as microscopic examination, heavy mineral studies, identity of fossils, or chemical tests. Nature of the wall rock does not serve as a definite signpost unless the vein occupies a rock-contact, but it may contribute useful auxiliary evidence wherever a fault has brought two types of rock into juxtaposition. For example, if the country-rock consists of horizontal beds and the drift passes through a fault from a higher into a statigraphically lower formation, the vertical component of displacement is established although the horizontal component remains to be determined.

Less reliable but often helpful are the physical features of fault zones.

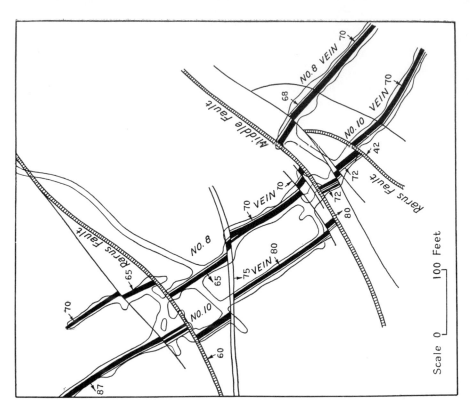

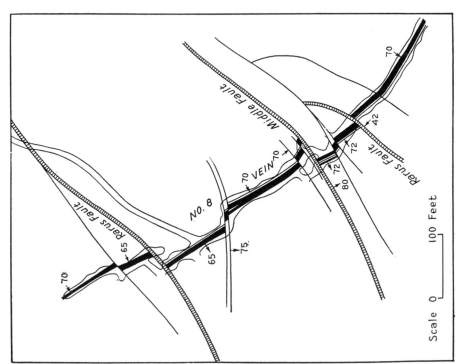

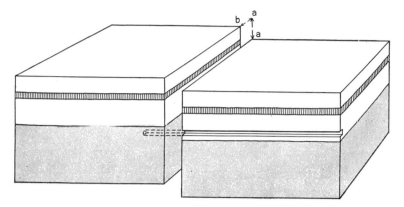

Fig. 115—Drift passing into a lower stratum beyond a fault. Stratigraphy determines vertical but not horizontal component of displacement.

As these are described in the standard texts on structural geology, they require only enumeration here, together with a few comments.

Drag. This word is used in two senses: (a) the trail of sulphides or other vein-matter in the crushed material of the fault zone; (b) the bending of bedding, cleavage planes, etc., near the walls of the fault, due to friction.

Slickensides. Grooves or scratches on the walls of the fault indicate the direction in which the walls have slipped past each other. While indicating the direction, they may leave the sense of the movement in doubt. For instance horizontal slickensides mean that the opposite wall moved (relatively) horizontally and not up or down, but they may not indicate whether the horizontal movement was to the right or to the left. The sense of the movement may sometimes be determined by

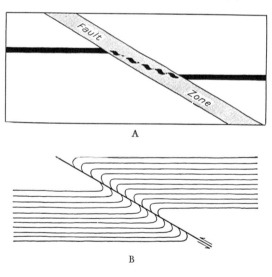

Fig. 116—A: Dragged ore (black) in fault zone. B: Drag in bedding adjoining fault. (Idealized diagrams)

Fig. 114 (opposite)—*Left:* Initial development work gave erroneous impression that only one vein existed. (Schematic diagram based on description.) *Right:* After geologic mapping, continued development discovers a new vein on each side of the fault. Portion of 1400-foot level, Mount View Mine, Butte, Mont. (*After* Linforth, *Ore Deposits of the Western States*)

rubbing your hand along the fault surface; the surface feels smoothest when the hand is moved in the same sense as the corresponding fault-wall. The shapes of slickensides and the trails or ridges of sheltered rock behind hard projections have been used as criteria.[7] Remember, however, that slickensides record only the last movement on the fault-surface; earlier slickensides may be obliterated by later ones. Furthermore, different planes in the same fault zone may indicate widely contrasting directions of movement.

Gouge. There is a widely prevalent belief that normal faults carry gouge whereas reverse faults do not. This may be true in individual districts and, where experience has shown it to be reliable, it may serve as a very useful guide. As a general proposition, however, it is without foundation; there are numerous examples of gouge-bearing reverse faults and, although gouge-free normal faults are not common, they unquestionably exist. Nor is it true that the amount of gouge or the width of the fault zone is any criterion of the amount of displacement on a fault. I have seen gouge zones many feet wide on faults of only a few inches displacement, whereas faults on which there has been a displacement of 200 feet or more have been almost invisible.

Sympathetic Faults, parallel to the fault plane, are likely to have the same direction of displacement as the main fault, a direction which may be determined by matching up the segments of veinlets or bedding planes displaced by the minor fault. But here again the possibility of movement in different directions along different planes during the history of faulting must not be overlooked.

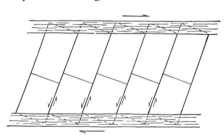

Fig. 117—Probable manner of development of complementary (antithetic) shears. (Idealized diagram)

Complementary Shears in the fault zone sometimes give rise to a structure analogous to fracture cleavage. The shear-planes cross the zone diagonally, usually at a small angle, and at their ends curve toward parallelism with the fault-walls. The acute angle points in the direction in which the opposite wall moved.

Tension Fractures in the rock adjoining the fault zone usually meet the walls at a rather large angle. If they curve on meeting the fault plane it is usually in such a direction as to bring them more nearly perpendicular to the wall.

[7] Willis, Bailey, *Geologic Structures* (1st Edition) pp. 56–57. New York: McGraw-Hill, 1923.

They may also appear within the fault zone if the material is brittle and not too badly crushed. Tension fractures, unlike complementary shears, stand with their acute angle pointing in the direction in which the rock on their own side (not the opposite side) of the fault plane has moved (Figure 118).

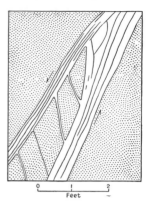

These criteria are dependable only where the faulting has been of the simplest sort. Some faults have had a complex history and have served as places of weakness throughout a whole series of adjustments, thus recording displacements in a variety of directions. The physical features just listed are most dependable when several or all of them agree in pointing to the same conclusions.

Fig. 118—Tension fractures between slips in a fault fissure of normal displacement. Newman Mine, Rico Mountains, Colorado. (*After* Ransome, *U.S.G.S.*)

Local Pattern. Aside from the evidence that is visible in and adjoining an individual fault, the pattern of faults in the district may offer an indication of the direction of movement, provided there is reason to believe that the faults were formed at substantially the same time and thus were caused by the same major forces. Under these conditions, parallel faults are all likely to have the same direction of movement and if two sets of faults intersect at a fairly large angle they are likely to be complementary. (See p. 300.) The rule regarding movement on conjugate faults may be stated thus: Consider the block or wedge between two intersecting faults. If the block moved away from the intersection along one fault, it moved away on the other as well. Applied to

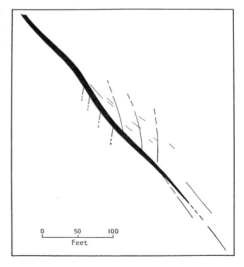

Fig. 119—Relation of tension fractures to a fault fissure of normal displacement. Real del Monte, Mexico. (*After* Thornburg, *Economic Geology*)

faults whose intersection is steep, this means that if movement on one set is right-hand in sense, the movement on the other set is left-hand. Applied to faults whose intersection is horizontal it means that if one set is reverse the other set is also reverse; if one set is normal the other set is also normal.   Thus at Kalgoorlie, Western Australia, (Figure 120) the lodes are cut by two sets of faults having similar strikes but opposite dips; both sets are reverse faults.   Since it is difficult to be sure that one is dealing with conjugate sets, this rule can be relied on only in districts in which it is supported by local experience. Where no past records are available, the most that can be said is that it affords a better basis for a guess than flipping a coin.

Multiple Dislocations

Whether or not the faults in a district belong to one or to more than one period of deformation is not always easy to decide, but it is unavoidably the key to any rational analysis of the faulting.   Even though one fault offsets another, it is still possible that both belong to one general period produced by a single orientation of forces, for a system of faults does not necessarily spring full-fledged into being; more often it grows progressively as stress is relieved by yielding in one place and builds up in another.   Thus slipping may occur on faults of set A (Fig. 121), then on one or more members of set B offsetting set A, then again on the same or on different members of set A and so on.   In such cases an attempt to reduce the faulting to distinct successive periods leads either to contradictory results or to postulating an unmanageable multiplicity of stages of deformation.   When there actually have been separate stages of faulting, the faults

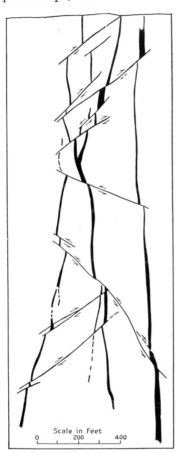

Fig. 120—Pattern of conjugate faults displacing vein system. Section through Main Lode system, Kalgoorlie, Australia. (*After* Stillwell and Finucane, *W. A. Geol. Surv.*)

of a particular age are sometimes, though not always, recognizable by a characteristic attitude, by a diagnostic type of gouge, or by a filling of calcite or some other mineral.   If you can identify faults of successive ages by such distinguishing marks, you can proceed to solve the problem in stages by first restoring (graphically) the younger displacements, then the next older set, and so on.   In a mine in Mexico I had the satisfaction of "unfaulting" a block of ground that had been cut into a veritable hash by two sets of faults. Fortunately, the circumstances were ideal for reconstructing the original conditions. Two pre-fault veins of opposite dip joined downward affording a datum for measuring both the horizontal and vertical components of displacement on each fault. With this information, a longitudinal section, some paste

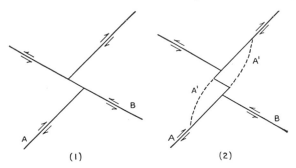

Fig. 121—Quasi-contemporaneous faults formed by progressive adjustment. *Stage (1)*: B offsets A. *Stage (2)*: further movement on A offsets B. (Idealized diagram)

and a pair of scissors were all that was necessary, first, to restore the displacement on a set of steep reverse faults and then to put back into place the blocks that had been dislocated by what proved to be three flat-dipping normal faults. The result (quite unanticipated at the start) was that nine different orebodies all turned out to be parts of a single shoot about 3000 feet in pitch length. Unfortunately all the pieces of the oreshoot had already been found and both of its ends (now in surprising places) had been explored. At any rate the solution of the fault problem terminated a fruitless search for more of the small orebodies and indicated that any hope for further ore lay in the discovery of an entirely new shoot.

False Walls

Faults that are nearly parallel to a vein are particularly hard to interpret. The margins of a vein are vulnerable surfaces for post-vein movement and if the movement is small, it may merely develop a gouge seam marking the wall of the vein. But if movement is large and the fault crosses the vein at an imperceptibly small angle the vein may be pulled apart or "pushed together" depending on the direction of the movement. Pulling apart produces an interval of fault surface between two segments of vein matter. The miner, mistaking the fault for the vein-wall, may follow it or follow one of its branches, missing the seg-

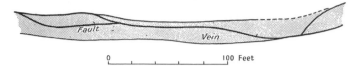

0   100 Feet

Fig. 122—"False walls" formed by faults within a vein.
Bourne, Oregon.

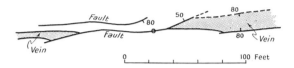

0   100 Feet

Fig. 123—Vein "pulled apart" by nearly parallel
faults. Bourne, Oregon.

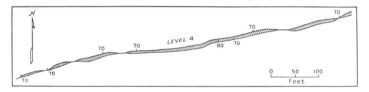

Fig. 124—Lensing of vein by post-vein faulting nearly parallel to walls.
Plan of No. 4 level, Black Pine Mine, Elk City, Mont. (*After* Shenon
and Reed, *Trans. A.I.M.E.*)

ment of vein matter altogether. If the movement has been in the opposite direction, the vein may be "doubled-up" so that two portions of the orebody lie side-by-side, separated only by the fault-plane. What the miner mistakes for a "good wall" may then be only a fault-plane within the orebody. That "walls" should always be penetrated at intervals by drill holes or crosscuts is not only good geology but sound routine mining practice; yet there are cases in which geologists have made themselves enviable reputations by merely recommending the application of this rule if it has been neglected.

Pitfalls in Fault Solution

Once the true displacement on a fault has been determined at one point, one might logically expect that the displacement at all other points would be the same in direction and amount. Although this is a useful working hypothesis, it is unfortunately not always correct. Hinge faults and scissors faults are fairly common, as might be expected on theoretical grounds, for all faults die out ultimately and one of the ways in which this can happen is through a diminishing amount of displacement from place to place along the fault plane. This variation may be so gradual as to be negligible in a given mine or district or it may be abrupt enough to be a real factor in the structural solution. Hinge and pivotal faults may be less common, however, than the literature would suggest, for one may suspect that in more than one instance an observer mistaking apparent displacement for true displacement has naively inferred that planes of unlike attitude have been displaced in contrasting amounts or even in opposite directions.

Aside from the possibility of hinge or scissors movement, faults may vary locally in amount of displacement by changing into flexures or into distributed dislocation. This may even happen abruptly, as when a fault in quartzite becomes a family of small slips in a slate. If a fault

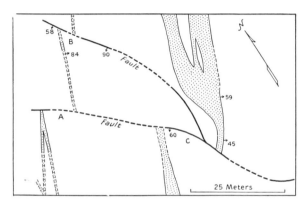

Fig. 125—Fault splitting into two branches. The displacement at *A* is not the full measure of the displacement of the vein at *C*. Colquiri, Bolivia. (*Courtesy of* F. S. Turneaure)

splits into branches, each of them may assume part of the displacement, so that there is danger of erroneously applying the measurement on a branch to the solution of the main trunk of the fault. Alternatively, a wedge between two faults may be a horst or a graben, with the result that displacement along either branch is greater than along the simpler part of the fault zone.

Recurrent displacement may produce even more confusing results. After the United Verde Extension orebodies had been discovered, as mentioned earlier in this chapter, it became evident that the displacement of the ore-zone was considerably greater than that of the sediments which overlay it. What had happened was this: The orebody was displaced in pre-Cambrian times, the surface was leveled by erosion, and in Paleozoic times the sediments were laid down. Then in the Tertiary, following an outflow of basaltic lava, there was further move-

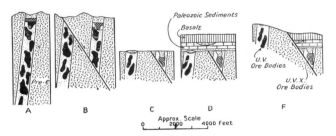

Fig. 126—United Verde Fault. Cross sections showing successive
stages in displacement. (*After* Ransome, Intl. Geol. Cong.)

ment on the fault.   This displaced the sediments and, of course, further
displaced the ore-zone.   But until the geologists had fully confirmed this
sequence of events, the possibility was open that there had been only
one period of movement, namely the one which displaced the sediments.[8]
If this had been true, the orebody which was found could hardly have
been the displaced part of the United Verde orebody.   Such a possibility
was intriguing, for it would have meant not only that the lost top was
still to be sought, but that the orebody that had been found had an
undiscovered lower segment somewhere in the footwall of the fault!
It was not until about $200,000 had been spent in searching for a second
displaced top that this possibility was abandoned.

On a smaller scale, a condition of this sort is not uncommon: A fault
displaces a vein.   Then a dike cuts the fault.   Then, later movement
on the fault perhaps in the opposite direction from the first displaces
both the vein and the dike.   In such a case the displacement of the dike
is an entirely misleading guide to the displacement of the vein.

Pre-Mineral or Post-Mineral Age?

Faults that have actually displaced orebodies are, by definition, post-
mineral.   It is not always easy, however, to be sure that a given fault *is*
post-mineral even though the ore ends against it, since examples of ore
ending against pre-mineral faults are not uncommon.   Thus, if a pre-
ore fault displaces a "favorable" bed which has later been replaced by
ore it is easily mistaken for a post-ore fault; the same is true of a pre-
ore fault displacing a fracture which has later received mineralization.
In a system of cognate fractures it is common, if not indeed characteristic, that a fracture of one set ends against a fracture of the other set;
similarly a tension crack may end against a shear.   If a slight change
in the orientation of forces keeps one set of fractures closed while per-

[8] Joralemon, Ira B., Personal communication.

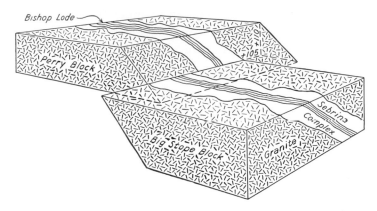

Fig 127—Ore-locus displaced by pre-mineral fault. Bishop, Cal. (*After Schroter, E. & M. J.*)

mitting the other set to open and receive mineralization, the result closely simulates post-ore faulting. The miners' "feeders and bleeders" —cross seams which form the beginning and end of an oreshoot—are, in some cases at least, slips which allowed the walls to gap in the interval between the "feeder" and the "bleeder." (Which is "feeder" and which is "bleeder" depends on which way you look at the oreshoot.)

This situation is especially deceptive if a little post-ore movement has taken place across a pre-existing jog in a vein,[9] or along one set of pre-ore fractures, as this may develop new gouge and make any mineralization in the fracture look like drag-ore. Examples in the Coeur d'Alene district of pre-ore fracturing with a little post-ore movement are discussed on page 304.

A correct diagnosis is vital because ore that has been cut off by a post-mineral fault is sure to exist beyond it unless, by pure chance, the fault coincided with the end of an orebody or unless some malign influence of erosion, leaching, or slicing has destroyed the displaced part of the orebody after it was faulted. But if the fault against which the ore ends is pre-mineral, the philosophy of the search is entirely different. In this case the fault is part of the fracture pattern, whether the fracturing be of one or of more than one age, and may thus have exerted an influence on ore deposition. The search is not for a displaced part of the orebody but for a displaced part of the localizing structure (which may or may not have been mineralized) or else for a new locus or mineralization.

[9] Hulin, Carlton D., Structural control of ore deposition, *Economic Geology*, vol. 24, pp. 19–20, 41–44, 1929.

No fool-proof rules can be given for distinguishing pre-mineral from post-mineral faults. The decision must rest on all that is known about the geological setting, but some of the obvious criteria may be tabulated:

POST-ORE FAULTS.

1. Slickensiding or brecciation of the ore itself. Drag ore in the fault zone.
2. Observable offsetting of veins or orebodies.
   Caution: A slight post-ore displacement on a pre-ore fault may produce deceptive slickensides and drag. Offsetting of the mineralized loci must be distinguished from offsetting of the mineralization itself.

PRE-ORE FAULTS.

1. Mineralization in the fault plane—ore in fractures, breccia and vugs.
   Caution: The fault may carry mineralization of post-ore age. This is usually recognizable because the minerals are not the same as those of the ore. Calcite, pyrite, gypsum and supergene minerals are the commonest ones.
2. Localizing effect of the fault on ore.
   Orebodies habitually (not merely fortuitously) adjacent to the fault, whether due to channelizing of solutions by the fault or wider opening of fissure on one side than on the other.

OREBODIES DISPLACED BY INTRUSIVES

Somewhat akin to faulting is the disruption of orebodies by later intrusions. The Homestake orebodies are cut by a series of rhyolite dikes in such a way that in order to reconstuct an undistorted picture of the orebearing formation it was necessary to remove the dikes (figuratively speaking). In at least one instance a missing part of the orebody was found entirely enclosed by dike matter.

In the Pewabic mine at Hanover, New Mexico, one orebody appears to end at the contact of a porphyry dike and is so shown in a published map of the workings.[9a] Recognizing that the dike was post-ore, Schmitt recommended development beyond it, and as a result an additional half million tons of 15% to 25% zinc ore was found.

A striking case of disruption of ore by a sill occurred in the Northern Empire mine in Ontario. The vein had been developed to a depth of 640 feet when it encountered the sill, which was found to be 550 feet thick.[10] On sinking a shaft through the sill, the vein was found below it with virtually no horizontal displacement.

9a Schmitt, Harrison, The Pewabic Mine: *Bull. G.S.A.*, vol. 50, p. 818, plate 2A, 1939.

10 Bruce, E. L., Structural relations of some gold deposits between Lake Nipigon and Long Lake, Ontario: *Econ. Geol.*, vol. 34, p. 360, 1939.

Benedict, P. C., and Titcomb, J. A., Geology of the Northern Empire mine: *C.I.M.M. Trans.*, vol. 50, pp. 412–423, 1947.

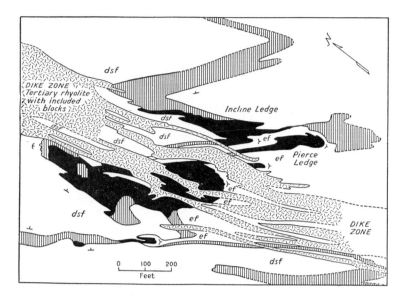

Fig. 128—Ore-locus displaced by intrusive dikes. Generalized plan of 1850 level, Homestake Mine, S. D. *dsf*: DeSmet formation. *Vertical hatching*: Homestake formation. *ef*: Ellison formation. Orebodies shown in black. (*After* Mc-Laughlin, *E. & M. J.*)

Most interruptions of orebodies by dikes and sills do not displace the orebody except to the extent that separation normal to the walls has provided space for the intrusive. Thus a dike, if normal to the plane of a vein, will cause no interruption of the dip or strike, although a dike intersecting a vein obliquely displaces it in a direction normal to the walls of the dike.[11] In rather exceptional cases there has been fault movement either before, during, or after the act of intrusion; this merely adds itself to the effect of the wall-separation.

Intrusives earlier than the ore have a different significance, of course. Ordinarily they are not difficult to recognize but, occasionally, deceptive cases appear. At Noranda, Quebec, intrusions of metagabbro within the orebody seemed on first examination to be post-mineral but more detailed study showed that they were locally mineralized and led to the conclusion that they had been resistant to the remarkably selective replacement which had converted the surrounding rhyolite breccia into sulphides. Dikes of diabase younger than the metagabbro are also

[11] *Cf.* Goodspeed, G. E., Dilation and replacement dikes: *Jour. Geol.*, vol. 48, p. 176, 1940. In contrast to the ordinary or dilation dike, Goodspeed describes dikes which have apparently been introduced by replacement. These would not necessarily displace the vein at all, since the dike-walls have not been separated. Replacement dikes, however, would be likely to occur along shear zones.

probably pre-mineral, but their contacts with the ore are in most places so sharp that there is still difference of opinion as to whether they are pre- or post-ore.[12]   Similarly dikes in the Alamos district, California, were at first thought to be younger than the veins, and this erroneous concept encouraged early fruitless exploration for severed vein segments. Moehlman's [13] work, which clearly showed that the dikes were older than the veins, serves to illustrate most of the criteria that apply to cases in which a decision is difficult:

The veins penetrate the dikes for short distances though they pinch quickly.

The dikes are commonly mineralized with introduced quartz and sulphides near veins and show low though appreciable gold values.

Veins in many cases follow post-dike faults.

Veins generally swing parallel to dike contacts.

Although some veins pick up again beyond the respective dikes, the dikes appear to have guided upflow of solutions, as some of the oreshoots at least, rake parallel to the intersections (in this example, 25 degrees).   Therefore a vein which is orebearing on one side of a dike is often not orebearing beyond it even if it picks up again.

AFTER DISLOCATIONS ARE RESTORED

In a mine that abounds in faults, the geologist's first and most obvious task is to solve the fault problems, but this is by no means the end of his endeavors.   Just as the pieces of a torn-up letter have to be fitted together before the writing can be read, so the faulted blocks have to be restored to their original relative positions before the geologist can begin the work that would have been the first order of business in a mine that was free of faults.   The same consideration applies to ore disrupted by dikes or sills.

The attack begins with reconstructing a series of plans, sections and, perhaps, models of the structure as it appeared before faulting, the faults themselves being either omitted or shown in such unobtrusive fashion that they do not distract attention from the pre-ore patterns.   Incidentally, an attempt to construct such a restoration may disclose erroneous assumptions in the solution of the fault problems and lead to a correction of mistakes or inaccuracies.   Once the pre-fault condition is restored, the stage is set for attacking such problems as the distribution

---

12 Price, Peter, Geology and ore deposits of the Horne mine, Noranda, Quebec: *Can. Inst. Min. and Met. Bull.,* No. 263, p. 139, 1934.

13 Moehlman, R. S., Dikes and veins in the Alamos district: *Econ. Geol.,* vol. 30, pp. 750–764, 1935.

of values in the primary ore, the pattern of veins, and the controls of primary ore deposition.

SELECTED REFERENCES

Billings, Marland P., *Structural Geology*. New York: Prentice-Hall, Incorporated, 1942.

Haddock, M. H., *Disrupted Strata*. London: Technical Press Limited, 1938.

Hills, E. Sherbon, *Outlines of Structural Geology*. New York: Nordeman Publishing Company, 1940.

Lahee, Frederic H., *Field Geology*, 4th Edition, Chapter 8, (pp. 201–262), Fractures and fracture structures. New York: McGraw-Hill Book Company, Incorporated, 1941.

Nevin, C. M., *Principles of Structural Geology*, 3rd Edition. New York: John Wiley and Sons, Incorporated, 1942.

Willis, Bailey and Willis, Robin, *Geologic Structures*, 3rd Edition. New York: McGraw-Hill Publishing Company, 1934.

15

Persistence of Ore in Depth

*All mines become completely exhausted at some point in depth. There-
fore the actual distance to which ore can be expected to extend below the
lowest level grows less with every deeper working horizon.*
—Herbert C. Hoover [1]

Much of the romance of mining springs from uncertainty as to what
a deeper level will disclose—the hope of rich reward pitted against
anxiety lest the ore disappear altogether. This hazard is never completely eliminated, yet from the viewpoint of sound business, as contrasted with the outlook of the gambler, the less uncertainty the better
for all concerned. Toward minimizing the risk, geological methods
are able to offer considerable help, first in predicting the shape and position that the orebodies will have at deeper levels; second, by providing
the basis for an intelligent guess as to how deep the ore is likely to extend and by recognizing at an early stage the signs of approach to the
bottom of commercial values.

PROBABLE POSITION AND SHAPE AT DEEPER LEVELS

There are definite advantages in being able to predict the position and
shape that the ore will assume as it is followed to deeper levels. The
degree to which prediction is possible depends on the regularity of the
orebody and particularly on the definiteness of the geological control of
ore. Exact prediction is perhaps never attainable, but in some mines,
as for example the Homestake, the outlines of orebodies can be projected with remarkable precision for one or two levels and with reasonable accuracy for several hundred feet. A downward projection involves two factors: the angle of pitch and the shape of the oreshoot.

[1] *Principles of Mining*, p. 32. New York: Hill Publishing Company, 1909.

PITCH

Significance

If an orebody consists of a shoot in a vein, its shape is more or less tabular—thin in one dimension and relatively extensive in the other two. Its outline, as seen in longitudinal section, may be quite irregular, like the nondescript shape of an amoeba, but more commonly it resembles some modification of an ellipse even though the actual curve is by no means an ideal mathematical one. The long axis may be horizontal, vertical, or inclined; that is to say, the pitch [2] may vary from zero to 90 degrees.

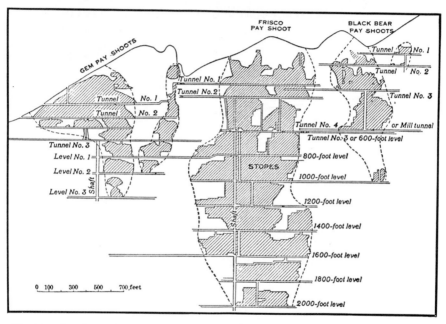

Fig. 129—Steeply pitching ore-shoots. Helena-Frisco Mine, Coeur d'Alene District, Idaho. (*After* Ransome and Calkins, *U.S.G.S.*)

Even if the orebody does not lie within a vein but consists, for example, of a mineralized zone of shattering or a replacement of sedimentary rock, it may nevertheless show a tendency to elongated shape, and if so, the plunge of its long axis is likely to be a critical factor in its behavior in depth.

---

[2] *Pitch* is the angle between the long axis of the orebody and the strike-line of the vein. This angle is measured in the plane of the vein. *Rake* or *plunge* (the two terms are synonymous) is always measured in a vertical plane. It is the angle between the long axis of an orebody and its horizontal projection.

A correct prediction of the pitch of an orebody is important, partly for safety in protecting property rights and partly for economy in laying out development work. The Morning orebody in the Coeur d'Alene district pitches steeply westward so that in depth the ore begins to cross the endline into the adjoining Star property. If it is possible to foresee such a condition in the earlier stages of development,

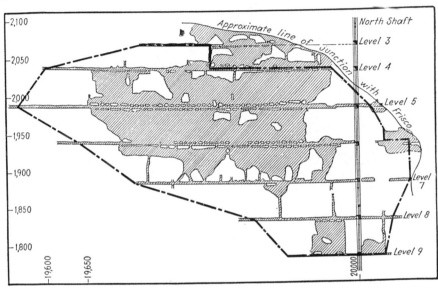

Fig. 130—Gently pitching ore-shoot. The dashed lines indicate limit of ore reserves, thus outlining ore-shoot, which is incompletely stoped. Longitudinal projection of "footwall vein" workings. San Francisco del Oro, Chih., Mexico.

the owners may find it advantageous to acquire the appropriate neighboring ground.

Furthermore, in planning a development program, it is desirable to place the main shaft near the center of gravity of the ore, or in any case, not in such a position that the ore quickly pitches away from the shaft, requiring a longer drift or crosscut on each successively deeper level. Similar considerations apply in laying out adits. Many an adit has been aimed to cut a vein at a point directly down-dip from the outcrop of its oreshoot, ignoring the possibility of other than 90-degree pitch. Not a few mines have been abandoned (temporarily at least) when such adits intersected discouragingly poor parts of the vein. Even if the preliminary development is by diamond drilling, recognition that the pitch will not necessarily be 90 degrees will avert negative conclusions from too few holes, and, if the probable pitch is known, the chance of cutting ore with the earliest holes is increased.

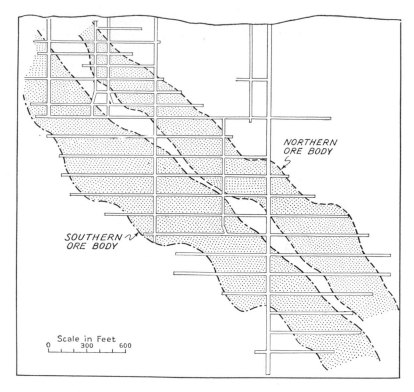

Fig. 131—Elongated plunging ore-shoots, controlled by plunging folds. North Broken Hill Mine, New South Wales. Longitudinal section looking west. (*After* Garretty and Blanchard, *Economic Geology*)

Criteria

The most direct evidence of the degree and direction of the pitch of an oreshoot is, of course, the observed trend of its boundaries. But in the early stages of development, the exposures may be inadequate to disclose the true pitch or, for that matter, to reveal any trend at all. Therefore, supplementary criteria may be useful either in confirming the preliminary indications or in serving alone as a basis of prediction. Any such predictions are admittedly far from infallible, yet they may provide the basis for better betting odds than the neutral assumption that the pitch will be 90 degrees.

1. *Observed Trend of Oreshoot.* The pitch of a shoot may be evident from the limits of ore on successive levels or from the shapes of stopes. If not, a more detailed record of the variation in values and width as shown, for example, by plotting curves of equal value or equal width on a longitudinal section, may disclose a consistent elongate arrangement. There are exceptional cases, however, in which such curves do not parallel the main direction of the shoot.

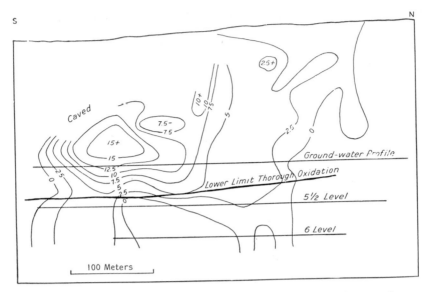

Fig. 132—Lines of equal ore-width used as a guide to the behavior of an ore-shoot in depth. Veta Colorada, near Parral, Chih, Mexico. The shape of the ore-shoot in depth was predicted from data taken above the 5½ level. Deeper development disclosed widths as shown below this level. These were found to correspond closely with the predicted outlines. (*After* Schmitt, *Trans. A.I.M.E.*)

This is true when the main oreshoot is the aggregate of a series of minor shoots whose individual pitches are oblique to that of the assemblage or when richer or wider streaks cross the main axis. In such cases the main trend is not evident until enough of the minor shoots have been exposed to reveal whatever broader pattern may exist.

For this reason and also because the margins of the shoot may be irregular in

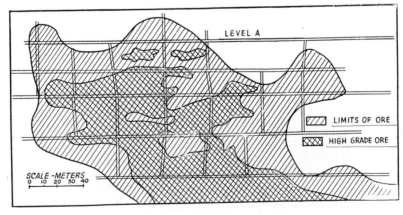

Fig. 133—High-grade ore within lower-grade shoot. Longitudinal section. Llallagua, Bolivia. (*After* Turneaure, *Economic Geology*)

detail, the trends disclosed in the earlier stages of development may be deceptive. They inspire greater confidence if they correspond with other criteria such as those listed in the succeeding paragraphs.

2. *Pitch of Other Oreshoots in the Same Vein.* More often than not, all or most of the oreshoots in any one vein have similar pitches.

3. *Pitch of Oreshoots in Neighboring Veins.* In the Burke portion of the Coeur d'Alene district, there is a series of parallel veins and nearly all of the oreshoots on them have very steep pitches approximating 90 degrees. In Grass Valley (California) it is a local "law" that "the shoot will, as a rule, pitch to the left of an observer standing on the apex of the vein and looking down in the direction of the dip." [3] Johnston [4] attributes this to the pitch of intersections of steep northeasterly-striking fractures ("crossings") with both the east- and west-dipping veins.

4. *Plunge of Rock Structure.* Replacement orebodies, especially those in tightly folded or schistose rocks very commonly follow the plunge of the folding. Even if the mineralization in such rocks has a vein-like form, the oreshoots are rather likely to be elongated in the direction of the regional plunge, as in the Porcupine and many other districts in the pre-Cambrian rocks of Canada.

As guides to the plunge of major structure, the plunges of minor features such as those listed below are most useful, as they usually correspond in direction if not in exact angle, to the axes of major folding. However, in some exceptional cases, minor folds stand at large angles to the major fold axes, and, in other still more unusual examples, the elongation of original rock-features is normal rather than parallel to the plunge of major folding. Because of these exceptions, the attitude of minor features is most dependable as a guide in regions where repeated instances of correspondence have already been observed.

The most useful guides are:

a. Plunge of drag folds
b. Intersection of cleavage with bedding
c. Lineation: [5]

Elongation of original features of the rock: pebbles in conglomerate, fragments in clastic or igneous breccias, amygdules or spherules in lavas, oölites in oölitic rocks.

Lensing of beds due to: structural pinching off (boudinage) or to rotation or rolling during folding.

Intersection of structural planes, giving "pencil cleavage": cleavage with bedding (cf. *b.* above); two cognate cleavages.

Parallel orientation of prismatic minerals (especially hornblende).

---

[3] Lindgren, Waldemar, The gold quartz veins of Nevada City and Grass Valley Districts, California: *U.S. Geological Survey 17th Annual Report,* pt. 2, p. 160, 1896.

[4] Johnston, W. D., Jr., The gold quartz veins of Grass Valley, California: *U.S. Geological Survey Professional Paper 194,* p. 49, 1940.

[5] Cloos, Ernst, *Lineation.* G.S.A. Memoir 18, 1946, pp. 16–21.

5. *Pitch of Intersections of Localizing Structures.* The position of an ore-shoot may have been predetermined by the intersection of two structural features. If one of them is a vein, the other may be either a fracture, a second vein, or a favorable formation. If a fracture, and it is not exposed or clearly visible, the dip and strike of nearby minor fractures may give a clue to its attitude. Similarly, minor stringers may indicate the attitude of a major intersecting vein. Examples of pitching shoots localized by intersections with favorable rock formations are given in Chapter 11.

If conditions are such that the plunge of an intersection cannot be measured directly, it can be calculated from the dips and strikes of the intersecting features; in fact, such a calculation, graphic, or trigonometric, serves as a useful check on a projection even when a direct measurement can be made.

6. Somewhat similar to (5) is *the plunge of a curve or angle in the strike* of a vein as shown on the plan of a level. If the same curve or angle appears on successively deeper levels in such a position that it can be interpreted with confidence as a consistent change in the attitude of the vein, then a line, vertical or inclined, as the case may be, connecting the points of curvature from level to level, is likely to have structural significance. If such a line parallels the indicated boundaries of an oreshoot, the probability is that the shoot is related to a true structural feature and is not accidental or erratic.

7. *Direction of Movement on Fault Fissures.* From the theoretical considerations discussed in Chapter 12, it would be expected that if a system of fissures had been formed and opened by forces which continued to operate without change in their orientation, any intersections of fissures, or any changes in attitude of a given fissure (say from a shear direction to a tension direction) would take place along lines normal to the direction of the slip along the shear-surfaces of the system. If so, oreshoots localized by vein intersections or by changes in vein attitute should pitch normal to this direction of slip. Hence, on a dip-slip fault, whether normal or reverse, oreshoots should have gentle pitches and on a strike-slip fault they should have steep pitches.

This concept, though meriting further testing, can have but limited usefulness as a criterion, since it would apply only in districts whose stress history is simple and whose rocks are uniform in strength. Like other structural criteria, it is further limited because influences quite independent of the nature of fracturing can control precipitation of ore.

CHANGES IN SHAPE

The probable shape of the orebody is predicted by projecting the plan of the orebody downward along the line of the pitch, but one must take into consideration any tendencies which may effect the shape. The Homestake orebodies, for example, maintain the same general shape from level to level, but since the ore is localized within a bed that is complexly folded, there are important changes in the detail of its outline. Some of the minor folds become tighter, some become more open; certain portions of the beds thicken and others thin. These tendencies become evident from a study of the trend of each element in the structure, interpreted in the light of familiarity with the mechanics of folding and the behavior of compressed folds.

If an oreshoot is on a vein, it should be studied carefully in longitudinal projection, noting any trends in its boundaries. In conjunction with the longitudinal section, closely spaced cross sections are compared, and the downward projection, if indicated by structural features, is sketched on each of them. Instead of vertical cross sections, inclined cross sections normal or parallel to the pitch of structural features may be helpful. As a check and supplement to these studies, any known oreguides are projected downward. If, for example, the ore is localized by the intersection of a vein and a bed, each is projected independently and the two projections compared with the projection of the oreshoot. In fact, the projection of intersecting loci may prove easier and more reliable than the projection of the oreshoot itself.

HOW DEEP WILL THE ORE GO?

PRACTICAL IMPORTANCE

Whether consciously or not, all plans for equipment and all valuations take into account some sort of guess as to probable life, and this unavoidably involves a consideration of the probable depth.

If mining is approaching the bottom of the ore, the sooner the fact is recognized the better, for it may change the whole development program and completely alter the company's financial policy. Suppose, for example, that the management contemplates a reduction in operating costs to be achieved by sinking a new shaft and improving the hoisting equipment. If there is a large developed ore reserve and reason to expect that the ore will continue, the new shaft is a wise investment. But if the principal orebody is likely to bottom within the next few levels, it will be more prudent to continue with existing facilities. And in this case the emphasis shifts from routine development of a known shoot to an active search for new orebodies.

Again, where sinking is expensive because of water or other difficulties, the question of whether or not to open a deeper level may be difficult to decide, and geological warning of an approaching bottom may clinch the matter, or at least dictate exploration by drilling rather than sinking.

In the valuation of mines and prospects the expectation of extension in depth is obviously a vital factor. Its application is discussed in Chapter 18.

BOTTOM OF OREBODY OR BOTTOM OF MINING?

Bottoming does not usually take place in such an abrupt manner that on one level there is abundant ore and on the next deeper level there is none. Instead, the common experience is that with a decline, whether steady or irregular, in tenor or in quantity per level, the margin of profit approaches zero. Indeed, profit may decline purely as a result of the increased cost of mining at greater depth without any change in the ore itself, but this is essentially a matter of economics rather than geology.

In considering bottoming attributable to geological factors, it is essential to recognize a clear distinction between the bottoming of an individual oreshoot and the bottoming of an assemblage of oreshoots which, in the aggregate, make up the future ore-reserve of the mine. In the Hollinger mine, for example, any single oreshoot rarely extends through more than a few hundred feet of depth, yet the orebodies, as they appear on the mine model, resemble a crowded school of fish and, as an assemblage, have a much greater over-all depth than any single oreshoot. New oreshoots are found at depth as old ones are bottomed, and at over 4000 feet the productive zone is still orebearing. Thus if the orebodies in a district are many and closely spaced, the bottoming of any particular one need cause no serious concern, and the problem then consists in predicting the depth below which no further orebodies will occur. But if only one orebody is known, no matter how large it may be, its continuation is a critical question.

EMPIRICAL RULES FOR DEPTH EXTENSION

Certain rules have been used in mine valuation as a basis for calculations that involve probable extension of an individual oreshoot in depth. It is common practice, in estimating the amount of ore that may be counted on with reasonable safety, to assume that the ore will extend downward for a distance at least equal to half the horizontal length of the shoot as exposed on the bottom level. This assumption has some support from actual experience and is a safe guide in the sense that if applied to a large number of orebodies in different districts it will not lead to an overestimate. However, it can be badly wrong in individual cases and it can lead to seriously incorrect conclusions if used for the purpose of predicting the *maximum* amount of ore that exists.

Another "rule" is that the largest horizontal cross section of an orebody is halfway between its top and its bottom. A modified form of this statement is that there will be as much ore below the level on which the stope-length is greatest as there is above it. Either of these statements would be applicable to an orebody which has the shape of a symmetrical almond, a shape which many orebodies do approximate, at least in a rough way. But not a few are shaped like carrots, some erect and some inverted, and one of these would prove woefully embarrassing to a geologist who estimated its tonnage in accordance with the "rule." Even barring exceptions, the rule is often difficult to apply; if an unknown amount of the upper part of the orebody had been removed by erosion there would be no data for calculating the extent of the lower half.

In spite of objections, there are instances in which these "rules" offer the only basis for a guess. But if anything is known about the habits of the district or about the structural controls, such knowledge provides a sounder basis for prediction than do rules of thumb.

MINERALOGICAL VS STRUCTURAL BOTTOMING

Bottoming of an orebody where attributable to geological factors may take place in one of two ways: the valuable mineral may dwindle in amount until the grade is less than economic requirements, or, alternatively, the orebody may become shorter or thinner until it is too small to be profitable.

A mine whose life depends on a group of orebodies rather than on a single one may bottom either because successively deeper orebodies become progressively leaner or because the orebodies themselves become more widely spaced if not altogether absent. Thus the bottoming, whether of a single orebody or of a group, may take place either through change in mineralogical content or through change in structure. Even though the two types of change may and often do go hand in hand, they are best understood if considered separately.

MINERALOGICAL BOTTOMING

A diminution in the quantity of valuable mineral per ton of ore is often, though not always, accompanied by diminution in quantity of associated minerals. As the ore-mineral and its associates disappear, their place may be taken by increasing amounts of some of the non-valuable minerals which are already present or by new minerals which accordingly come to be recognized as unfavorable omens. This sort of change may take place not only with depth but outward away from the center of the orebody in all directions—downward, laterally, and (if erosion has not removed the evidence) upward. For most oreshoots lie encased in a larger body of low-grade vein matter.[6]

This curious but very common localization of valuable (or for that matter non-valuable) minerals in shoots often corresponds with local variation in the nature of the wall rock or in the structure of the ore-channel but in some cases no relationship to recognizable features is evident. Conceivably, variations in the proportions of minerals may reflect intricacies in the paths of solution-flow or delicate physico-chemical influences as yet little understood. We still have much to learn about the causes of oreshoots. But in any case, where the border of an oreshoot is marked by the same sort of mineralogical change on all sides, the bottoming of the shoot, although taking place in depth (as it must if it is to be called bottoming), can hardly be regarded as a consequence of depth itself.

It is otherwise when a downward mineralogical change is different from that in other directions, for then we may suspect that depth in itself is the determining factor. Our suspicion will not necessarily find confirmation, however, since the change may correspond with some change in the nature of wall rock or in structure of the ore channel which happens to take place in a downward direction.

Change of Mineralogy with Wall Rock

A mineralogical change in the ore on passing into a different wall rock is not uncommon. Thus in the San Dimas District in Western Mexico, the rich silver-gold veins in andesite pass downward into rhyolite with undiminished size, but the gold- and silver-bearing minerals, along with their accompanying gangue minerals (rhodonite and manganiferous calcite) disappear abruptly at the contact while the quartz becomes coarse and in places amethystine. Here it seems inescapable that change in the precipitating power of the wall rock is the essential cause of the mineralogic change.

Change of Mineralogy with Structure

The mineralogy of a vein may be influenced by change in the structure of the channel-way without any change in the wall rock. In a mine in Grass Valley (the Norambagua), the dip of the vein changes at intervals from steep to gentle. The steep portions consist of shear-zones made up of slabs and slivers of mineralized wall rock which is strongly pyritized and carries high gold-values, whereas the flattest portions of

---

[6] Wisser, Edward, The environment of orebodies: *A.I.M.E. Tech. Pub. 1026*, p. 3, 1939.

the vein are inclusion-free and filled with nearly barren quartz. The absence of pyrite in the flat stretches is attributable to the lack of inclusions which would have offered abundant surfaces for reaction and precipitation.

Mineralogical changes that are attributable purely to changes in character of wall rock and in structure of vein may mark the end of an individual oreshoot, but they do not necessarily mean that deeper ore will not be found in the district or even in the same ore-channel; the ore is likely to "make" again if favorable wall rock and structure can be found at greater depth. In this respect they differ from changes that are attributable to the direct influence of depth.

CHANGES OF MINERALOGY BECAUSE OF ZONING

There are many examples of mineralogical changes of a sort which can be ascribed only to the influence of depth itself or at least to proximity to the probable source of mineralizing solutions, which ordinarily is deeper than the site of deposition. Bottoming of copper orebodies by change to massive pyrite is common; so is bottoming of lead-zinc orebodies with disappearance of galena accompanied by change in color of sphalerite from light to dark and an increase in the amount of pyrite. The classic examples of change, downward and inward toward a "hot center"—silver-zinc passing into copper at Butte and copper passing into tin in Cornwall—are familiar to all students of ore deposits.

Nature of Hypogene Zoning

The "zonal theory," [7] which has been developed to explain these observations, is based on the concept that the minerals present and their relative proportions bear a relationship to the conditions which prevailed at the time of deposition and that these conditions changed gradually along the path of the solutions from their source toward the surface. Of the "conditions," probably the most influential is temperature. But pressure may also play a part, especially where the reactions of deposition involve a gas phase. In addition to temperature and pressure, a somewhat less tangible yet probably real factor is the chemical potency of solutions by virtue of the dissolved substances which they carry; presumably this potency declines as the solutions become enfeebled through reaction and deposition in the course of their travel. The resultant of all these factors as exemplified at any place may be termed the intensity

[7] Spurr, J. E., A theory of ore deposition: *Economic Geology*, vol. 2, pp. 781–785, 1907.

Emmons, W. H., Primary downward changes in ore deposits: *American Institute Mining Metallurgical Engineers, Transactions*, vol. 70, pp. 964–992, 1924.

of mineralization at that place. Zoning implies declining intensity upward or outward from the source.

Higher rock temperatures at depth than at the surface and, in fact, a rather uniform increase with depth have been observed in all deep mines and deep boreholes. This "normal" temperature gradient is modified by presence of still-warm intrusives and by heating of rock in the neighborhood of channelways through which hot solutions are ascending. Thus the successive isotherms may, in their idealized form, have shapes varying from horizontal layers in the case of a "normal" gradient to concentric domes or vertically standing concentric cones or cylinders.

Local heating along a channelway is more rapid the greater the quantity of solution that moves along it; hence, geotherms may rise in a very local manner in the neighborhood of a path of hot rapidly rising solutions. Similarly, other factors of intensity may vary with the channelway and the volume of flow. Therefore it is not to be expected that zonal changes will necessarily take place at the same depth or the same distance from the source along all channelways, nor is it surprising that in some districts the zoning is of a broad and uniform nature while in others the zonal change occurs at different elevations on different veins.

Accordingly we may recognize zoning on all scales ranging from the proportions of a region through those of a district to those of a single vein. Of most practical significance is the distinction between district-wide zoning and localized or "spot" zoning, even though no sharp dividing line can be drawn between the two.

District-Wide Zoning

Throughout some districts the bottoms of the lowest oreshoots on the veins are points on an imaginary gently rolling surface;[8] where the depths of some of such orebodies are known, the approximate positions of the bottoms of others can be predicted by projecting this surface. Thus in the Parral district, Mexico, the orebodies (except those in the immediate vicinity of the city) bottom at a roughly constant elevation of 1700 meters, which means 50 to 300 meters below their outcrops.[9]

Similarly, in fissure veins in the northern part of the Boulder batholith (Montana), Billingsley and Grimes[10] find that the productive portions do not as a rule extend more than 1000 feet below the flat roof of

---

[8] Wisser, Edward, Environment of ore bodies: *American Institute Mining Metallurgical Engineers, Technical Publication No. 1026*, p. 1, 1939.

[9] Barry, John G., Cited by Schmitt, Harrison, Determination of oreshoot bottoms: *Engineering and Mining Journal*, vol. 134, p. 52, 1933.

[10] Billingsley, Paul, and Grimes, J. A., Ore deposits of the Boulder batholith of Montana: *American Institute of Mining and Metallurgical Engineers, Transactions*, vol. 58, p. 307, 1918.

the batholith (out of 100 veins, only four were productive below this depth). In the Rimini [11] district in this region, the bottoms of all the important orebodies lie at an elevation of 5500 ft. ± 500 ft. In at least three instances rather thorough exploration 300 to 500 feet below the bottom of the ore failed to find anything except very small orebodies. In the Rimini orebodies, at least in those whose mode of bottoming has been studied, galena disappears (in one shoot within a vertical distance of 100 feet), and the proportion of quartz and barren pyrite increases with increasing depth.

Localized Zoning

In contrast to the conditions at Rimini, the mineralogical change in some districts takes place at different elevations in different orebodies, for reasons already suggested. A striking case of vertical change within individual groups of orebodies has been carefully studied at Morococha, Peru.[12] Within each group or "ore cluster," silver, lead and zinc ores change downward into copper ores and finally bottom in heavy pyritic material. The succession is:

(Top)

Galena and sphalerite

Sphalerite and tetrahedrite-tennantite

Tetrahedrite-tennantite, enargite, and pyrite

Enargite, chalcopyrite, and pyrite

Chalcopyrite and pyrite

Pyrite, often with magnetite

(Bottom)

The heavy pyrite begins to appear as a downward-spreading core surrounded by a thinning sheath of copper ore. The entire change takes place within a depth-range of 500 feet in some of the ore clusters, but in others it requires more than 1000 feet.

Mineralogical changes which take place in the direction of the probable source of solutions sometimes coincide with changes in the structure of the channelway. In such cases it is difficult to decide whether the dominating influence is zonal or structural. This is true in some replacement deposits of the manto-chimney [13] type in limestone. At

[11] McKinstry, H. E., and Svendsen, R. H., Unpublished mining report, 1937.

[12] Graton, L. C., Burrell, H. C., and others, The Morococha District: *Copper Resources of the World, 16th International Geological Congress,* Washington, pp. 536–537, 1933.

[13] Prescott, Basil, Limestone replacement deposits of the Mexican province: *Engineering and Mining Journal,* vol. 122, p. 246, 1926.

Hayward, M. W., and Triplett, W. H., Occurrence of lead-zinc ores in dolomitic limestone in northern Mexico: *American Institute of Mining and Metallurgical Engineers, Technical Publication No. 442,* 1931.

Erupcion-Ahumada, vanadium and molybdenum minerals begin to appear where the manto steepens and becomes a chimney.[14]   (These minerals, although products of oxidation, presumably represent elements present in the primary mineralization.)   At Gilman, Colorado,[14] the lead and zinc minerals of the mantos give place, in the chimney, to massive pyrite.   A similar change occurs in the Nitt Mine (Magdalena District, New Mexico) although here the distinct manto-chimney relationship is lacking.   The lead-zinc replacement in the orebodies of the upper levels changes to massive pyritic copper ore in depth, followed by rapid pinching out.

District-Wide vs. Localized Zoning

Some if not all localized zoning may represent merely a modification of district-wide zoning in which the boundaries of zones, instead of being relatively even surfaces, are highly irregular, rising abruptly and steeply in the neighborhood of channelways or in response to other local causes.   If this is so, the distinction between district-wide and localized zoning is essentially one of degree, yet the two contrasting conditions are worth recognizing.   Where it is known from ample experience throughout a particular district that the productive zone bottoms at a fairly uniform elevation or on a gently inclined surface, the chances of finding ore by exploration below this surface are not encouraging. But if bottoming of commercial ore has been shown to take place at greatly contrasting elevations in different orebodies or along different ore-channels, it is much more difficult to assign any definite depth to the bottoming of a given mine.   For, even though a characteristically deeper non-productive zone, encountered below the ore, may discourage still deeper exploration on that part of the channelway, this does not preclude the possibility, or even the expectation, that ore at greater depth may be found on another channelway or even on another part or branch of the same one.

Vertical and Horiztonal Aspects of Zoning

A map of the Butte district shows a zone of zinc-bearing veins surrounding the central zone of copper veins.   Viewed in vertical section, the copper mineralization underlies the zinc mineralization at depths which increase outward from the center of the district.   Somewhat similar relations have been observed in other districts, though as a rule

---

[14] Schmitt, Harrison, Determination of oreshoot bottoms: *Engineering and Mining Journal*, vol. 134, p. 52, 1933.

the arrangement in a horizontal dimension is better established, or at least more readily observable, than in the vertical. Where successive zones are bounded by surfaces whose forms rudely approximate those of the layers of the upper half of an onion, the rate at which downward change takes place as compared with horizontal change will depend on the shape of the "onion" and this varies greatly in different districts both in slope and regularity. For that matter the arrangement may not be onion-like or dome-like at all but more nearly cylindrical or conical, if indeed any geometrical figure proves remotely descriptive. But where adequate development in a district has disclosed a reasonably regular three-dimensional shape, the arrangement of mineralization at the surface tells something of what may be expected at depth below a given incompletely developed deposit. Thus an inner downward-flaring barren zone may give warning as to the nature and approximate depth of bottoming that may be expected; similarly an inner tin zone surrounded by silver-bearing veins will suggest that silver ore at the surface may give way to tin in depth.

Relation of Zoning to Classes of Ore Deposits

Although local experience, properly interpreted, is the most dependable guide to possible zonal changes, this guide unfortunately is not always at hand. In a district where orebodies have not been developed through intervals great enough to disclose changes in mineralogy, the nature of whatever mineralization is exposed may hold a clue as to what might be expected in depth. In this connection, the genetic class to which an orebody belongs may be significant.

In Hydrothermal Deposits. Of Lindgren's [15] classes of ore deposits, those belonging to the hydrothermal group (deposited by "hot ascending waters . . . charged with igneous emanations") are the ones most pertinent to a consideration of zoning. This group is divided by Lindgren into three sub-groups: epithermal, mesothermal, and hypothermal, according to whether the depth of deposition was shallow, intermediate, or deep.

Inherent in the classification is the assumption that both temperature and pressure vary with depth, an assumption which, in the main, is probably correct. However, where intrusive bodies have ascended to positions relatively close to the surface, the average rate of increase in tem-

[15] Lingren, Waldemar, *Mineral Deposits*, 4th edition, pp. 207–212. New York: McGraw-Hill Book Company, 1933.

Lindgren, Waldemar, The relation of ore deposition to physical conditions: *International Geological Congress*, X, Mexico, *Compte Rendu*, pp. 701–724, 1907.

TABLE 10

Minerals of Hydrothermal Deposits

X–Common or characteristic. (x)–Sparse or occasional. ?–Doubtful occurrence (contingent on classification of specific deposits)

Ore Minerals

	Hypothermal	Mesothermal	Leptothermal	Epithermal
Magnetite	X	(x)		
Specularite	X	(x)	(x)	
Pyrrhotite	X	(x)		
Cassiterite	X	(x)		
Arsenopyrite	X	X	(x)	(x)
Bismuthinite	X			(x)
Molybdenite	X	X	(x)	(x)
Bornite	X	X	(x)	(x)
Gold (native)	X	X	X	X
Pyrite	X	X	X	X
Sphalerite	X	X	X	X
Galena	X	X	X	X
Chalcopyrite	X	X	X	X
Enargite (Famatinite)		X	X	(x)
Chalcocite		X	(x)	(x)
Jamesonite		(x)	X	X
Bournonite	(x)	X	X	
Boulangerite	?		X	?
Silver (native)			X	
Cobaltite			X	
Niccolite			X	
Smaltite			X	
Ruby Silvers			(x)	X
Polybasite			(x)	X
Pearceite			(x)	X
Stephanite			(x)	X
Marcasite				X
Stibnite		(x)	(x)	X
Bismuth (native)				X
Argentite			(x)	X
Cinnabar		(x)		X
Selenides				X
Realgar				X
Orpiment				X

Gangue and Rock-Alteration Minerals

	Hypothermal	Mesothermal	Leptothermal	Epithermal
Garnet	X			
Pyroxene	X			
Amphibole	X			
Forsterite	X			
Ilvaite	X			
Vesuvianite	X			
Anorthite	X			
Wallastonite	X			
Axinite	X			
Scapolite	X			
Biotite	X			
Muscovite	X			
Topaz	X			
Tourmaline	X	(x)		
Albite	X	X		
Epidote	X	X	X	X
Quartz	X	X	X	X
Sericite	(x)	X	X	(x)
Chlorite (high iron)	X	(x)		
Chlorite (low iron)		(x)	X	X
Carbonates	X	X	X	X
Fluorite	X	(x)	(x)	X
Rhodonite	X	X	(x)	
Siderite		X	(x)	
Rhodochrosite			X	X
Barite		(x)	X	X
Dickite		(x)	X	X
Adularia			(x)	X
Alunite				X

perature from the surface to the intrusive must be more rapid the shallower the intrusive. Therefore, a strict correspondence between temperature and depth is not to be expected, nor is it necessarily true that temperature and pressure must vary together. Indeed, high temperature at shallow depth can accompany low pressure, a fact which Lindgren clearly recognized. Accordingly, Buddington has proposed a class, xenothermal, for ore deposits formed at high temperature but at shallow depth and low pressure.[16] Thus, since ore deposits have formed above intrusives that were emplaced at various depths, it is probable that the temperature gradient has not been the same in all localities and, indeed, that the gradient in a particular deposit did not remain constant during the whole time required for deposition; the temperature at any point along a channelway would depend on the temperature of the rock when solutions began passing through it, the temperature and quantity of the solutions and the time during which they had been flowing. Insofar as the minerals present and their proportions are dependent on temperature, the rate at which mineralization changes with depth will vary, even among deposits belonging to the same class. But in spite of the fact that temperature, depth, and pressure must be regarded as variables which are capable of a considerable degree of independence, the fact remains that most hydrothermal deposits fit with more or less satisfaction into the Lindgren type of classification.

One must remember, of course, that this threefold division into epithermal, mesothermal, and hypothermal is set off by boundaries which, though convenient, are arbitrary in the sense that they are man-made, as must always be the case when a naturally continuous series is subdivided. Instead of three classes a larger (or smaller) number might be established. In fact, Graton [17] has introduced a fourth class, leptothermal, comprising a well defined group of closely related deposits on both sides of Lindgren's border line between epithermal and mesothermal, and in addition has proposed a fifth class, telethermal, to include ores deposited far from their magmatic source (the lead-zinc deposits of the Mississippi Valley are the outstanding example of this class). Thus Graton's classification would be: Telethermal and epithermal (both deposited at shallow depth but under unlike conditions), leptothermal, mesothermal, hypothermal.

Since these classes are intergradational, mineralization belonging to

[16] Buddington, A. F., High temperature mineral associations at shallow to moderate depths: *Econ. Geol.*, vol. 30, pp. 205–222, 1935.

[17] Graton, L. C., The depth zones in ore deposition: *Economic Geology*, vol. 28, pp. 513–555, 1933.

one class may, in depth, or even laterally, take on the characteristics of
the next deeper and warmer class. Thus there are examples, some of
which will be mentioned shortly, in which epithermal mineralization
changes in depth to leptothermal. But such a change does not necessarily affect the continuity of the ore. For instance, it is not to be
expected that an epithermal vein will cease to be productive on entering
the leptothermal zone nor, conversely, that it will continue to be productive *until* it enters that zone. The usefulness of the classification,
for present purposes, is that the deposits belonging to each class have
their own characteristics with respect to the nature of the mineralogical
changes that they experience and the rate at which such changes take
place.

In *telethermal* deposits, at least those of the Mississippi Valley type,
zonal changes with depth are not the critical factor, so far as bottoming
of mines is concerned. Even granting that the distribution of mineralization around the Ozark Uplift and similar relations in the Wisconsin
field represent true zonal arrangement,[18] its dimensions are of regional
rather than local magnitude and no corresponding vertical changes have
been apparent within the depth opened by zinc-lead mining. That the
depth of mining has been very limited is attributable to structural and
stratigraphic factors; ore deposition has been controlled so delicately by
fracturing, and especially by receptive beds within the limestone series,
that these factors far outweigh any considerations of zonal change in determining the depth to which any mine or group of mines will extend.

In *epithermal* deposits, changes in mineralization with depth are characteristically conspicuous and abrupt. Whether this is to be explained
by steeper temperature gradient or by other influences which are prevalent near the surface, such as sudden reduction of pressure on entering
shallow shattered zones, boiling, escape of gas, and mingling with surface
waters (causing cooling, oxidation and chemical reactions), is still a
matter for investigation. In some districts, epithermal deposits show
"telescoping" [19]—that is to say, types of mineralization which might
otherwise have occurred in orderly successive zones have been crowded
together into a narrow vertical range. Some epithermal ores appear
to have deposited in complex sequence and under changing conditions
with correspondingly abrupt variations in the proportions of minerals
present. In these the lack of orderly arrangement renders predictions

[18] Emmons, W. H., Origin of the deposits of sulphide ores of the Mississippi Valley: *Econ.
Geol.*, vol. 24, pp. 230–234, 1929.
[19] Spurr, J. E., *The Ore Magmas*, pp. 292–308. New York: McGraw-Hill Book Company,
1933.

hazardous. But despite the ever-present danger of abrupt changes, "the failure of ore in depth and the distribution of oreshoots around centers are aspects in zoning which may be well-exhibited . . ." [20]

The behavior of the typical epithermal precious metal vein with depth is well described by Wisser: "The salient feature . . . is a body (or a number of bodies) of quartz or quartz and calcite. Base metals are sparse toward the top of this body, but they increase in depth to a horizon where they reach a maximum. Below this horizon the base sulphides continue to the lowest explored depths with no universal tendency either to increase or decrease. . . . With most epithermal precious metal veins, there is a single zone of ore body expectancy, appearing as a roughly horizontal band in longitudinal vertical projection of the veins. The bottom of this band may be recognized by the fact that the vein there 'looks splendid but doesn't run,' i.e., the gangue and base sulphides persist but the precious metal content has suddenly dropped." [21]

This decline in precious metals with depth, so common in epithermal deposits, may be compensated by an increase of base metals on approaching leptothermal conditions. This occurs at Casapalca, Peru,[22] and at Fresnillo, Mexico.[23] But more commonly, the base-metal sulphides, though conspicuous, are too sparse to make commercial ore. As Graton [24] points out, "the base metals have so low a ratio of value to weight that . . . [they] would have to increase scores to thousands of times as fast as the precious metals fall off if the same money value of the ore is to be maintained throughout." If the increase is only gradual, the interval that will intervene before the base metals attain commercial proportions may be hundreds or even thousands of feet. Furthermore, it is possible that solutions which ultimately deposit precious metal ores may in some cases never have carried enough lead, zinc, or copper to make commercial base-metal ore in any zone.

Textural changes sometimes accompany the mineralogical changes. Schmitt [25] describes an orebody near San Francisco del Oro (Mexico),

[20] McLaughlin, D. H., and Sales, Reno H., *Ore Deposits of the Western States* (Lindgren Volume—Rocky Mountain Fund Series), p. 691. New York: American Institute Mining Metallurgical Engineers, 1933.

[21] Wisser, Edward, in Symposium, Some observations in ore search: *A.I.M.E. Tech. Publ. No. 1209*, p. 31, 1938.

[22] McKinstry, H. E., and Noble, J. A., The veins of Casapalca, Peru: *Economic Geology*, vol. 27, pp. 502–522, 1932.

[23] Stone, J. B., and McCarthy, J. C., Mineral and metal variations in the veins of Fresnillo, Zacatecas: *American Institute Mining Metallurgical Engineers, Technical Publication No. 1500*, 1942.

[24] Graton, L. C., The depth zones in ore deposition: *Economic Geology*, vol. 28, p. 543, 1933.

[25] Schmitt, Harrison, Determination of oreshoot bottoms: *Engineering and Mining Journal*, vol. 134, p. 52, 1933.

whose bottom is marked by spectacular coarsening of sulphides: chalcopyrite crystals as much as two inches in diameter and galena crystals
as much as six inches. Many limestone replacement deposits of the
"funnel" type bottom in coarse breccias. Similarly in one mine in

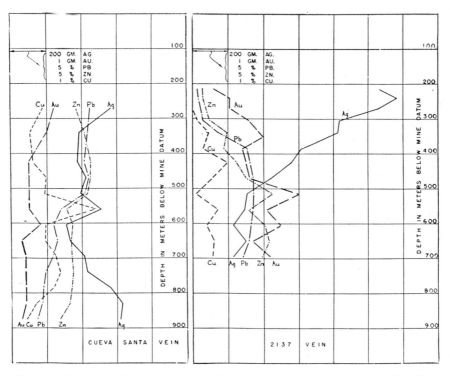

Fig. 134—Graphs showing variation in metal content with depth on two veins in Fresnillo,
Mexico. (*From* J. B. Stone and J. C. McCarthy, *A.I.M.M.E. Tech. Pub. 1500*)

Parral,[26] the ore passes downward into a silicified breccia below which
is an open breccia not filled with mineral matter. Wisser [27] notes that
a silver vein at Real del Monte changes 50 meters below the bottom of
its ore to an open fissure filled with boulders. "Some interstices between
the boulders are big enough for a man to crawl into. The boulders are
coated with quartz crusts but insufficient quartz deposited in the crusts
even to begin to fill the large interstices. Above, in the heart of the
vein zone, the vein is a quartz-cemented breccia, but openings are
scarce." Wisser notes, however, that the major veins of the same group

[26] Schmitt, Harrison, Determination of oreshoot bottoms: *Engineering and Mining Journal,*
vol. 134, p. 52, 1933.
[27] Wisser, Edward, Some observations in ore search (Symposium): *American Institute Mining
Metallurgical Engineers, Technical Publication No. 1209,* p. 34, 1940.

show fewer signs of decrease of intensity of mineralization at depth and, in fact, often show intense silicification.

In contrast to these striking changes, epithermal gold ores in the Cripple Creek District have reached no permanent mineralogical bottom at 3000 feet or more,[28] although individual shoots die out and others come in. Loughlin compares the fracture system to an apple tree with spreading branches: Down in the trunk the fractures become tighter and more restricted. Thus the decline in productivity is here due to structural rather than mineralogical factors.

In most epithermal precious metal deposits mining has ceased, for the present at least, at depths of from a thousand feet or less to 3000 feet below the present surface. Thus at Goldfield, less than 2400 feet, at El Oro, 1500 feet, at Comstock, 3000 feet, and at Zacatecas, less than 1500 feet.

In some if not all of these districts it is probable that these figures do not represent the full original range of temperature-pressure conditions conducive to ore deposition. First, erosion has removed an unknown amount from the top of the ore-bearing zone—probably least at Goldfield where the earth's surface during ore deposition was less than a thousand feet above the present surface.[29] Second, it is not clear in all cases that bottoming represents a zonal rather than a structural change. However, at Tonopah it does appear that mining started at the top of the orebearing zone and continued to its mineralogical bottom. There, Nolan[30] shows that the productive zone is a dome-like shell only 600 to 1000 feet thick, whose top reaches the surface only in the center of the district and even there in but isolated places. The bottom of the zone is roughly parallel with the top, both top and bottom lying deeper in the outskirts of the district than in the center. Since the zone is symmetrical with respect to rock alteration and truncates structure— rock formations as well as faults—Nolan concludes that it records the form of the isotherms as they existed at the time of ore deposition.

Leptothermal ores have, by and large, a considerably better record for depth-extension than have epithermal. At Casapalca, Peru, the vein system is productive through a vertical range of over 4000 feet and no indication of bottoming has been reported. At the highest levels the ore shows definite epithermal characteristics, but the mineralization soon

[28] Loughlin, G. F., Some observations in ore search (Symposium): *American Institute Mining Metallurgical Engineers, Technical Publication No. 1209*, p. 25, 1940.

[29] Ransome, F. L., Geology and ore deposits of Goldfield, Nev. *U.S. Geol. Surv. Pro. Paper No. 66*, p. 31, 1909.

[30] Nolan, Thomas B., The underground geology of the Tonopah Mining District: *Univ. of Nevada Bull.*, vol. 29, No. 5, p. 13, p. 42, 1935.

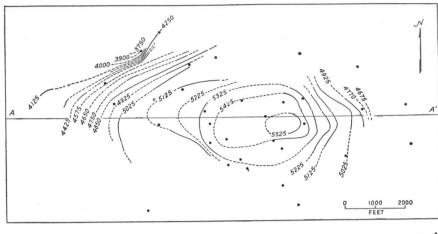

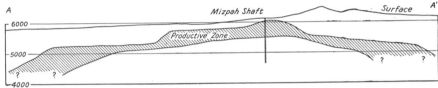

Fig. 135—*Above:* Sketch map showing contours on lower surface of productive zone, Tonopah, Nevada. *Below:* Cross section along line A-A′ showing dome-like shape of productive zone. (*After* Nolan, *University of Nevada Bulletin*)

changes to leptothermal and while there is a continuing change with increasing depth, it is so gradual that the deepest levels are still in mineralization that can be considered leptothermal.

The zinc ores of the outer zone at Butte, which have leptothermal affiliations, give way inward and presumably downward to mesothermal

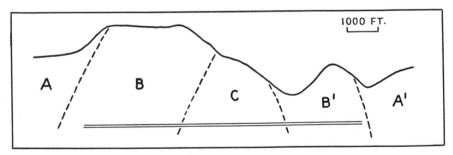

Fig. 136—Zoning of mineralization, Casapalca, Peru. Longitudinal section along vein-system looking east. *A:* Outer zone, quartz and calcite, pyrite, tetrahedrite, stibnite, realgar, spotty silver. *A′:* Botryoidal calcite and stibnite begin to appear. *B:* Intermediate zone, quartz, some calcite, pyrite, sphalerite, galena, tetrahedrite, bournonite, high silver. *B′:* Mineralization as in zone *B* with more calcite, less quartz, some rhodochrosite. *C:* Central zone, quartz, pyrite sphalerite, galena, less silver. (*After* McKinstry and Noble, *Econ. Geol.*)

copper ores which have been mined to depths of over 4000 feet.

The Michigan copper deposits, though of an uncommon type not easy to classify, may also belong to the leptothermal group. They have been mined to a vertical depth of 6000 feet, and where mining ceased it was not because of any radical zonal changes but the result of a gradual diminution in copper content per ton accompanying consistent thickening of the ore-locus—a change due essentially to structural causes.

Not all leptothermal ores have proved minable to any such extreme depths, but where operations have ceased at shallow horizons, as notably in the Cobalt District and in the Tomboy and Smuggler Union mines at Telluride, Colorado, the impoverishment has usually been found to coincide with changes in wall rock or to reflect other influences independent of depth-temperature environment.

Mesothermal deposits, together with some in the leptothermal class, offer the best opportunities for practical application of zonal theory, since here the mineralogical changes are not so extremely gradual as to be imperceptible nor yet too rapid and erratic to be predictable.[31] Some mesothermal deposits show recognizable changes in mineralogy within a range of 1000 feet or less, but others show no consistent change throughout a much greater interval. On the Mother Lode, although shoots of ore occur intermittently, there is no consistent change in the nature of mineralization through the explored range of more than 5000 feet. A number of other mesothermal deposits have been mined to depths of 3000 to 6000 feet; notable are Butte, the Coeur d'Alene, and Kirkland Lake.

In the Burke portion of the Coeur d'Alene district the locus of bottoming appears to be a curved surface sloping away from a stock of monzonite. Near the stock several mines bottom in non-commercial mineralization consisting of fine-grained garnet, magnetite and marmatite at elevations of 3000 feet or more, whereas the Morning mine, three miles from the stock, is still mining ore at depths well below sea level.

Hypothermal ores were deposited at such great depth that zonal change is gradual within the interval of the few thousand feet accessible to mining. Vertical changes are known—for example, at Noranda, Quebec, where individual orebodies increase in copper content downward and then bottom by abrupt falling off in values in both copper

---

[31] McLaughlin, D. H., and Sales, Reno H., Utilization of geology by mining companies: *Ore Deposits of the Western States* (Lindgren Volume—Rocky Mountain Fund Series), p. 691. New York: American Institute Mining Metallurgical Engineers, 1933.

and gold.[32]   Yet shoots of low-grade but probably commercial ore have been found at depths of more than 6000 feet.[33]

Certain districts of spotty gold ores having some of the characteristics of pegmatites have been described as the denuded roots of orebodies, but it is rarely possible to prove that better or different ore ever existed at higher elevations or that other shoots of the same ore do not exist at deeper levels.   With the possible exception of some tin veins, I do not know of any hypothermal ore, payable at the surface, which has been shown to bottom for reasons of zoning.   This is not to say that all hypothermal deposits will necessarily extend to great depth, for many shoots have proved to be small and quickly exhausted, but in such cases the reason is usually structural and the danger of reaching depths which have been too great to favor mineralization is negligible.

Conclusions.   Hypothermal mineralization need occasion little fear of consistent unfavorable change in mineralogy due to zonal causes, although this does not eliminate the possibility of dying out of individual shoots which may have been localized by structural or by more obscure influences.   In the case of epithermal and xenothermal deposits, there is a double hazard.   To the ever-present question of structure is added the uncertainty as to the range of favorable temperature-pressure conditions.

Although the foregoing considerations supply a background for judgment as to the general order of depth-extension that may be expected and the degree of risk involved, they are not in themselves sufficiently quantitative to serve as a basis for predicting specific changes either in mineralogy or in commercial tenor at definite depths.   For any approach to a quantitative basis, a thorough study of local conditions is indispensable.   The need for factual data is tersely emphasized by McLaughlin and Sales: [34]

"A careful record of facts must be built up by detailed field and laboratory work to make hypogene zoning really of direct value in mining work. . . . Diagnostic minerals must be recognized, limits defined, sequences established and distribution mapped in relation to rocks, structure, and ore bodies.   The work necessarily rests on a thorough understanding of the geology, and it can rarely be carried on to an effective stage if undertaken too early in the examination of a district.   Sample

[32] Price, Peter, Geology and ore deposits at the Horne Mine, Noranda, Quebec: *Canadian Institute Mining Metallurgical Engineers, Bulletin 263*, p. 108, 1934.

[33] *Annual Report,* Noranda Mines, Ltd., for the year ending Dec. 31, 1944.

[34] McLaughlin, D. H., and Sales, R. H., Utilization of geology by mining companies: *Ore Deposits of the Western States* (Lindgren Volume—Rocky Mountain Fund Series), p. 691. New York: American Institute Mining Metallurgical Engineers, 1933.

maps, records of production, and stope maps afford exceedingly valuable data from which distribution of metals or of ratios of minerals may often be determined and correlated with other features indicative of zoning."

In Pyrometasomatic Deposits. Closely allied to hypothermal deposits is the group known as pyrometasomatic. This group includes contact metamorphic deposits in limestone near the margins of granular intrusives, but the inclusive term, pyrometasomatic, recognizes the fact that the group is not restricted to the vicinity of contacts. Although carbonate rocks are the typical hosts, a few pyrometasomatic deposits occur in schists and gneisses which may or may not originally have contained alkaline earth carbonates. Calcium and magnesium, if not supplied by the host rock, must have been introduced by ore solutions, as the distinguishing trait of the deposits is the presence of silicates of these elements. But most pyrometasomatic deposits may be regarded as hypothermal deposits whose host rock was limestone.[35]

Their temperature of deposition was high, at least during the silicate stage. Although deposition of silicates was closely followed by scheelite, magnetite, and cassiterite (where these minerals are present), the base metal sulphides are usually distinctly younger and in some districts they extend well beyond the skarn zone where they form deposits having mesothermal characteristics. Lead and zinc ores usually persist to greater distances from the contact than do copper ores and thus may form a distinct outlying zone. Traced inward, the copper deposits characteristically give way to a barren silicate zone next to the intrusive. Doubtless a similar zonal relation is to be found at depth where parts of the intrusive underlie the deposits.

From a practical standpoint, however, mineralogical changes are less important than structural changes. Of the pyrometasomatic deposits, Bateman [36] says: "They are vexatious deposits to exploit because of their relatively small size, their capricious distribution within the aureole of contact metamorphism, and their abrupt terminations. . . . Their development must be undertaken with caution, and the optimism attendant upon mining such concentrated and often rich bodies frequently gives way quickly to disappointment upon the sudden termination of the orebody."

In Pegmatites. Pegmatites probably form, or at least begin to form, at temperatures higher than those of hypothermal deposits. Their depth-range is so great that no mine starting on a productive pegmatite

[35] Graton, L. C., The depth zones in ore deposition: *Econ. Geol.*, vol. 28, p. 531, 1933.

[36] Reprinted by permission from *Economic Mineral Deposits* by Professor Alan M. Bateman, published by John Wiley & Sons, Inc., 1942, p. 20.

is likely to reach a horizon too deep for further deposits. This does not mean, however, that any one pegmatite body will have great persistence in depth; in fact, pegmatites are notorious for their irregular structure and may pinch out with very little warning. Zonal arrangement of minerals within pegmatite bodies is common (see p. 279), but these changes are usually rudely symmetrical with respect to the walls and to the center and are not an expression of depth.

Except for tin ores recovered in the oxidized zone, few if any pegmatites are mined as sources of base or precious metals. They are the source of industrial minerals such as mica, feldspar, beryl, and spodumene. They are also the home of rare metals such as tantalum, columbium, and thorium, which are recoverable chiefly because of coarseness of texture; even though the aggregate tenor in some of these metals is minute, the crystals are large enough to be seen and picked out. The rare metals usually occur in small pockets or segregations which are so quickly exhausted that the cost of looking for additional occurrences vastly exceeds that of extracting the minerals once they are exposed.

In Magmatic Deposits Proper. Of the ores "formed by concentration in igneous magmas," some have remained at the site where they accumulated during differentiation of the magma; others have moved to new positions, whether within the intrusive body or in its adjoining wall rocks.

Those ores that have accumulated by gravitative differentiation and remained *in situ* normally occupy zones or bands which are more or less horizontal in attitude. The chromite bands and the Merensky platinum-bearing horizon in the Bushvelt Complex occur in flat-lying layers; any repetition in depth is conditional upon the "stratigraphy" of the enclosing igneous complex. Analogous structurally is the stratiform chromite of the Stillwater Complex in Montana [37] although here the layers have been up-ended so that extension in depth depends on what originally was horizontal continuity.

Ores that have been intruded or injected into new positions must have traveled as melts, and while it is conceivable that some of their components might crystallize before others, one would hardly expect them to show zoning of the sort familiar in hydrothermal deposits. If the melt carried any significant quantity of water or other mineralizer, its effects might be difficult to distinguish from those of hydrothermal solutions, but even so they would be comparable to hypothermal rather than cooler and shallower deposits. Any changes in depth would at most

---

[37] Sampson, Edward, in *Ore Deposits as Related to Structural Features*, pp. 11, 12. Princeton. N. J.: Princeton University Press, 1942.

be no more pronounced than in hypothermal ores. In short there is a lack of clear examples of ores assigned to this class which have been unprofitable in depth by reason of downward changes in nature of mineralization.

The extension of injected bodies in depth as well as in other directions depends on the openings which they were able to find or make for themselves and therefore expresses structural rather than mineralogical control. Thus ilmenite-magnetite deposits like those of Lake Sanford [38] (Tahawus, N. Y.) have band-like to lenticular shape. Injected deposits having the form of dikes or of sills as at Kiruna might be expected, from analogy to intrusive rocks, to be continuous to their source, though the source is not necessarily downward nor is structural thinning precluded.

In some districts where genesis by magmatic differentiation was formerly accepted, this mode of origin has been questioned by more recent workers. The magnetites of New York and New Jersey are now variously interpreted as pyrometasomatic, hypothermal, or as metamorphosed iron formations—a lack of agreement which may reflect actual differences in character between individual deposits. Whatever their origin, most geologists agree that so far as their structure is concerned they behave as though they were highly folded sedimentary beds, so that extension in depth depends on the shapes of the folded structures.

In regard to the sulphide ores of Sudbury, all authorities agree that, with the possible exception of the disseminated blebs in the norite, the sulphides have been transported to their present position; some of the geologists who have studied them intimately in recent years postulate solutions similar to if not identical with hydrothermal solutions.[39] Downward, as well as in other directions, individual orebodies are limited in a broad way by proximity to norite or to "offset rock" (quartz diorite) and in greater detail by the continuity of zones of shearing or brecciation.[40] There is no evident reason to believe that, apart from structure, the factor of depth in itself should impose any limit on ore occurrence.

[38] Osborne, F. F., Certain magmatic titaniferous iron ores and their origin: *Econ. Geol.*, vol. 23, pp. 724–761, 1928.

Mine Staff, MacIntyre development of National Lead Co. at Tahawus, N. Y.: *Mining and Metallurgy*, vol. 24, p. 510, 1943.

[39] Bateman, Alan M., Magmas and ores, *Econ. Geol.*, vol. 37, p. 5, 1942.

Davidson, Stanley, Structural aspects of the geology of the Falconbridge Nickel Mine, Sudbury District, Ontario, *Can. Inst. M. and M. Bull. No. 414*, p. 504, 1946. Also *Transactions*, vol. 49, p. 504, 1946.

[40] Anonymous, Canadian operations (of International Nickel Co.), *Canadian Mining Journal*, vol. 67, pp. 326–330, 1946.

Change of Mineralogy due to Supergene Processes

Ores that owe more or less of their value to supergene processes are, by their nature, related to an erosion surface and hence will cease to be commercial, or at least show a marked change in mineralogical character, at a relatively shallow depth below this surface. The erosion surface to which the ore is related, however, may not be the present surface of the earth; it may be an old surface which has been buried or tilted or one that has been planed off by subsequent erosion.

Two geologically different types of ore may be distinguished, depending on whether profitable values are in the zone of oxidation or in the zone of supergene sulphide enrichment. In some cases the material of both zones is minable.

Of the deposits minable in the oxidized zone, some are commercial merely because oxidation has softened the ore and thus reduced the cost of mining and treatment. Others (residual deposits) are minable because chemical action has removed valueless elements and thereby concentrated the valuable metal. Some of the ores of iron, manganese, nickel, aluminum, gold, lead, and tin belong in this category. If the evidence indicates that the ore will not be minable below the zone of oxidation, an estimate of the depth of this zone is called for. Generally speaking, the oxidized zone will extend to the groundwater level and unoxidized material will appear below it, so that the problem resolves itself into an estimate of the depth of the water level, making use of the principles of hydrology. This generalization finds exceptions in cases (not uncommon) in which the water level has been raised or lowered as a result of the events in recent physiographic history. Where the water level has been lowered in times so recent that oxidation has not yet caught up with it, the bottom of oxidation is likely to be highly irregular, extending downward along fractures and permeable zones and often leaving islands of unoxidized material stranded above it. Similar irregular bottoms may possibly be occasioned by oxidation below the water table along channelways of artesian circulation. When, instead of being lowered, the water level has been elevated, the oxidation is to be correlated with the older, deeper water table and not with the elevation at which water stands at present.

Deposits which are minable in the secondary sulphide zone begin at the bottom of oxidation and extend downward for varying depths. Where the present water level lies below the bottom of oxidation, the secondary ore is experiencing oxidation encroaching from above, but, especially in arid regions, large tonnages of secondary sulphide ore may still exist.   Secondary enrichment is a highly important factor in many copper deposits and also in some silver deposits.   In the copper deposits, the oxidized capping may or may not carry an appreciable quantity of metal.   Beneath it, sulphide enrichment begins, usually abruptly, and extends downward to depths that vary with the conditions in different districts.   At Butte, some supergene chalcocite persists to depths of 3000 feet below the bottom of oxidation, and at Bingham, Utah, the zone of supergene enrichment is 1400 feet thick.   These thicknesses are rather exceptional, however; in most disseminated copper deposits the enriched zone has a thickness of 150 to 300 feet, less commonly 450 feet or more.[41]   While the bottom of enrichment is abrupt in some districts, especially where the primary sulphide is massive it is more commonly gradational; in most "porphyry" copper deposits the bottom of mining, if determined by downward decline in enrichment, is an "assay bottom," that is, mining ceases at the point where grade falls below costs and not on a definite geological boundary.   In some cases, however, the bottom of enrichment does not constitute the bottom of mining; at Bingham (Utah), Ely (Nevada), Ajo (Arizona), and Chuquicamata (Chile) the primary ore, although leaner than the supergene material, is still minable.   In such cases the ultimate bottom is a matter of structural or of primary mineralogical bottoming rather than of cessation of enrichment.

Secondary copper deposits of the "porphyry" type are usually tested thoroughly by drilling in advance of mining, since huge tonnages have to be proved before installing a treatment plant.   Here the geologist's contribution lies mainly in making a preliminary appraisal to decide whether or not a test is worth while and, later, in preventing errors in the interpretation of the results of drilling and test-pitting.   His deductions are based partly on his general knowledge of ores and geologic processes and partly on clues afforded by the specific mineralogy and texture of the oxidized material.   These matters are discussed more fully in Chapter 10.   The proportion of primary to secondary copper and, therefore, an index to the probable tenor of the protore may sometimes be estimated from mineralogical and mineralographic evidence (see Chapter 5).   Plotting metal content or metal ratios on a system of cross sections usually affords a valuable guide to the interpretation of enrichment.

[41] Bateman, Alan M., *Economic Mineral Deposits*, p. 284.   New York: John Wiley and Sons, Inc., 1942.

STRUCTURAL BOTTOMING

If a particular ore deposit consisted purely and simply of open space filling in a zone of brecciation, one would naturally expect that the ore would terminate with the bottom of brecciation, in which case a prediction of the depth to which it would extend would be merely a problem in structural geology. However, structural controls are rarely as simple and definite as this. In some cases a structual locus of one type terminates in depth; yet the ore continues downward following a different locus. In other cases the ore terminates by mineralogical change before the bottom of the favorable structure is reached. As Schmitt [42] has pointed out, the behavior depends on the relation of the favorable structural horizon to the favorable mineralogical zone, or, in simplified terms, the relation of "ground preparation" to depth. If ground preparation extends below the depth which is mineralogically favorable, the ore terminates by mineralogical bottoming; if ground preparation of a suitable kind does not extend to the bottom of the favorable mineralogical zone, the ore may terminate by structural bottoming.

These considerations are somewhat theoretical, but they do call attention to a significant distinction between structural and mineralogical bottoming. A change in mineralogy marking passage downward into a zone too deep to be favorable to commercial mineralization marks the permanent bottom of the ore, at least so far as that particular ore channel is concerned, but an unfavorable change due purely to structure may be only the bottom of an individual oreshoot. So long as the zonal bottom has not been reached, the ore is likely to resume if favorable structural conditions repeat themselves at depth. At Norseman (Western Australia) an oreshoot had bottomed along a nearly horizontal line at a depth of about 800 feet and the operation was abandoned. Examination several years later showed that the bottom was purely a structural one, attributable to the pinching of a fracture zone with steepening of its dip.[43] There was no downward change in the nature of mineralization and the ore was of a high-temperature type in a region where gold ores had been followed to depths of several thousand feet. A study of the structure suggested the probability that the fracture would flatten again, and subsequent drilling checked this conclusion.

[42] Schmitt, Harrison, Determination of oreshoot bottoms: *Engineering and Mining Journal,* vol. 134, p. 53, February, 1933.

[43] McKinstry, H. E., Norseman mine, Western Australia, in *Ore Deposits as Related to Structural Features,* p. 224. Princeton, N. J.: Princeton University Press, 1942.

Deeper development has opened up a series of new shoots and disclosed over 800,000 tons of 7 dwt ore to a depth of 2200 feet.

With Weakening of Fracturing

Types of Downward Termination

A vein may pinch out in depth or it may "fray out" by changing to a zone of stringers. Either the pinching or the fraying often coincides with a change in the dip of the fracture. If minable ore is coextensive with sustained vein-width or with intense fracturing, the lower limit of the ore, when viewed in longitudinal section, may appear as a horizontal line, but more often it represents a shortening of the shoot from level to level in a shape which appears on the projection as a blunt prong or a group of prongs. The last gasp may be a small detached orebody

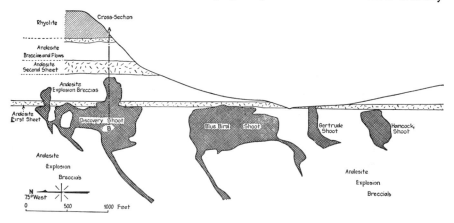

Fig. 137—Bottoming of ore shoots by narrowing into downward projecting prongs. Longitudinal projection, Camp Bird Vein, San Juan District, Colorado. (*After* Spurr, *Econ. Geol.*)

off the end of one of the prongs. Instead of a prong, there may be a pipelike continuation which extends downward indefinitely and seems to be the feeder of the orebody. It may or may not be large enough to follow downward in mining. The downward tapering may, it is true, reverse itself, giving what may be termed an "hourglass" shape. Such behavior is always the hope when the shoot appears to be constricting, but only occasionally does it materialize. Shortening of a shoot, indicating an approaching bottom, may be evident in a purely geometrical projection on a longitudinal section. Such a trend, not always obvious from the stope-outlines, may be revealed more delicately by plotting, on the longitudinal section, curves of equal vein-thickness (isopachs) or of equal assay values.

A group of veins may merge downward into a single vein which may be either stronger or weaker than its upper branches. Alternatively the veins of the group may pinch individually, either in *echelon* fashion or according to no recognizable pattern.

A lode, consisting of a zone of fractures, may cease to be orebearing as the individual fractures become smaller and fewer. This appears to have been the manner of bottoming in the Teck Hughes mine in the Kirkland Lake district, where the "Main Break" became lean at a depth of about 4800 feet. The lode was explored to over 6000 feet but consisted only of tight stringers said to be similar in mineralogy and metal content to those of the higher levels but carrying shoots too few and small to encourage deeper development. Whether or not a similar apparent bottoming will occur in other mines on the Main Break and, if so, at what depth, is not yet known.

Many bulky deposits, including some that are called disseminated, consist of a complex system of small, closely-spaced fractures and differ from lodes only in being more or less equidimensional in plan rather than long and narrow. When the ore bottoms, it is usually by decline in number and size of the fractures. Some of the fractures may extend downward along restricted shatter-zones until these lodelike bodies become too small and poor to mine. Alternatively the ore may continue downward as a pipelike chimney. Such a pipe under a ring-shaped orebody at Cananea [44] (Sonora) was exceptionally rich.

With great changes in depth, the nature of fracturing may be expected to change correspondingly. This follows not only from theoretical considerations but from a comparison of epithermal with hypothermal deposits.[45] Tension cracks and breccias, since they involve increase in the volume of the mass as a whole, are the predominant mode of fracturing close to the surface, whereas shearing is most common in deep-seated deposits. The resulting mineralization changes from dominantly open-space filling in the very shallow deposits to replacement of shears and highly selective replacement [46] of wall rock at great depth. It is impossible to assign any definite depth to this change, since it occurs at much greater depth in competent rocks than in incompetent ones,

[44] Perry, V. D., Copper deposits of the Cananea District, Sonora, Mexico: Copper Resources of the World, XVI *International Geological Congress,* Washington, vol. 1, p. 417, 1935.

Joralemon, Ira B., The unexpected in the discovery of orebodies: *American Institute Mining Metallurgical Engineers, Technical Publication No. 340,* p. 7, 1930.

[45] Butler, B. S., Some interrelations of structure, mineralogy and association with intrusive bodies; *Ore deposits as related to structural features,* p. 3. Princeton: Princeton University Press, 1943.

[46] Graton, L. C., The depth zones in ore deposition: *Economic Geology,* vol. 28, p. 529, 1933.

and furthermore, it probably varies with the nature of loading and rate of application of force. As a matter of fact, the change with depth is so gradual that in few if any individual districts is it noticeable within the range opened by mining, and a clear-cut example observed within a single mine is difficult to cite.

On Faults

If a fault is expected to intersect an orebody in depth, the question of whether or not it will form the ultimate bottom of the orebody depends partly, but not entirely, on whether the fault is younger or older than the mineralization. If it is younger, the continuation of the ore must exist somewhere on its footwall side. To this statement there are only two exceptions: (1) the case in which the fault happens to coincide with the original bottom of the ore, and (2) the case in which the segment on the footwall side has been raised (relatively) into a position above the present erosion surface. Searching for ore below a post-ore fault does not differ in principle from solving any other fault problem.

If, on the other hand, the fault is pre-mineral, there is no positive assurance that ore exists or ever existed on its footwall side. Whether or not there is ore to be found depends on the geological conditions in the individual case. If a favorable structure, whether it be a receptive rock formation, a breccia zone or a fracture, has been displaced and then mineralized, the chances are reasonably good that the mineralizing solutions will have found their way into it on the lower side of the fault as well as on the upper side unless the displacement was so great that the structure was out of their reach. However, an orebody below a pre-ore fault may be narrower or wider, richer or leaner than the corresponding orebody above it. In the case of orebearing fractures not in existence before the faulting but formed either at the same time or later, there is no reason to expect that their extensions exist below the fault although new and distinct veins may appear on the footwall side.

A remarkable example of bottoming on pre-ore faults is to be seen in the Kennecott District [47] in Alaska. Typically, each vein widens downward toward a bedding plane fault and is widest at its base, which rests

[47] Bateman, Alan M., (Ed., W. H. Newhouse) The ore deposits of Kennecott, Alaska: *Ore Deposits as Related to Structural Features*, p. 190. Princeton, N. J.: Princeton University Press, 1942.

Bateman, Alan M. and McLaughlin, D. H., Geology of the ore deposits of Kennecott, Alaska: *Economic Geology*, vol. 15, pp. 1–80, 1920.

Lasky, S. G., Transverse faults at Kennecott, Alaska, and their relation to the main fault systems: *American Institute Mining Metallurgical Engineers, Technical Publication No. 152*, 1928; reprinted, *American Institute Mining Metallurgical Engineers, Transactions*, vol. 85, pp. 303–317, 1929.

on the fault.　Below a fault no extension of the vein is to be found, but new veins appear and bottom similarly on other faults which mark deeper stratigraphic horizons.　The ultimate bottom of productivity is formed not by any single fault but by greenstone which underlies the folded limestones and dolomites in which the veins occur.

With Change of Wall Rock

Any indication that a change in wall rock is to be expected with depth is a danger signal.　As someone has said, "An orebody is a miracle"; its creation requires a combination of favorable conditions, and if wall rock is one of them, a different wall rock may make the difference between ore and waste, or at least between abundant ore and only moderate quantities.　Thus the wall rock of the ore that is being mined in any

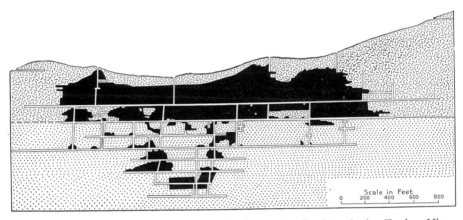

Fig. 138—Abrupt decline in productivity with change of wallrock in depth.　Tomboy Mine, Telluride, Colorado.　Longitudinal section looking northeast.

district is likely to be a more favorable formation than others which adjoin or underlie it, for if only the less favorable formation had been exposed, mining might never have been undertaken.　Therefore, despite numerous happy exceptions, it is general experience that a change in wall rock is a change for the worse rather than for the better.

The experience of the Dome Mine is well known.　Its great orebodies were in conglomerate.　When the workings deepened and encountered the underlying greenstone, the orebodies became so much poorer and scarcer that, for a time, hope for the future of the mine was given up even though the same formation where exposed on the other side of the district was known to be highly productive.　As it turned out, enough ore was eventually found in the greenstone to keep production going until further development down the plunge discovered new orebodies in the sediments, but the story stands nevertheless as one of the many examples of falling off of productivity with change of wall rock.

Probably the most famous example of disappearance of ore with change of wall rock is in Cobalt, Ontario, where veins in the Cobalt Conglomerate were phenomenally rich but either pinched or continued as barren gangue veins as they went down into the underlying Keewatin lavas.

In the Kalgoorlie District (Western Australia), a thick, folded intrusive sill of quartz dolerite constitutes the favorable horizon, and the series of altered volcanics (the Older Greenstone) that underlies it is a poor ore-carrier. "Lode after lode of the Eastern Lode System has died in depth where it encountered the Older Greenstone contact, and the bottom of others can be predicted with fair accuracy." [48] It is true that in part of the district orebodies have been found below the contact but rarely more than a very few hundred feet below it. "Experience has shown that orebodies in the Older Greenstone where they do occur are apt to be one of two kinds: (a) small discontinuous pipes of rich ore, or (b) extremely low-grade tabular bodies."

In general, the greater the contrast in rock type, the more radical the change in the ore. In many districts of the Western United States, the crystalline basement underlying younger sediments and volcanics is a probable ultimate bottom. [49] Although there is no geological law that prohibits the ore from extending below this basement, the change both in rock type and in structure is usually so pronounced that few orebodies persist through it.

Although an impending change of wall rock is to be viewed with alarm, it sometimes turns out to be a false alarm. The ore may continue into another type of rock with supreme disregard for considerations of petrology. It may even improve when followed into another deeper formation, although such experience is uncommon because mineralization in the less favorable of two formations is so often unconducive to the starting of operations. But the Sunshine Mine in Idaho operated for years as a small and obscure producer from a vein in a sedimentary phyllite known as the Wallace Formation. With depth it entered the St. Regis, an alternation of slates and quartzites, and suddenly blossomed into the largest and richest silver mine then operated in the United States.

[48] Gustafson, J. K., and Miller, F. S., Kalgoorlie geology re-interpreted: *Economic Geology*, vol. 32, p. 304, 1937.

[49] Schmitt, Harrison, Determination of oreshoot bottoms: *Engineering and Mining Journal*, vol. 134, p. 52, 1933.

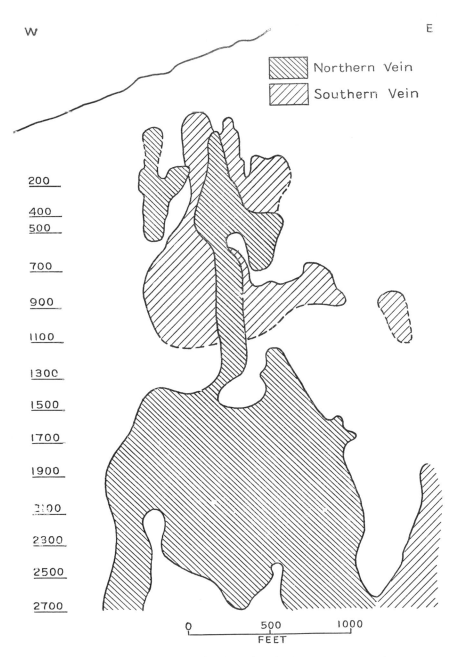

Fig. 139—Shortening of ore-shoot followed by lengthening at greater depth. Sunshine Mine, Idaho, longitudinal section. (*After* Sunshine Mining Company, *Annual Report*, 1941)

Such spectacular improvements are exceptional, but they are just common enough to make it unsafe to toll the funeral knell until the deeper rock has been adequately tested. But in any case, the stratigraphy should be deciphered, and the structure projected so that any impending change may be anticipated. If entry into a different wall rock is in prospect, any large financial commitments should be held in abeyance until extension in depth has been verified by drilling or sinking. This precaution can be ignored only when abundant experience in the district has shown that the new wall rock does not have a malign influence.

OTHER MODES OF STRUCTURAL BOTTOMING

With Pinching or Swelling of Replaced Beds

Ore that is a replacement of a permeable or chemically receptive bed is likely to pinch if the bed pinches. If, on the other hand, the bed thickens, the ore is likely to thicken with it. The thickening, however, may be compensated by a falling off in grade. In the Calumet Lode (Michigan), where copper ore is a replacement of the matrix of a conglomerate, the lens of conglomerate becomes longer and thicker with depth. With this enlargement the grade falls off until on the lower levels the lode is no longer payable. Interestingly enough the total amount of copper present on each level is about the same, but since the copper is distributed through a larger volume of conglomerate, the amount of metal per cubic foot is decidedly less [50] at depth.

With Change in Folded Structures

The replacement of a favorable bed by ore may be controlled by the structure of the bed. If ore is localized by a fold, it is in danger of terminating if the fold dies out. At Elkhorn, Montana,[51] an orebody at the surface is at the crest of a plunging anticline. As the anticline broadens in depth, the group of orebodies divides into two pendants, one on each limb of the fold, and both eventually die out, the deeper one below the 2200 foot level.

In Sedimentary Deposits

Aside from heavy minerals in placers, iron and manganese are the principal metals that occur as sedimentary deposits. In general such ores are remarkably continuous along both dip and strike; their exten-

---

[50] Butler, B. S., Burbank, W. S., et al. The copper deposits of Michigan: U.S. Geological Survey Professional Paper 144, p. 189–190, 1929.

[51] Weed, W. H., Geology and ore deposits of the Elkhorn mining district, Jefferson County, Montana: U.S. Geological Survey 22d Annual Report, pt. 2, p. 478, 1901.

sion in depth is controlled by rock-structure, chiefly the nature of the
folding.   If the beds are flat-lying, the ore will, of course, bottom when
the base of the orebearing stratum is reached.   If the beds have been
folded, the bottom of the ore will be determined by the depth of the
syncline.   Aside from these simple structural factors, it is important to
consider the possibility of interruption by faulting or by pinching-out
on the limb of a fold.

Despite their usual great continuity, sedimentary deposits terminate
eventually, whether at the ultimate limit of an original sedimentary
basin or at an unconformity where erosion has removed the orebearing
bed.   Such terminations, of course, may take place either laterally or
in depth, depending on the shape of the original deposit with respect to
the later folding or tilting.

Some of the ores both of iron and of manganese owe their commercial
value to supergene processes and, for this reason, become unpayable at
relatively shallow depth below the related erosion surface even though
the stratigraphic formation continues.

DEPENDABILITY OF GEOLOGICAL INFERENCE

From these considerations it will be clear that ore deposits of different
geological types differ vastly in their expectancy of continuation in
depth.   In some deposits it would be dangerous to count on as much
as a hundred feet below the deepest openings.   In others a thousand
feet or even several thousand feet may be anticipated with a reasonable
degree of assurance.   Although the genetic nature of the deposit is
strongly indicative, confidence is increased if other deposits of the same
type in the same district have been shown to extend to great depth.
The best of geological evidence, however, does not take the place of ore
blocked out by development work.   Even on the Rand, where ore is
exceptionally uniform and continuous, one of the largest mines (the
Randfontein) encountered at depth an unexpected barren area which
interrupted the ore throughout a horizontal length of over 8000 feet
along the reef.

Although geological assurance of extension in depth can justify preliminary expenditures for purchase and development, it should never be
allowed to bear the responsibility of heavy further commitments when
the continuity of ore can be confirmed by underground development.
For instance, it may be good business policy to exercise an option if
time is short and geological assurance is good, but even the most convincing geological evidence should be substantiated by underground
development or at least by drilling before building a mill, a long motor

road, or a power plant. In general it is safest to make sure that enough ore is in sight to amortize these expenditures before incurring them.

SELECTED REFERENCES

Emmons, W. H., Primary downward changes in ore deposits, *American Institute of Mining and Metallurgical Engineers*, Transactions, vol. 70, pp. 964–992, 1924.

Graton, L. C., The depth zones in ore deposition, *Economic Geology*, vol. 28, pp. 513–555, 1933.

Schmitt, Harrison, Determination of oreshoot bottoms, *Engineering and Mining Journal*, vol. 134, pp. 52, 1933.

Schmitt, Harrison, Extension of oreshoots with comments on the art of ore finding, *American Institute of Mining and Metallurgical Engineers*, Technical Publication No. 164, 1929.

Symposium, Some observations in ore search: Question 3. Are there any criteria by which ore can determine when mining operations have reached the roots of an ore deposit? *American Institute of Mining and Metallurgical Engineers*, Transactions, vol. 144, pp. 132–146, 1941. Also: Technical Publication 1209, 1940.

Wisser, Edward, The environment of ore bodies, *American Institute of Mining and Metallurgical Engineers*, Transactions, vol. 144, pp. 96–110, 1941. Also: Technical Publication 1026, 1939.

16

FIELD EXPLORATION

Nay if I understand anything, greater wealth now lies hidden beneath the ground in the mountainous parts of your territory than is visible and apparent above ground.   Farewell.
—AGRICOLA DE RE METALLICA, 1556 [1]

IN THE world-wide search for new ore deposits, mining and exploratory organizations follow two somewhat contrasting methods.   Some companies examine the most promising of the properties that prospectors and promoters submit to them, no matter where the properties are located.   Other companies center their operations in a particular district or region, thus covering a narrowed field but studying it more exhaustively.   Within a particular region there are, in turn, two plans of campaign.   One is to examine old mines and new discoveries, concentrating attention on places where ore or signs of ore have already been found.   The other is to investigate the tract systematically, undertaking actual prospecting in the places that seem most promising.   The methods are not mutually exclusive, of course; some companies combine two or all three methods of approach.

Which of the methods is best depends partly on the kind of organization that undertakes the work.   The large mining companies with field men in every part of the accessible world are in a position to follow up prospects regardless of location.   Smaller companies lacking an international organization do better to concentrate on a very few nations, states or districts.   Whether the bailiwick is wide-spread or restricted, a campaign of inspecting prospects, keeping in touch with local developments, and trying to be the first on the scene when a discovery is

---

[1] Translation by Herbert Clark Hoover and Lou Henry Hoover.   London: The Mining Magazine, 1912.

made, is really a series of prospect examinations by methods which will be described in a later chapter. The type of exploration which will receive attention in the ensuing pages is the systematic investigation of a sizable area whether in territory newly opened for prospecting or in an older region whose possibilities have not been exhausted. Work of this sort is undertaken either by companies formed for the specific purpose or by exploration departments of the large mining organizations.

Reserves and Concessions

The exploration of a large tract is usually carried out under some form of government concession, an arrangement which works out to the benefit both of the government and the concessionnaire. It is to the advantage of a nation or colony to see that its resources are developed as rapidly as is consistent with orderly economic progress, and this means that the exploration should be in hands that possess the requisite technical skill and have access to the necessary capital. If the region holds promise, some mining or exploration company will be glad to undertake the work, provided there is adequate assurance that it will reap the reward of its labor if any rewards are forthcoming. Should the exploration program produce no results the company must pocket its loss; therefore, it is justified in seeking to reserve for itself a reasonable amount of ground without being too closely fenced in by competitors who are sure to rush in as soon as a discovery is made. In some countries this is arranged by granting the exploratory company a temporary concession covering many square miles. For example the company may be allowed a year for preliminary exploration after which it must give up three quarters of the reservation and at the end of three years must drop three quarters of the remainder, retaining only a selected sixteenth of the original concession. In the absence of a government concession, a similar advantage, though on a smaller scale, may be gained by taking options on groups of claims from private owners and planning to exercise the options only on those claims which prove to be of definite interest.

No matter which method is followed, it is rarely feasible to retain control of the entire tract for any prolonged period; in the case of a government concession the terms of the agreement forbid it and in the case of options the payments that become due make it too expensive. Therefore, although the development of promising ground may proceed apace, the first and immediate objective is not so much one of orehunting as of prompt rejection of the unpromising parts of the area. This calls for application of the principles of orehunting "in reverse."

Initial Reconnaisance

Since time is of the essence, it is important to reconnoitre the whole tract, using methods that will give the most information at the earliest date. This usually means examining the best rock exposures first.   Where to look for them depends on the nature of the terrain.   In the bush-covered hills of western Mexico, experience soon shows that the only continuous natural exposures are in high cliffs and along water courses; accordingly the most rapid method of reconnaissance consists of running traverses up one arroyo and down the next.   In the desert of Western Australia the best rock-exposures are on the ridges and along the shores of the dry salt-lakes.

Preliminary reconnaissance of a large tract in Labrador [1a] was carried out by flying over it and sketching from the air the main geographic and geologic features.   Many areas of gossan could be seen from the plane, and their locations were recorded.   In the most interesting looking areas ground parties were landed on lakes and they prospected the shores from canoes, making sketch maps of the gossans and conspicuous geological features.   The field of search was widened beyond the reach of rapid prospecting by encouraging the Indians to bring in samples and specimens; the more promising of the Indians' finds were then examined.

These few examples bring home the fact that since each type of country presents its own problems, the first few days or weeks are well spent in sizing up the lay of the land in order to select the most effective plan for more detailed reconnaissance.

Even though a year or more may be available for selecting the best parts of the concession, the time is likely to prove all too short.   Compared with the detailed study that selected areas will later receive, the preliminary examination will necessarily be hasty and superficial and the selection will have to be based on incomplete evidence.   For this reason there is always a risk of rejecting ground that contains ore.   This risk has to be faced candidly, balancing the danger of making a mistake against the expense of insuring against it.   The selection and rejection cannot be infallible but must be based on the most intelligent guess that can be made in the light of the available knowledge.

Classification and Selection of Ground

After geological reconnaissance, portions of the tract can be classified into several categories, as for instance: (1) ground in which there are

---

[1a] Gustafson, John K., Personal conversation.

known orebodies or promising indications, (2) ground on which favorable structural conditions are known to exist, (3) ground on which no favorable conditions are known to exist, (4) ground on which favorable conditions are believed to be absent. A distinction is to be made between mere absence of positive indications and actual presence of negative indications. Rocks that are clearly younger than the oreforming period are definitely unfavorable, hence ground in which these rocks extend to depths below the reasonable limits of mining, as in down-faulted blocks or post-ore intrusions, can be rejected with confidence. Presence or absence of rock alteration is often a useful guide.

Although lack of alteration is discouraging, it may not be a negative indication, for in some camps the wall-rocks are altered only a few inches or a few feet from ore. However, most epigenetic deposits are surrounded by altered zones several feet to many hundreds of feet across. In one district in South America the veins are in red sandstones and shales which are conspicuously bleached even along the smallest mineralized fractures; here large areas of unbleached rock offer little hope. In general, rocks which lack fracturing and alteration—rocks which the prospector would call "dead-looking"—can be put in the least interesting class so far as hydrothermal deposits are concerned. But the behavior of rock structure in depth must always be considered. Where dips are gentle, favorable formations may lie beneath unfavorable, and where unconformities are present, a post-ore formation may conceal productive rocks.

Methods of Investigation

Mapping. For systematic investigation of an area, some kind of map is indispensable, whether to show geological features or merely to plot observed ore and mineralization. Just what sort of base to use for it will depend on what maps are already in existence. If government topographic and geological surveys have been made, they serve as an excellent base for recording the results of broad-scale reconnaissance and prospecting. However, since many regions in which mineral exploration is undertaken are remote and little known, any maps that exist at all are likely to be so sketchy and generalized that the exploring party will have to make its own map as it goes. For large tracts the methods are similar to those used by the government surveys and are well-described in the texts on field geology.[2] Hills and prominent land-marks may be tied together by a triangulation net, prepared by means of a

2 See references at the end of Chapter 1.

theodolite, a plane-table, or a compass, according to the accuracy required. Intermediate measurements may be made by pacing, measuring-wheel, or automobile "speedometer," depending on the terrain.

For most purposes, however, aerial photographs form much the most satisfactory and economical base-maps (see p. 19). But in mentioning them it may not be amiss to say that although they are virtually indispensable in a modern exploratory campaign, they are merely a means of map-making to be supplemented by other exploratory methods. Airplane photography is not in itself a method of ore-finding. A few years ago a strong company undertook an ambitious air-survey over a large area, but on completing the photography were not disposed to provide further funds to follow it with geological work. Whether or not the geological work would have found ore will probably never be known, but in any case it is clear that without it the survey had small chance of returning its cost.

The cost of air photography varies, of course, with location, scale and other factors. As an indication of general order of expense, mapping of 15 square miles in Canada with prints on a scale of 1 inch to 500 feet is estimated as about $40 per square mile.[3] An accurate contour map made from the photographs costs about $65 a square mile.

To be most useful, a reconnaissance map should show at least the broader features of the geology, and it should indicate the location of any mines or prospects and all outcrops of veins or mineralized rock. If there are mines which have yielded ore in the past, the amount of production should be indicated graphically, for example by circles of contrasting size proportional to the number of pounds or ounces of metal from each mine. If enough information is available, such a map will at once bring out the trends of ore-bearing belts and show their relation to rock structure and intrusive bodies.

Reconnaissance maps on small scales ranging from a few thousand feet up to several miles to the inch will be adequate to serve as a basis for eliminating large hopeless areas and outlining the ground that is worth more careful attention. For large tracts considered as a whole, mapping on larger scales is not likely to be warranted. But when attention turns to the study of the promising subdivisions or to the solution of specific problems, maps of much larger scale, ranging from 1000 feet down to 100 feet to the inch will be needed for selected tracts. In addition to the geological features these maps should show all veins and ore-outcrops. Using them as a basis, the extensions of known ore-

[3] Gayer, R. G., Mechanical aids in prospecting: *Western Miner*, June, 1946. Abstract, *Mining Magazine*, vol. 75, p. 121, August, 1946.

structures are projected longitudinally for reasonable distances and on their dips down to plausible limits of mining. This serves to outline the parts of the tract that are definitely known to be of interest. The remaining areas can then be studied critically with a view to rejection in case there is no reason to expect that they will be ore-bearing. When the time arrives for actual development, maps of still larger scales will be needed. At this stage the mapping methods revert to those discussed in the early chapters of this book.

Geophysical Surveys.[4] In planning the exploration of a large tract, the possibility of using geophysical methods always deserves consideration. Whether or not these methods can be helpful in any given case depends on the type of ore-occurrence that may be expected. Geophysics is not a cure-all; in situations to which it is not adapted it may prove useless even if not downright misleading. But where it is applicable, it is a rapid method of outlining areas that merit further exploration and of eliminating unfavorable ground.

Geophysical methods may be used either to obtain direct evidence of the existence of orebodies or merely to investigate subsurface structural conditions. Direct detection is most successful if the ore is distinctly different in its physical properties from the surrounding rock; that is, if the ore is magnetic or electrically conductive or exceptionally heavy and massive. If the ore itself is not amenable to direct detection, the use of geophysics in tracing contacts under concealed overburden or determining the depth to key horizons is often helpful. Generally speaking, the simplest methods have been the most successful; geomagnetic surveys have found more ore than all other geophysical methods combined, although they are, of course, applicable only to certain types of deposits. Methods directed to the interpretation of structure rather than the direct recognition of ore itself are most successful where the structure is simple. Unfortunately this is the case in only a few mining districts; too often the structure is so complicated that the geophysical results are subject to a variety of alternative interpretations. Just as in other types of investigation, the deciding question must always be: Specifically what may we expect to learn by this method?

Prospecting

Role of the Prospector. After the least promising areas have been rejected, the emphasis shifts from the elimination of hopeless ground to

---

[4] See Chapter 4.

the active search for ore within the selected claims or concessions. Here geology, geophysics, or a combination of the two can be of assistance in pointing to the most promising places; but at best these techniques are aids to ore search rather than substitutes for it. Actual discoveries must be made either by finding ore that is naturally exposed or by exposing it artificially, whether with the drill or the pick and shovel.

Some finds are purely accidental. The first silver vein in the Cobalt district (Ontario) was exposed while excavating a railway cut, and the copper-nickel ore at Sudbury was discovered in a similar manner. More freakish finds, like that made by the hunter who, picking up a stone to throw at a bear, noticed that the stone was heavy, are told and retold not because they are common but because they are exceptional. Despite the many entertaining anecdotes of accidental discoveries, it is safe to say that the majority of mines that are known today have been found by purposeful prospecting.

Geological deduction, followed by drilling and underground work deserves credit for an increasing number of orebodies in districts that are known to be mineralized but so far these methods alone have discovered few, if any, entirely new districts.

It is neither a disparagement of geologists nor a startling revelation to state that prospecting is best done by a prospector. Not that a knowledge of geology is a handicap—quite the contrary. But prospecting requires not only specialized experience but an unusual temperament, combining exceptional endowments of both patience and optimism—patience to go over the ground methodically, literally leaving no stone unturned; optimism to believe that even though today's work was disappointing, tomorrow's will surely strike it rich. The debt that the mining industry owes the prospector will never be reckoned. Some of his kind have reaped rich reward, but most of them have worked cheerfully year after year with nothing but a grubstake to show for their labor. Yet they would not have it otherwise nor exchange the bright hope of sudden wealth for the monotony of steady wages with nothing to dream of at the end of the trail but social security.

Prospectors' Methods. The good prospector works methodically, knocking a corner off every outcropping rock and cracking open pieces of float, especially if they are dark or rusty-looking. If he suspects them of containing gold, he may need to roast them in a fire or in a forge to free the gold particles before grinding and testing in the pan. Gravel and soil are likewise panned to reveal heavy minerals.

The prospector's manipulation of the pan has been described as follows: [5]

"He fills his pan half full of water, throws into it a shovel-full of dirt, first picking out the pebbles, stirs the mass with his fingers till the water is fully charged with clay and gradually winnows out all the clay. Filling the pan again with water, he gives it a peculiar circular motion and each little wave of sand passes off till the whole is winnowed off, and at last he sees specks of gold shining free in the bottom of the pan."

Panning is the rough-and-ready field method of testing gold deposits, but even if gold is not the object of search, a few flakes of the yellow metal may point to the presence of ore. Most lead, zinc, copper, and silver deposits of the cordilleran type carry a little gold, and, since gold is so nearly indestructible, it survives oxidation and attrition longer than any of the other metallic minerals associated with it. It migrates down hill or downstream, sometimes for several miles, and so forms a guide that may be followed back to the parent outcrop.

Besides gold, a few other heavy minerals, derived from base-metal deposits, may appear in the pan, though they do not retain their identity so far from the outcrop. Cerussite from lead deposits may be found in the detritis, and even pyrite may survive if erosion has been especially rapid. Limonite grains are common, but they can come from such a variety of sources that they have little significance unless they can be recognized as special types that are known locally to be associated with ore. The same may be said of garnet, magnetite, and ilmenite. Some other heavy minerals that are recovered in the pan may be valuable for their own sake. These include cassiterite, platinum, chromite, tantalite, columbite, wolframite, monazite, and zircon.

The prospector, if he finds any of these significant minerals by panning, or if he picks up pieces of ore or vein-matter in the float, can be sure that they have not been transported *up*hill and that the source must be at some higher point. As he proceeds up the stream or gulley the indications become more abundant. Should they disappear abruptly he knows that he has gone above the source, so he returns, perhaps picking up indications leading up a branch stream. Failing this he searches the adjoining hillslopes for an outcrop.

Panning and float-tracing succeed best in unglaciated country, although in some areas of mountain glaciation they can be used to advantage. In regions of continental glaciation like the Canadian Shield they are of little help, since the materials of the till are carried tens and

[5] Lakes, Arthur, *Prospecting for Gold and Silver*, p. 13. Colliery Engineering Co., Scranton, Pa., 1895.

even hundreds of miles and become so scattered and mixed that there is little hope of tracing them back to their source.

Coordination of Prospecting and Geology. It might be contended that in examining a region the prospecting should be postponed until after the geologizing is completed, in order to concentrate the search in the most likely places, but it is a fact that prospecting discloses information about ore occurrence and mineralization which helps to round out the geological picture. Thus prospecting and geology may proceed simultaneously, each aiding the other. The prospecting may be done either by men who travel with the survey party or by men who are free to move about as they see fit, though keeping in touch with the geologists and surveyors. Which plan is followed depends on the personnel available and the nature of the terrain.

Ore-Search and Development

When float and heavy minerals have been traced to their source, or when other localized indications of ore have been found, the next step is to uncover the mineralized rock by digging a series of trenches. The trenches, or at least the first exploratory ones, should be at right angles either to the rock structure or to the probable strike of the veins. When a vein is found, trenching may well follow along its strike so as to expose it continuously, although, if the ore is in the form of a wide body, the job of stripping it completely may be out of the question, and it usually suffices to expose it by a series of cross trenches. If the overburden is so deep that continuous trenching is impractical, the bedrock is tested by a series of closely spaced pits.

Trenching, since it is a cheap method of investigation, is useful not only in ore-search but in the elimination of unpromising ground. Thus, in a glaciated district covered by thin drift, a series of trenches across the structure will find any veins that are present at the bedrock surface or quickly and definitely disprove their presence.

Indications pointing to ore at depths too great for trenching may be tested by drilling. The alternative, underground work through a tunnel or a shaft, being much more expensive, will be undertaken only where drilling is impractical or where the chance of finding ore is exceptionally good. The indications of ore below the reach of trenches or test-pits may consist of geophysical anomalies, definite structural guides, or leached gossans and cappings presumably underlain by sulphide ore.

Once the presence of ore is confirmed, whether by trenching, drilling, or sinking, any further investigation and development follows the methods outlined in Chapter 17.

EXAMPLES OF METHODS IN FIELD EXPLORATION

Exploring the Nkana Concession

A highly successful program of exploration, carried out on the Nkana Concession in Northern Rhodesia in 1927–29, is described by Parker and Gray.[6] From an original concession of 1800 square miles, special grants aggregating 150,000 acres were to be selected. That is, 87% of the area had to be eliminated on the basis of two field seasons' geological work and prospecting. As a direct result of the geological work three large copper mines (Mulfulira, Chambishi, and Baluba) with drilled reserves of 162,000,000 tons [7] of 4% copper ore were developed and an extension of a fourth mine, the now-famous Roan Antelope, was found.

The success of the work is all the more remarkable because the ore, as such, does not outcrop and was found only by drilling below the oxidized zone. Even oxidized outcrops are scarce, and the country is covered by fairly dense scrub except for occasional open grassy flats called *dambos*. The field work was planned in a novel manner in order to make the most effective use of base camps. The camps were established in the centers of circular areas each 8 to 12 miles in diameter, spaced over the whole concession without overlap or any attempt to cover the spaces that fell between the contiguous circles except where there was special reason for doing so. Two field parties, each consisting of a geologist, a prospector, and native helpers, would make headquarters at a base camp. Each party would set out in the morning to make a traverse outward along the radius of the circle. On reaching the circumference they would take an offset of about a mile on the chord of the circle and return along another radius, reaching camp again by the end of the day. The two parties worked in opposite directions from the camp, but in order to minimize the personal equation, the parties would alternate in direction with each other on successive days. The traverses were made by pace and compass, although in some cases measuring wheels were used. Natives searched for outcrops within 100 to 200 yards of the line of traverse and all outcrops, as well as soil colors and nature of vegetation were plotted on the map. Before starting the radial traverses, stream beds and valleys were examined; in fact most of the outcrops were found at this stage.

---

[6] Parker, R. J., and Gray, Anton, Prospecting and geological survey of the Nkana Concession, Northern Rhodesia: 1927–1929: *Institution of Mining and Metallurgy*, vol. 45, pp. 317–331, 1936. Abstract, *Mining Mag.* vol. 54, pp. 181–185, March, 1936.

[7] by 1936.

The whole area was surveyed in a single field season and the resulting map showed the general structure. The second season's work consisted in an accurate survey of the parts of the area underlain by the productive horizon (the Mine Series) or younger formations, rejecting from consideration the areas occupied by rocks older than this. In the detailed survey, base-lines were laid out parallel to the strike and traverses were made at right angles to them at quarter-mile, or at most, half mile intervals. Where outcrops were scarce, pits were sunk to determine the character and structure of the formations.

Based on this work the 150,000 acres were selected so efficiently that they covered all of the possible orebearing horizon down to a depth of 4000 to 6000 feet and, although three great mines were developed within the concession, no commercial copper deposits have since been found in the rejected ground.

Prospecting in Uganda

Another example of systematic prospecting, the examination of an area of 155 square miles in the West Province of Uganda, East Africa is described by Wilson.[8] The area consisted of grassland at lower elevations and forest in the higher country. In the forested uplands, parallel lines were cut through the bush on 2400 foot centers. This interval was chosen because, under the conditions, a disseminated base-metal orebody would have to be at least 1200 feet long to be of interest and even if it were not intersected by a traverse line it would disclose its presence by float which would roll down the hillsides or be carried downstream for at least an equal distance. Prospecting was carried out along with line-cutting by parties each consisting of two Europeans and eighty natives. Along the traverse lines, stakes were driven at 300 foot intervals (corrected graphically to true horizontal measurement), and, where overburden was deep, a test pit was dug at each alternate stake (i.e., every 600 feet). Pits were also put down in each stream valley that crossed the traverse line and a traverse was run along each valley to tie into the adjoining traverse. Sand from the pits and from stream beds was panned for traces of gold and cassiterite and, as a check on observations, composite samples of the black sand from panning were made up, each representing 5000 feet of traverse, and these samples were sent to a laboratory for assay so that if values were found the pits could be re-examined.

In areas that merited detailed examination, straight traverse lines were

[8] Wilson, N. W., Rapid systematic prospecting in mountainous country: *Mining Magazine*, vol. 58, pp. 9–20, January, 1938.

run at 300 or 600 foot intervals and along them all vegetation was cut out to a width of 20 feet. This usually disclosed an outcrop somewhere within the cleared strip. From the results of prospecting a geologic map on the scale of 1:10,000 was constructed.

Prospecting in Eastern Canada [9]

The vast pre-Cambrian shield of Canada has been the scene of widespread prospecting since the early years of the present century. Until the mid-twenties the search was carried out by independent prospectors; not until a discovery had been made would the mining companies ordinarily take over the development work. But beginning about 1925, after the discovery of Noranda, the competition for properties became so intense, and naturally-exposed croppings became so scarce, that companies and syndicates were willing to take up any group of claims on which promising mineralization had been found or on which the geology was considered favorable. In doing so the companies incurred considerable risk, but with their ample financing they could undertake a more thorough and systematic search than a prospector's grub-stake could have permitted. As a consequence many concealed ore deposits have been discovered which prospectors alone could never have found. Through experience these methods have taken on a well established pattern adapted to the peculiar problems of the terrain. The portion of the Canadian Shield south of the subarctic barren-land is a flat to rolling country, dotted with lakes and swamps that interrupt the forest of second-growth timber. The lakes and streams are the key to transportation. They afford waterways for canoes and furnish bases for airplanes which are equipped in summer with pontoons and in winter with skis for landing on the ice. Between seasons there is a month during which the air transport is suspended because the lakes in the north are frozen and those in the south are clear, hence neither type of landing-gear can be used. For local transport the labyrinth of waterways connected by portages provides canoe routes. Away from the waterways, travel is by foot, and the going is slow except where good trails have been cut. Transportation of heavy machinery is least difficult in winter when tractors and horse-drawn sleds can make their way over the frozen lakes and along "winter roads" through the bush.

As the region is glaciated, much of the bedrock is covered by till and swamp-muck, but where outcrops do occur they are likely to present fresh rock and practically unoxidized ore.

---

[9] *Cf.* Bell, L. V., Geology in prospecting, with special reference to Western Quebec: *Can. Inst. Mining & Met. Bull.* No. 289; also *Trans.* vol. 39, 1936, pp. 235–256.

Since outcrops are snow-covered in winter, all prospecting and geologizing is confined to the summer months; the best time is during the very few weeks in April or May after most of the snow has melted but before the leaves have come out and obscured the view. Later in the season prospecting is still feasible if one can brave the attacks of the black-flies from mid-June to mid-July. Geophysical work and diamond drilling are entirely practical in winter as well as in summer, however. In fact, this type of work is usually easiest when the swamps and lakes are frozen.

A description of the examination and prospecting of a group of claims in the Chibougamau district of Quebec will illustrate the methods that are used through the region.[10] The claims had been staked by prospectors who entered the area in 1928 and discovered chalcopyrite showings. A little trenching had exposed a streak of copper-gold mineralization on one of the claims but no systematic prospecting was done at that time. Ten years later, when interest in the district revived, a Canadian-American group took an option on the claims. Early in the summer a group of twelve men, including a foreman, a geologist, an engineer, and a cook, went in by airplane and established a camp on the edge of the lake. The geologist began making a preliminary traverse through the bush between claim lines and soon found that zones of shearing had a trend a little north of east and that, as already suspected, the claims covered an area of anorthosite and an area of altered greenstone and basic dikes separated by a belt of granite. The engineer with a rodman and two axemen began clearing lines through the bush. The first line was a base-line through the center of the tract, parallel to the general strike of the shear zones. This was marked by stakes at 400 foot intervals; then through each stake a line was laid out crossing the structural trend. Along each line, bushes, saplings and interfering boughs were trimmed out to a width of five to ten feet so as to give an unobstructed view along the line. As soon as the first few lines had been cut, the geologist with a helper began mapping the outcrops along each line and plotting the exposures in the bush within 50 feet of it.

This mapping indicated that the zone in which shears were most numerous was about 4000 by 1000 feet in dimensions. In this zone intermediate lines were cut, making the interval 200 feet, and all outcrops were mapped.

As examination disclosed quartz stringers and mineralization on a

---

[10] For purposes of description the sequence of events is here somewhat idealized. Actually the work was done intermittently over a period of years and some of the operations were repeated by various field-parties.

number of the outcrops, these exposures were enlarged by stripping off the moss that had encroached on their edges and, where the mineralized streaks passed under soil cover, trenches were extended along them as far as pyritization could be followed or, where the soil became too deep for trenching, one or two test-pits were sunk along the line of strike.   Along the best-looking streaks, the workmen freshened the rock by drilling shallow holes with hand-steel and blasting off the top foot or so.

The next step was to sample the "showings."   The geologist measured off five-foot intervals along each of the sulphide streaks and with lumberman's crayon marked off crosslines perpendicular to the strike for the width of the mineralization.   The samplers cut channels along these lines and sacked the chips.   The geologist, while supervising the sampling, mapped the detailed geology of each "showing" and plotted the location of the sample-channels.   The work was laid out so that the first batch of samples would include one or more from each of the best-looking parts of each showing and thus give an early idea as to how the richest "ore" would assay.   By the next airplane that went out, the first consignment of samples was dispatched to the assayer and when, ten days later, the pilot brought back the returns, anticipation was tense.   The unhappy ending of the story was that, although several of the samples showed excellent values, it was evident that the average was not encouraging.   From then on the sampling of the showings was completed more as a precaution against missing something good than with any genuine expectation of making a mine. When, toward the end of the summer, this work had been completed, the option was dropped.

This example, in which the property was rejected as soon as the probability of finding ore had been definitely excluded, is selected because it is common and typical.   There have been dozens of cases, however, in which identical methods have succeeded in finding ore carrying highly encouraging values and in which the surface prospecting has been followed by drilling and then underground development with the result that a highly profitable mine is brought into production.   The disappointments are all in the year's work, and, if areas are selected with good geological judgment, there is a favorable chance that out of several investigations one successful mine will result.   The main objective is to test each tract with the maximum speed and the minimum expenditure that will yield conclusive results.

Exploration for Iron Ore in the Lake Superior Region [11]

Methods which have been worked out through half a century of exploration on the iron ranges of Minnesota and Michigan are applicable, with appropriate modifications, to other regions, such as Brazil and Labrador, where the ore occurs in sedimentary "iron formations."

Geological Setting

The "iron formations" in the Lake Superior Region are pre-Cambrian sedimentary beds which, in their primary unaltered condition, carry an average of only about 25% Fe in the form of the carbonate, siderite, and the silicate, "greenalite," [11a] along with cherty silica. It is only in favored places, where underground waters have slowly percolated through the iron formation, oxidized the iron to hematite and "limonite," and leached out part of the silica that the iron content attains the 40% to 50% that is the minimum for merchantable ore.[12] These minable portions constitute only a small fraction of the whole iron formation. On the Mesabi Range the formation in its productive portion covers a surface area of 135 square miles, whereas the aggregate area of all the ore bodies of commercial grade is about 15 square miles, or less than 8% of the exposed surface. On the Gogebic Range the iron ore deposits constitute only about 1% of the surface area of the iron formation.

Steps in Exploration

The figures just cited mean that, although an iron ore body presents a relatively large target for ore-search, the area in which it may occur is very much larger. Since testing all the iron formation by drilling or underground work would be out of the question, it is necessary to restrict detailed exploration to the most favorable portions. Thus there are three steps in exploration: (1) outlining the areal extent of the iron formation, (2) determining the favorable areas within the iron formation, eliminating unfavorable areas, and (3) testing the favorable areas for the existence of ore.

[11] This section is based on notes prepared by Stanley A. Tyler.

[11a] Greenalite, as the term was formerly employed, includes three species, all hydrous silicates containing iron: minnesotaite, stilpnomelane and greenalite. Magnetite and martite are present in most of the taconite of the Mesabi range. Gruner, John W., *Mineralogy and Geology of the Mesabi Range*. St. Paul, Minn.: Commissioner of the Iron Range Resources and Rehabilitation, 1946, pp. 7–17.

[12] Lower grade ores which are especially amenable to artificial concentration are mined in a few places.

Outlining the Areal Extent of the Iron Formation

Preparing a geologic map showing all outcrops within the area under consideration is usually regarded as an essential initial step. Since the area to be covered is large and the scale of the map is small, a pace-and-compass traverse is usually accurate enough for this purpose. The information to be derived from geologic mapping alone is likely to be incomplete, however, because much of the bedrock in this region is concealed by soil, glacial deposits and unconsolidated material. But it is often possible to outline areas of iron formation with a high degree of accuracy by carefully tracing areas of magnetic attraction. Although the iron in the formation is chiefly in the form of hematite and limonite, there is usually enough magnetite to distort the earth's magnetic field and produce a local anomaly. The contact between the iron formation and the associated slates or quartzites is usually marked by a sharp change in the general intensity of the magnetic field. The magnetic attraction is usually intense enough to affect the ordinary dip needle (see p. 121), and this is the instrument most commonly used, although instruments which are more delicate but also more time-consuming may have to be employed [13] when the magnetic attraction is very weak. They give little added information, however, in areas of moderate to high magnetic intensity.

Determining Favorable Areas Within the Iron Formation

Having outlined the iron formation, the geologist's next task is to select the areas within it which are favorable to ore occurrence and this, in effect, means areas favorable to oxidation and leaching. Guides to these areas may be grouped as stratigraphic and structural. In connection with these geological guides, the results of the magnetic survey aid in outlining favorable areas.

Stratigraphic Guides. Other things being equal, the most favorable beds are those which were originally highest in iron and lowest in silica, thus requiring less leaching to change them into ore. But chemical composition of the original bed is not the whole story, since the rate of leaching is governed partly by permeability. Highly permeable beds with a rather low iron content have in some cases been altered to ore, whereas richer non-permeable horizons were not leached. Ferruginous chert, in which the iron oxide was originally deposited directly as a chemical sediment along with the chert, had little pore space. In con-

[13] R. H. B. Jones recommends the Hotchkiss Superdip. Geologic interpretation of magnetic exploration on the Mesabi Range, Minn.: *A.I.M.E. Tech. Pub. No. 2038,* 1946.

trast, rock in which the iron was originally in the form of siderite or greenalite, although initially low in porosity, could become porous when the iron-bearing minerals were oxidized; and this pore space is so distributed as to give the water access to all portions of the rock. The size of each chert grain is so small that for each grain there is a large surface area in proportion to the volume. This condition favors solution and removal of the chert and thus leads directly to natural ore concentration.

Susceptibility to leaching is determined not only by the original nature of the beds but by metamorphism, which, by increasing the grain-size of the chert and causing the iron and silica to combine into iron silicates, tends to inhibit natural concentration.

Which beds possess the favorable features of high iron content and susceptibility to leaching will usually be known through familiarity with the local stratigraphic column taken in conjunction with data acquired from geologic mapping and from any holes that have been drilled. Degree of metamorphism may be inferred from similar data insofar as it varies from one bed to another. In its broader aspects it is not strictly a stratigraphic guide but conforms instead to zones which are independent of the bedding yet discernible from wide-scale geologic mapping.

Structural Guides consist of the features which have facilitated the flow of circulating waters. The most favorable conditions are:

1. Wide areas of outcrop. These afford broad areas of intake and expose large surfaces of iron formation to the attack of groundwater.
2. Fractures, which permit passage of solutions. They have been especially influential where the beds are only gently folded, as on the Mesabi Range.
3. Faults, which tend to brecciate ferruginous chert portions of the iron formation, producing permeable channelways. A fault may also constitute one side of a trough (see below).
4. Pitching troughs. These may be formed by:
a. A syncline having an impervious basement or the intersection of a dike with an impervious bed (Marquette and Gogebic districts).
b. A fault: Bringing a basic sill against the iron formation. (Marquette District.) Bringing impervious slates or footwall quartzite against a rich, relatively pervious portion of the iron formation.

These geological criteria, used to eliminate portions of the iron formation which are unfavorable to leaching and to select areas that are structurally favorable, may be supplemented by data from magnetic observations. The preliminary magnetic survey was designed to outline the iron formation as a whole; a resurvey of areas of special interest, using more closely spaced readings, will bring out additional information.

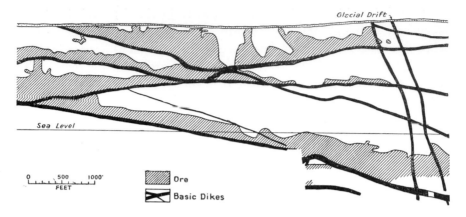

Fig. 140—Ore localized by oxidation and leaching guided by intersection of dikes with iron formation. Longitudinal section of part of iron formation of the Gogebic District. (*After* Gruner, Economic Geology. *Data from* Oliver Iron Mining Company)

This may aid in stratigraphic correlation, since some beds have higher magnetic intensity than others, and it may disclose structural details by revealing the trend lines of the more strongly magnetic beds. But valuable as these measurements are for geological purposes, they do not constitute direct guides to ore. First the magnetic readings vary not only with the magnetite content but also with the depth, dip, and shape of the magnetic body. Second, and quite apart from this consideration, strongly magnetic belts are actually unfavorable. The magnetic intensity depends not on the iron content but on the amount of iron that is present as magnetite, and this is increased by metamorphism and decreased by oxidation. Metamorphism, as already explained, tends to inhibit leaching. Oxidation destroys existing magnetite by converting it slowly into hematite and since oxidation goes hand in hand with enrichment the enriched ore may actually have a lower magnetite content than the parent iron formation. Therefore, the ore within a given formation is marked by low rather than high intensity.[14] For these reasons the common belief that high magnetic attraction is a favorable indication of an orebody in the Lake Superior District is a popular fallacy.

Drilling

Favorable areas are tested by drilling, using either diamond drills or churn drills according to the consistency and attitude of the ore and rock. The usual practice is an alternation or combination of the two

---

[14] Jones, R. H. B., Geologic interpretation of magnetic exploration on the Mesabi Range, Minn.: *A.I.M.E. Tech. Pub. No. 2038*, p. 13, 1946.

methods (see p. 109). Holes are spaced 200 to 300 feet apart on the
Mesabi Range [15] and, since the dip is gentle there, they are usually
drilled vertically. On other ranges where the orebodies have a variety
of shapes and attitudes, closer spacing and inclined holes may be necessary. For example, on the Cuyuna Range where the formation dips at
about 70 degrees, the holes are inclined and are drilled on cross sections
300 to 400 feet apart, but this interval is later bisected. Zapffe [16] says
that on each cross section holes should not be more than 100 feet apart
and 50 feet is better.

Prospecting for Scheelite (Tungsten Ore)

The remarkable behavior of some minerals in ultra-violet light furnishes
a quick and useful method of finding and identifying them. The
method has been widely used in recent years in prospecting for tungsten
ore in which the metal occurs as scheelite. In ordinary light this mineral is inconspicuous and easily overlooked, but in ultra-violet light it
glows with a beautiful fluorescence.

Light-Source. As sources of ultra-violet light there is a choice of
several types of lamp, giving various ranges of wave-length.[17] The
color and intensity of fluorescence varies not only with the species and
composition of the mineral but also with the wave-length of the light;
scheelite does not fluoresce in light of 3200 to 4000Å but yields excellent results with a cold-quartz tube which gives 60% to 90% of its
radiation in the 2537 Å range. Lamps of this type,[18] made either in
portable forms operated by batteries or in laboratory models operated
through a transformer from a house current, are the ones most commonly used in testing scheelite and other fluorescent minerals.

The fluorescent color of scheelite varies with its chemical composition.
Scheelite is one end-member of the isomorphous series, scheelite-powellite
($CaWO_4$–$CaMoO_4$). This fact is of practical interest because molybdenum, if present in excess of 1%, is an objectionable impurity in tungsten ore. Molybdenum-bearing scheelite fluoresces with a white rather
than a blue-white color, while powellite fluoresces golden-yellow. As
minor differences in color are not conspicuous unless compared side-by-

[15] Wolff, J. F., Derby, E. L., and Cole, W. A., Sampling and estimating Lake Superior
Iron Ores: *Tr. A.I.M.E.*, vol. 72, p. 645, 1925.

[16] Zapffe, Carl, Estimating in the Cuyuna iron ore district, Minnesota: *Tr. A.I.M.E.*, vol. 72,
p. 662, 1925.

[17] Vanderwilt, J. W., A review of fluorescence as applied to minerals, with special reference
to scheelite, *A.I.M.E., Tech. Pub. No. 1967*, pages 4–6, 1946. Describes the types of lamps
and discusses effects of differing wave-lengths.

[18] Sold by Ultra-Violet Products, Inc., 5205 Santa Monica Boulevard, Los Angeles, or Warner
& Geiger, 405 Ninita Parkway, Pasadena, California.

side, any quantitative estimates of molybdenum content are made with the aid of an analyser [19] consisting of a card on which are mounted eleven fluorescent comparison-standards varying from 0 to 4.18% Mo and one of 48% Mo.

Exclusion of Daylight. Since fluorescence can be recognized only in the virtual absence of visible light, prospecting for scheelite, except in underground workings, is usually carried on at night, or else specimens are brought into camp for examination in a darkened room. But for outdoor work in daytime, Eardley-Wilmot [20] uses a hood of lightweight black cloth, familiarly known as a "doodle-skirt." The hood is open at its top and bottom. Through the hole at the top the operator sticks his head, tying the cloth about his neck. Near the bottom of the hood is a wire hoop about two feet in diameter and below this a frill which lies on the irregular rock surface to shut out light. About a foot above the bottom there are two arm holes fitted with sleeves into which the operator inserts his forearms and the lamp. This device, permits observations even on sunny days.

Sampling Scheelite. Quantitative estimates [21] of the tungsten content of rock in place can be made by using the Rosiwal principle, familiar to petrographers, which is based on the assumption that the area of a mineral on an exposed surface is proportional to its volume in the rock-mass.

Precautions. Estimates of the percentage of scheelite based on fluorescence are more often too high than too low, because the brilliantly glowing grains give an exaggerated impression of their abundance. In a mine in Argentina the grade was grossly overestimated because the scheelite occurred on minute fractures along which the rock broke and exposed disproportionately large amounts of scheelite. Estimates become more reliable as the operator becomes familiar with the ore of a particular mine and gains experience by repeatedly checking his estimates against assays.

Scheelite is not the only substance that fluoresces. Other fluorescent minerals include some varieties of silica (opal, chalcedony and hyalite),

[19] Developed by Ralph S. Cannon, F. S. Grimaldi, and K. J. Murata of the U. S. Geological Survey and sold by Ultra-Violet Products, Inc.

[20] Eardley-Wilmot, V. L., Tungsten: Canadian and world situation, *Can. Min. & Met. Bull.* No. 367, p. 446, November 1942. Also *C.I.M.M. Trans.*, vol. 45, p. 446, 1942.

[21] Walker, W. S., Tungsten prospecting in the Gilmour Lake area, and Some notes on the ultra-violet ray method: *Can. Mining Jour.*, vol. 63, pp. 145–149, March 1942. Abstr. *Chem. Eng. & Min. Rev.* (Melbourne), July 10, 1942.

Jolliffe, A. W., and Follinsbee, R. E., Grading scheelite deposits with an ultra-violet lamp, *Can. Min. & Met. Bull.* No. 358, pp. 91–98, February 1942. Also *Tr. C.I.M.M.*, vol. 45, pp. 91–98, 1942.

which glow yellowish to greenish, some calcites which may appear red, white or yellowish, some scapolites, and fluorite, which usually phosphoresces. Certain organic substances also fluoresce; for example, oil (white to purplish white) which sometimes spatters the walls of mine workings; certain lichens, fish, and lizards. However, an experienced technician will have relatively little difficulty in distingushing scheelite from oil and organisms (especially lizards). Scheelite is distinguished from other fluorescent minerals by the color of its fluorescence, but this should always be confirmed by testing physical properties, especially hardness and heaviness (H = 4½–5 sp. gr. 5.9–6.1).

Other Fluorescent Minerals. Fluorescence can be used in exploration for a few minerals other than scheelite. Some uranium minerals fluoresce, usually in green tones. Some zircons appear orange. Willemite (zinc silicate) fluoresces brilliantly, but this fact is of practical interest only at Franklin Furnace, N. J., since the mineral rarely occurs anywhere else.

SELECTED REFERENCES

Mapping—See references at end of Chapter 1.
Aerial Surveying—See references at the end of Chapter 1.
Geophysical Prospecting—See references at the end of Chapter 4.

Prospecting

Idriess, I. L., *Prospecting for Gold*, 293 pp. Sydney, Australia: Angus and Robertson, Limited, 1933.
McClelland, James F., Lynch, W. W., and Judd, Edward K., Prospecting, development and exploration of mineral deposits, in *Mining Engineers Handbook*, 3rd Edition (Robert Peele, Ed.), pp. 10–21 to 10–33. New York: John Wiley and Sons, Incorporated, 1941.
von Bernewitz, M. W., *Handbook for Prospectors*, 4th Ed. New York: McGraw-Hill Book Company, Incorporated, 1943.

17

Examining and Developing Prospects

My Lord, if you was to take all the . . . minerals out of these . . .
mountains, the . . . mountains would fall to pieces.
— Reply of an Australian mining expert
to a titled member of the board of
directors of an English company.[1]

A prospect is a potential ore producer which is still in its early stages of development; not until there is enough ore to support a substantial output does the property achieve the dignified status of "mine." A prospect may be merely an untouched ledge of outcropping vein-matter, or it may be a former mine that has produced thousands of tons, reduced again to the status of prospect by the removal of all of its developed ore. These and other types of prospects have in common the fact that the ore [2] reserves consist chiefly of hopes.

The value of a prospect hinges on the probability that these hopes will materialize. Once in a blue moon you will see a prospect so obviously good that the probability is almost a certainty. But such a prospect will not be going begging. Unless you arrive at the scene very promptly after its discovery someone else will have financed it and will have it under active development. Barring exceptional finds of this sort, most of the prospects that you will have occasion to see will be idle or in only desultory operation, waiting for capital with which to develop them. The very fact that such a prospect is inactive is a sign that something is wrong with it. No doubt other engineers have been there before you and have turned it down for good reasons of their own. But this does

[1] Recounted by Wilfred G. Burchett, *Pacific Treasure Island*. Melbourne: Cheshire, 1941.
[2] Again I am using "ore" in the technical sense of the word. A body of metal-bearing material is not an ore reserve until someone proves that it can be treated at a profit.

not necessarily mean that it is hopeless, for the records abound in examples of properties, repeatedly rejected, which have finally been made into highly profitable operations; local folklore delights in reciting the names of eminent engineers and geologists who once turned down what is now the leading producer in the district. That many a prospect after long dormancy has evolved into a prosperous mine merely emphasizes the fact that every prospect presents a problem to be solved. Recognizing this, the first question that you will ask when you see an inactive prospect is, "Where is the catch?" This is not pure cynicism; it is merely a direct approach to the crux of the matter. If you can see a chance of overcoming the obvious obstacle, the prospect calls for further investigation. But if the "catch" lies in probable lack of ore or in some circumstance that nothing can alter, the sooner you recognize the fact the better.

"The Weakest Link"

Joralemon [3] has very lucidly explained that a successful mine depends on a whole chain of favorable conditions and if a single link is too weak the strength of the other links is immaterial. For instance if a zinc prospect is in the *sierra* of Mexico three days by mule train from a railway, the question whether the average grade is 15% or 18%, or whether the ore in sight consists of 10,000 or 40,000 tons is unimportant. The question is whether or not there is a possibility of developing an enormous deposit large enough to pay for the construction of rail facilities to service it. If a brief study of the geologic structure or, at most, a few test pits or drill holes should show that no huge tonnage is present, detailed sampling and ore estimation are unwarranted. In the face of transportation problems the limited amount of ore is sufficient reason for rejection.

Problems: Operating and Geological

The problem that has to be solved may be one of transportation, of metallurgy, of mining, of geology, or of business. Some of these problems may have solved themselves automatically since the last engineer rejected the prospect—transportation by a newly projected railroad or highway; metallurgy by a recent advance in technique; a business problem by the death of an unreasonable owner or by an increase in price of the metal. But if the problem still exists the hope of making the prospect into a mine is by overcoming obstacles that previous examiners

[3] Joralemon, I. B., The weakest link, or Saving time in a mine examination: *E. M. & J.*, vol. 125, pp. 536–540, Mar. 31, 1928.

have not dared to face.   The copper mines at Cerro de Pasco, Peru, were known for three centuries but came into sizable operation only through the courage of the Haggin-Hearst interests in building a railway and establishing mining and smelting plants at the top of the Andes.   The Bingham property in Utah was well known but idle for years until D. C. Jackling developed the then-novel plan of large scale, low cost mining.

Geological problems, including the whole question of whether or not ore exists and how it can be found, are to be solved either by better insight into the structure than previous examiners possessed or undertaking development that no one else has dared to try.   Success in solving ore-finding problems has by no means been limited to geologists and engineers, of course.   Some of the most spectacular discoveries have been made by men who merely played hunches, either failing to realize that they were confronted by unfavorable odds or having enough gambling spirit to take long chances.   Those who have tried thus and failed have been written down as fools; those who succeeded are hailed as men of courage and vision.

The speculative element will continue to play an essential part in the development of prospects, but a wise decision as to whether or not the critical problems are worth solving can best be reached when the facts are assembled and analyzed.

EXAMINATION AND INVESTIGATION OF PROSPECTS

The critical information about a prospect comprises not only such observations as can be made in the field but also data that might be termed historical—the record of work that has been done in the past and particularly of the ore and indications of ore that have been disclosed.   The blend of observation and history varies in its proportions according to the stage of development that the prospect has attained.   If the workings consist only of a few trenches or open cuts their annals are short and simple.   But if the prospect is an old mine it is likely to have a long and perhaps checkered career whose chronicle is more enlightening than anything that can be observed on the ground, particularly if the workings are partly or completely inaccessible.

PRELIMINARY INSPECTION

An examination begins with a quick preliminary trip over the surface and through the underground workings (if there are any) to gain a general impression of the whole property and also to decide whether any further examination at all is worth while.   A quick size-up of non-geological questions such as the probable cost of operation and the amount of capital required may make it obvious that the grade and tonnage would have to exceed all reasonable expectations if the property is to be of interest. Occasionally it happens that, after an exhaustive and expensive examination, a prospect is turned down by the head office because of difficult metallurgy, lack of water, distance from transportation, or some other condition that should have been evident before the examination was commenced. When this occurs the usual reason is that the management did not give the prospect serious attention until the time for a final decision arrived. The full blame for this omission can hardly be placed on the geologist, yet it is his duty, not as a geologist but as an intelligent individual, to call attention to obvious operating problems at an early stage in the inquiry and to urge that they receive the attention of engineers who are qualified to make a decision.

In the preliminary examination you will observe, among other things, the general geological setting, the amount of development work that has been done, the shape of the orebodies, if there are any—whether vein-like, manto-like or otherwise—and the geographical setting with respect to other near-by mines. On this preliminary sight-seeing trip the owner or his representative will probably act as your guide and give you abundant information, some of which you will believe and some you will take with a grain of salt. When you finish the preliminary inspection you will present a recommendation for or against making a detailed examination. If it appears to you that an inexpensive piece of development will tell more than an examination, you may wish to recommend this instead. Should you propose continuing, you will state what kind of work should be done, how long it will take and, if the estimate lies within your province, how much it will cost.

DETAILED EXAMINATION

First-Hand Information

In laying out your plan for a more detailed examination you will have to decide how much mapping and sampling will be necessary and where to begin it.

Mapping. Some sort of mapping is always desirable, if only to stimulate observation and aid the memory, but whether the map should be a simple sketch or an accurate survey depends on the particular problem that needs solving. For purposes of appraisal a rough sketch map is likely to suffice, because in nine cases out of ten the potential value of the prospect does not hinge on the precise location and exact form of the geological features. If the prospect proves worthy of development, an accurate map will be necessary, but even then the map need not extend far from the mineralized areas unless there is reason to solve a definite problem in rock structure. It is true that some geologists recommend plane table mapping of the surface on all examinations. Schmitt, for example, points out that, since the examiner has to walk over the outcrops, he may as well carry a stadia rod and have the locations recorded accurately. This practice is a decided advantage to a company or a consultant that specializes in the investigation of some particular district, for then the results of a series of prospect examinations will eventually build themselves into a valuable map of the whole area. But in this case the mapping has a definite purpose related only indirectly to the examination of the individual prospect. The procedure is not an exception to the rule that detailed cartography is warranted only where there are specific reasons for it.

If there are underground workings on several levels you will need a map in order to see the relation between one level and another and between the underground workings and the surface. Usually an engineering map (lacking geology) will be available, but if not you will have to make at least a quick tape-and-compass survey. On the map you will place such geological features as seem essential, especially veins, faults, apparent ore-limits, and obvious rock-contacts.

Sampling, like mapping, will be either selective or exhaustive depending on whether or not a precise result is necessary. In the early stages of the examination you will need to take only enough samples to determine whether or not the ore that has been exposed is of sufficient grade to encourage further development. If a few channel samples in the places that look best, or in ore that the owner considers the richest, should turn out to be poor, there is little incentive to do an exhaustive job of sampling. If the results of previous sampling are available, a few "spot checks" will confirm or discredit the reliability of the work. If ore has been mined and shipped there may be little left to sample, and the records of shipments may give a better idea of the grade than any samples that you could take in the mine. However, no great amount of money should be spent on the basis of unconfirmed records of shipments. Remember that "the record of past production is a measure, not of what is left, but of what is not left." [4] In any case it is hardly worth while to spend the time and money to make the precise deter-

---

[4] Raymond, R. W., Ancient history and modern investments: *E. & M. J.*, pp. 457–458, March 10, 1906. Cited by Hoover, Theodore J., *The Economics of Mining*, p. 125. Stanford: Stanford University Press, 1933.

mination of the tenor of a few tons of exposed ore if the potential value of the prospect depends on the grade of a large tonnage that has not yet been found.   But when you *do* take a sample, cut a real channel; a few well-cut samples are worth more than a host of hastily-taken ones.

The number of samples that you take will depend to some extent on whether you will have a chance to take more in case the first results should turn out better than you expected.   If the property is so remote that you will not be able to go back to it conveniently, you will do better to take too many than to wish you had taken more.   And in no case should you leave the prospect without enough samples and notes to enable you to frame some sort of statement as to size, grade, and tonnage in terms that are at least roughly numerical rather than vaguely descriptive.

The Time for Detailed Work.   The admonition against unduly detailed mapping and sampling should not in any sense suggest that exhaustive work is always out of place in a prospect examination.   As soon as you are convinced that the extension of the ore or the chance of finding new bodies depends on a correct interpretation of the structure, you are amply warranted in doing as thorough a mapping job as may be necessary to get the correct answer.   Similarly, once it is apparent that you must determine the grade of the exposed ore in order to make intelligent recommendations for or against further development work, a careful program of sampling is indicated and you should spare no pains in arriving at a completely dependable result.

Observations in Old Mines.   In an old mine, much of the evidence regarding the occurrence of the ore is likely to have disappeared with the removal of the ore itself and is to be reconstructed only by inference. The size and width of the stopes will give an idea of the dimensions of the orebodies, but large stopes that have broken through to the surface may be pitfalls figuratively as well as literally; they have usually been widened by natural caving or enlarged purposely by mining wallrock to serve as fill in the underground workings.   Likewise, the length of a stope, as indicated by timbering and chutes in the back of an underground level may give a false impression of the amount of ore mined; it is common practice to start stoping in ore of low or marginal grade in the hope that it may improve upward.   If the ore fails to improve, parts of the stope, particularly the end-portions, are abandoned at a height of one or two rounds above the level.

Remnants of the original ore will be scarce.   Even pillars, which give the best opportunity to observe the nature of the original mineralization, are unlikely to constitute fair samples of the ore since the poorest parts of the orebody are the ones that are apt to be left.   However, if pillars are systematically and regularly spaced they may be taken as representative of the ore; a floor pillar, with stopes both above and below it, is likely to be a true example of the type of ore that was mined.

If you are counting on ore extending beneath the lowest known level, be sure that you have actually seen the bottom of the mine and, if the deepest workings are under water, do not recommend paying any portion of the purchase money until they have been pumped out.   It may suit the owner's convenience to fill in or cover over a winze connecting with the deepest level in order to conceal the embarrassing fact that the orebody has bottomed.   The absence of any deeper workings on the map is not conclusive, for almost invariably there are more workings in an old mine than the map indicates.   This is either because the management did not take the trouble to bring the maps up to date before shutting down or because "leasers" worked the mine after formal operations had ceased.

Evidence from Dumps.   The dumps from old workings tell a great deal about the history and geology.   The cubical content of a waste dump is an index to the depth of a shaft or the extent of underground workings.   The tonnage in a dump of mill tailings indicates the tonnage of ore that has been treated (unless too much has been washed or hauled away).   Reckoned together with the record of metal or concentrate produced, it gives an idea of the grade of the mill heads.   Aside from their informational interest, dumps of tailings or of mine waste may carry enough recoverable values to make payable feed if a new mill should be built, so they should be sampled whenever there is reason to expect that they contain appreciable metal.

A mine dump is a mineral and rock collection containing specimens of all of the material that was encountered in the workings and, since the rock nearest the shaft or portal is likely to be the first that was encountered in the course of development it even gives some idea of the arrangement of formations.   The best ore will be gone, of course, but a diligent search will usually disclose a few remnants of it.   If ore is unnaturally abundant or conspicuous, it should be viewed critically. Occasionally pieces of good ore from a more prosperous mine are "planted" on a dump to arouse the enthusiasm of the examiner.   I have seen angular pieces of gold-bearing quartz on a lakeside dump where all the other material was water-worn gravel and, elsewhere, pieces of fresh sulphide on a dump of oxidized rock and gossan.   A geologist will be amused rather than deceived by naïve attempts of this sort.

Historical Data

The correct appraisal of the possibilities of an old mine may depend largely on historical data. Being second-hand, such evidence needs to be interpreted with discrimination. For example, interested parties or even cheerful kibitizers are prone to encourage the belief that a large tonnage of profitable ore has been left in the old workings. Whether ore actually remains or not depends largely on the conditions that prevailed during the final months of operation, hence it is always pertinent to make searching inquiry as to why the mine closed down.[5] Invariably a plausible reason is forthcoming. Most commonly, inefficient management gets the blame, but almost as often the ostensible reason is either litigation or some technical problem that could be overcome by modern practice, such as metallurgical difficulties, inability to handle heavy flows of water, or high costs due to hand operations. The history may prove that these handicaps actually existed but, even so, it is likely that they were only contributing causes. The most common real reason is the one that is least frequently mentioned—lack of ore.

The Myth of Minable "Leavings." The most deceptive type of old mine is the one that operated when costs were so high that only rich ore could be mined at a profit. Surely, it would seem, there must be lots of low grade ore left. But this conclusion does not necessarily follow for two excellent reasons. First, a peculiarity of ore, particularly precious metal ore, is that it is so commonly found in streaks and bunches. A vein that averages ten dollars a ton is likely to be made up of gangue averaging a dollar or less with streaks or spots that carry $20 to $30. The "old timers" were good miners and good sorters, especially in countries where labor was plentiful. By selective mining and close sorting they could win profits from a ten-dollar vein even though ore of lower than twenty-dollar grade would not stand shipment charges. If so, the parts of the vein that they left will average closer to one dollar than to ten.

Second, it cannot be assumed that all ore that was lower than profitable grade has been left unmined. To see why this is so let us inquire into the history of the later stages of a typical mining venture. After a period of profitable operations the rich ore becomes scarcer and scarcer

---

[5] Theodore Hoover lists ten reasons why mines close down: (1) Change of nature of ore with depth (2) Exhaustion of ore (3) Shift in price of metals (4) Influx of water (5) Caving of large stopes or levels (6) Bad management (7) Need to convert property into other forms of capital (8) Prohibitive depth (9) Premature abandonment (10) Increase or change in legislative measures. Hoover, T. J., *The Economics of Mining*, pp. 34–35. Stanford: Stanford University Press, 1933.

until the manager encounters difficulty in keeping up the grade of his mill heads.   But at least he is breaking even financially and he has had luck before, so he keeps one or two development headings going in the hope that they will break into more of the old high grade.   When the last of the "sweetening stopes" is cleaned out the mill heads drop still lower and the manager looks for a way to cut expense.   The obvious way is to shut down development and lop a couple of dollars from the costs.   Even though the mill heads fall still lower, the operation continues to break even and no serious complaint comes from the home office.   Then, one month, the account is in the red but the manager, being a congenital optimist (as most good managers are) writes the chairman an encouraging letter promising better returns next month. This goes on until the semi-annual report comes out and shows a heavy loss.   The directors hold a meeting and decide to send an engineer to the property.   He reports that there is no more profitable ore in sight and recommends a specific piece of development work.   If this finds no ore there is another directors' meeting.   Everyone is very gloomy. Somebody says, "Let's shut her down," and a telegram goes forth to the manager.

Note that for six months or a year the mine has been running at or below costs and the costs for much of that time included no development work.   In the mill, old machinery has been patched but not replaced, so there has been no maintenance charge.   If total costs were normally ten dollars, the costs in this last period were seven or eight and the mine did not close until all of the seven dollar ore and most of the six dollar ore was mined out.

These depressing observations explain why the hope of finding large tonnages of low grade ore in sight on reopening a mine should be tempered with a good deal of skepticism.   But to find ore already developed is one thing and to discover new ore by fresh development work is quite another.   The latter has been accomplished time and again, whether through better luck, better insight into geological controls, or a greater willingness to take long chances than fell to the lot of the former management.

Utility of Compiled Data.   Possibilities that had escaped the notice of previous operators may become obvious when historical information is analyzed systematically.   In a surprising number of old mines no one has even taken the trouble to assemble the data that are needed to answer the most obvious questions: How much ore did the mine produce?   What was the average grade?   What parts of the mine did the ore come from and where were the richest shoots?   The information that provides the answers will not be found in ready-made form. It will have to be ferreted out through days or weeks of persistent search for published records and unpublished reports as well as by soliciting the testimony of people who were acquainted with the property when it was operating. Analyzing and plotting this information requires even more patience and persistence than finding it, but whatever tedium it entails will be more than compensated by the thrill of discerning a clear indication of structural control or, better still, by the recognition of a promising guide to ore discovery.

Sources of Information

Published Records. A certain amount of authoritative information in regard to the ore occurrence, past production and geology is usually to be found in published reports, particularly those of the government and state geological surveys.

In the United States and most parts of the British Empire, as well as in many Latin American countries, nearly every mining district has been described either in general or in detail, and many of these reports include not only the geology but the history and records of production for the more important mines of any district.

Next to governmental sources are technical periodicals whose back numbers, if consulted in a library, divulge either a description of the property at some stage of its career or news notes relating to production or to changes in management. To assemble this information may require a protracted search through the files, but it may yield critical information when other sources fail. If there is a good index, the search is shortened. The California Division of Mines office in San Francisco, for example, has a very detailed index to items in old numbers of the *Mining and Scientific Press.* By following these through it is possible to reconstruct production records for almost every mine in the state.

The files of newspapers published in mining communities often contain much historical information. It is customary in Australia, for example, to publish fortnightly reports of development and production for each mine, and the back files of the Melbourne and Bendigo papers contain an almost complete history even of small prospects.

The annual reports of mining companies provide a continuous record of production and finance.

Unpublished Reports. Reports written by previous geologists and engineers are, of course, greatly to be prized. Their value varies with the competence of the author, and they always need to be read critically, but at the worst they cannot fail to give some information that is of use.

An old geological map is almost too much to hope for, but occasionally such a thing turns up. Even a map that merely shows the limits of the ore and indicates which parts of a drift were on the vein and which were off can be a wonderful aid in reconstructing the shapes of the orebodies. Failing this, a set of level maps and a longitudinal section showing stoped areas may supply the data for drawing cross sections and afford a good guess as to the ore-distribution.

Old assay maps, if available, are a cause for rejoicing, and every effort should be made to obtain them unless there is reason to believe that no such records were kept. On one occasion an assay map of an inaccessible mine in Oregon was badly needed and after much inquiry a copy was discovered in the possession of the widow of the engineer who made it. The good lady was willing to sell it for $100 and at this price it was the cheapest piece of information obtained during the whole course of the examination. On the other hand, an engineer who had previously sampled another set of workings offered us his results for $2000, but as we had access to all of the same workings and could repeat the sampling for half this expense we declined the offer.

In practically all mines there are or have been records of shipments to the smelter or mint. The local smelting companies are usually very cooperative in allowing accredited engineers to consult their copies of the smelter returns. This is often a laborious proceeding, however, as each carload is recorded on a separate sheet and a long history of production is represented by hundreds if not thousands of such sheets.

An old mine office is likely to be crammed with files of information, most of it useless but some of gem quality. A file of correspondence in one Mexican mine office not only revealed the fortunes and vicissitudes of the mine but provided many an evening's fascinating reading from the letters describing activities during successive revolutions. If a mine office has been without a custodian the files are likely to be in extreme disorder. In a building high in the Rockies an associate and I found the floors of two rooms strewn ankle-deep with papers and we succeeded in sorting out two storeboxes full of records. Some of the documents had been chewed by mice, but enough figures were preserved to permit the plotting of data in the form of an assay map. On another occasion an assay book was discovered in the bottom of an abandoned shaft.

Testimony of Old Residents. Men who worked in the mine during its previous periods of operation are usually more than willing to reminisce. Their stories are always worth a hearing even though they seldom lose glamour in the telling. No sooner does a mine close down than rumors begin circulating and the ore becomes richer with every year of aging legend.

Naturally, the more responsible the position the former employee occupied, the more trustworthy his information is likely to be. Muckers and drillers, even though they worked daily at the faces, may not have known the grade of the ore except by hearsay, and this is especially true of gold ore since its value cannot be judged accurately by its appearance. It is less true of base-metal ore, for the old-timers, particularly those who have leased and prospected, became remarkably good at "eyeball assaying," albeit their errors were likely to be on the high side. Close agreement between the stories told by two men independently is not necessarily a satisfactory confirmation, since both stories may have emanated from the same source and the narrators may have been convinced after the passage of years that they personally saw the conditions that they describe.

The information given by bosses and engineers is likely to be relatively reliable since these men were in a position to know the facts and had reason to remember them. Nevertheless they cannot always be believed implicitly. I have repeatedly had occasion to interview former mine superintendents and later to compare their statements with their own reports written during the operating period. (Lest I be suspected of taking unfair advantage, I may add that in most cases I did not know of the reports at the time of the interview.) Almost without exception the superintendent's memory paints a rosier picture than do his records. This is not, as a rule, because of insincerity. Psychologists would agree that rich ore and handsome widths make a vivid impression on the mind; material of indifferent grade leaves a feeble imprint, while poor and narrow ore evokes a positively unpleasant memory which the mind tries to erase. If an aging superintendent quotes definite figures they are likely to be correct, but if he says in a vague way, "I'm sure that section must have averaged better than an ounce," the chances are that he is unintentionally exaggerating.

The fact that old recollection and local folklore are notoriously inaccurate does not mean that they should be disregarded. A shrewd sifting of evidence may point toward the truth, and by putting two and two together (and sometimes dividing by four) the investigator may succeed in reconstructing some semblance of the correct picture. Tradition and local gossip, like other data, should receive their proper weighting for degree of probability and take their place in the array of indirect evidence.

Conclusions from Examination

The examination of a prospect usually leads either to an appraisal of its value or to recommendation as to whether or not it merits development. If the examiner recommends development, he should describe in specific terms the work that he proposes. The nature and extent of the work will depend on the type of problem that the prospect presents, and, in this respect, any prospect is likely to fall into one of three intergrading types:

1. Ore-exploitation prospects. In this type there is no serious question as to the quantity of the material; the main problem is whether or not it can be treated at a profit. The question is: *What can you do with it?*
2. Ore-extension prospects. Some ore has been found and its grade is good enough provided a sufficient tonnage can be developed. The question is: *Is there any more ore?*
3. Ore-hunting prospects. Here conditions are encouraging (otherwise the property would not be a prospect at all) but more and better ore has to be found than has been encountered thus far. The question is: *Where is the ore (if any)?*

Ore-Exploitation Prospects. The "What-can-you-do-with-it?" type of prospect is exemplified by the low-grade magnetite of the East Mesabi Range in Minnesota or by the ilmenite deposits of Lake Sanford, N. Y., (as they must have appeared before metallurgical research was undertaken). Akin, but somewhat different in its problems was the great zinc-lead deposit at Sullivan, B. C., as it existed before the perfection of the selective flotation process.

In such prospects the amount of ore is manifestly very large. It is true that the existence of some specified tonnage has to be demonstrated beyond a doubt before undertaking large expenditure, and the demonstration may require drilling or other methods of development under geological guidance; but the question at the outset is not whether the amount of material is one million or a hundred million tons, but whether the material is really ore in the technical sense. The critical questions are: Can a marketable product be made? What will be the revenue per ton? What will it cost to mine and treat the ore? Geology may be of help in determining the mineralogical state of the metal and perhaps in predicting the nature of the ground insofar as it may effect mining methods, but the major problems are those of sampling, cost estimation, economics, and metallurgy.

Ore-Extension Prospects. In most prospects which the geologist has occasion to consider seriously, a certain amount of ore has been found, and the critical question is whether or not more ore can be developed. If some or all of the development faces are still in ore, the answer to this query is obviously "Yes." The important question is "How much?" A three-dimensional portrayal of the ore in its geological setting is the basis for a tentative projection. Trends inferred from the distribution of values, taken in conjunction with trends in the geologic structure, give an indication of the probable direction of the continuation. Here the principles discussed in the chapter on extension of ore in depth come into use. As to size, the magnitude of the ore-localizing structures and the habits of other orebodies in the district serve as guides.

If, however, the limits of the known ore have been reached and the future depends on finding new orebodies, the prospect is really an ore-hunting or "Where-is-it?" prospect, except for the consideration that the outlook is more promising than if no ore existed.

Ore-Hunting Prospects. The "Where-is-it?" type of prospect demands the utmost in application of geological judgment. The examiner has to form an estimate not only of the probability of finding ore, but also of the probable value of the ore if found. Stated thus, the proposition seems almost as conjectural as the old question "How long is a piece of string?" but the solution is not always as indeterminate as this might imply. Serious development is rarely undertaken except in a district where some orebodies have been proved to exist or where there is at least an outcrop of gossan or altered rock. One may reasonably expect that if a new orebody is found, it will have a size and grade comparable to other orebodies in the district or indicated by the magnitude of the croppings. While surprises are always possible, these indications give some idea as to the probabilities.

Search for new ore will test the possibilities of whatever guides can be recognized, whether outcrops, gossan, altered zones, or favorable structural conditions. Whether development will consist of an exhaustive search in a large block of ground or of a quick test of a restricted site will depend on how sharp and definite the available guides appear to be.

ACQUIRING PROSPECTS

The admonition to "first catch your rabbit" applies with full force to the examination and development of prospects. Once caught, the next concern is to make sure that it does not escape. So tying up a prospect with the necessary legal safeguards is essential to the enjoyment of the ultimate rewards of successful development.

Companies occasionally acquire prospects by taking up claims on public land but more often by dealing with a prospector who either staked the ground himself or acquired it from someone who did.   In this case it is important to make sure that the holder's title is valid under the laws of the land, and that the arrangements for taking over the property from the owner are satisfactory and binding.   Although these are commercial or legal matters, the geologist has a direct interest in them, first because he sometimes has to act as an advance agent in arranging a deal, second because his opinion should influence the terms of the agreement and third, because the terms govern, in some degree, the program of development that he will recommend.

Prospects on Public Land

The laws of most mining countries permit an individual or a company to undertake prospecting and mine development on any land that is not privately held or otherwise reserved.   In some countries, mining rights can be acquired even when the surface rights for agricultural and other purposes are already owned privately.   Each nation and, in some nations, each state or province has its own mining code, and it would be futile here to attempt to outline even those of the nations in which geologists are most likely to have occasion to work.   It may be of interest, however, to mention some general similarities and differences.

In most countries there are two general steps or stages in acquiring mining rights.   The first, variously called staking, pegging, or denouncement confers a temporary right to develop the mineral deposit. To maintain the right, the miner has to perform some minimum of assessment work or "manning," or else pay a tax.   In some countries he must do both, though usually the expense, apart from the actual cost of the work, is small.   This makes it possible to give the ground a preliminary test and reject it without serious expenditure if it proves disappointing.   The second step, called patenting, taking up a concession or securing a crown grant, usually calls for an official survey and the payment of substantial fees or taxes.   It gives a more secure and permanent right to exploit the ground and is intended to safeguard a mining organization in making the investments and improvements that are necessary to continuing operations.

The theories of mining rights are more divergent than the actual practical effects.   In the United States, mineral land, if open for prospecting, belongs in theory not to the government itself but to the people individually and may be exploited by any citizen [6] who stakes a claim.

---

[6] Van Wagenen, Theo. F., *International Mining Law*, p. 98.   New York: McGraw-Hill, 1918.

He may not be dispossessed by the government even for non-compliance with regulations, but only by another citizen who is able to establish a better claim.   In most other countries, mineral rights are the property of the nation or of the crown.   Private individuals can secure only leases, though these may be of long duration.   Thus in Mexico the term is thirty years, subject to renewal, and in Western Australia 21 years, renewable for an additional 21 years.

The size of claims differs greatly in different countries.   In the United States a lode claim is a parallelogram (not necessarily a rectangle) 1500 feet long and 600 feet wide.   In British Columbia it is 1500 feet square, in Quebec it is forty acres and in Mexico one hectare (2½ acres).   Qualifications for prospecting also differ.   In the United States, prospecting is "free," that is, no license is required, but claims may be staked only by citizens or by aliens who have expressed intention of becoming citizens.   An individual can stake as many claims as he likes.   In British Columbia a staker need not be a citizen but he must hold a "free miner's license" (the miner, not the license, is free) and cannot hold more than one claim on the same lode though he may hold claims on other lodes.   In Ontario the holder of a "mining license" may stake out three claims for himself and three on behalf of each of two other persons.

Of all mining laws the most peculiar is that of the United States, which provides for "extralateral rights," whereby the holder of the outcrop or "apex" of a lode may follow the lode down its dip even though it passes outside the vertical projection of his own side lines.   By the same token he does not have the right to mine, even beneath his own claim, a vein whose outcrop has been discovered on his neighbor's ground.   This rule, which was moderately satisfactory on the simple, well-behaved veins of the Mother Lode in California, has caused endless confusion in other districts where the ore is not in veins at all or where the veins are complex and faulted.[7]   It has been abandoned by common consent in some camps (Bisbee, for example) in order to avoid litigation, claim owners agreeing among themselves to abide by vertical side lines.   Where it is in force, it applies only to claims that were staked

---

[7] Shamel, Charles H., *Mining, Mineral and Geological Law*, pp. 200–283.   New York: Hill Publishing Co., 1907.   Describes a number of interesting court cases.

Lindley, Curtis H., *American Law Relating to Mines and Mineral Lands*, pp. 565–618.   San Francisco: Bancroft Whitney Co., 1914.   "Lindley on Mines" is an exhaustive three-volume treatise.

DeSoto, Emilio D., and Morrison, Arthur R., *Mining Rights on the Public Domain* (*Morrison's Mining Rights*) 16th Edition.   San Francisco: Bender-Moss Co., 1936.   Sums up mining law on apex and most other U. S. problems.   Apex and extralateral rights: pp. 198–224.

on public land; this in general means only in the Western states. In the East and Middle West, where land is owned in fee simple, the owner of the surface has complete ownership of the mineral rights below his property but not outside it.

Although the doctrine of extralateral rights grew up through custom in California, later adopted in other Western states and ultimately sanctioned by act of Congress, the doctrine, whether or not the California miners were aware of the fact, can be traced back through Derbyshire to Germany in the seventh century[8] and probably to Roman law. However, it has been abandoned in every country in which it was ever used except in the United States and in Southern Rhodesia, where it was introduced by Cecil Rhodes' American advisers.

In all other British countries and in Latin America the claim boundaries are vertical planes extending downward both from the side lines and the end lines. As a general rule the holder of mining rights may work any ore within his boundaries and none outside them.

These examples of divergent practices should be sufficient to indicate the importance of becoming familiar with the laws of the country in which one happens to be working.[9]

Prospects in Private Hands

Most of the prospects that the geologist has occasion to examine are in the possession of a prospector or a promoting group, and the purpose of the examination is to decide whether or not to purchase the property. However, a final decision may await not only the outcome of the examination but also the outcome of development work. Since the examination, not to mention the development, involves considerable expense, the prospective purchaser will want to be absolutely sure that, if and when he decides to take over the property, it will still be available, otherwise a wily owner may raise his price when he suspects that the examiner is favorably impressed, or may sell to a competitor who becomes interested on finding that a serious examination is under way. Therefore it is customary to have a definite and binding agreement in writing before a detailed examination begins.

However, a brief inspection or preliminary examination may well precede any serious discussion of terms. This serves to avoid the sort

---

[8] Van Wagenen, Theo. F., *International Mining Law*, p. 291. New York: McGraw-Hill, 1918.

[9] The U. S. Bureau of Mines has published digests of the mining laws of most foreign countries in about 65 Information Circulars with numbers between 6102 and 6798. Consult U.S.B.M. publication lists, Subject index, under name of country. The laws in some countries have been changed, of course, since these summaries were published.

of anticlimax that would result if, after months of haggling and negotiation culminating in the signing of a contract, the examiner turns the property down at the end of a two-days' visit.   But since the preliminary inspection is brief, the purchaser's acquaintance with the property is of necessity incomplete when he and the seller meet to arrange terms. This puts a premium on the examiner's ability to size up the potentialities as accurately as possible in the very limited time available.

The Geologist as Negotiator.   The geologist, while making his preliminary inspection can often help materially in arriving at mutually satisfactory terms.   He is likely at this time to become acquainted with the owner and can understand both his and the investor's problems, so that during the course of the inspection he may find opportunity to sound out the owner regarding the sort of terms that he would expect and at the same time, if authorized to do so, explain the sort of deal that would be satisfactory to his own principals.   Confidence established at this stage can smooth the path toward successful negotiations.

Whether or not the geologist has been instrumental in arranging the deal, he should always be given full particulars concerning the terms of the contract, otherwise he cannot be expected to make intelligent recommendations for or against undertaking development, nor can he lay out a wise program.   An example may help to make this clear.   Let us suppose that the purchase price of a property has been fixed at $50,-000 with no substantial payment due until the end of 18 months.   If the geologist considers that there is a good chance of finding a commercial orebody by driving a 700-foot tunnel, he will recommend that this work be undertaken.   If, on the other hand, the purchase price of the same property is $250,000 and a payment of $75,000 must be made in 90 days, he will either turn the property down or will recommend two or three quick diamond-drill holes in the hope that one or more of them will cut rich ore before the first payment is due.

Options.   In the exciting days of the last century rich mines were sold for cash after a period of only a few days or weeks in which to carry out the examination and sampling.   Under modern conditions, however, where few prospects are obviously rich at the start and production comes only after a large expenditure, a reasonably long period is allowed before any cash payment is required.

A typical agreement might be somewhat along these lines: The purchaser receives an option good for two years, to buy the property for a specified price.   (The periods of time here are purely illustrative.) During the first 90 days, allowed for examination, he has no obligation except, perhaps, to show some signs of activity.   At the end of this period he may have to make a small cash payment or none at all, but he must decide whether or not he wishes to undertake development work. If he decides to go ahead, he must then spend an agreed amount each month. At the end of the first six months he is required to make a cash payment followed by similar and increasing payments at the end of each six-month period until the end of the two-year option period, these payments applying against the ultimate purchase price. At any time during the two-year period he may relinquish the option and withdraw without any further obligation, although, of course, he loses what he has already paid as well as what he has spent on development. If he continues to the end of the two years, he must then decide whether or not to exercise the option. If he elects to do so he pays the purchase price, or an installment of it, and takes over the property.

Naturally the amounts, time periods, and terms vary widely to suit individual cases, but certain principles are generally recognized: No cash payment is expected before examination, and, unless substantial ore is in sight at the start, no cash is required before the termination of a reasonable period for development. In other words, the purchaser should not be required to pay for the privilege of spending his money on development. This principle is sometimes modified in the case of a very promising prospect whose vendor has small but pressing financial obligations or needs a few hundred dollars a month for living expenses, as under such conditions a relatively small amount of cash may be more important to him than a much larger payment at a later date.

An intelligent vendor will understand that the larger the cash payment and the earlier it is required, the less likely is the purchaser to exercise the option. A company which might be unwilling to pay $10,000 before the property was tested might very willingly pay $50,000 after development work had provided sufficient encouragement. The prospector, if he has confidence in his property, will usually see the wisdom of allowing time for thorough testing in the faith that it will measure up to his expectations and warrant a larger payment than he could expect to get if the date were set too early.

Protection to Vendor. The obligation to do development work is proper as a protection against the purchaser's tying up the property for a long period and doing little or nothing. To have a property optioned and turned down by a reputable company always gives the prospect a black eye, even though insufficient work was done to demonstrate the absence of ore. The agreement may provide for carrying out a rigidly specified piece of work, such as sinking a shaft in a certain location, but usually the purchaser wishes to use his own judgment as to the place in which the work is to be done and be free to modify his own plans as new information comes to light. More often, therefore, the purchaser guarantees to spend a minimum amount of money per month or to work a certain number of man-shifts, reserving the right to use his own discretion as to the where and how.

If some ore is in sight the prospective purchaser may wish to mine and ship or mill it in order to determine its grade and metallurgical characteristics. The vendor, at the same time, is entitled to protection against an operator who might mine out the ore, pocket the profits, and abandon the workings. Therefore most agreements take the form of a "lease and option." The prospective purchaser, known as the lessee, has the right to mine the ore, paying a royalty which will, in case the option is exercised, apply against the purchase-price. The royalty is usually based on the "net smelter return" since this is a definite figure which can be determined without question, whereas a royalty based on the profits would involve matters of bookkeeping which might be subject to controversy. What constitutes a fair royalty depends on the richness of the ore that exists or is likely to be found, and usually varies from 5% to 20%. Only in districts of exceptionally rich ore is the royalty higher; 10% to 15% is a common figure. Sometimes the royalty is on a sliding scale, the percentage stepping upward with the grade.

Participation by Vendor. As alternatives to outright purchase, various kinds of participatory agreements may be made between the investor and the owner. The investor may, for example, agree to install a plant to bring the property into production, the owner taking his compensation in the form of a royalty on production or a percentage of the profits. The most common arrangement provides for the formation of a company to develop and operate the mine and for the issue of stock to both parties. The owner usually receives a minority rather than a majority of the stock, because the investment required to develop and equip the property is likely to be greater than the value of the undeveloped prospect; therefore the investor is entitled to control in order that he may conduct the operation in accordance with his best technical judgment.

A common form of agreement might be somewhat along these lines: Henry Hardrock, prospector, sells the property to New Company and receives 150,000 shares of stock in New Company in payment for his mining rights. The investor—let us call it National Mining and Finance Co.—buys 200,000 shares by putting $200,000 into the treasury of New Company and this cash is available for development and construction. When and if further funds are required, N.M.F.C. buys additional stock, thereby making further cash available and increasing its own interest in New Company. These figures are, of course, only for illustration; the amounts, actual and relative, depend on the value of the property and the expenditures that are likely to be required to bring it to production. Not infrequently an arrangement is made whereby N.M.F.C. gets back part or all of its investment before Henry Hardrock begins to receive dividends; this may be accomplished by issuing either preferred stock or notes to N.M.F.C. Naturally, a great variety of deals is possible, varying from out-and-out cash purchase to a straight partnership.

Legal and Geological Counsel. In writing a contract, a good attorney, especially one experienced in mining transactions, can suggest ways of accomplishing the specific purposes that are intended, and, by foreseeing many of the possible occasions for disagreement, can word the document in unequivocal language that will forestall litigation at a later date. The geologist should not attempt to be his own lawyer, but he can help in drafting a contract by holding a proper perspective before the negotiating parties. Having his own opinion as to the maximum that the property might eventually be worth in the event of reasonably successful development, he is in a position to insist that the owner's compensation or participation should not be more than a fair proportion of this amount, and that the period elapsing before the first payment be ample for the development to put ore in sight if it exists.

DEVELOPING PROSPECTS

Development Policy

Progressive Elimination of Risk. A million dollars is not an unusual amount to spend in bringing a prospect to the stage at which it has an outlook for profits which have a present value of, say, two million dollars. Yet the probability of making a raw prospect into a profitable producer is rarely better than one in ten and often no better than one in twenty or one in fifty. What, one may ask, is the justification for spending a million dollars on odds of one in ten in order to win a prize of two million? Surely this is, on the face of it, a poor bet. The answer is that by no means all of the million dollars is risked against one-in-ten odds. The whole program for developing a prospect should consist of a series of steps, each designed to eliminate an element of risk. The expenditure to which a company commits itself at each step should never exceed an appropriate fraction of the potential prize, a fraction which is determined by the odds judged to exist at the moment.   As each step eliminates another hazard, a larger commitment becomes justifiable.   If a prospect potentially worth $2,000,000 survives to the stage at which say $700,000 must be put up for purchase and equipment, the major hazard as to the existence of ore should have been eliminated by the establishment of a blocked-out ore reserve.

To illustrate the principle of *balancing the odds against the expenditure,* let us look at another example in greater detail.   Let us suppose that a vein has been prospected by trenches and shows ore that promises a gross profit of $5 a ton if it can be mined at a rate of 200 tons a day. The ore has been exposed for a length of 200 feet, but the vein is still covered at both ends so that its total length is not disclosed, although more remote trenches show that it cannot extend more than 2000 feet. That is, so far as anyone can tell there *may* be a length of nearly 2000 feet or say 1000 tons of ore per foot of depth.   If the ore should extend to a depth of 500 feet the orebody would contain gross profits of $2,500,000 or, say $1,000,000 when reduced to present value.   Now if there is one chance in 100 that this amount of ore exists or one chance in 50 that half as much exists, the expenditure of $1,000 for trenching is a very attractive bet.

Suppose, now, that this trenching has been completed, and that the ore has been shown to extend for a length of only 700 feet and to represent 400 tons per foot of depth.   The structure is now better understood and the chance of extending to a depth of 500 feet is judged to be one in ten.   The gross profit if this amount of ore is found would be $1,000,-000 or, reduced to present value and deducting cost of plant, about $700,000.   Since the one in ten probability of achieving this profit would be worth $70,000, a proposal to prove existence of the ore beyond reasonable doubt by spending $50,000 would be attractive, especially if there is a reasonably good chance that the ore will go deeper.

The Concept of Amortization Tonnage.   In the example just described, it would not be necessary to develop the ore to a depth of 500 feet before deciding to take over the property.   In fact, to develop that much ore might occasion an excessive investment in advance-development and might unduly delay the return of capital.   Let us assume that in this particular case the smallest scale of operation that would yield reasonable operating earnings would be 100 tons a day and that at this rate of production the unit earnings would be $4 a ton.   Assume, furthermore that a plant to mine and treat this tonnage would cost $150,000. To return this amount with sufficient interest to cover a moderate operating risk would require an ore supply of about 2 years or 60,000 tons.

This amount of ore, which is the amount required to amortize the investment, may be termed the "amortization tonnage."

If exactly this tonnage exists, there will of course be no significant profit, but if at least this tonnage is shown to be present and there is, in addition, a reasonable chance of finding more, the company is in a very enviable position. It cannot lose, and it has a chance of winning, possibly very handsomely. Therefore it may safely take up the property and install equipment for production. But if development work shows that an amortization tonnage does *not* exist, the work of examination and testing can be considered completed and the prospect should be abandoned forthwith.

With amortization tonnage as an initial hurdle, the development is planned accordingly. We immediately lay out drilling, tunnelling, or other development to determine as quickly as possible whether or not the 60,000 tons exist. In the present instance, since the ore would have to extend to an average depth of 150 feet, we test it at this depth. If there is no ore at 150 feet, the possibility that the ore may extend to 50 or 75 feet does not interest us.

Briefly restated, the steps in applying the concept of amortization tonnage are: (1) As soon as the grade and general nature of the deposit become apparent, calculate the cost of a plant having sufficient capacity to treat the ore at a reasonable profit. (2) Calculate the tonnage of ore that would amortize this expenditure. (3) Visualize an orebody or group of orebodies embracing this tonnage. (4a) Once it is evident that no such tonnage exists, abandon the prospect, or (4b) if ore of these dimensions is shown to exist, proceed with plans for bringing the property into production. This need not preclude further development if it appears that a still larger plant might be warranted.

Setting a Definite Objective. The cost of demonstrating whether or not an amortization tonnage exists is much the most speculative part of a development campaign. This is the initial ante in the game of mining, and it is risky because the player does not know what cards he will draw or what the size of the pot will be. If the ante is the cost of developing an amortization tonnage, its limit is the cost of proving that ore does not exist. The expenditure on a prospect may be less than this limit, whether because the requisite ore is found at an early stage or because the investor becomes discouraged, but it will not be more, for no one will continue looking for ore after he has convinced himself that there is none to be found. The most satisfactory sort of prospect is the one in which the limit is low in comparison with the prize and, by and large, this is the one in which there is a definite ore-locus to be tested. If the target is the intersection of fissures with the Bonanza limestone within 500 feet of the Top Notch Fault, the cost of determining whether or not ore exists there will be relatively small. But if the ore, assuming that it exists at all, may be anywhere within a square mile and at any depth down to 5000 feet, the expenditure can go on and on without coming to any definite conclusion. There is always a temptation to send good money after bad in the effort to bail out a failure, and it is true that great orebodies have been found after a long series of disappointments. The Irish bull, "Never stop until you have put in another round," is often quoted, but company after company has gone broke by not knowing when to quit. The type of prospect known to the profession as a "teaser" can keep on consuming capital to the point where even if ore is finally discovered it does not pay a reasonable return on the large amount that is already invested.

A critical question, then, is "What will it cost to prove that the expected ore does not exist?" This may seem like a negative form of question, for the geologist's function is not to turn down prospects but to find ore. True enough—yet the discovery of ore is by no means the only possible outcome; if one successful prospect in ten is a very good score, we need to know what each of the nine failures is going to cost. If a property potentially worth $200,000 can be proved or disproved for $10,000 worth of drilling, the bet is a good one. But if it can be tested only by underground work costing $50,000, it is not attractive unless the odds are much better than one in ten, or unless the potential prize is several times $200,000. The risk-money can be kept within bounds by setting up for each prospect a definite objective, or set of objectives, and if ore is not found, promptly abandoning the operation. This is not to say that new information disclosed in the course of development should be ignored. For instance a drill hole may demonstrate the absence of the ore that is sought but disclose evidence of another vein that was not known to exist. In this event, however, the whole operation is due for deliberate reappraisal. It becomes a new prospect to be judged on its own merits just as though no time or money had been previously spent on the property.

A series of decisive tests, each test proving or disproving a structural hypothesis in a different prospect, is more likely to find ore than a long-drawn-out blind search for ore on a single property, even one which seemed at first to offer more encouragement than any of the long-shot bets.

Methods of Development

Surface Development. Compared with underground work, surface development is so inexpensive that it pays to expose the bedrock to the greatest degree possible by trenches and test-pits before starting any shafts or tunnels unless, perchance, a very short piece of drilling or crosscutting might serve to demonstrate in a conclusive manner the absence of extensive ore.   There are circumstances, of course, in which surface development would yield little information, as where the ore-bearing horizon is covered by deep glacial drift or by flat-lying beds. But an outcrop, even if it is a gossan and therefore gives little direct evidence of grade, should indicate the extent of the mineralized zone, throw some light on the nature of mineralization and point to the best places for deeper development.   Trenching, moreover, offers a rapid method of solving certain structural problems, a method which, surprisingly enough, geologists with their minds fixed on geological procedures sometimes overlook.   If two workmen in a day can uncover the bedrock and disclose the amount and direction of displacement on a fault, the result is more convincing and less expensive than an equal amount of the geologist's time devoted to deductive methods of solving the problem.   Trenching requires little equipment; a few picks and shovels are all that is necessary.   But if a large amount of work is to be done, it may pay to contract for the use of a small power shovel, a mechanical ditch digger, or a tractor equipped with a bulldozing blade.[10]   If ample water under high pressure is available, the method known to placer miners as ground-sluicing [10a] may be even cheaper and is capable of providing a more extensive exposure.   This method has been used in many prospects, perhaps the most spectacular of which was the famed "silver sidewalk" at Cobalt, Ontario.

Where the overburden is too deep for either trenching or ground-sluicing, a series of test-pits to bedrock discloses the nature of the underlying material.   As a labor-saving substitute for deep trenching, the practice of crosscutting the structure by a line of inclined diamond-drill holes is widely used in Canada.   This is particularly advantageous if there are parts of the property where the overburden is so thick that trenches would not expose a complete cross section.   Local depressions in the bedrock surface should not be left untested, as they may be due

[10] Grimes, R. A., Exploring drift-covered areas with a bulldozer: *E. & M. J.*, vol. 140, p. 53, Sept., 1939.

[10a] Boericke, W. F., *Prospecting and Operating Small Gold Placers*, 2nd Ed., p. 69.   New York: Wiley, 1936.

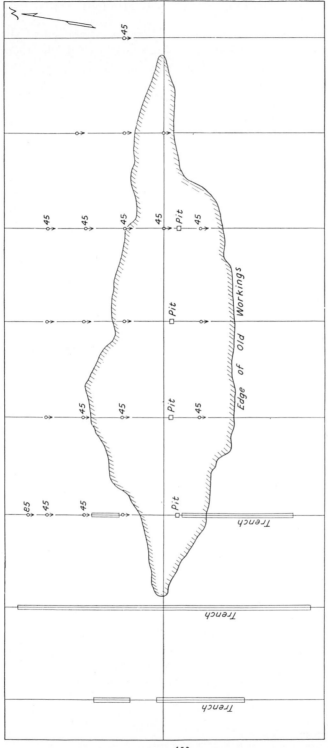

Fig. 141.—Example of a system of surface development. Trenches, pits and drillholes (indicated by arrows) are all placed on cross-section lines. (Idealized diagram to illustrate method recommended by Raymond Brooks) Scale, 1:4000

to deep erosion where oxidation of sulphides or alteration of the rocks has softened the rock—just the places where ore might be found.

As an example of systematic surface development the procedure used by Raymond Brooks [11] in opening up a series of copper deposits in the Belgium Congo is worth describing. The ore was oxidized and occurred in wide but somewhat elongated bodies which were to be exposed by trenches, test-pits, drill-holes, and, in some cases, underground crosscuts. The feature of the method was that all of the work was concentrated on regularly spaced parallel lines crossing the axis of the outcrop. This made it possible to plot all information on a series of cross sections without projecting any data. Thus the structure and assays on each section were factual and they involved a minimum of interpolation.

As a preliminary to laying out the cross-section lines, a base line was surveyed along the long dimension of the orebody and if the outcrop curved, boomerang-fashion, the base line was deflected through the necessary angle to keep in the middle of it. The base line was marked with stakes at 100-meter intervals, but since these stakes were destined to destruction by trenching, a permanent landmark was set four meters toward the zero end of the base line from each 100-meter stake, i.e., at 96 meters, 196 meters, etc., and marked with a zinc tag. A line was then surveyed through each stake at right angles to the base line and was marked by stakes at 30-meter intervals, tagged "96 + 1N," "96 + 2N," or "296 − 2S" etc. The trenches were put in parallel to these cross lines but 4 meters away from them so as to cross the even hundred-meter points of the base line. The trenches were dug 1 meter wide and 2 to 5 meters deep. If the depth had to be more than 2 meters, side benches like firing steps were dug in order to (1) allow shoveling in two stages, and (2) protect the bank from caving.

Drilling vs. Underground Development. If the prospect survives the test of surface development the next step is to probe at greater depth, and we are faced with a choice between drill holes and full-sized underground openings.

Drilling is much the cheaper method and is preferable wherever the nature of the ore is such as to yield decisive results. One traditional objection to drilling is that "you can't mine ore out of a drill hole"; that is, if drilling finds ore, the underground work will have to be done anyway (unless of course open pit mining is indicated). But whether ore is found or not, the cost of the drilling cannot be considered an injudicious waste of money. If it discovers ore, the subsequent investment

[11] Personal communication.

in underground exploration is subject to a much lower risk factor and, moreover, the workings can be laid out to open up the ore in the most direct and economical manner. If, on the other hand, the drilling demonstrates absence of ore, the cost of underground work is saved. Even in districts where the ore is so spotty that the core or sludge cannot be expected to show whether mineralized matter is payable or not, to say nothing of giving a reliable indication of grade, drilling may nevertheless have a real function. If it merely serves to outline areas that are barren of mineralization, it narrows down the zones that will have to be tested by more expensive methods.

From the foregoing it might seem that drilling is an advantageous mode of development under any and all conditions, but this is not so. There are some circumstances under which drilling is uneconomical and others under which it is uninformative. As explained in Chapter 3, diamond drilling is slow and expensive in blocky or mixed hard-and-soft ground. Churn drilling is excessively expensive in really hard rock. Under such unfavorable conditions, any form of drilling may give less information for the money than underground work. Moreover, the topography may be such that excessively long holes would be required to reach the objective. Thus a vein cropping out well down a slope and dipping into the mountain side is hard to reach from any position on the surface. In general, holes of excessive length are unsatisfactory, partly because they are likely to deviate and miss anything but a large target, and partly because enough of them to give a satisfactory test may entail heavy expense. Drilling becomes less advantageous the smaller the orebodies and the spottier the ore, because a larger number of holes is required to give a dependable sample or to avoid missing an orebody.

Shaft vs. Adit. After preliminary drilling, or instead of it, comes underground work. Here again we are faced with a choice: "Do we sink a shaft or do we drive a tunnel?" In some types of terrain the question answers itself; if the ground is level a shaft is the only possible way of gaining depth; if the slopes are steep and the vein crops out on the flank of the hill, a tunnel can follow it in from the grassroots. But if a crosscutting adit is necessary in order to tap the vein, the decision may not be so obvious.

A shaft complies in spirit, though perhaps not literally, with the time-tested Cornish rule: "Follow the ore even if it flies up a church steeple." [12] If the ore bottoms at shallow depth, the shaft discloses the fact im-

---

[12] A shaft for permanent operations should be placed in the wall (preferably the footwall), but a shaft for preliminary testing gives quicker information if sunk on the vein itself.

mediately. It has the disadvantage, however, that muck has to be handled in cramped quarters and hoisted to the surface; when the shaft reaches the water level the water has to be pumped or bailed. For these reasons a shaft costs at least twice as much per foot as an adit. An adit, however, may take more feet to reach and open up the ore. If it cuts the vein below the bottom of the ore the footage is increased by the necessity of a raise. If the oreshoot rakes in an unexpected direction the adit may miss it and necessitate a drift of unknown length. Thus the choice between shaft and adit is something of a gamble. If the adit finds the ore where expected, the gamble succeeds and usually makes subsequent operating cheaper and easier.

In laying out exploratory workings it is desirable to place them in such positions that they can be useful for operating purposes when and if the ore is mined. This consideration can easily be overemphasized, however. Especially in the early stages of development, the prime consideration is speed and economy of results. After the ore is developed, the operation can readily afford a properly placed shaft or adit, a luxury which may be poor economy until the ore is known to exist.

Equipment. The amount of mechanical equipment that should be provided for developing a prospect depends on a variety of considerations, some, though not all, of which are geological. Naturally the cost of providing and installing equipment has to be balanced against the cost of doing the work without it and so depends on the amount of work to be done. Suppose that an old mine tunnel lacks five feet of cutting the projection of a vein and that the question of doing any further work depends on the appearance of the vein when it is cut. Unless a portable compressor is handy, it will be cheapest to drive the five feet by hand drilling, even though the cost per foot is extremely high. Similarly, if development is through a shaft, a hand-operated windlass made from scrap timber may tell the story for less cost than even the freight on a gasoline or electric hoist. But if there is a strong chance that several hundred feet of work will be done on the vein after cutting it, a hoist compressor, track, and cars will readily pay for themselves.

And if it were certain that the mine would be operated after the development period, it would pay to put in full permanent equipment and begin immediately to take advantage of the economy of efficient operation.

These considerations however leave out of account the time factor which is sometimes more important than direct cost. Can the ore question be settled by crude methods before the mechanical equipment could be installed, or, on the contrary, would hand operations be so slow that waiting for proper equipment would save time in the end?

In all of these questions, the geological conditions, by determining the minimum amount of work that will be done and the odds for and against the possibility of additional development and subsequent operation, may be the deciding factor.

Other questions affect the decision, to be sure, and prominent among them is the location of the property. Near a railroad or highway the equipment can be brought in and removed with very little expense, whereas at the end of a long pack trail the cost of transportation may be so high that the equipment is not worth removing and thus has no salvage value. Another consideration is the availability of equipment. In this respect a company that is continually operating mines and developing prospects has a distinct advantage over a group that has been organized to develop a single property. The continuing company is likely to have a hoist, a compressor, and a variety of miscellaneous equipment left over from some other job, and afterward can use it to advantage on still another prospect, obviously a more economical procedure than buying it new and, if the results are disappointing, selling it on the second-hand market.

Cost of Development

Some illustrative cost figures have been given in Chapter 18. The direct costs of development work on a prospect with reasonably efficient equipment should be comparable to those in small mines. Frost [13] gives as an average for development work in mines handling 150 to 250 tons a day: Drifting and crosscutting ($5' \times 7'$) $12.17 per ft., including $5.30 for labor; raising, $11.15, including $4.90 for labor. These costs do not include depreciation or overhead, which, of course, will be relatively high in a prospect where there is no production to share the expense. Small prospects driving only two or three headings would be comparable to only a 25- to 50-ton operation, and costs would be somewhat higher, even without overhead. Shaft-sinking, according to Frost should cost $15 to $20 a foot for each compartment of shaft; a two-compartment shaft 100 feet deep should cost $3,000 to $4,000. Rock drilling equipment for breaking 25 to 50 tons a day would cost about $14,000—including compressor, drills, sharpening equipment, and accessories, but not transportation or installation.

Many other cost figures could be cited but, as most of them are for out-dated conditions, the foregoing, based on experience in mines in

[13] Frost, Hildreth, Jr., Equipment for preliminary mining investigations, *Deco Trefoil*, Denver Equipment Co., pp. 5–8, April, 1945.

continental U. S. in 1944, are probably as useful as any. Costs vary widely, of course, not only with the nature of the rock and the locality, but also with changing industrial conditions. Until labor and material costs reach some degree of stability, past records can be of only moderate assistance.

Selected References

Examination of Prospects

Gunther, C. Godfrey and Fleming, Russell C., *The Examination of Prospects.* New York: McGraw-Hill Book Company, Incorporated, 1932.

Joralemon, Ira B., The weakest link; or saving time in a mine examination, *Engineering and Mining Journal,* vol. 125, pp. 536–540, 1928.

Reid, J. A., and Huston, C. C., Practical examination of mineral prospects, *Transactions, Canadian Institute of Mining and Metallurgy,* vol. 48, pp. 270–283, 1945.

Westervelt, William Young, in Peele's *Mining Engineers' Handbook,* 3rd Edition, pp. 25–02 to 25–32, Mine Examinations, Valuations and Reports. New York: John Wiley and Sons, Incorporated, 1941.

Valuation of Prospects—See references at end of Chapter 18.

Development of Prospects

Eaton, Lucien, *Practical Mine Development and Equipment.* New York: McGraw-Hill Book Company, Incorporated, 1934.

Mining Law

Van Wagenen, Theo. F., *International Mining Law.* New York: McGraw-Hill Book Company, Incorporated, 1918.

U. S. *Bureau of Mines,* Information Circulars (about 65 reports, numbered between I.C. 6102 and I.C. 6798, 1926–1934, summarizing mining laws by countries. Consult U. S. Bureau of Mines, Subject Index, under name of country.

18

Valuing Mining Properties

A mining property has a definite value only by virtue of its ability to produce a profit over a term of years.

— Baxter and Parks [1]

Just how much a mining property is worth is a question that the geologist is likely to be called upon either to answer or to help in answering. It is true that in some mines the question is purely one of engineering and economics. If the amount of ore and its grade are fully known, the operation is comparable to a manufacturing business with its raw material on hand and awaiting treatment. But as most mines have ore reserves for only a few years, their value depends in large measure on future ore whose amount and grade can be estimated only by taking geological factors into account. In the valuation of prospects, geological considerations are even more weighty. This chapter will concern itself primarily with the geological factors of valuation, but to this end a review of the underlying economic principles is indispensable since the two phases are so closely interrelated.

VALUATION OF OPERATING MINES

Purposes of a Valuation

Valuation of operating mines for purposes of outright purchase is rather uncommon, because mines that are producing profitably are rarely for sale. No owner is likely to part with a property except for a price that is at least as much as he thinks it is worth, and such is the optimism of mine owners that the price is usually greater than a prudent purchaser

---

[1] Baxter, Charles H., and Parks, Roland D., *Mine Examination and Valuation*, page 118. Houghton: Mich. College of Mines and Technology, 1933.

is willing to pay. This divergence in viewpoint is readily understandable. The owner knows the habits of the ore; he has seen the mine come through various misfortunes; he has faith that more ore is to be found than meets the eye. So he is unwilling to part with the goose that lays the golden egg for the price of the next two or three eggs, whereas the potential buyer is inclined to suspect the health and longevity of the goose, especially if the goose is for sale. Furthermore, the owner is rarely an individual. So large an expenditure of money is required to bring a mine to the stage of profitable operation that the resources of a partnership, or more commonly a corporation, must eventually be called on. Individuals may sell their interests, but a company does not ordinarily commit suicide by disposing of its assets so long as its profit and loss account is in the right column.

Valuations for purposes other than sale are common, however. They are often needed for purposes of merger, for preparation of tax statements, for the settlement of estates, or for appraising the value of shares on the market. Where such a valuation is merely for bookkeeping purposes, it may consist of little more than a formality that can be carried out by applying fixed rules. But if the interests of any large group of owners are involved, it is necessary to use methods designed to achieve a result that is fair to all parties concerned. To this end it is imperative to take into account a number of intangible factors, some of which may involve a large element of judgment.

Basis of Valuation

The "fair market value" of a mine has been defined as "the price at which a willing and able buyer and a willing and able seller would effect a *bona fide* trade." [2] But the divergence in outlook between the buyer and the seller has already been suggested, and this divergence is all the more difficult to take into account when no actual sale is contemplated; for in this case the buyer and the seller are both imaginary characters, and the appraiser who seeks a meeting-ground for their opposing views must put himself in the place of the two mythical individuals at one and the same time.

It might be held that from the standpoint of both buyer and seller the matter could be approached as a problem in bookkeeping by setting up the assets of the concern and deducting the liabilities. This is true in principle but far from simple in practice, for there still remains the crux of the problem: How to assign a fair value to the assets. The most

[2] Copper Producers Tax Committee, *Factors for Determining Copper Mine Values*, Brief to Bureau of Internal Revenue, 1926, privately printed, page 4.

tangible of the assets of a mining company are the ore in the mine and the plant that has been built to treat it.   Of the two, the ore is much the more important, for without it the plant has little value.   A concentrator that cost two million dollars is hardly worth its weight in scrap metal if it has no ore to treat.   The original cost, which may or may not appear on the books, is of no significance; the mountains of the West are full of derelict properties in which hundreds of millions of dollars have been invested, but which could not today be sold as sheep pasture.   On the other hand, most successful mines could not be bought for hundreds of times the original cost of the property and plant.

The basic asset then is the ore.   Yet, despite its solid appearance, ore may be elusive.   In the commonly accepted definition, ore is that part of a geologic body from which the metal or metals that it contains may be extracted profitably.[3]   In this sense, what is ore today may not be ore tomorrow.   Millions of tons of copper-bearing rock were ore in 1930 when the price of copper was 18 cents a pound, but ceased to be ore in 1932 when the price fell to 5 cents.   Much of it was ore again in 1942 when the price was 12 cents.

Since ore has no assignable value that is independent of the cost of mining and treating it, the only rational basis of valuation is earning power.   Yet it is not *present* earning power that determines the value but rather the outlook for future earnings.   For this reason every valuation is in the nature of a prophecy rather than a factual inventory.   The factors that enter into such a prophecy are many.   Some of them are technical, involving geology, mining methods, and metallurgy, but of fully equal importance are questions of economics and politics, both national and international.   Even the more technical considerations do not fall within a single professional field.   If the valuation is made by one individual, the person chosen to make it is likely to be a mining engineer or a geologist; if a mining engineer, his knowledge of geology is one of the skills that he brings to bear in arriving at his conclusion; if a geologist, he acts only partly in his professional capacity and partly by employing his experience in fields which are only indirectly related to his own specialty.   He will do best to limit his calculations so far as possible to technical problems.   Not that he can ignore the broader economic and political factors, but he can detach them from his own com-

---

[3] Lindgren, Waldemar, *Mineral Deposits,* page 13.   New York: McGraw-Hill, 1933.

A more precise definition of ore is that of J. F. Kemp: "In its technical sense an ore is a metalliferous mineral or an aggregate of metalliferous minerals, more or less mixed with gangue, and capable of being, from the standpoint of the miner, won at a profit; or from the standpoint of the metallurgist, treated at a profit."   *Trans. Canadian Mining Institute,* vol. 12, p. 367, 1909.

putations by making certain assumptions in regard to future prices and costs. These assumptions should be so clearly labelled that the economist or business man can, for his own purposes, revise the valuation up or down in accordance with his own conception of future conditions.

Factors Determining Value

The valuation, then, comes down to estimating what the earnings of a mine throughout its future life are worth today. Three factors enter into such an estimate: (1) the amount that the mine will earn each year, (2) the number of years that it will continue to produce, and (3) the present value of these future earnings.

These three factors cannot be determined independently of each other. Annual earnings and life both depend on the rate of production, and this should be chosen in such a way as to give the highest present value.[4] The rate of production directly determines the life of the mine, for, obviously, if a given amount of ore is to be mined, the higher the annual rate the shorter the life. The rate of production also determines the annual profit, not merely because the annual profit is the number of tons times the profit per ton, but also because the profit per ton itself increases with the scale of production, owing to lowering of costs by large-scale operation. Furthermore, since lowering of costs permits a lower grade of ore to be mined, an increase in the annual capacity may in effect increase the ore reserve and thus extend the life of the mine.

Annual Profit

The profit to be expected each year might be calculated by estimating all of the expenditures that will be incurred during a year and deducting this from the total value of metals that will be sold. Most engineers, however, are accustomed to thinking in terms of values and cost per ton mined and have in their experience a basis for judging the reasonableness of figures so expressed. Therefore, it is usually preferable to compute annual profits by multiplying the rate of production in tons by the profit that is estimated for each ton. Profit per ton, in turn, is the difference between value of recoverable metal content per ton and cost of production per ton. Each of the factors involved *viz.* (a) grade of ore, (b) price of product, (c) costs, (d) rate of production, merits separate comment.

[4] *Cf.* Hotchkiss, W. O., and Parks, R. D., Total profits vs. present value in mining, *A.I.M.E. Tech. Pub. No. 708*, 1936.

FitzGerald, Norman D., Optimum rate of working mineral deposits, *Mining & Met.*, September, 1938, pp. 401–402.

Grade of Ore

The starting point for an estimate of profits is the amount of metal in the ore, for no process can recover more metal than nature provided and the main question is how much of it can be brought to the market and turned into cash. The heart of the matter, then is grade, but this term without qualification may be ambiguous and the various senses in which it is used need to be distinguished.

Sampled grade is the tenor of the ore in place as determined by underground, surface, or drill-hole sampling.

Millhead grade is the grade of the ore as it comes from the mine and goes to the mill. In calculating it one must make appropriate allowance for dilution (see below).

Recoverable grade is the millhead grade less metallurgical losses (see Chapter 22). It must be determined by a metallurgical test if a close calculation is necessary. For preliminary estimates, the experience with similar ores in the district or elsewhere will serve as a basis.

Liquidation grade is the amount paid by the smelter or other purchaser per ton of ore mined.

Price of Product

The value of a mine's product, whether concentrate, bullion, or refined metal, fluctuates with the market prices of metals. The prices of gold and silver are fixed, so far as the United States is concerned, by act of Congress and government regulations. This fact does not mean, however, that they are permanently stable; the statutes are subject to repeal or amendment, and the problem of future prices is essentially political. The prices of other metals, though pegged in war time, have normally been governed by laws of supply and demand, and, while they can never be predicted with confidence, they are essentially questions of economics. In their prediction, past history serves as a useful guide, but it is far from infallible.

A purely mechanical projection of the price curve is almost as likely to give the wrong trend as the right one and even a projection that takes all economic factors into account can be little more than an enlightened guess. Current quotations have, at least, the advantage that they represent the meeting-ground of a large number of the shrewdest and best-informed minds; their chief shortcoming is a tendency to myopia; to metal traders, a temporary glut or shortage may loom larger than the longer outlook. That they can be sadly in error at times is all too evident from a glance at the staggered curves of the past, but anyone who can do better has an opportunity to make himself very, very rich by dealing in metal futures without bothering his head about mining investments. Instead of today's quotations, an average of the past ten, fifteen, or twenty years may seem more conservative, although it can prove just as wrong, especially in troubled times. Its chief merit is that it avoids the danger that today's price is a peak or trough in the curve of longer trend.

What price, then, is the unhappy valuing engineer to use? If his client is an experienced business man, entitled to an opinion of his own in regard to economic trends, a geologist will do well to confine his predictions to matters of science and engineering, leaving his principal to do his own crystal gazing in regard to price. To facilitate the forecast, he may supplement an estimate of earnings at current prices with a table showing the difference that would be introduced by each price change of, say, one cent per pound or ounce of metal. If the client is likely to be unacquainted with such matters, the geologist will have to shoulder the responsibility and make the best guess he can. There are no dependable rules.

The prices received by mines that sell their metal in the from of crude ore or mineral concentrates depend partly on the market prices of metals and partly on sales arrangements which are matters for negotiation between the mine and the smelting company. Smelter schedules are discussed in Chapter 23.

Cost of Production

Direct and Indirect Costs

In an operating mine, the best guide to costs is past experience as recorded in the books of the concern. But since the value of the mine depends on costs in the future rather than in the past, the recorded costs call for analysis and perhaps revision, taking into account any anticipated changes in rate or methods of production as well as current trends in cost of labor and materials. To this end, it is usually necessary to break the cost items down into such categories as labor, materials, and general expense, both in total and per unit (e.g., per ton or per pound of metal). Even though the books may already segregate the items in some such manner as this, the treatment which may be entirely satisfactory for purpose of an annual report is not always the one which applies correctly to a valuation. The guiding principle is that annual income should include everything that accrues directly or eventually to the benefit of the mine owner or stockholder and should include

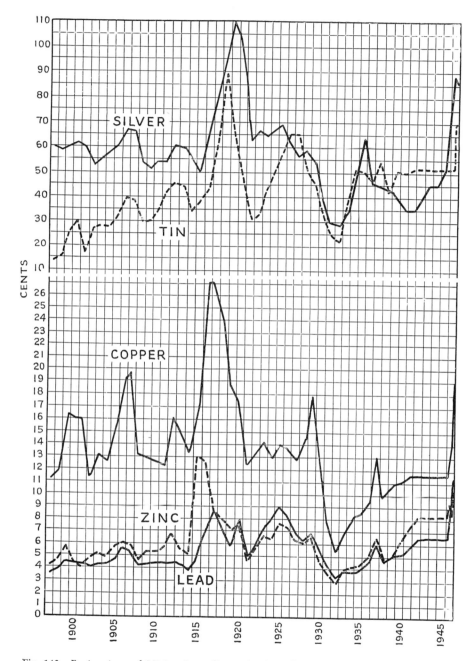

Fig. 142—*Engineering and Mining Journal's* graph of metal prices. *Silver:* U. S. open market quotation in cents per ounce. *Tin:* Straits, New York in cents per pound. *Copper:* Domestic, New York, f.o.b. refinery, in cents per pound. *Zinc:* East St. Louis in cents per pound. *Lead:* New York in cents per pound. (*Courtesy of* McGraw-Hill Publishing Company)

nothing which does not fit into this category.   The items that are most likely to need recasting are: overhead, or general expense, depreciation, depletion, and development costs.

Accounting Items

General Expense.   Usually this includes such items as salaries of executives and office staff, insurance and local taxes.   Income taxes are usually not included in "general expense" but are shown separately. Since they form a very sizable item of expense, often, in fact the largest single item, they must not be overlooked.

Some accountants distribute a large portion of overhead expense into direct operating costs on some pro-rata basis which may or may not be very reasonable; others charge general expense with items which are really a part of direct production cost.   For purposes of valuation it is convenient to include as general expense all items which are approximately the same from year to year and do not vary with the number of tons produced, reserving for unit operating costs those expenses which apply directly to the production of a ton of ore or a pound of metal. This facilitates an estimate of costs for possible alternative rates of production.

Depreciation.   Depreciation is an item that is entered on the books in order to take into account the wear and tear on plant and machinery. For simplicity of calculation, a mine plant should resemble the original one-hoss shay.   The plant should serve its purpose until the ore is exhausted and fall to pieces as soon as the last ton goes through the mill. Obviously this does not happen in actual practice.   Machinery needs to be repaired and replaced from time to time, and the expenditures for this are handled on the books in a variety of ways.   Some companies charge practically all equipment directly to operating; others charge it to a capital account which is then credited each year with an amount that may or may not be a realistic representation of actual wear and tear.   At one extreme is a large mine whose concentrating plant was long ago charged off and, although it is likely to function for many years and could not be replaced for several million dollars, is carried on the books at one dollar.   What is good practice from the standpoint of accounting need not concern us here.   For purposes of valuation a distinction should be made between "depreciation" and "maintenance," even though no such distinction may appear in the accounts.   Depreciation, in the strict sense, is purely a book charge whose function is to indicate that not all of the operating surplus is true profit.   For estimating taxable income and for many other purposes this is a proper deduction; in fact, were it omitted the figure for profit would be misleading. For purposes of valuation, however, it is simpler to ignore depreciation altogether. If the equipment is already in existence, it has little or no value except as an adjunct to the operation of this particular mine; the money that bought it is water over the dam and very little of it could be recovered should the mine close tomorrow no matter how good the condition of the machinery. If a new or enlarged plant will be needed at a later date its cost should be discounted to present value and deducted from the present value of future profits.

The expenditure that has to be made year by year in order to keep the plant in efficient operating condition is a proper item of operating cost and belongs under "maintenance" or some such heading. Unless the accounts are critically analyzed, expenditures for current items of equipment may be misleading, since they may be high in a year in which new mine cars or ball mills are bought and low in a year in which current replacements are postponed. A realistic figure may be arrived at by averaging the expenditure for machinery, etc., over a period of years, providing the plant is in essentially the same condition as at the beginning of the period and does not face a major expenditure for replacement in the near future.

Depletion. Depletion is analogous to depreciation but applies to the ore reserve rather than to the plant. It takes into account the fact that a mine is a "wasting asset." If the entire ore reserve were to be mined out in a single year, the cost of acquiring the ore (purchasing and developing the property) would be a very important part of the expenditure for the year. If a tenth of the ore reserve is mined each year, something on the order of a tenth of the cost of acquiring the ore reserve will properly be chargeable each year as depletion. From the standpoint of valuation, however, the ore reserve was purchased when operations began and constitutes part of the capital investment rather than an item to be deducted from the earnings which eventually reach the stockholders.

For this reason "costs excluding depreciation and depletion" are the usual ones which are considered in appraising the earning power of a property.

Development Cost. The current cost of searching for new ore and preparing it for stoping is an unavoidable expenditure in mining operations. If, each year, the amount of ore developed is substantially equal to the amount mined, the year's expenditure for development is a realistic part of that year's production cost. In some properties, however, development is adding rapidly to ore reserves; in others it is failing sadly to keep pace with extraction and, therefore, ought to be increased unless there is little hope of finding new ore. In still other mines, development work is done spasmodically; sinking the shaft, say, 600 feet and opening up four new levels in a single year, then doing no further important development work for three or four years. In all of these cases the development expense for any one year gives a deceptive idea of the cost per ton. Under such conditions, a figure for "development expense per ton developed" gives a better basis for future expenditure. This figure may be computed by taking the total development cost over a period of years and dividing it by the tonnage mined plus the increase (or minus the decrease) in ore reserves from the beginning to the end of the period. Such a figure needs to be modified, of course, if ore finding is becoming much more difficult and expensive or if, on the other hand, exceptionally fertile fields have recently been discovered and remain to be fully tested.

Rate of Production

In an operating mine, a plant of some sort is already in existence and the immediate minimum rate of production is determined by the capacity of this plant, provided, of course, that there are no physical obstacles to prevent the delivery of ore at this rate. If this rate uses up the ore in a very short time, so much the better from the standpoint of profit per ton and present value of anticipated earnings. The present size of the plant need not, however, place an *upper* limit on the assumed rate of production. If calculation shows that the expense of increasing the plant capacity is more than offset by a higher valuation due to increased rate of production, the estimate should be based on the higher rate.

Since a high rate of production gives (*a*) high profits per ton, (*b*) high annual profits and (*c*) a quick return of capital, it might at first sight appear that the higher the rate of production the better. This is indeed true in a general way, but there are practical considerations that impose a limit well short of infinity.[5] This may be illustrated by an extreme example. Suppose that an orebody consists of half a million tons and no more is believed to exist. A plant large enough to exhaust it in a single year would cost, say two million dollars, all of which would have to be written off in one year at four dollars a ton. At the other extreme a plant that would exhaust the ore in no less than a hundred years might cost less than $20,000 or four cents a ton, but since its

---

[5] *Cf.* Warner, Robert K., Metal resources and their conservation, *Journal of Political Economy*, vol. 44, 1936, p. 217.

capacity would be only 16 tons a day, the cost of operation would be excessive, the annual earnings small and the present value of any earnings after the first 30 years [6] would be negligible. A calculation on any reasonable set of assumptions would show that the highest present value lies somewhere between these two extremes. [7] In practice it usually works out that the optimum rate is one that would exhaust an ore deposit in 10 to 15 years.

Regardless of arithmetical abstractions, the nature of the orebody is likely to be the determining factor in influencing the rate of production. In underground mines the tonnage that can be produced each day is governed by the number and size of stopes, and this, in turn, is limited by the time required to prepare the ore for mining. A conservative assumption is that a level a year can be developed. Although this rate can be doubled or even quadrupled under favorable circumstances, any attempt to push the production to too high a rate is merely an invitation to a temporary stoppage with each unforeseen difficulty. A safe and comfortable rate of production can ordinarily be based on the amount of ore per foot of depth, making the assumption that the equivalent of a 100- to 200-foot vertical interval can be mined out annually.

Although in theory the present value is at a maximum if the mine is brought, as soon as possible, to the highest production rate that the orebody will support, it is not always good business policy to step up the production at such an early stage. Until the property receives recognition as a profitable producer, additional capital is likely to be available only at a high rate of interest. After success is established, money can be borrowed at a lower rate or stock can be issued at a favorable price. Therefore, a mine may well begin with a trial period of relatively small operation, enlarging its capacity out of earnings or by increase of capitalization at a later stage. This consideration needs to be taken into account in forecasting the rate of production.

Life

How long a mine can continue to operate depends in the last analysis on how much ore there is in the ground. For even though low metal prices or high costs may terminate an operation, the real cause of suspension is that what had been ore is no longer ore in the technical sense of the term. The amount of ore that is available for future mining

[6] Cf. Berry, Edwin S., Present value in its relation to ore reserves, plant capacity and grade of ore: Mining & Met., July, 1922, p. 11.

[7] FitzGerald, Norman D., Optimum rate of working mineral deposits: Mining & Met., vol. 19, September, 1938, p. 401.

cannot always be calculated accurately, but always there is a minimum amount which can be measured and sampled or else the mine is not a mine at all but merely a prospect. The calculable tonnage, including some that is believed, even though not conclusively proved, to exist, is known as the *ore reserve*.

Ore Reserves

Classes of Ore Reserves. Paradoxically enough, no one can be sure how much ore there is in a mine until it has been mined out; therefore, at best, ore reserve figures are estimates rather than certainties. The tonnage of ore that is exposed on all sides by workings can be calculated with reasonable accuracy, but the tonnage that exists beyond or below any workings can be estimated only by making certain assumptions. It is, therefore, conventional to divide the ore reserve into categories based on the degree of assurance of its existence. Of several classifications that have been proposed, all based on the same principle, the oldest and probably the most widely used divides the ore reserve into three classes as follows:

> *Positive Ore* or *Ore Blocked Out.* Ore exposed and sampled on four sides, *i.e.*, by levels above and below and by raises or winzes at the ends of the block. This definition applies to veins; for wide orebodies the workings must be supplemented by crosscuts.
> *Probable Ore.* Ore exposed and sampled either on two or on three sides. (Authorities differ.)
> *Possible Ore.* Ore exposed on only one side, its other dimensions being a matter of reasonable projection. Some engineers use an arbitrary extension of 50 to 100 feet. Others assume extension for half the exposed dimension.

Although these definitions are relatively rigid, they fail to specify one important factor—the distance between the workings that expose the ore. This factor is pertinent because there is always a chance that somewhere within the block there may be a barren patch, and this chance is greater as the distance between exposures is greater. Therefore, in order that ore may be considered "Proved" or "Blocked Out," the workings in which sampling has been done should not be more than some specified distance apart; yet no arbitrary standard can be set up, because different types of ore vary in their regularity and dependability. In a spotty erratic orebody the spacing must be closer than would be permissible in a large uniform orebody. Recognizing this, Hoover [8] says, "In a gen-

---

[8] Reprinted by permission from *Principles of Mining* by Herbert C. Hoover, p. 19. Copyrighted, 1909, by the McGraw-Hill Book Company, Inc.

eral way a fair rule in gold quartz veins below influence of alteration is that no point in the block shall be over fifty feet from the points sampled. In limestone or andesite replacements, as by gold or lead or copper, the radius must be less. In defined lead and copper lodes, or in large lenticular bodies such as the Tennessee copper mines, the radius may often be considerably greater,—say one hundred feet. In gold deposits of such extraordinary regularity of values as the Witwatersrand Bankets, it can well be two hundred or two hundred and fifty feet."

The regularity of the ore determines not only the maximum permissible spacing, but also the number of sides on which the ore must be exposed in order to assure its presence. Although ore of an erratic

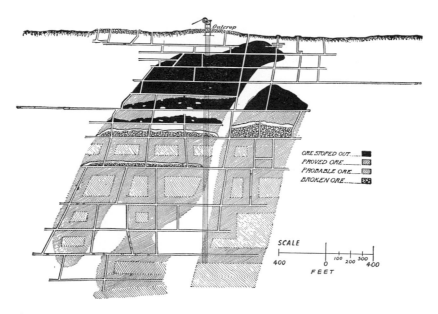

Fig. 143—Longitudinal section of a mine showing classification of exposed ore. (Reproduced by permission from Hoover, H. C., *Principles of Mining*, copyright 1909 by the McGraw-Hill Book Company, Inc.)

nature needs to be blocked out on four sides, as called for in the conventional definition of positive ore, a uniform orebody whose structure is well understood might be counted on with reasonable confidence if it were exposed on only two sides. Hoover, therefore, proposed categories based on more flexible definitions which allow some leeway to the judgment of the individual:

Proved Ore. Ore where there is practically no risk of failure of continuity.
Probable Ore. Ore where there is some risk yet warrantable justification for assumption of continuity.

Prospective Ore. Ore which cannot be included as "Proved" or "Probable," nor definitely known or stated in any terms of tonnage.

Another set of terms, which allow rather wide latitude to the individual, has been adopted by the U. S. Geological Survey and the U. S. Bureau of Mines. Instead of "Proved," "Probable," and "Prospective," these Bureaus use "Measured," "Indicated," and "Inferred," defined as follows:

Measured ore is ore for which tonnage is computed from dimensions revealed in outcrops, trenches, workings, and drill holes, and for which the grade is computed from the results of detailed sampling. The sites for inspection, sampling, and measurements are so closely spaced, and the geologic character is defined so well, that the size, shape, and mineral content are well established. The computed tonnage and grade are judged to be accurate within limits which are stated, and no such limit is judged to differ from the computed tonnage or grade by more than 20 per cent.

Indicated ore is ore for which tonnage and grade are computed partly from specific measurements, samples, or production data, and partly from projection for a reasonable distance on geologic evidence. The sites available for inspection, measurement, and sampling are too widely or otherwise inappropriately spaced to outline the ore completely or to establish its grade throughout.

Inferred ore is ore for which quantitative estimates are based largely on broad knowledge of the geologic character of the deposit and for which there are few, if any, samples or measurements. The estimates are based on an assumed continuity or repetition for which there is geologic evidence; this evidence may include comparison with deposits of similar type. Bodies that are completely concealed may be included if there is specific geologic evidence of their presence. Estimates of inferred ore should include a statement of the spacial limits within which the inferred ore may lie.

This classification leaves room for considerable deduction from geological background. It is well suited to its intended purpose, the estimation of the reserves of a district or a nation. It is less satisfactory for valuing a single mine.

Which of the various schemes of classification is preferable depends partly on individual taste, partly on the nature of the ore, and partly on the usage in any particular region. There is an obvious advantage in using terms that are rigid enough to enable two engineers to arrive independently at similar figures. When a substantial proportion of the ore is actually exposed and sampled on four sides, the fact can be expressed by calling it either "positive" or "blocked out." But where relatively little has been exposed in this manner, yet the ore is so regular that its existence is well assured without complete blocking out, a large tonnage might qualify as "proved" which could not be called "positive." In this case, "proved" might convey the more accurate impression of the ore reserve. In any case, since there is considerable diversity in the sense in which the terms are used by different engineers, it is well to define them when an ore estimate is presented, thus:

Positive ore (ore blocked out on four sides by workings not more than 200 feet apart) ....148,000 tons.

So far as "possible" or "prospective" ore is concerned, my personal conviction is that any attempt to set down a definite tonnage in this category is likely to be more misleading than helpful. Either the mine contains more, and often a great deal more ore than any engineer would dare to estimate as prospective, or else some of the ore estimated as prospective does not exist. Most mines that have been in operation for ten years or more have already produced more ore than was estimated as "possible" in the early stages of development. I believe that it is preferable to express prospective or possible ore in terms of tons per foot of depth or per foot of linear extension and then discuss the higher and lower limits of expected extension.

The depth to which ore will extend is likely to be one of the critical factors in determining the probable life of a mine. The geological factors governing extension in depth are discussed in Chapter 15.

Estimation of Ore Reserves

The tonnage of ore reserves is estimated from maps and sections that show the limits of ore and the average grade of the workings that have been sampled. (The methods of averaging a series of samples are described in Chapter 2.)

Cut-off Grade and Ore Limits. In order to outline the ore, one must draw a dividing line between ore and waste. Just where to draw this line can be one of the most difficult problems in ore estimation. In the first place, it demands a correct decision as to the *cut-off grade, i.e.,* lowest grade that will meet costs, yet the over-all cost as shown on the books is not necessarily the proper one to use for this purpose.[9] Let us say that the expense of production consists partly of fixed expense amounting to $1500 a day in overhead, maintenance, etc., regardless of the tonnage mined, and partly of variable expense amounting to $3.50 for each ton mined. Clearly the addition of any marginal ore which yields better than $3.50 will add to the profits so long as the fixed ex-

---

[9] *Cf.* Lawford, E. G., How much of the vein is ore: *E. & M. J.*, vol. 125, 1928, p. 54.

pense remains unaffected.   However, there is rarely [9a] any justification for deliberately diluting good ore with waste or for the not uncommon practice of keeping a high-grade stope in reserve to use as a "sweetener." If the distribution of the ore is such that all the high-grade ore can be mined out first and at once, the present value is decidedly higher than if a steady average grade is maintained by mining high- and low-grade ore together.[10]   To say this, however, is not to commend the practice known as "picking the eyes (or eye-teeth) out of the mine."   If the rich spots can be mined selectively only at a relatively high cost per ton, and if their removal increases the subsequent cost of mining the remaining low-grade ore, the selective procedure is poor economy in the long run.

Furthermore, the cost varies with the rate of production.   There are properties in which only a modest tonnage of ore would be calculable if the cut-off were placed at 5% copper, but five times as much ore could be estimated if the cut-off were at 3% and a huge reserve could be shown with the cut-off at 1%.   So, in these cases, what is ore and what is not depends on the cost, but the cost, in turn depends on the scale of production; the scale of production depends on the amount of ore, and the amount of ore depends on the cost.   The only way out of the circle is to calculate the reserves using alternative cut-off grades [11] and to prepare a corresponding series of calculations of present value.

Establishing the *ore limit* is simple if the vein has well-defined walls and the oreshoots have abrupt boundaries.   But in many mines the values decline gradually or irregularly from the vein into the walls on both sides or from the oreshoot into barren vein-matter at the ends, top, or bottom.   If so, it is not always correct to draw the dividing line at the last assay which shows minable grade.   Swanson [12] has shown from a consideration of frequencies that a block of low-grade but minable ore is likely to contain a large, and sometimes predominating, proportion of individual assays which are below the grade-limit.   A series of samples, all of them within a minable shoot, *may* start (at the limit of the shoot) with a high value but it is more likely to start with a low one. Therefore, to draw the limit closely around all the high samples would

[9a] The desirability of maintaining an even grade for reasons of efficient mill operation may justify this procedure in isolated cases.

[10] Berry, Edwin S., Present value and its relation to ore reserves, plant capacity and grade of ore: *Mining and Metallurgy*, July, 1922, p. 11.

[11] For ore whose values are made up of three metals, say lead, zinc, and silver, H. I. Altshuler has devised an ingenious triangular diagram from which all possible combinations of values for any cut-off grade may be read.   *See* Determining cut-off grades with triangular co-ordinates: *E. & M. J.*, vol. 139, October, 1938, p. 35.

[12] Swanson, C. O., Probabilities in estimating the grade of gold deposits: *Can. Inst. M. & M. Tr.*, vol. 48, pp. 324–327, 1945.

give a tonnage that is too low and an average that is too high. If the limits of ore are recognizable from geological observation, this may show where to place the dividing line. Otherwise the proportion of low-grade assays within the body must serve as a guide.

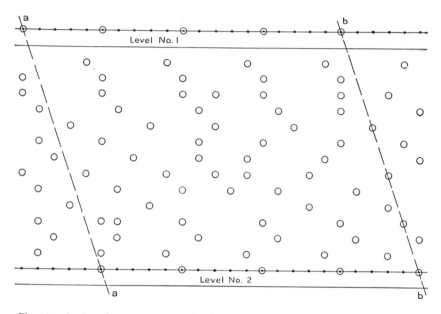

Fig. 144—Semi-random arrangement of rich spots in a low-grade ore-shoot. Open circles represent high-grade spots. Dots represent samples. Establishing ore limits by connecting the outermost high samples on each level (*a-a-b-b*) would exclude part of the ore from the estimate. (Idealized diagram)

When the ore-outline is based partly or wholly on the results of diamond drilling, it must be drawn with due regard to the structure. If a series of holes all indicate ore at the same stratigraphic horizon, it is reasonable to assume that the ore forms a continuous layer (A, Figure 145). The same is true if the intersections line up well, especially if the line is parallel to vein-walls or banding visible in the core. But if the ore is in different stratigraphic horizons in different holes (C), and particularly if it is missing in one or more holes, the conclusion is that it occurs in disconnected lenses. Similarly it is dangerous to correlate intersections which do not lie on a straight line or regular curve (D).[13]

Dilution. An orebody can rarely be mined so cleanly that no waste is broken with the ore. If the vein is narrow, good practice demands that the stope be no wider than necessary, yet few stopes are less than three feet wide and then only where the vein is steep, the walls well-

[13] Moehlman, R. S., Diamond drilling in exploration and development: *A.I.M.E. Tech. Pub. No. 1858*, 1945, p. 17.

marked, and no timbering is necessary.   Ordinarily 4 or 4½ feet should
be allowed as a minimum mining width.   It is true that narrow veins
can sometimes be mined by resuing or by sorting in the stope, thus keep-

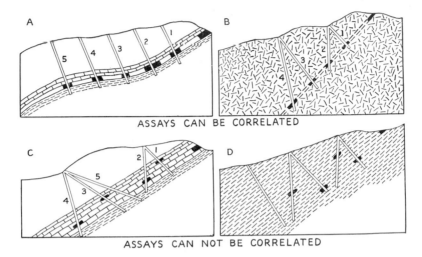

Fig. 145—Correlation of assays in drill holes.   A: Ore has limestone hanging
wall and shale foot wall.   B: Wallrock is granite.   Intersections line up and apparently represent a vein.   C: No. 5 hole, bored as a check, showed no ore.
D: Ore apparently is in disconnected shoots.   (After Moehlman, Trans. A.I.M.E.)

ing the ore separate from the wall rock, but in this case there is almost
certain to be some loss of ore in the "fines" left in the stope.   Methods
of calculating sample averages for minimum mining widths are described
in connection with sampling in Chapter 2.

But dilution of ore by waste is not limited to narrow veins, nor are
its results covered by adjusting calculations to minimum mining width.
Some wall rock is sure to slab off and, especially where the ore limit is
an "assay wall," it is impossible to break to the margin of the ore without, in places, breaking through it.   Dilution is least where the walls
are strong and the rock breaks cleanly away from them.   It is greatest
where the wall is irregular and the rock is weak or shattered.   Of the
various mining methods, shrinkage stoping is likely to give the highest
dilution.   Most engineers allow at least 10% for dilution under the most
favorable circumstances, and 15% or 20% if considerable sloughing is
to be expected.   In an operating mine a conversion factor can be established by comparing the sampled grade with the millhead grade.

Ore Supply Beyond Developed Reserves

Some ore deposits are of such limited extent or can be explored so
cheaply that their full size can be determined at an early stage in the

operations. These are rather exceptional, however. In the ordinary mining venture the development work that would be required to explore to the ultimate depth and to find all of the orebodies that can possibly exist would be excessively expensive and would tie up so much capital that it would be impracticable. Usually it is economical to develop only enough ore to guarantee the investment for plant construction and then push development only a very few years ahead of extraction. It is for this reason that mines continue to operate for many years beyond the life of the ore reserve that is in sight at any one time. For this reason also, a mining property can rarely be bought for a price represented by the life of its ore reserve, and this is true whether it is a prospect or a going concern and whether the criterion of value is an actual sale or the daily quotation of a share on the market. Therefore, the outlook for ore beyond known reserves has a value which cannot be ignored, even though its magnitude is a matter of geological judgment and its existence involves a sizable element of risk. The seriousness of the risk varies greatly in different types of deposits.

As an approach toward a concrete appraisal of this consideration, McLaughlin [14] has proposed a classification of ore deposits "according to the assurance of ore supply that they are ordinarily capable of providing with the amount of exploration that is customary in good current practice." According to the categories of risk involved he sets up three classes:

I. *Plenemensurate orebodies*—those capable of being fully measured and sampled at an early stage in the operations.

II. *Partimensurate orebodies*—those in which prospects for ore in addition to proved reserves remain a substantial element until the later stages of the life of the mines based on them.

III. *Extramensurate orebodies*—those difficult to explore and measure much in advance of mining, in which the value of prospects for ore based on geologic evidence exceeds the value of proved reserves throughout most of the life of mines supported by them.

Class I includes most placer deposits and other orebodies which have definite bottoms, whether limited by the depth of oxidation or enrichment as in the case of lateritic bauxite ores and most "porphyry" coppers, or by shallow structural bottoms as at Cobalt, Ontario, or bounded by property lines as in the outcrop mines of the Rand.

Class II includes a great variety of ore deposits which have in common the characteristic that the ore is likely to extend much farther or deeper than the limits to which development can economically be carried at

[14] McLaughlin, Donald H., Geological factors in the valuation of mines: *Econ. Geol.*, vol. 34, 1939, pp. 589–621.

any one time, or that even if individual orebodies have been delimited there is good reason to expect that new ones will be found beyond such limits.   To name only a few of the examples cited in the original paper:

Lead-zinc ores of the Mississippi Valley type; copper sulphide lodes such as Mufulira in Northern Rhodesia; repetition of separate gold-bearing lodes along well-defined loci, as the Dome Mine in Ontario; hypothermal lead-zinc-silver lodes, notably Broken Hill, New South Wales.

Class III includes deposits whose extension or repetition depends almost wholly on geological evidence.   Such deposits rarely have large developed ore reserves and could be assigned only a moderate value on conventional methods of estimation.   They periodically face the danger of exhaustion yet they may, nevertheless, enjoy long and profitable lives if bold and intelligent development is kept well ahead of extraction. Among such deposits are some of the massive sulphide copper mantos of Morococha, Peru; similar lead-zinc-silver mantos and pipes of Tintic, Utah; and small, structurally controlled orebodies such as those of Bendigo, Victoria.

Present Value of Future Earnings

Compound Interest Method

The value of a mine is not the simple sum of annual profits throughout its future life.   This fact will be evident when it is recalled that a dollar which will not be received for a year or for ten years is not worth as much as a dollar in hand today.   The principle is the same as that of buying for $75.00 a Savings Bond which, in ten years, will pay $100.00.   For this reason it is necessary to reduce the amount of each future installment of profits to its present value.   This may be done in accordance with a modification of the formula for compound interest:

$$V_p = \frac{1}{(1+r)^n}$$

where V_p is the present value of $1.00 due in n years and r is the rate of interest.[15]   Obviously, if the installment is, say $250,000 instead of $1.00, we multiply V_p by 250,000.   Instead of reducing each install-

---

[15] This formula assumes that the interest is compounded annually. If, instead, we wish to stipulate that interest be compounded more than once a year, the formula is

$$V_p = \frac{1}{\left(1+\frac{r}{t}\right)^{tn}}$$

where t is the number of times a year that interest is compounded. The notation in these formulae follows that of Baxter and Parks.

ment separately to its present value, we may use the formula for the present value of an annuity:

$$V_p = \frac{(1+r)^n - 1}{r(1+r)^n}$$

where V_p is the present value of an annuity of \$1.00 a year for n years and r is the interest rate.

Example:

A mine is expected to earn \$80,000 a year for ten years. A certain investor wishes 9% a year on his investment. What is the present value of the anticipated income at this rate of interest?

$$V_p = 80,000 \times \frac{(1.09)^{10} - 1}{(1.09)^{10} \times .09} = 80,000 \times \frac{2.367 - 1}{.21303}$$

$$= 80,000 \times \$6.417 = \$513,360$$

Tables are published for the rapid calculation of the present value of an equal annual installment. (Table 11)

Hoskold Method

Another method of estimating present value is based on the financial policy of British coal mining companies of nearly a century ago and, while the policy is no longer followed, the method of valuation is still in common use. In order to put its shares on a basis comparable to bonds, the company would in effect say to its shareholder: "If you care to invest £100 in the enterprise, we will pay you a dividend each year and return your £100 when the mine is exhausted." Recognizing that the mine was a "wasting asset" and would be worth virtually nothing at the end of 25 years (or whatever may have been its estimated life), the company, in order to have the £100 available for the shareholder, set aside an appropriate amount each year and put it out at compound interest so that it would amount to £100 at the end of the period.

In order to compute the present value of annual earnings in conformity with this principle, H. D. Hoskold,[16] a British mining engineer, developed the formula:

$$V_p = \frac{1}{\dfrac{r}{(1+r)^n - 1} + r'}$$

[16] Hoskold, H. D., *Engineers Valuing Assistant.* London: Longmans, Green & Co., 1st Ed. 1877, 2nd Ed. 1905.

PRESENT VALUE

of $1 or £1 per year for *n* years at ——% interest, compounded annually.

n	1%	1½%	2%	2½%	3%	4%
1	.9901	.9852	.9804	.9756	.9709	.9615
2	1.9704	1.9559	1.9416	1.9274	1.9135	1.8861
3	2.9410	2.9122	2.8839	2.8560	2.8286	2.7751
4	3.9020	3.8544	3.8077	3.7620	3.7171	3.6299
5	4.8534	4.7826	4.7135	4.6458	4.5797	4.4518
6	5.7955	5.6972	5.6014	5.5081	5.4172	5.2421
7	6.7282	6.5982	6.4720	6.3494	6.2303	6.0021
8	7.6517	7.4859	7.3255	7.1701	7.0197	6.7327
9	8.5660	8.3605	8.1622	7.9709	7.7861	7.4353
10	9.4713	9.2222	8.9826	8.7521	8.5302	8.1109
11	10.3676	10.0711	9.7868	9.5142	9.2526	8.7605
12	11.2551	10.9075	10.5753	10.2578	9.9540	9.3851
13	12.1337	11.7315	11.3484	10.9832	10.6350	9.9856
14	13.0037	12.5434	12.1062	11.6909	11.2961	10.5631
15	13.8651	13.3432	12.8493	12.3814	11.9379	11.1184
16	14.7179	14.1313	13.5777	13.0550	12.5611	11.6523
17	15.5623	14.9076	14.2919	13.7122	13.1661	12.1657
18	16.3983	15.6726	14.9920	14.3534	13.7535	12.6593
19	17.2260	16.4262	15.6785	14.9789	14.3238	13.1339
20	18.0456	17.1686	16.3514	15.5892	14.8775	13.5903
21	18.8570	17.9001	17.0112	16.1845	15.4150	14.0292
22	19.6604	18.6208	17.6580	16.7654	15.9369	14.4511
23	20.4558	19.3309	18.2922	17.3321	16.4436	14.8568
24	21.2434	20.0304	18.9139	17.8850	16.9355	15.2470
25	22.0232	20.7196	19.5235	18.4244	17.4131	15.6221
26	22.7952	21.3986	20.1210	18.9506	17.8768	15.9828
27	23.5596	22.0676	20.7069	19.4640	18.3270	16.3296
28	24.3164	22.7267	21.2813	19.9649	18.7641	16.6631
29	25.0658	23.3761	21.8444	20.4535	19.1885	16.9837
30	25.8077	24.0158	22.3965	20.9303	19.6004	17.2920
31	26.5423	24.6461	22.9377	21.3954	20.0004	17.5885
32	27.2696	25.2671	23.4683	21.8492	20.3888	17.8736
33	27.9897	25.8790	23.9886	22.2919	20.7658	18.1476
34	28.7027	26.4817	24.4986	22.7238	21.1318	18.4112
35	29.4086	27.0756	24.9986	23.1452	21.4872	18.6646
36	30.1075	27.6607	25.4888	23.5563	21.8323	18.9083
37	30.7995	28.2371	25.9695	23.9573	22.1672	19.1426
38	31.4847	28.8051	26.4406	24.3486	22.4925	19.3679
39	32.1630	29.3646	26.9026	24.7303	22.8082	19.5845
40	32.8347	29.9158	27.3555	25.1028	23.1148	19.7928
41	33.4997	30.4590	27.7995	25.4661	23.4124	19.9931
42	34.1581	30.9941	28.2348	25.8206	23.7014	20.1856
43	34.8100	31.5212	28.6616	26.1664	23.9819	20.3708
44	35.4555	32.0406	29.0800	26.5038	24.2543	20.5488
45	36.0945	32.5523	29.4902	26.8330	24.5187	20.7200
46	36.7272	33.0565	29.8923	27.1542	24.7754	20.8847
47	37.3537	33.5532	30.2866	27.4675	25.0247	21.0429
48	37.9740	34.0426	30.6731	27.7732	25.2667	21.1951
49	38.5881	34.5247	31.0521	28.0714	25.5017	21.3415
50	39.1961	34.9997	31.4236	28.3623	25.7298	21.4822

TABLE 11

PRESENT VALUE

of $1 or £1 per year for **n** years at ——% interest, compounded annually.

n	5%	6%	7%	8%	10%	12%
1	.9524	.9434	.9346	.9259	.9091	.8929
2	1.8594	1.8334	1.8080	1.7833	1.7355	1.6901
3	2.7232	2.6730	2.6243	2.5771	2.4869	2.4018
4	3.5460	3.4651	3.3872	3.3121	3.1699	3.0373
5	4.3295	4.2124	4.1002	3.9927	3.7908	3.6048
6	5.0757	4.9173	4.7665	4.6229	4.3553	4.1114
7	5.7864	5.5824	5.3893	5.2064	4.8684	4.5638
8	6.4632	6.2098	5.9713	5.7466	5.3349	4.9676
9	7.1078	6.8017	6.5152	6.2469	5.7590	5.3282
10	**7.7217**	**7.3601**	**7.0236**	**6.7101**	**6.1446**	**5.6502**
11	8.3064	7.8869	7.4987	7.1390	6.4951	5.9377
12	8.8633	8.3838	7.9427	7.5361	6.8137	6.1944
13	9.3936	8.8527	8.3577	7.9038	7.1034	6.4235
14	9.8986	9.2950	8.7455	8.2442	7.3667	6.6282
15	10.3797	9.7122	9.1079	8.5595	7.6061	6.8109
16	10.8378	10.1059	9.4466	8.8514	7.8237	6.9740
17	11.2741	10.4773	9.7632	9.1216	8.0216	7.1196
18	11.6896	10.8276	10.0591	9.3719	8.2014	7.2497
19	12.0853	11.1581	10.3356	9.6036	8.3649	7.3658
20	**12.4622**	**11.4699**	**10.5940**	**9.8181**	**8.5136**	**7.4694**
21	12.8212	11.7641	10.8355	10.0168	8.6487	7.5620
22	13.1630	12.0416	11.0612	10.2007	8.7715	7.6446
23	13.4886	12.3034	11.2722	10.3711	8.8832	7.7184
24	13.7986	12.5504	11.4693	10.5288	8.9847	7.7843
25	14.0939	12.7834	11.6536	10.6748	9.0770	7.8431
26	14.3752	13.0032	11.8258	10.8100	9.1609	7.8957
27	14.6430	13.2105	11.9867	10.9352	9.2372	7.9426
28	14.8981	13.4062	12.1371	11.0511	9.3066	7.9844
29	15.1411	13.5907	12.2777	11.1584	9.3696	8.0218
30	**15.3725**	**13.7648**	**12.4090**	**11.2578**	**9.4269**	**8.0552**
31	15.5928	13.9291	12.5318	11.3498	9.4790	8.0850
32	15.8027	14.0840	12.6466	11.4350	9.5264	8.1116
33	16.0025	14.2302	12.7538	11.5139	9.5694	8.1354
34	16.1929	14.3681	12.8540	11.5869	9.6086	8.1566
35	16.3742	14.4982	12.9477	11.6546	9.6442	8.1755
36	16.5469	14.6210	13.0352	11.7172	9.6765	8.1924
37	16.7113	14.7368	13.1170	11.7752	9.7059	8.2075
38	16.8679	14.8460	13.1935	11.8289	9.7327	8.2210
39	17.0170	14.9491	13.2649	11.8786	9.7570	8.2330
40	**17.1591**	**15.0463**	**13.3317**	**11.9246**	**9.7791**	**8.2438**
41	17.2944	15.1380	13.3941	11.9672	9.7991	8.2534
42	17.4232	15.2245	13.4524	12.0067	9.8174	8.2619
43	17.5459	15.3062	13.5070	12.0432	9.8340	8.2696
44	17.6628	15.3832	13.5579	12.0771	9.8491	8.2764
45	17.7741	15.4558	13.6055	12.1084	9.8628	8.2825
46	17.8801	15.5244	13.6500	12.1374	9.8753	8.2880
47	17.9810	15.5890	13.6916	12.1643	9.8866	8.2928
48	18.0772	15.6500	13.7305	12.1891	9.8969	8.2972
49	18.1687	15.7076	13.7668	12.2122	9.9063	8.3010
50	**18.2559**	**15.7619**	**13.8007**	**12.2335**	**9.9148**	**8.3045**

TABLE 11 *(Continued)*

PRESENT VALUE

of $1 or £1 per year for **n** years at ——% interest, compounded annually.

n	14%	16%	18%	20%	25%	30%
1	.8772	.8621	.8475	.8333	.8000	.7692
2	1.6467	1.6052	1.5656	1.5278	1.4400	1.3609
3	2.3216	2.2459	2.1743	2.1065	1.9520	1.8161
4	2.9137	2.7982	2.6901	2.5887	2.3616	2.1662
5	3.4331	3.2743	3.1272	2.9906	2.6893	2.4356
6	3.8887	3.6847	3.4976	3.3255	2.9514	2.6427
7	4.2883	4.0386	3.8115	3.6046	3.1611	2.8021
8	4.6389	4.3436	4.0776	3.8372	3.3289	2.9247
9	4.9464	4.6065	4.3030	4.0310	3.4631	3.0190
10	**5.2161**	**4.8332**	**4.4941**	**4.1925**	**3.5705**	**3.0915**
11	5.4527	5.0286	4.6560	4.3271	3.6564	3.1473
12	5.6603	5.1971	4.7932	4.4392	3.7251	3.1903
13	5.8424	5.3423	4.9095	4.5327	3.7801	3.2233
14	6.0021	5.4675	5.0081	4.6106	3.8241	3.2487
15	6.1422	5.5755	5.0916	4.6755	3.8593	3.2682
16	6.2651	5.6685	5.1624	4.7296	3.8874	3.2832
17	6.3729	5.7487	5.2223	4.7746	3.9099	3.2948
18	6.4674	5.8178	5.2732	4.8122	3.9279	3.3037
19	6.5504	5.8775	5.3162	4.8435	3.9424	3.3105
20	**6.6231**	**5.9288**	**5.3527**	**4.8696**	**3.9539**	**3.3158**
21	6.6870	5.9731	5.3837	4.8913	3.9631	
22	6.7429	6.0113	5.4099	4.9094	3.9705	
23	6.7921	6.0442	5.4321	4.9245	3.9764	
24	6.8351	6.0726	5.4509	4.9371	3.9811	
25	6.8729	6.0971	5.4669	4.9476	3.9849	
26	6.9061	6.1182	5.4804	4.9563		
27	6.9352	6.1364	5.4919	4.9636		
28	6.9607	6.1520	5.5016	4.9697		
29	6.9830	6.1656	5.5098	4.9747		
30	**7.0027**	**6.1772**	**5.5168**	**4.9789**		
31	7.0199	6.1872	5.5227			
32	7.0350	6.1959	5.5277			
33	7.0482	6.2034	5.5320			
34	7.0599	6.2098	5.5356			
35	7.0700	6.2153	5.5386			
36	7.0790	6.2201				
37	7.0868	6.2242				
38	7.0937	6.2278				
39	7.0997	6.2309				
40	**7.1050**	**6.2335**				
41	7.1097					
42	7.1138					
43	7.1173					
44	7.1205					
45	7.1232					
46	7.1256					
47	7.1277					
48	7.1296					
49	7.1312					
50	**7.1327**					

TABLE 11 *(Concluded)*

where V_p is the present value,

> r is the "safe rate" on redemption of capital
> r' is the "speculative rate" to the purchaser on redemption of capital
> n is the number of years of life.

The basis of the formula is that each installment of annual earnings consist of two parts: (1) an interest payment to the investor and (2) a return of part of his capital, which might then be reinvested at compound interest to build up a "redemption fund." Since money invested in a mining enterprise is subject to a decidedly higher risk than money invested in government bonds or placed in a savings bank, the formula embodies two rates of interest, r, a relatively low "safe rate" and r', a relatively high "risk rate" or "speculative rate."

Mining companies no longer provide so thoughtfully for their stockholders' future and, in fact, the average mining investor prefers to take his full dividend and either reinvest it himself or spend it as his fancy dictates. But if he is discerning, he understands that he will get his money back in the form of dividends or not at all and that part of his dividend is not real earnings but a return of capital which he may if he likes put into a redemption fund. That the flesh-and-blood investor does not dutifully set apart the appropriate portion of dividends and invest it safely does not mar the logic of the theory. The fact is that the Hoskold principle is a recognized standard which valuation engineers understand and many taxation authorities accept. Tables based on it are widely published [17] and are readily available for quick calculation (Table 12). Several criticisms and refinements of the Hoskold formula have been offered,[18] but the figures of the original tables are still the ones in common use.

The *"safe rate"* in common use when Hoskold's tables were pub-

---

[17] Grimes, John Alden, and Craigue, William Horace, *Principles of Valuation*, p. 46. New York: Prentice-Hall, Inc., 1928.

Hoover, Herbert C., *Principles of Mining*, pp. 46–48. New York: Hill Publishing Co., 1909.

Baxter, Charles H., and Parks, Roland D., *Mine Examination and Valuation*, pp. 228 ff. Houghton: Mich. College of Mines and Technology, 1933.

[18] O'Donahue, T. A., The valuation of mineral properties: *Institution of Mining Engrs.*, vol. 32, p. 399, 1906. Notes on the valuation of mineral properties, *Institution of Mining Engrs.*, vol. 43, p. 19, 1912. O'Donahue's criticism is in regard to deferment. He maintains that although the capital should pay the risk rate during the period of deferment, the interest should be compounded not at the risk rate but at the safe rate.

Morkill, D. B., Formulas for mine values: *Mining & Scientific Press*, vol. 117, p. 276, 1918. Morkill maintains that the investor is not entitled to a risk rate on all of his investment during the entire life of the mine. The risk rate should apply only to that portion of the capital which has not yet been returned.

lished was 3%, but since the beginning of the present century 4% has been widely used. It is true that, in view of present bond yields, 2% might be more realistic, but the rate is, in a sense theoretical, and 4% has been used so long that it is still very commonly employed for purposes of comparison though not necessarily as a basis for an actual cash transaction.

The *"risk rate"* varies with the type of mine and must be determined largely by the judgment of the engineer or the investor. An equity in any business venture faces a greater danger of loss than does the purchase of high-grade bonds and is, therefore, entitled to a higher rate of interest. The average mining investment should yield a still higher rate. Although some mines are no more hazardous than sound industrial enterprises, others, particularly those whose developed ore reserves are limited, involve a large element of risk over and above the normal uncertainties of markets and costs. Herbert Hoover [19] writes, "Mining business is one where 7% above provision for capital return is an absolute minimum demanded by the risks inherent in mines, even where the profit in sight gives warranty to the return of capital." At a later date, Theodore Hoover [20] said, "To be satisfied with less than 10 per cent annually would show a lack of acumen, and a much higher rate would not be exorbitant for most mining ventures." When the copper companies were revalued as of 1913 to establish depletion for taxation purposes, the Bureau of Internal Revenue, then interested in a low valuation, maintained that an appropriate risk rate should be at least 10%,[21] although the large copper mines especially the porphyry coppers, are among the least hazardous of mining ventures. As bank interest at the time of the discussions was about 5%, this meant that the Bureau considered relatively safe mining ventures as entitled to a risk rate 5% higher than bank interest. With the lowering of interest rates all along the line in recent years, it might be logical to use lower rates than those recommended in the first quarter of the century. Nevertheless, 8% is a figure still widely used and 6% would still seem low for the most stable mining business. These considerations apply merely to the risk rate for use in the Hoskold formula; the total annual income to which a mining investment is entitled should, of course, be very considerably higher because it includes return of capital, but this consideration finds separate expression in the formula.

[19] Hoover, Herbert C., *Principles of Mining,* page 43. New York: Hill Publishing Co., 1909.
[20] Hoover, Theodore Jesse, *The Economics of Mining,* p. 154. Stanford: Stanford University Press, 1933.
[21] Copper Producers Tax Committee, "Factors for Determining Copper Mine Values," Brief to Internal Revenue Bureau, 1926. Privately printed. p. 80.

"HOSKOLD TABLES"

Present value of $1 or £1 per year for *n* years allowing interest to purchaser at ——% and redemption of capital at 2%

n	3%	4%	5%	6%	7%	8%	9%	10%	12%	15%
1	.9701	.9615	.9524	.9434	.9346	.9259	.9174	.9091	.8929	.8696
2	1.9046	1.8690	1.8347	1.8016	1.7698	1.7390	1.7093	1.6805	1.6529	1.5503
3	2.8030	2.7266	2.6542	2.5856	2.5204	2.4585	2.3995	2.3433	2.2384	2.0975
4	3.6681	3.5383	3.4174	3.3044	3.1987	3.0996	3.0064	2.9187	2.7577	2.5470
5	4.5013	4.3074	4.1295	3.9657	3.8145	3.6743	3.5541	3.4228	3.2035	2.9226
6	5.3043	5.0371	4.7956	4.5761	4.3759	4.1924	4.0237	3.8681	3.5903	3.2412
7	6.0786	5.7303	5.4197	5.1411	4.8897	4.6617	4.4541	4.2642	3.9281	3.5148
8	6.8255	6.3894	6.0057	5.6654	5.3617	5.0888	4.8424	4.6187	4.2281	3.7522
9	7.5463	7.0168	6.5567	6.1533	5.7966	5.4790	5.1944	4.9379	4.4940	3.9601
10	8.2422	7.6151	7.0758	6.0825	6.1986	5.8368	5.5149	5.2267	4.7320	4.1438
12	9.5639	8.7291	8.0283	7.4316	6.9175	6.4700	6.0768	5.7287	5.1398	4.4532
15	11.3863	10.2223	9.2742	8.4872	7.8232	7.2556	6.7648	6.3361	5.6235	4.8117
18	13.0375	11.5338	10.3410	9.3719	8.5688	7.8925	7.3152	6.8165	5.9987	5.0838
20	14.0535	12.3218	10.9701	9.8856	8.9963	8.2537	7.6245	7.0843	6.2051	5.2313
25	16.3344	14.0410	12.3122	10.9624	9.8794	8.9911	8.2494	7.6207	6.2129	5.5181
30	18.2983	15.4679	13.2959	11.8133	10.5652	9.5557	8.7222	8.0224	6.9132	5.7257
40	21.4797	17.6818	15.0250	13.0623	11.5532	10.3567	9.3847	8.5796	7.3230	6.0040
50	23.9102	19.2964	16.1751	13.9231	12.2215	10.8905	9.8210	8.9427	8.5859	6.1796

TABLE 12

Present value of $1 or £1 per year for **n** years allowing

n	3%	4%	5%	6%	7%	8%	9%
1	.9709	.9615	.9524	.9434	.9346	.9259	.9174
2	1.9135	1.8775	1.8429	1.8096	1.7774	1.7464	1.7164
3	2.8286	2.7508	2.6772	2.6074	2.5411	2.4781	2.4182
4	3.7171	3.5839	3.4599	3.3442	3.2360	3.1345	3.0393
5	4.5797	4.3792	4.1954	4.0265	3.8706	3.7264	3.5925
6	5.4172	5.1388	4.8876	4.6599	4.4524	4.2626	4.0883
7	6.2303	5.8649	5.5400	5.2492	4.9874	4.7505	4.5350
8	7.0197	6.5593	6.1555	5.7986	5.4808	5.1960	4.9393
9	7.7861	7.2237	6.7370	6.3118	5.9370	5.6043	5.3069
10	8.5302	7.8597	7.2870	6.7921	6.3601	5.9798	5.6424
12	9.9540	9.0529	8.3014	7.6651	7.1194	6.6462	6.2320
15	11.9379	10.6648	9.6370	8.7899	8.0797	7.4757	6.9557
18	13.7535	12.0906	10.7865	9.7363	8.8724	8.1494	7.5353
20	14.8775	12.9507	11.4658	10.2864	9.3270	8.5313	7.8607
25	17.4132	14.8307	12.9152	11.4380	10.2640	9.3086	8.5159
30	19.6004	16.3883	14.0807	12.3427	10.9867	9.8991	9.0074
40	23.1148	18.7750	15.8072	13.6496	12.0102	10.7224	9.6841
50	25.7298	20.4643	16.9879	14.5211	12.6798	11.2530	10.1148

TABLE 12

Present value of $1 or £1 per year for **n** years allowing

n	4%	5%	6%	7%	8%	9%
1	.9615	.9524	.9434	.9346	.9259	.9174
2	1.8861	1.8512	1.8175	1.7859	1.7538	1.7236
3	2.7751	2.7002	2.6292	2.5618	2.4978	2.4370
4	3.6299	3.5027	3.3842	3.2735	3.1697	3.0723
5	4.4518	4.2621	4.0879	3.9273	3.7789	3.6413
6	5.2421	4.9810	4.7447	4.5298	4.3335	4.1531
7	6.0021	5.6622	5.3588	5.0865	4.8400	4.6166
8	6.7327	6.3080	5.9337	5.6014	5.3043	5.0371
9	7.4353	6.9208	6.4728	6.0794	5.7309	5.4203
10	8.1109	7.5204	6.9788	6.5235	6.1240	5.7707
12	9.3851	8.5798	7.9019	7.3233	6.8235	6.3874
15	11.1184	10.0059	9.0958	8.3374	7.6958	7.1459
18	12.6593	11.2368	10.1017	9.1749	8.4038	7.7523
20	13.5903	11.9643	10.6858	9.6542	8.8042	8.0918
25	15.6221	13.5113	11.9031	10.6369	9.6143	8.7710
30	17.2920	14.7427	12.8485	11.3856	10.2218	9.2738
40	19.7928	16.5225	14.1797	12.4187	11.0469	9.9479
50	21.4822	17.6834	15.0263	13.0633	11.5540	10.3573

TABLE 12

TABLES"

interest to purchaser at ———% and redemption of capital at **3%**

10%	11%	12%	15%	18%	20%	25%	n
.9091	.9009	.8929	.8696	.8475	.8333	.8000	1
1.6874	1.6594	1.6324	1.5562	1.4867	1.4438	1.3466	2
2.3611	2.3066	2.2546	2.1118	1.9860	1.9101	1.7436	3
2.9496	2.8651	2.7853	2.5705	2.3865	2.2778	2.0449	4
3.4680	3.3517	3.2430	2.9555	2.7148	2.5750	2.2813	5
3.9278	3.7793	3.6417	3.2830	2.9887	2.8201	2.4716	6
4.3383	4.1579	3.9919	3.5650	3.2205	3.0257	2.6281	7
4.7068	4.4953	4.3019	3.8102	3.4193	3.2004	2.7590	8
5.0395	4.7977	4.5780	4.0252	3.5915	3.3508	2.8700	9
5.3410	**5.0702**	**4.8255**	**4.2153**	**3.7421**	**3.4815**	**2.9653**	**10**
5.8664	5.5413	5.2504	4.5359	3.9926	3.6974	3.1205	12
6.5034	6.1063	5.7548	4.9076	4.2778	3.9406	3.2920	15
7.0073	6.5484	6.1460	5.1892	4.4902	4.1202	3.4164	18
7.2878	**6.7928**	**6.3607**	**5.3414**	**4.6037**	**4.2156**	**3.4817**	**20**
7.8476	7.2765	6.7830	5.6361	4.8210	4.3970	3.6045	25
8.2631	7.6325	7.0912	5.8473	4.9746	4.5245	3.6898	30
8.8291	8.1128	7.5040	6.1251	5.1743	4.6891	3.7985	40
9.1856	**8.4129**	**7.7600**	**6.2946**	**5.2948**	**4.7878**	**3.8630**	**50**

(Continued)

TABLES"

interest to purchaser at ———% and redemption of capital at **4%**

10%	12%	15%	18%	20%	25%	n
.9091	.8929	.8696	.8475	.8333	.8000	1
1.6944	1.6388	1.5620	1.4921	1.4489	1.3510	2
2.3790	2.2709	2.1261	1.9986	1.9218	1.7533	3
2.9807	2.8130	2.5941	2.4068	2.2963	2.0598	4
3.5134	3.2827	2.9884	2.7425	2.5999	2.3008	5
3.9878	3.6933	3.3249	3.0233	2.8509	2.4952	6
4.4129	4.0550	3.6152	3.2615	3.0618	2.6553	7
4.7955	4.3758	3.8681	3.4659	3.2412	2.7892	8
5.1416	4.6622	4.0901	3.6431	3.3957	2.9028	9
5.4558	**4.9191**	**4.2865**	**3.7981**	**3.5299**	**3.0004**	**10**
6.0041	5.3604	4.6178	4.0559	3.7516	3.1590	12
6.6693	5.8844	5.0015	4.3489	4.0009	3.3340	15
7.1946	6.2896	5.2912	4.5663	4.1242	3.4603	18
7.4861	**6.5112**	**5.4472**	**4.6820**	**4.2812**	**3.5263**	**20**
8.0637	6.9438	5.7467	4.9017	4.4640	3.6495	25
8.4868	7.2553	5.9585	5.0548	4.5907	3.7337	30
9.0479	7.6615	6.2296	5.2487	4.7501	3.8384	40
9.3852	**7.9020**	**6.3877**	**5.3605**	**4.8414**	**3.8979**	**50**

(Continued)

"HOSKOLD TABLES"

Present value of $1 or £1 per year for **n** years allowing interest to purchaser at ——% and redemption of capital at 5%

n	6%	7%	8%	9%	10%	12%	15%	18%	20%	25%
1	.9434	.9346	.9259	.9174	.9091	.8929	.8696	.8475	.8333	.8000
2	1.8334	1.8004	1.7685	1.7378	1.7081	1.6517	1.5737	1.5028	1.4589	1.3597
3	2.6730	2.6034	2.5374	2.4746	2.4148	2.3036	2.1547	2.0238	1.9451	1.7727
4	3.4651	3.3491	3.2405	3.1388	3.0433	2.8687	2.6414	2.4474	2.3332	2.0895
5	4.2124	4.0421	3.8851	3.7398	3.6049	3.3625	3.0544	2.7980	2.6497	2.3397
6	4.9173	4.6869	4.4770	4.2852	4.1091	3.7970	3.4088	3.0925	2.9124	2.5422
7	5.5824	5.2872	5.0217	4.7816	4.5634	4.1817	3.7156	3.3430	3.1335	2.7090
8	6.2098	5.8467	5.5238	5.2346	4.9742	4.5242	3.9835	3.5583	3.3219	2.8487
9	6.8017	6.3685	5.9872	5.6490	5.3470	4.8304	4.2190	3.7450	3.4841	2.9672
10	7.3601	6.8555	6.4157	6.0289	5.6861	5.1055	4.4274	3.9083	3.6249	3.0687
12	8.3838	7.7353	7.1799	6.6990	6.2784	5.5780	4.7784	4.1793	3.8569	3.2333
15	9.7122	8.8525	8.1325	7.5209	6.9948	6.1364	5.1823	4.4851	4.1159	3.4134
18	10.8276	9.7698	8.9002	8.1728	7.5554	6.5636	5.4838	4.7091	4.3037	3.5416
20	11.4699	10.2897	9.3297	8.5335	7.8626	6.7942	5.6438	4.8266	4.4017	3.6077
25	12.7834	11.3344	10.1805	9.2399	8.4583	7.2345	5.9444	5.0447	4.5824	3.7282
30	13.7648	12.0994	10.7934	9.7419	8.8771	7.5387	6.1482	5.1908	4.7025	3.8074
40	15.0463	13.0785	11.5658	10.3668	9.3931	7.9075	6.3913	5.3630	4.8435	3.8992
50	15.7619	13.6158	11.9840	10.7016	9.6670	8.1008	6.5170	5.4512	4.9154	3.9456

TABLE 12 (Continued)

"HOSKOLD TABLES"

Present value of $1 or £1 per year for *n* years allowing interest to purchaser at ——% and redemption of capital at 6%

n	5%	6%	7%	8%	9%	10%	12%	15%	18%	20%	25%
1	.9524	.9434	.9346	.9259	.9174	.9091	.8929	.8696	.8475	.8333	.8000
2	1.8594	1.8255	1.7927	1.7612	1.7307	1.7012	1.6453	1.5679	1.4974	1.4539	1.3554
3	2.7232	2.6510	2.5826	2.5175	2.4557	2.3969	2.2872	2.1404	2.0112	1.9335	1.7630
4	3.5460	3.4245	3.3111	3.2050	3.1055	3.0119	2.8408	2.6177	2.4271	2.3148	2.0746
5	4.3295	4.1498	3.9845	3.8318	3.6904	3.5590	3.3225	3.0214	2.7703	2.6248	2.3203
6	5.0757	4.8305	4.6079	4.4049	4.2191	4.0483	3.7451	3.3668	3.0579	2.8817	2.5188
7	5.7863	5.4699	5.1862	4.9305	4.6988	4.4879	4.1182	3.6654	3.3023	3.0977	2.6823
8	6.4632	6.0708	5.7234	5.4135	5.1355	4.8846	4.4499	3.9258	3.5122	3.2817	2.8191
9	7.1078	6.6362	6.2231	5.8586	5.5344	5.2441	4.7463	4.1548	3.6943	3.4401	2.9352
10	7.7217	7.1682	6.6888	6.2694	5.8995	5.5709	5.0124	4.3572	3.8535	3.5778	3.0349
12	8.8632	8.1416	7.5287	7.0015	6.5434	6.1416	5.4697	4.6987	4.1182	3.8048	3.1967
15	10.3797	9.4036	8.5953	7.9150	7.3345	6.8333	6.0117	5.0931	4.4181	4.0594	3.3745
18	11.6896	10.4661	9.4745	8.6545	7.9652	7.3776	6.4290	5.3895	4.6394	4.2455	3.5021
20	12.4622	11.0812	9.9758	9.0709	8.3165	7.6780	6.6559	5.5481	4.7564	4.3432	3.5683
25	14.0939	12.3529	10.9948	9.9057	9.0129	8.2677	7.0946	5.8496	4.9763	4.5259	3.6907
30	15.3724	13.3242	11.7576	10.5206	9.5191	8.6918	7.4046	6.0587	5.1269	4.6500	3.7729
40	17.1591	14.6460	12.7750	11.3278	10.1752	9.2355	7.7956	6.3180	5.3113	4.8013	3.8718
50	18.2559	15.4376	13.3731	11.7957	10.5511	9.5441	8.0143	6.4609	5.4119	4.8834	3.9250

TABLE 12 (*Concluded*)

With very speculative mining ventures the risk rate should perhaps be 25%, 50%, or even higher, but since the Hoskold formula loses its significance in such cases, it is sounder to value mines of this type by applying a "discount for hazard," as explained in a later section.

Comparison of Methods

Estimates of present value by the two methods—the annuity formula and the Hoskold formula—depend on dissimilar modes of approach and consequently will not give identical results unless all of the interest rates are purposely chosen so as to make the final figures identical. For example, the present value of $1.00 a year for 20 years at 8% and 4% (Hoskold formula) is $8.80. The annuity method would give the same present value if the interest rate were taken at about 9½%. For a longer life the equivalent rate by the annuity method would be lower.

The annuity concept is the simpler of the two and is satisfactory for most purposes. The Hoskold principle, however, calls attention to the fact that a mine is a "wasting asset" and permits comparison between mining investments and industrial securities or government bonds.

Discount for Hazard

Using a speculative interest rate in the Hoskold formula takes care of the normal risk in a reasonably well-established mining venture. But when the future of a mine depends largely on finding new ore which may or may not prove to exist, or on any other highly uncertain factor, an appropriate risk rate would be so high that the Hoskold valuation would lose most of its meaning. In such cases, and they are common, it is more reasonable to estimate the present value (without attempting to be more precise than the data warrant) on the assumption that a continuing ore supply will be available, and then discount the present value by whatever factor seems appropriate to the hazard involved. The hazard factor is by its nature a matter of opinion, but since it usually depends on geological conditions, the geologist should be the person best qualified to make an enlightened guess. He may reach his opinion through some such mode of reasoning as this: "I cannot be sure that any ore will be found below the present deepest level. But from my experience and from what is known of ore deposits of this type I consider it probable that more ore will be found. I can state the probability in this way: If you were operating a hundred properties of this type I would expect that in twenty of them you would find that the ore continued. While this particular property might or might not be one of the twenty you would come out with a profit from your hundred properties if you valued them all on this basis."

If the geologist considers, then, that there is one chance in five that his guess will turn out to be correct, he divides the present value of profits by five in arriving at his valuation. Often there is reason to apply more than one risk factor to the same mine. It may appear, for example, that there are nine chances in ten that 100,000 tons of ore, estimated as proved, will yield the profits that are assigned to it. Beyond this, it may appear that there is one chance in two of developing 150,000 tons and one chance in 10 of developing a still further 200,000 tons. In this case the present value of the proved ore is multiplied by 9/10, the value of the next 150,000 tons by ½ and the value of the final 200,000 tons by 1/10.

To set down calculations of this sort in a report might mislead the reader into believing that the estimate is more precise than it can actually be, but the geologist's mental process is based, whether consciously or not, on some such train of reasoning.

Deferment

The figures of the basic valuation tables assume that the first installment of income will be available a year hence. But in many cases some time must elapse before operations begin. If the plans call for a development campaign or for building a plant, production may not start for one, two, or three years, and, even then, income will not be available until working capital has built up to a safe level. This consideration may be introduced into the valuation by first calculating the present value just as though profitable production were to begin immediately, and then discounting this value by compound interest for two years or whatever period will intervene. Special tables are published incorporating "years deferment" into the valuation.

Summary

The steps in valuing an operating mine may be summarized as follows:

1. Calculate the ore reserve and grade as sampled.
2. From the sampled grade, calculate the mill-head grade, allowing for dilution.
3. Using mill-head grade and percentage of recovery, calculate the content of metal recovered per ton of ore.
3a. If the product is sold in the form of concentrate, calculate the "smelter liquidation value" of the ore.

4. Estimate the operating cost. This includes cost of:
   Mining the ore
   Milling the ore
   Freight on metal or concentrate (unless deducted in 3a)
   Development cost
   Maintenance of plant and equipment

It should not include depletion, nor should it include depreciation except insofar as this item is represented by plant maintenance.

Taxes, insurance and overhead are usually estimated at a later stage in the calculation and deducted from profit, since they do not vary directly with the tonnage. They are nevertheless a part of cost and it may be convenient to include them here.

5. Subtract cost from revenue to obtain profit per ton.
6. Estimate probable rate of production in tons per year and multiply by the profit per ton to obtain annual profit.
7. Divide ore reserves by annual production to obtain life of ore reserves.
8. Discount annual profits to obtain present value of future annual profits.
9. Estimate ultimate tonnage that may be expected beyond present reserves and discount this to present value.
10. Assume a factor expressing the probability that the tonnage estimated in (9) will be found and multiply it by the present value of such ore (9 × 10).
11. Add present value of developed ore and present value of potential ore (8 plus 10).
12. Having determined the present value of the ore reserves, deduct from it the present value of the first cost of the plant.
13. If production is not to begin immediately, apply a discount for deferment.

Naturally there are various ways of achieving the same results that the steps just outlined are intended to accomplish; this procedure is merely one of a number that might be used.

Valuation of Prospects

Purpose of Valuation

Most prospect examinations are undertaken in order to decide whether or not to spend money on a property. The expenditure may include purchase money, cost of development and cost of building a plant when and if sufficient ore is assured. Not all of these expenditures come due at once, and contracts are usually so arranged that the investor may abandon the venture at any stage with no further obligation. If the prospect is under development, new information bearing on the value of the property will come to light from time to time, hence a new or revised estimate may be advisable each time a fresh installment of expenditure is faced, thus disclosing any outlay which is out of line with what the mine may ultimately be worth and the odds that it will turn out favorably.

An accurate and precise valuation is desirable if enough facts are available. But if they are not (and usually they are not) the valuation may consist merely of a mental calculation or a few figures set down in a notebook for the examiner's own guidance. Whether the computations be exact or rough, the recognized methods of mine valuation should be the guide.

Methods of Valuation

So far as general principles are concerned, the valuation of a prospect is carried out in the same way as the valuation of an operating mine; in practice the difference is largely a matter of emphasis. In the prospect, where the amount of developed ore may be small or negligible, the emphasis is likely to be on the value of undiscovered or undeveloped ore. This value is largely a matter of judgment in assigning the values to two large unknown quantities: (1) the amount and value of ore that may be expected in the event of success and (2) the discount for hazard, which depends on the probability of finding this ore.

The element of judgment is so important that the job of appraising a prospect is one for a man of the greatest possible experience. Such work is too often entrusted to a young and unseasoned engineer who either becomes discouraged too quickly by the lack of developed ore or else lets his imagination run wild to picture enormous potential ore reserves in a setting that is not appropriate for them. As Locke says, "judging a prospect is indeed a precarious task; there is scarcely another in engineering with fewer rules to guide and more alternatives from which to choose; and scarcely another so tempting to the dreamer, nor in practice, so abandoned to rules of thumb." [22]

Factors in Valuation

Profit

The factors used in calculation are the same as for operating mines: annual profit, life, risk rate or discount for hazard, and capital expenditure. Profit, of course, is a prime consideration; if the difference between revenue and costs will clearly be on the red side of the ledger, the question of tonnage will be of no significance, for a negative quantity multiplied by any number, however large, is still negative. At the

[22] Locke, Augustus, *Leached Outcrops as Guides to Copper Ore*, page 1. Baltimore: Williams and Wilkins Co., 1926.

same time, the economies in large-scale production will not be overlooked in case there is a chance of a really huge tonnage. Because of
the difference between a mine and a prospect, some of the factors deserve special comment.

Revenue

Revenue depends, of course, on the grade of the ore, the proportion
of metal that is recoverable, and the sales price of the product. If most
of the ore is still to be developed, the grade has to be a guess based on
the sampling of such ore as has been found and on the grade of other
ore in the district. Assuming a given tenor, you can predict the recovery and the grade of the concentrate with sufficient accuracy for preliminary purposes if you have a working knowledge of mineralogy and
of metallurgical processes (see Chapter 22). The sales price of the
product depends on the same considerations as those for an operating
mine. Other deductions from gross revenue—charges for transportation and smelting—may be ascertained by making the necessary inquiries from reliable sources.

Costs

In a new prospect, costs are not a matter of record as they would be
in an operating mine. In forecasting them there are two avenues of
approach; one is by detailed estimate, the other is by comparison.

The *detailed estimate* is the method usually employed by engineers,
particularly at the stage when plans for operation are well advanced.
The method consists of setting down all prospective items of operating
expenditure per day, per month, or per year, adding them up and dividing by the proposed rate of production. No method is more accurate than this if it is correctly carried out. But in order to carry it
out properly one must be able to anticipate all items of expenditure
and to estimate correctly the amount of each item. This can be done
only by an engineer of long experience. The inexperienced man is
sure to omit some important item which will turn up in the accounts
at some embarrassing later stage. Nor is it sound to estimate the costs
and then add 50 or 100 percent for contingencies. If the estimate is
so inaccurate, one might as well guess at the costs in the first place.

Particularly unreliable are cost estimates of this sort prepared by
prospectors or promoters who are unaccustomed to sizable operations.
A "leaser" may know quite accurately how many tons a man can get
out in a day, but he is almost certain to overlook the necessity for clerks,
engineers, and assayers, and for depreciation, fire insurance and a hun-

dred and one other small items that go to make up a sizable charge for overhead expense.

Although the necessity for a detailed estimate has to be faced sooner or later, the geologist, in the course of his preliminary size-up, will do better to use the *comparison method*. This means finding out what the costs are in nearby operations or, if there are no operating mines in the district, reviewing the costs in similar mines elsewhere. By fixing in his mind the operating costs in the successive mines that he sees in the course of his work, the geologist can build up a series of standards to which he can compare new operations. He will need, of course, to make adjustments and modifications to take account of special local conditions. The most important variables are:

Width of vein and physical nature of the ore (since these factors determine the mining method that can be used).
Hardness of the ore and consequent cost of drilling and breaking.
Nature of the ground as determining necessity of timbering.
Depth from which the ore has to be hoisted.
Amount of water to be pumped.
Local wage rates.
Power costs.
Cost of transportation, not only for the product from mine to market but for incoming supplies and equipment.
Taxes.

All of these factors may vary within rather wide limits, but the chance for serious error here is outweighed by uncertainties in estimating development costs, especially for small orebodies.

Table 13 is a tabulation of the cost of mining by various methods based on a series of articles by M. J. Elsing.[23] In adapting these figures to the present purpose, development costs are excluded, since they depend not so much on the method of mining as on the size, shape and spacing of the orebodies, and should therefore be estimated separately. The usefulness of these figures is subject to certain reservations: (1) They represent costs in the interwar period; post-war costs are likely to be higher. (2) They represent, for the most part, relatively large mines. (3) They are for the United States; where wages are higher but other costs lower, as a rule, than in most other countries.

Development Costs. The cost of orefinding is too often overlooked or lightly dismissed. Many a small mine has paid handsomely as long as it was in ore but when the known ore was exhausted the search for

[23] Elsing, M. J., Summary of the cost of mining, E. & M. J., vol. 133, p. 611, 1932. Also articles on costs by individual method, same vol., pp. 161, 323, 376, and 521.

the next orebody has consumed the profits from the last bonanza.   Thus the mine has struggled along with no consistent profit until an unusually wide interval between oreshoots has finally put the operation literally on the rocks.   If a mine is to be successful in the long run, the

TABLE 13

Mining Costs in the United States
(Data from Elsing [24])

Method of Stoping	Cost of Stoping per Ton		Total Mining Costs ex-Development per Ton
	Range	Average	Average
Caving	$ .14– .34	$ .23	$ .58
Open Stoping (Tri-State)	.37– .60	.50	.82
Sublevel Caving	.52– .60	.56	1.03
Top Slicing			
Iron Country	.63– .66	.65	.98
Western	.82–1.89	1.15	1.52
Shrinkage	1.28–2.74	1.46	1.74
Cut and Fill	1.16–2.98	1.84	2.92
Square Set	1.63–3.50	2.28	3.45

expenditure for development, year in and year out, must be well within the operating margin.   Development cost per ton mined is not subject to estimate from past records, as it would be in an operating mine, but depends largely on the probable size, shape, and spacing of the expected orebodies.   For ore that has not yet been found, these factors are unknown; but the geologist should be in a better position than anyone else to estimate them, since they depend on geological conditions.

If the prospect is an old mine and the upper levels have been worked in the past, the ratio of stoped to unstoped ground will often be the best available guide, although one must make due allowance, of course, for any geological changes in depth, such as downward decline in secondary enrichment, changes in structure, and difference in favorability of wall rock.

Example: Let us say that a vein has an average width of five feet, that in the old workings 25% of the length of the orebearing zone was of

24 Elsing, M. J., Summary of the cost of mining, E. & M. J., vol. 133, p. 611, 1932.   Also articles on costs by individual methods, same vol., pp. 161, 323, 376, 521 and 573.

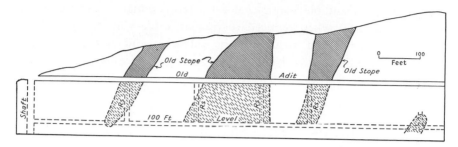

Fig. 146—Estimation of probable development footage based on size and distribution of ore-shoots exposed on adit level. (Idealized diagram)

stoping grade, and that the length within which orebodies occur is one thousand feet. On this basis the future development cost would be estimated in the following manner:

$$\text{Ore on each level: } \frac{.25 \times 1000' \times 5' \times 100'}{12.5 \text{ cu. ft/ton}} = 10,000 \text{ tons}$$

Cost of developing each level:	Total	per Ton
Drifting: 1000 ft. @ $15	$15,000	1.50
Shaft-sinking: 100 ft. @ $75	7,500	.75
Raising (say 4 raises)	6,000	.60
Total	$28,500	2.85

In this case, the probable development cost, $2.85 per ton would be relatively high and might be almost as much as the direct mining cost.

Rate of Production

Rate of production, life and potential ore are interdependent, of course. But as explained earlier in this chapter, the most economical rate of production is usually determined by the rate at which ore can be developed. The daily rate for an underground mine can be taken, for purposes of rough calculation, as about half the number of tons per vertical foot; e.g., for 1000 tons per vertical foot, one 150-foot level or 150,000 tons can be developed in a year, and this would be enough to supply a mill having a capacity of 500 tons per day.

Life

Life is even more difficult to predict in a prospect than in an operating mine. In a prospect, however, there are so many other uncertain factors that an exact prediction of life is not essential unless there is reason to expect that the ore will bottom at shallow depth. If there is a reasonable chance that ore will be found to a depth of 1000 or 1500 feet, a life of ten years is a suitable assumption for a trial estimate.   Any earnings beyond this term, when reduced to present value and discounted for hazard, would not add greatly to the valuation and any danger of a shorter life can be covered by assuming an appropriate hazard factor.

Potential Ore

Just how large a mine any given prospect will grow to be is one of those uncertainties which add a fillip to the mining business.   But in spite of the fact that any prediction must necessarily be little more than an intelligent guess, it need not be, on the one hand, a vague expression in which all arabic numerals are cautiously avoided nor, on the other, a merely arbitrary figure picked out of the air; usually, one can at least set up some range of possibilities.   What is the smallest amount of ore that may reasonably be expected, and what is the largest tonnage that may ultimately be found?

Where the question is a matter of the ultimate size of a known ore-body, the extreme lower limit is automatically fixed; it is the tonnage of ore in sight.   An upper limit may usually be assigned with some degree of confidence.   If the ore is in a vein exposed on the surface, its width is ordinarily disclosed by trenching.   Longitudinally the ends of the ore may or may not have been reached.   If not, the maximum length is limited only by the nearest barren trench or other exposure on the prolongation of the vein, unless structural conditions impose more restricted limits.   If the full size at the surface has been determined, the information is very helpful, but it is not safe to assume that the size at depth will be the same.   It may be larger or smaller, depending chiefly on structural conditions.   At any rate, the probability of enhanced size at depth does not deserve much credit in a valuation unless it is based on definite geological indications.

The depth to which an orebody will extend is usually the most difficult matter to forecast; this problem has already been discussed in Chapter 15.   However, it is not always essential in the prospect stage to predict the ultimate depth.   If you feel confident of extension for a few hundred feet or if, on the contrary, you expect bottoming at very shallow depth, you can make a decision as to whether or not to recommend further development, even though there is no basis for forecasting the limit in more specific terms.

If there is a chance of additional orebodies, or if, for that matter, the prospect is one in which no ore has yet been discovered, the basis for an enlightened guess must be sought in the habitual size of deposits of the same genetic or structural class, the magnitude of known ore loci and especially the size of other ore deposits in the same district.   One would hardly be likely to base a valuation of a narrow gold-quartz vein on an assumed tonnage of ten million, nor, on the other hand attempt to value an expected one-per-cent porphyry copper deposit where there was room for no more than 100,000 tons.

Analogy to other deposits in the district will fail to provide a very definite index if the known deposits vary from small to large and from lean to rich.   But since small and lean deposits are much more common than large rich ones, the discount for hazard tends to compensate the uncertainty of dimensions and tenor.   If, in a given district, the chance of finding a ten-million-dollar orebody is reckoned as one in 400 and the chance of finding a $500,000 orebody is one in 20, the prospective values of both types when discounted for hazard are about the same.

Discount for Hazard

Assigning a discount for hazard is usually the critical factor in the valuation of a prospect, yet no definite rules or directions can be written. Although there are many sources of risk, the principal one depends on the probability (or improbability) of developing an adequate ore-supply.   The odds must be judged from the nature of the prospective ore deposit, the sharpness of local ore-guides, and the habits of the district, particularly the size and spacing of other known deposits.   If orebodies occur at intervals of a few hundred feet, the chance of finding ore on any limited group of claims is much better than it is if the orebodies are far between.   If many orebodies are known, the chances of finding new orebodies are good provided considerable ground within the mineralized area remains unexplored.   But if only one orebody has been found, the risk factor is much less favorable; for there is reason to fear that the lone body may be a freak and that no others exist.   Yet this is not necessarily damning, especially if little exploratory work has been done, for there must have been a moment in the history of such productive fields as Butte and Leadville when only one orebody was known.

Capital Investment

The capital investment consists of three elements: (1) the purchase price of the property, (2) the expense of developing enough ore to start production, and (3) the cost of equipping the mine to produce.   The purchase price will be evident from the agreement with the owner.   If there is no agreement, the chief purpose of the examination will be to determine the maximum that you can recommend paying; this involves solving the valuation problem in reverse, with cost of property as the unknown factor. The expense of development can be estimated by methods that already have been explained. Only the amount of development that is necessary to put the mine in production need be considered in estimating capital expenditure; once mining starts, further development, although chargeable to a capital account, is no longer part of the initial capital expenditure. For the capital cost of equipping for production, a good horseback figure is $1000 per ton of daily capacity. The actual expenditure may range from half this to twice this, depending on the size and nature of the plant. The equipment costs are highest where power, transportation routes, and living quarters have to be provided.

Examples of a Tentative Valuation

Let us assume that an orebody has been shown to contain 1000 tons per foot of depth and that an economical rate of operation is 500 tons per day. At this rate the costs are estimated at say $7.50 per ton and the revenue per ton at $13.00.

Revenue per ton	$ 13.00
Operating cost (including development, maintenance and taxes)	7.50
Profit per ton	$ 5.50
Annual operating profit (150,000 × $5.50)	$825,000
Present value of operating profits (factor, $1 per year for 10 years at 8% and 3% deferred two years, 5.1)	$4,200,000
Capital cost of equipment	500,000
Present value of est. earnings	3,700,000
Discounted for risk (factor taken at 30%)	1,110,000
or in round figures	$1,000,000

If the life had been taken at 15 years, the present value factor would have been 6.41 instead of 5.1. But in this case the risk factor would be higher; if it had been taken at 25% instead of 30%, the valuation would have been $1,119,900 or substantially the same as estimated before.

A more refined calculation might have taken into account the different degrees of risk for various lengths of life and might have made a distinction between the hazard of developing enough ore to justify equipping the mine for production and the risk after starting operations. The following calculation shows, however, that in the earlier stages of development, a computation that attempts to take these factors into account gains nothing in real accuracy, since the determining feature is the choice of risk factors, which are matters of personal judgment. It is also intended to show the absurdity of carrying such a calculation to six significant figures.

Annual operating profit, (as above)		$825,000
Present value as of date of starting operations:		
Present value of 3 years' profits (2.48)	2,046,000	
Discounted for risk (90%)		1,841,400
Present value of next 7 years' profits		
(3.50)	2,887,500	
Discounted for risk (60%)		1,732,500
Present value of 10 years life		3,573,900
Deferred 2 years (.857)		3,062,832
Less capital cost of equipment		500,000
		2,562,832
Present value, discounted for risk (40%)		1,025,133

Computation vs. Guess

Since so many of these factors have to be assumed and, particularly, since the risk factors are so largely a matter of personal judgment, one may pertinently ask: "Why bother to go through all this calculation? Why not guess the value and have done with the matter?" It is quite true that an engineer of long experience can set a reasonable value on a prospect by employing a species of intuition, but to those who have not acquired this sixth sense, a calculation is excellent mental discipline. A little arithmetic may serve to keep imagination within reasonable bounds. It may show that on no plausible assumption is the property worth the cost of testing or, on the contrary, it may indicate that with reasonably successful development the prospect has all the elements of an attractive gamble.

SELECTED REFERENCES

Mine Valuation

Baxter, Charles H. and Parks, Roland D., *Mine Examination and Valuation*, 2nd Edition. Houghton: Michigan College of Mines and Technology, 1939.

Louis, Henry, *Mineral Valuation*. London: Charles Griffith and Company, 1923.

Hoover, Herbert C., *Principles of Mining*. New York: McGraw-Hill Book Company, Incorporated, 1909.

Hoover, Theodore Jesse, *The Economics of Mining*. Stanford University Press, 1933.

Truscott, S. J., *Mine Economics*. London: Mining Publications, Limited, 1937.

Mining Costs

Croston, John J., Effect of revaluation on the gold mining industry, *American Institute of Mining and Metallurgical Engineers*, Technical Publication No. 709, 1936. World gold production costs, part 1, the Americas, *Mining and Metallurgy*, pp. 324–327, July, 1937.

Elsing, Morris J., (Series of articles on costs by various mining methods), *Engineering and Mining Journal*, vol. 133, p. 13, p. 79, p. 161, p. 323, p. 376, p. 521, p. 573; summary of the cost of mining, p. 611, 1932.

Finlay, John R., (revision by Notman, Arthur), Cost of Mining, in Peele's *Mining Engineer's Handbook*, 3rd Edition, pp. 21–03 to 21–41. New York: John Wiley and Sons, Incorporated, 1941.

Wright, C. W., *Mining Methods and Costs at Metal Mines of the United States*, U. S. Bureau of Mines Information Circular 6503, 1931. (See also numerous U. S. Bureau of Mines Information Circulars on individual mines and districts —consult U.S.B.M. Publication List).

19

Geological Work at an Operating Mine

What privilege it is for a geologist to live and wrestle for months and years with a tough problem, watching it forced by the steady penetration of underground workings, to yield and at last surrender, so that its inner secrets may be known.

—L. C. Graton [1]

Nearly all large mining companies and a great many small ones employ geologists, either as occasional consultants or as full-time members of their staffs. It might perhaps be expected that the extent to which any company utilizes geology would depend on the acuteness of its ore-finding problem. This is true in some degree, but it is not the only deciding factor.

Many mines with large reserves of ore and no immediate difficulties in developing more employ geological staffs—obviously not from motives of charity or sentiment—while other mines whose ore is scarce and hard to find seem to get along (not to their best advantage, geologists think) without geological advice.

Even though a mine may have no orefinding problems at the moment, the day is sure to come sooner or later when new orebodies will be needed. As Lindgren [2] said, "when the miner has an abundance of ore he gets along comfortably without the geologist, but when the ore resources grow slim, he calls the geologist forthwith." This is like postponing the call for a doctor until the patient is about to die. Too often a mine has passed maturity and faces the search for new ore only to find that the critical facts of ore occurrence have been stoped out along with the

---

[1] Graton, L. C., Ore deposits, *Geology, 1888–1938*, G.S.A. Fiftieth Anniversary Volume, 1941, p. 505.

[2] Lindgren, W., Research in processes of ore deposition: *Tr. A.I.M.E.*, vol. 76, p. 291, 1928.

ore itself and are preserved, if at all, only in the mind of a superannuated foreman.

Although this is to be expected in mines which have never employed a geologist, it is all too common where a geologist has been in residence but was either unaware of the advisability of keeping detailed records or was unsuccessful in convincing the management that his time would be well spent in doing so.

When, as it must to all mines, the day for shutting down finally comes, there should be good assurance that the pumps can be pulled without abandoning any worth-while chances of finding further ore. This is possible only when the problems of occurrence and genesis of the ore have been thoroughly investigated and subjected to the acid test of development during the era of operations.

"Theoretical" or "Practical"?

There are still a few mine superintendents who scorn a geologist as a theorist, capable, perhaps, of wisdom after the event but of little practical use when it comes to "putting ore in the box." Other executives, and their operating staffs as well, hold their geological departments in the highest respect and invariably consult them on all questions that have a geological aspect. The reason for these contrasting attitudes is usually to be sought in the personalities and attainments of the individuals who have personified geology on the local scene.

Two particular types of geologists very unlike in training and mental outlook have both, unfortunately, failed to win a high rating for the profession. The first of these, and he comes first because, historically, he was the first in the field, is the geologist of primarily scientific interests who writes imposing reports on the petrology, the stratigraphy, and even the origin of the ore but lacks either the quantitative type of mind or the practical mining experience to translate his ideas into tons of ore, percentage of metals, and feet of depth. He is capable of fulfilling a highly useful function, but only in partnership with an individual who can be called a mining geologist with the emphasis on the mining.

Contrasted with the "pure" scientist is the self-styled "practical" type of geologist who is content to log drill holes, put faults on the map, and direct the activities of the sampling crew. He knows little and cares less about theories of ore deposition, scorns as "long-haired geology" any speculation as to why the ore is where it is, and confines his recommendations to blind following of the vein or automatic riddling of the country with drill holes. His work could be done quite as effectively by any bright young engineer whose geological training was limited to a few undergraduate courses, all now forgotten except an ability to recognize the common minerals and put names on the more obvious rocks. Even so he is probably of more direct use than his more academic confrère, but both he and his employer probably fail to realize that they are getting and using only a small fraction of what geology has to offer.

The geologist who has earned the respect of the operating staff is likely to be a man who combines long underground experience with a broad scientific training. He is able to talk the miners' jargon and breathe in comfort the air of the underground workings (that unforgettable mixture of odors of rotting timber, acetylene, dynamite fumes, and strong tobacco smoke). He has developed the geological judgment that can be acquired only by visiting the working face every morning, guessing what it would look like after the next round and looking at it the following morning to see how badly he was in error. He has learned to see ore in terms of dollars per ton in a way that no one can do who has not had to request an appropriation to back his ideas and then watch the assay reports each night to find out whether he was courageous or just foolhardy. Yet all this experience, indispensible though it is, is little more than a seasoned mine captain has acquired. To it, the geologist adds the broader picture of ore occurrence and rock distribution gained by assembling the details into a unified set of plans and sections. These he interprets against the background of an understanding of geology that extends far beyond the platitudes of the classroom. Although he is thoroughly acquainted with traditional views, he does not hesitate to question the most cherished dogma of the science as soon as he finds it inconsistent with the clear testimony of the rocks. Yet he is not happy in rejecting it until he is able to offer instead an interpretation which is in accordance with proved principles of chemistry and physics, even though unorthodox geologically. Following a new idea through to its logical consequences and testing these against the observed facts is a trait which distinguishes a sound original thinker from a mere crackpot. In short, the truly practical geologist is a theorist and scientist in the highest senses of both terms.

PLACE OF GEOLOGISTS IN A MINING ORGANIZATION

In a mining company the stockholders are the owners of the corporation and the ultimate source of authority. The board of directors represents them and, while it decides questions of policy, especially financial policy, it delegates the responsibility for operations to a general manager or managing director who may make his headquarters at the home office (*e.g.*, New York, London, or Toronto) or at the principal scene of operations, depending on whether the company's activities are widespread or localized.   In any case there will be a man in local charge of operations, whether he is called the general manager or general superintendent. If he is responsible for milling and smelting as well as mining, he will have under him a mine superintendent.   The mine superintendent runs the mine, and his line of authority descends through the mine foremen and shift bosses to the miners and other "productive labor."

The point is that neither the resident geologist nor the consulting geologist (if there is one) appears in this line of authority.   Both are "staff officers," and their functions are advisory rather than administrative.   Strict observance of this principle may seem bureaucratic, but it will avoid no end of friction and jealousy.   The geologist's relations with the engineering department, the assay office, the foremen, the shift bosses and the miners will be close and he may make requests, explain his views and, when asked, proffer advice, but he must be careful not to give instructions, for to do so would be treading on the toes of the superintendent.   If the miner at the face says, "Shall I swing to the right or the left?" the geologist can talk the matter over with him, but his parting advice must be, "Do whatever the shift-boss says."

The Resident Geologist.   The exact place of the resident geologist in the flow-sheet of organization varies with different companies.   At some mines he is merely an assistant in the engineering department. This position is appropriate if the geologist is so young or irresponsible that he needs constant guidance, and it is moderately satisfactory if the chief engineer has at least a sufficient working knowledge of geology and appreciation of the geologist's methods to take full advantage of his findings and recommendations.   But unless the chief engineer is very understanding and co-operative, a mature geologist will not be happy, nor will he do his best work, under this arrangement.

More commonly the geological department has functions and independence parallel to that of the engineering department.   The geologist or (if there is more than one) the chief geologist, reports to the mine superintendent or directly to the general superintendent or general manager.   This is more satisfactory, at least from the geologist's point of view, for he can then talk to the man who has authority to give instructions, even though not all of his advice may be accepted.

Exceptionally, the engineering department, as well as the personnel concerned with sampling and exploratory drilling, are under the direction of the chief geologist.   This eliminates considerable duplication of functions and proves a happy arrangement provided the chief geologist is temperamentally suited to heavy administrative responsibilities (not all geologists are) and does not frustrate the ambitions of his subordinates.   In order that he may use his geological experience to best advantage, he must have sufficient assistance to relieve him of executive detail and allow him time for geological thinking.

The staff geologist lives at his mine—in fact, he almost lives *in* it. Until he knows every stope at least as intimately as does the mine foreman he cannot attain his maximum usefulness.

The Consulting Geologist.   Some companies employ consultants on occasion, to solve special problems; others retain them on a year-to-year basis to make regular visits to the mine where they hold frequent discussions with the operating and geological staffs.   The consulting geologist usually reports directly to the board of directors or to the general manager.   In some organizations the resident geologist is the immediate subordinate to the consultant, but usually this is not the case. The more usual arrangement whereby the resident geologist reports to the mine superintendent and is independent administratively of the consulting geologist might seem at first thought to create an awkward situation, but as a rule the relationship is amicable.   The resident looks up to an older and more experienced man and feels fortunate in having someone to appreciate his work and make constructive suggestions.   Indeed with this relationship the consultant may, in effect, tell the resident what to do and how to do it, yet he must be careful not to give formal instructions directly but instead allow them to come from the manager or superintendent (whichever is the geologist's immediate superior).

The resident geologist, in turn, must not abuse his close relationship with the consulting geologist (who may have the ear of the president and board of directors) by going over the head of the superintendent. If he cannot be loyal to his immediate superior he must be prepared to resign.

The consulting geologist is usually an alumnus of the hard school of underground mapping and drill-core logging that the staff geologist is going through, but unless he happens to have been brought up in the particular mine in question he can hardly be expected to know the orebodies as intimately as does the resident geologist.   Instead he contributes a background of broad geological experience that enables him to size up a situation quickly, suggest the most fruitful lines of investigation, and propose methods of attacking such problems as need to be solved.   In addition to his geological experience, he is likely to bring an acquaintance with the behavior-patterns of superintendents and boards of directors, for his job is not only scientific but diplomatic; often he has to act as a salesman of ideas and programs.

DUTIES OF STAFF GEOLOGISTS

Assembling Information

The geologists, whether the staff consists of one geologist or half a dozen, keep the mapping up to date and, in so doing, they study the sludge and core from exploratory drilling and plot the current assay returns on their geologic maps or on cover sheets to accompany them. In general, they compile and correlate all data regarding rocks, ore, and production that may have any possible geological significance.

Research

But the routine collection of data is only the foundation for the geologist's real work. He must fit facts together and interpret them in order to reveal a comprehensive picture of the ore occurrence. This task usually calls not only for three-dimensional analysis but for mineralogical and petrological investigation and, above all, for thinking constructively and testing the results of deduction.

In planning his work the geologist should strive to strike a proper balance between routine duties and scientific research. Although some men become so engrossed in the theoretical aspects of mine geology that they neglect opportunities to make themselves of immediate practical use, the more common failing is to allow daily routine to crowd out study and speculation on the broader problems of structure and ore deposition. Yet it is just these fundamental problems whose solution may in the long run prove of greatest importance to the future of the mine in leading to new ideas for major development projects. Moreover, it may benefit not only the mine itself but the science as a whole, for our ideas regarding ore deposition are greatly in need of the rigid testing and constructive revision which the men who live with the ore and follow its vagaries from day to day are in the best position to apply.

Cooperation with Operators

An enterprising geologist is always on the watch for ways in which he can be of genuine assistance to the operating staff. In some cases he can help them by supplying up-to-date maps showing the structure in relation to ore grades in drifts, raises, and stopes as well as his prediction as to conditions that will be encountered in new headings or on deeper levels. At Butte, "each mine is provided with a set of geologic maps that are posted at regular intervals.   In order to provide efficient service, the geologist is required to post these maps in pencil, based on his compass survey, as soon as the notes are taken instead of waiting for the monthly transit survey.   The pencil posting is erased when the final survey appears, but in the meantime the foreman has had the benefit of up-to-date information.   The same service is extended to the general superintendent."

Daily conversations with the foremen and the superintendent, in the office or underground, keep the geologist in touch with what is going on and what is planned and, at the same time, enable him to convey to the operators his understanding of the relations of geological features to mining and development.   To do so in a tactful and friendly way, preserving mutual respect and avoiding any semblance of patronizing or lecturing is an art not learned in technical courses but very essential to smooth cooperation.

Recommending Development

Planned Program.   Drawing on his familiarity with the mine and his understanding of ore occurrence, the geologist makes recommendations for new exploration and development.   He selects the most promising places for new ore and lays out exploratory work, whether in the form of drilling or underground openings.   His plans for development are not merely stabs in such haphazard places as his fancy dictates but should form part of a systematic program designed to exhaust, when completed, all reasonable possibilities with a minimum of expenditure.

Form of Recommendations.   Although recommendations may have been made informally from time to time, it is best to submit them in written form also.   The writing places the matter on record and avoids any misunderstanding as to just what was or was not recommended.   Formal recommendations describe the proposed work specifically in terms of footage and bearings rather than in generalized language.   It is convenient to submit a sheet for each prospect in some form such as this:

Prospect Recommendation

Prospect No. 231
Mine: San Diablo   *Level:* 4.
Location: C5 drift, 43 feet north of Station 452.
Work Recommended: Crosscut on bearing N 38 W
Object: To explore intersection of veins 32 and 34.
Distance: 400 feet
Grade: B
Date Started: (left blank)
Results: (left blank)

Before the prospect recommendation is submitted in final form, it is a good plan to go over the proposals with the mine foreman in order not only to enlist his cooperation but to elicit his suggestions. He may, for example, prefer to reach a certain part of the vein by a raise from Level 5, where there are facilities for disposal of the waste, rather than by a drift on level 4 where the muck would have to be hoisted through an already overworked winze. Should his preference differ from yours it is wise to defer to it if you can, but if you are convinced that he is seriously mistaken it is much better to take the time to convince him that the advantages of your methods outweigh his objections than to go over his head in a peremptory manner.

"Grading" prospects (as for example "Grade: B" in the illustrative form), gives the management an idea of the relative desirability and urgency of the working proposed. Some prospects offer very encouraging hopes of developing ore; others have relatively small chances and are recommended more for the purpose of disproving the possible existence of ore than with any confidence of finding it. Such prospects may be carried out when nothing more urgent or promising is in view or where a part of the mine is about to be abandoned. In some mines, raises or crosscuts are driven for the purpose of getting waste to fill the stopes, and, if a few D-grade recommendations are on file, the work may be done in places where it has at least an off-chance of finding ore.

The following system of grades has been found satisfactory:

A. Very good chance of finding ore.
B. Less definite assurance but good mining risk.
C. Fair prospect of finding ore.
D. Not very likely to find ore but recommended in order to exhaust possibilities.

Following up Development Work

The spaces following "Date Started" and "Results" are to be filled in later when and if the work is actually carried out, thus providing a complete history of the prospect. The geologist enters the information periodically in his own copy of the recommendation and either posts the superintendent's file copy or supplies the recipients of the original recommendation with a supplementary sheet each month. This gives footage of progress, location and average grade of any ore found, and a description of the geological conditions encountered.

After the recommended work has been started, the geologist will need to follow it closely. To write out a recommendation and then disappear from the scene would be like a general drawing up plans for a campaign and then going away on a world cruise while the army fights the battle. The unexpected is always rather more than likely to happen in mining, and it is rare that a geologist, however experienced, can picture the exact conditions that will be met in the course of new work. He should therefore be prepared to modify his recommendations to meet the actual conditions encountered and be ready to reappraise his expectations as the work progresses.

"Outside" Examinations

Aside from his work at the "home" operating mine, the geologist may be requested from time to time to examine outside prospects and mines. This work, in addition to offering him some diversion from the daily routine, helps to broaden his geological horizon. The methods employed in work of this sort are discussed in Chapters 17 and 18.

Services apart from Ore Search

Although the geologist's main job is to determine what development work is most likely to find ore and, by recommending, advising, cajoling, or imploring, to induce the management to undertake this work, his usefulness is not limited to the current problems of ore search. Even in those fortunate mines whose development problems are simple and whose ore supply is but a minor worry, an enterprising geologist can find plenty to keep him usefully occupied. For, apart from ore search, geology can aid in a great variety of problems; each mine has its own and the examples in ensuing pages are intended to be suggestive rather than exhaustive. Some of those dependent on the habits and nature of the ore will receive attention in the rest of this chapter. The succeeding chapter will be devoted to additional engineering problems quite independent of the ore itself.

As some of these problems are outside the recognized responsibility of the geological department, the management may not realize that geology can be of service in connection with them and so may not request the geologist to attack them. Therefore, if the geologist sees a way to be helpful and offers his services, he must do so tactfully, otherwise those in charge of other departments may misinterpret his motives and resent an implied criticism of the methods that they have been using. But if the assistance is offered diplomatically in a sincere spirit of helpfulness, it is likely to be accepted with good grace, and, if the geologist's suggestions eventually produce good results, they are sure to be appreciated.

Clean Stoping. The ideal in stoping—to recover all of the ore and none of the barren wall rock—is at best only imperfectly attainable and is especially difficult if the boundaries of the ore are irregular and hard to recognize. Under these conditions, a map based on the results of sampling or drilling and interpreted in the light of detailed geological structure will show the operators what ground to break and where to stop the stope. To be of real use it should be kept up to date for each stope floor. At the Homestake mine, where complexly folded stratigraphic horizons constitute the boundaries of orebodies, the geological staff has enabled the mine operators to improve the grade remarkably without an offsetting increase in mining costs.[3]

Similarly, in broad veins the payable streaks may constitute only part of the vein, say the band adjoining the hanging wall or the footwall. Detailed sampling, interpreted with proper regard to vein structure, may point to a mining method employing narrower stopes and yield a higher grade which outweighs the higher cost per ton. In caving systems an accurate record of conditions in the stopes may help to avoid dilution. In the Old Dominion mine [4] the time ultimately arrived for extracting crushed pillars from between old stopes. Here the footwall portion of the orebody, consisting of silicified quartzite and limestone was high-grade copper ore, carrying, in many places, over 4%; the hanging wall portion, consisting of diabase, carried 1.5% to 2%. The problem was to draw out the richer ore through chutes and leave the diabase except for the portion of it that was ore. As mapping had shown that practically all the ore was on the footwall of the diabase, both the undercutting and the draw could be regulated so as to recover all of the richer ore and stop drawing before the waste came in.

Layout of Workings. Since underground workings serve the double purpose of exposing ore and providing openings through which to extract it, there is room for significant economy in killing both birds with one stone. Where other considerations are equal, a haulage way, crosscut, or raise for fill should be placed in such a position that it will have a chance of finding ore. Conversely, exploratory openings should be spaced in such a way that they fit into the system of stoping and haulage that will be used later. At the Old Dominion mine, development on the 2200 level gave reason to expect that development below the level would find orebodies amenable to caving. Accordingly, preliminary exploration work was spaced to conform to this method of mining and,

[3] McLaughlin, D. H., in *Ore Deposits of the Western States*, A.I.M.E., 1933, p. 727.
[4] Bjorge, Guy N., and Shoemaker, A. H., in *Ore Deposits of the Western States;* A.I.M.E., 1933, p. 715.

as a result, all development work was later used for ore extraction.[5]

Whereas exploratory workings and temporary orepasses should be driven where they are likely to find ore, the aim in the case of permanent shafts and main haulage-ways is just the opposite. They should deliberately avoid orebodies, otherwise they will tie up pillars and blocks of ore and prevent their recovery until the mine nears exhaustion. Thus, in selecting locations for permanent workings, a structural projection of all ore zones is valuable as a guide. At one mine where a new shaft was contemplated, the ore zones were known to follow broad structural trends. The geologist plotted the probable orebearing areas on each of the next ten undeveloped levels and, by superimposing the plans, was able to suggest several alternative shaft-locations which would avoid any of these zones.

Although main haulage workings should be far enough from future stopes to avoid danger from caving, they should, at the same time, be as near to the ore as practicable in order to minimize the length of drifts and crosscuts, as this not only saves in development expense but makes for ultimate economy in haulage costs.

Ore Estimation

The annual or semi-annual estimate of ore reserves is ordinarily the responsibility of the chief engineer, but the geologist is often called into consultation in preparing it. If it is to be more than a perfunctory calculation, it must take geological conditions into account, especially in estimating probable and possible reserves where questions of continuity between and beyond known exposures are the deciding factors. On these matters the geologist should be in a position to offer sound advice.

Mineralogical Aids in Ore Treatment

In order to design an effective flow-sheet for treatment of an ore by any of the standard methods of ore-dressing, it is important to determine not merely the metal content of the ore but the identity, proportions and textural relationship of the minerals that compose it. Up until a very few decades ago, most metallurgists gave little attention to these questions and were content to control their tests entirely by chemical analysis or assay. But with increased experience in flotation they realized that the mineralogical nature of the metals and gangue had an important bearing on mill performance. Accordingly, metal-

[5] Bjorge, Guy N., and Shoemaker, A. H., in *Ore Deposits of the Western States*; A.I.M.E., 1933, p. 714.

lurgists are giving more and more attention to mineral identification and, in fact, are beginning to make significant contributions of their own to determinative mineralogy.   But it is still true as a general statement that the average mill-operator has something to learn from a well-trained mining geologist in the matter of acquaintance with minerals and skill in optical methods.[6]   Therefore, collaboration between the concentrating department and the geological laboratory is likely to be helpful in solving metallurgical problems.

The importance of knowing what minerals are present in an ore is obvious from a consideration of modern methods of ore treatment.   For example, although the ultimate purpose of flotation is to separate one metal from its associated elements, the task is accomplished not by separating metals, as such, but by separating minerals.   Therefore the choice of reagents depends somewhat on the mineral species in which the metal occurs.   And if two metals are combined in a single mineral, there is no hope of separating them by flotation or any other physical method.   If, for example, the mineral bournonite ($PbCuSbS_3$) is an abundant constituent of the ore, there is no need to waste time in attempting to make a clean separation of lead from copper in the concentrate.   Similarly, in an Idaho lead ore part of the lead occurs as jamesonite ($Pb_4FeSb_6S_{14}$), which contains only 40.16% lead; hence the ore does not yield a high-grade lead concentrate and there is no purely physical means of removing the antimony.

Likewise, the possibility of removing sulphur from iron ore depends on the mineralogical form in which it occurs.   Magnetite ores containing pyrite can be cleaned of most of their sulphur by magnetic separation because pyrite is not attracted by the magnet.   But if the sulphur is in the form of pyrrhotite, which responds to magnetic attraction, it cannot be separated efficiently by this means.   In treating copper-bearing magnetite ores chalcopyrite is left behind by the magnet and can then be collected in a copper concentrate, but if the copper is present as cubanite (which can hardly be distinguished from chalcopyrite except by microscopic methods), neither the copper nor the sulphur can be separated from the iron by a magnetic concentrator.[7]

Gangue minerals may interfere with flotation in surprising ways.   In Sudbury, the flotation plant performed irregularly at times for no apparent reason.   A geologist made counts to determine the mineralogical

    [6] For a discussion of laboratory methods see Chapter 5.
    [7] Schwartz, G. M., Solving metallurgical problems with the reflecting microscope: *E. & M. J.*, vol. 116, pp. 237–238, 1923.

    Schwartz, G. M., Review of the application of microscopic study to metallurgical problems: *Econ. Geol.*, vol. 33, pp. 440–553, 1938.   (Gives a full bibliography)

composition of the millfeed and of the concentrate when recovery was good and also when it was poor. A comparison led to the unexpected conclusion that biotite was the culprit. This mineral would build up in the flotation cells and periodically reach the point where it upset mill performance. After it had been floated off, performance would be good until another batch of biotite accumulated. Once the mystery was solved the difficulty was remedied.[8]

The texture of an ore may have a strong influence on problems of treatment. The grain-size of intergrowths, as of galena and sphalerite, for instance, will indicate the fineness of grinding that is necessary for a clean separation.[9] Gold at Wiluna (W.A.) is very difficult to recover in cyaniding because it occurs in particles less than a micron in diameter enclosed in arsenopyrite and the finest grinding that economy permits fails to expose all of it to the solvent action of solutions. Similarly, but on a larger order of dimensions, texture may determine the susceptibility of a copper ore to leaching. The ore of Castle Dome, Arizona,[10] consists of rock cut by fractures filled with chalcocite, covellite, and chalcopyrite. When crushed to half-inch size for leaching tests the ore broke along the veinlets and exposed the copper minerals to solutions. Some copper in the form of grains disseminated in the wall rock away from fractures escaped leaching but its proportion was small. However, sulphide particles surrounded by clay-like material were partly protected from the effects of leaching.

The resistance of gold particles either to amalgamation or cyaniding is sometimes found to be due to film-like coatings which the microscope reveals.

Another instance, in which shape and distribution of the members of a mineral aggregate proved more important than grain-size alone, is described by Cooke,[11] who found that magnetite could be freed from silica because it had an equigranular form, whereas specular hematite, being in interlocking laths, trapped particles of gangue.

The amenability of ore to treatment, since it depends on mineralogy and texture, is, in the last analysis, a reflection of geological conditions. This fact is neatly illustrated by Broderick's work[12] on the iron ores of the Lake Superior district where research has been in progress on the

[8] Yates, A. B.: Personal communication.

[9] Anon. The role of the microscope in ore dressing, Ore Dressing Notes, No. 4, Oct. 1935. American Cynamid Co., New York, 1935, pp. 12–16.

[10] Head, R. E., Microscopic study of an ore as an aid in copper leaching: E. & M. J., vol. 126, pp. 13–15, 1928.

[11] Cooke, S. R. B., Microscopic structure and concentrability of the important iron ores of the United States: U. S. Bureau of Mines Bull. 391, 1936.

[12] Broderick, T. M., Application of geology to problems of iron ore concentration: Tr. A.I.M.E., vol. 115, pp. 273–284, 1935.

beneficiation of low grade ore to replace the declining supplies of "merchantable" material. Using both field and laboratory methods, Broderick noted two types of iron-bearing material which cannot be concentrated profitably: (a) iron formation which has escaped oxidation and thus has its iron still in the form of greenalite or similar silicates and (b) iron formation which has been so strongly metamorphosed that a substantial portion of the iron has been converted into iron-amphibole. In both of these geologically contrasting types, too much of the iron is combined chemically with silica. Thus ores amenable to sink-and-float treatment are unmetamorphosed iron formations which have been oxidized and at least partially leached, but not all of these are suitable because the iron oxide and silica, though separate chemically, may be too intimately intermixed physically. Iron minerals in sufficiently large grains or bands are characteristic of certain stratigraphic members, notably the "wavy-bedded member" on the Gogebic Range, samples of which yielded a highly satisfactory concentrate carrying 59% Fe by the sink-and-float method at sizes of 10 mesh to 2 inches.

Publication of Scientific Findings

Apart from his regular duties the geologist owes it to his science to publish the results of important observations and discoveries. A description of a large mine or an important district is always worth publishing. In the case of an obscure mine, a geological description is likely to be of little more than local interest for its own sake, yet, since every ore deposit when studied exhaustively displays some unusual feature or illustrates some broad principle, an article centering on the chief problem and omitting irrelevant descriptive detail will always be of interest to colleagues. There is always a temptation to postpone publication until studies are a little farther advanced, but geological investigation, like "woman's work," is never done, and the solution of each problem exposes others which remain to be solved. Unless the geologist resolves at a certain stage to publish what he has, there is danger that he will be called to another district, if not to the Elysian Fields, before he gets his results in form for submission to a society or journal.

In writing articles for publication the geologist must remember that any information he acquires in the course of his work is the property of his employer and that he is therefore under obligation to obtain permission before publishing it. Fortunately, mining companies are becoming more liberal in granting permission to publish. They realize that they owe a good share of their success to knowledge that has accumulated through previous publication and that their only way of repaying any part of this debt is by making the results of their own experience available to the mining profession. They realize furthermore that even though one of their employees may devote part of his energy and attention to the preparation of an article, the resultant sharpening of his ideas as well as the personal stimulation that he derives from making a scientific contribution is likely in the end to render him more valuable to the company. It is quite true that under certain circumstances there are valid business reasons for withholding some of the facts about a property, but usually there is valuable information of a scientific nature that can be published without serious damage to the company's interests.

Selected References

Edwards, A. B., *Textures of the Ore Minerals and their Significance.* Melbourne: Australasian Institute of Mining and Metallurgy, 1947. Chapter 7: Applications to ore dressing.

International Nickel Company, Departmental organization (Geological Department), *Canadian Mining Journal,* vol. 67, pp. 325, 326, May, 1946.

McLaughlin, D. H. and Sales, Reno H., Utilization of geology by mining companies, in *Ore Deposits of the Western States,* (Lindgren Volume), pp. 683–729. *American Institute of Mining and Metallurgical Engineers, 1933.*

20

Engineering Geology in Mining

Economic geology . . . and engineering geology . . . are two impor-
tant branches of applied geology. There is, of course, much overlapping
and interfingering between them.

— W. J. Mead [1]

Aside from the techniques of ore-search and ore-appraisal, the operation of mines calls for the solution of a variety of engineering problems
inherent in the job of making holes in the ground. A geologist, because
of his knowledge of rocks—their structure, their distribution, their response to stress, and their qualities as aquifers—can often help in solving
these problems, even some of those which might appear to lie chiefly
within the province of the mining engineer. Although the mining
geologist, since his field of experience must, of necessity, have some limitations, may not always feel able to contribute all that the science can
possibly offer even toward the solution of problems which are essentially
geological, he should at least be able to recognize such problems when he
sees them and, by calling in a colleague specially versed in hydrology or
engineering geology, to save his employers from ultimate expense and
even from impending disaster.

Another type of service outside the conventional field of ore-search
is the exploration for convenient sources of materials, such as limestone
and concrete aggregate, that are used in connection with the mining
and processing of metallic ores.

Location of Workings

Sometimes a varied assemblage of rock formations offers a choice of the
type of rock in which to drive an opening. An example of economy

[1] Mead, W. J., Engineering geology: *Geological Society of America, Fiftieth Anniversary Vol-*
ume, 1941.

through geological planning is available in the Catskill Aqueduct.[2]   The stratigraphic section at the site of the Rondout Pressure Tunnel showed that the hard Shawangunk Grit was underlain by the relatively soft Hudson River shale and sandstone.   Accordingly, the tunnel was placed at a depth of 250 feet below sea level in order to take advantage of the cheaper and faster driving in the softer formation.   So accurate was the prediction that, although the tunnel was in the Hudson River formation and thus below the hard grit throughout all of its length, it was no deeper than necessary.   There was a distance of 500 feet in which the grit formed the roof of the tunnel through this deepest part of the syncline.

Such an opportunity for choice of elevation is rarely presented in mining work, where levels must be placed at fixed vertical intervals, but often there is scope for choice of horizontal position.   Especially in steeply dipping beds, a slight change in the proposed position of a drift can put it in a soft rock rather than a hard one.   Of course, softness of rock is not the only factor to consider.   Although soft slates or shales make for low costs in driving, they may occasion subsequent expense in timbering and repairs.   Thus a choice of formation may demand careful balancing of first cost against maintenance expense, and this choice depends largely on how long the drift is expected to remain in service. In any case, a map showing the projected positions of rock formations on a new level will enable the management to plan the layout in such a way as to take advantage of possible economies.

Even more important to consider in laying out workings is the position of faults.   Fault zones usually consist of soft or loose material.   Occasionally this is "picking ground," soft enough to be excavated without explosives yet firm enough to stand without timber, but such favorable conditions are rare.   More often the fault zone is loose, swelling ground requiring spiling and timbering and, at best, occasioning slow and expensive progress.   Workings in such zones are subject to continuing maintenance expense for repairs and retimbering and may even suffer damage from further movement on the fault during readjustment of the ground in the course of mining.   Therefore it is highly desirable to keep shafts, haulageways, pump stations, and drill holes for electric cables away from faults and other bad ground.[3]   A drift or crosscut which has to pass through a fault in order to reach its objective should

---

[2] Berkey, C. P., Engineering geology of the City of New York, *Guidebook 9*, 16th International Geological Congress, 1943, p. 100.

[3] Linforth, F. A., Application of geology to mining in the ore deposits at Butte, Montana, in *Ore Deposits of the Western States*, A.I.M.E., New York, 1933, p. 695.

be turned to go through it with the shortest feasible course. In addition to other disadvantages, faults below water level are apt to be water courses, as will be discussed in the following paragraphs.

WATER PROBLEMS

Pumping and drainage present serious problems in many mines and, since hydrology is a phase of geology, the well-trained geologist familiar with the behavior of ground-water can assist the management by forecasting conditions that will be found in new workings and by suggesting means of avoiding serious consequences.

Cone of Unwatering

When a shaft is sunk below the natural water table in rock that is reasonably permeable and homogeneous, pumping immediately begins to drain water out of the pores and crevices in the rock. As pumping continues, the water level is artificially depressed and assumes much the shape that a stretched membrane would have if one were to punch it downward with a stick. That is to say, the water table has the shape of a flat inverted cone with its apex at the shaft. This is known as the *cone of water-table depression* or the *cone of unwatering,* although in terms of strict geometry it is not a true cone, since its sides, viewed in cross section, are not straight lines but curves which steepen toward the shaft. The flow of water into the shaft is heaviest when pumping begins, but if sinking is stopped it gradually lessens and after some months becomes virtually constant. Accordingly the cone of unwatering assumes a shape which is practically stable as the flow of water into the shaft reaches a state of equilibrium with the supply of water entering the aquifer and percolating through it. If shaft-sinking is resumed, the process is repeated; the new cone is deeper and requires a higher rate of pumping to keep it drained.

If a drift is extended from the bottom of the shaft, the cone of unwatering is no longer a symmetrical cone; what was formerly the point of the cone is elongated into a horizontal line, the water table sloping upward from it at both sides and at the ends. If closely spaced crosscuts are driven from the drift, the cone assumes somewhat the form of a bathtub with flat-sloping sides. If upper levels are now driven from the shaft they will encounter little water until they are out far enough to reach the sides of the cone; then they will begin to tap the water reservoir, but unless they extend for long distances they will not materially lessen the flow that enters the deepest workings.

Variation with Nature of Rock

The more permeable the rock the flatter the gradient of the cone. Unconsolidated sands and gravels are highly permeable. Among the consolidated rocks, limestones and dolomites, if highly cavernous, are the most permeable. An example of the difficulties offered by cavernous rocks is found on the Rand, where attempts to sink through the dolomite overlying the Witwatersrand series were defeated by flows of water until the François cementation process made it possible to seal off the water-bearing formation. Next in order of permeability is sandstone, which, if not too highly metamorphosed, may indeed be more permeable than any but the most cavernous carbonate rocks. Then come lavas of recent origin with their zones of breccia, open tubes and connected vesicles. If permeable fractures are closely spaced, the water-filled fractures constitute a "curiously skeletonized hollow network."[4] The rock-mass behaves, so far as water is concerned, much as if it were homogeneous, with a cone of unwatering that is rudely symmetrical, though extending farthest from its axis along the most open and permeable fissures. If more than one formation is present at a given elevation, the "cone" may be highly irregular, extending farthest and deepest in the rocks that are most permeable. Thus the water table may be deep in a limestone and shallow in an adjoining porphyry. Below the water table a tight rock may "make" little water, whereas an adjoining permeable layer may yield copious flows.

In stratified and folded rocks the contrast in permeability between different beds and the variations in the attitudes of aquifers renders the movement of water so complex as to modify the ideal cone almost beyond recognition. With relatively impervious rocks like granite, quartzite, slate, and schist, the aquifers may consist of veins and faults constituting a system whose intricate geometry introduces problems which are extremely difficult to handle mathematically and for which, in fact, adequate data are rarely available. Workings in such rocks may encounter little or no water until they intersect a fracture, but when they do the flow of water may be extremely heavy.

The degree to which flows of water may be concentrated along fissures is illustrated by the experience in two districts in the Peruvian Andes. The Mahr [5] (Kingsmill) tunnel, 30,000 feet long, drains the Morococha mines by connecting with their workings about 1700 feet below the

[4] Tolman, C. F., *Ground Water*, p. 291. New York: McGraw-Hill, 1937.

[5] Anon., Mahr Tunnel encounters 20,000 g.p.m. flow: *E. and M. J.*, vol. 134, p. 414, 1933. Mahr Tunnel completed: *E. and M. J.*, vol. 135, p. 217, 1934.

surface.   During the driving of this tunnel the water emerging from its portal increased gradually, reaching 17,000 gallons per minute when the face had advanced to about 23,000 feet.   At that point the tunnel cut a fissure from which a flow of 50,000 g.p.m. gushed with such force as to prevent further advance for six months.   As the fissure gradually drained itself, the flow from it declined to 18,000 g.p.m. and the total flow from the portal decreased to 28,000 g.p.m.

At Casapalca [5a] a drainage tunnel in porphyritic andesite and silicified shale was carrying about 10,000 g.p.m., practically all of which came from fractures; about 90% of it was from a group of fissures a few hundred feet south of the Carlos Francisco shaft and the rest from a fault zone north of the shaft.   When a new drainage tunnel 600 feet deeper tapped the main fissures, the flow from them into the upper tunnel practically ceased.   The rock away from the fissures "made" so little water that the Carlos Francisco shaft could be sunk to 600 feet below the deeper tunnel without encountering flows of more than a few hundred gallons per minute, and these came in on minor fractures.   But, since experience indicated that the major fissures when tapped at this deep level would disgorge about 15,000 g.p.m. (later declining to 10,000 g.p.m.), the management took the wise precaution of installing a pump station capable of handling 17,000 g.p.m. before beginning to drift at this level.

Not all fractures are water-bearing, however.   Some are sealed with mineral matter or packed with impervious gouge.   But most faults and many veins constitute water-courses.   Therefore graphic projection of faults and of formations that are likely to be water-bearing into ground that is about to be entered makes it possible to anticipate flows of water.

Water-Filled Workings

Even more treacherous than water-bearing fractures and formations are old workings below the water-level.   Should new workings break into them, a sudden rush of water may cause loss of life, or, at best, serious inconvenience.   It is possible to guard against the menace by carrying a long drill hole ahead of the advancing face; then a heavy flow from the drill hole indicates danger ahead.   However, if no workings are known to exist, this precaution is likely to be neglected.   Of course the position of old workings is not a geological problem, yet the geologist, who has occasion in the course of his studies of ore distribution to compile the data from old maps and records, may have more informa-

5a Misener, R. H., The pumping station of the Carlos Francisco Mine, Casapalca, Peru: A.I.M.E. Tech. Pub. 1546, pp. 1-15, 1943.

tion on the subject than other staff members and may therefore be able to sound a warning when a new heading is approaching them.

Variation with Depth

Down to moderate depths the aggregate flow of water into a mine increases as the workings are deepened (allowing, of course, for the time required to reach equilibrium), but this increase does not continue indefinitely. The fractures become tighter and the rocks less permeable until at a depth varying from 2000 to 4000 feet there is little groundwater except along specially permeable aquifers and on the strongest fissures. The really deep mines of the world are dry at the bottom, or would be were it not for water that comes down through the workings.

Need for Data

This outline of principles has been wholly qualitative; I have made no attempt to state in numerical terms the slope of a cone of unwatering, the rate of flow to a sump, the time required to reach equilibrium, or the relative permeabilities of rock formations. Statistical data and formulas will be found in texts on hydrology, but as they are based chiefly on observation in water-supply wells in homogeneous aquifers of high permeability they are applicable only in principle to the problems of mining in rocks whose permeability depends chiefly on fractures.[5b] In the mining literature there is plenty of information on rates of pumping but little in the way of correlation of these data with the nature of rock formations and the shapes of water tables. There is room for a modern book on water problems in mining written from a geological standpoint.

GROUND MOVEMENT

Nature of Problems

When too much rock is taken out of underground openings, part or all of the openings collapse. Everyone knows this, of course, and part of the layman's distaste for going underground arises from apprehension lest the mine "cave in." The miner's contempt of this fear, arising from familiarity with walls and roof that stand year after year, sometimes leads him to imagine that a rock which "stands well" will continue to do so no matter how much support he removes. The problem

---

[5b] A recent mathematical treatment of flow of water into mine workings is: Theis, Charles V., and Stuart, Wilbur T., Groundwater investigations in the Iron River Mining District, Michigan: Paper presented at meeting of Society of Economic Geologists, New York, March 20th, 1947.

is to estimate what size and shape of opening may be excavated without serious danger, to foresee hazardous conditions, and to devise ways of preventing ground movement or at least of minimizing its disastrous effects. These are problems in mining engineering, but as Graton [6] says, "inasmuch as it is the *rocks* that fail, it would seem that much useful light on the phenomenon . . . can in the future be shed by the geologist, the particular specialist in rocks."

The mode of failure of mine workings depends somewhat on the nature and structure of the rock—its inherent strength-characteristics and the attitude of its surfaces of weakness. But if these factors are constant, the mode of failure varies with depth. Probably much of the disagreement among writers on rock failure would be cleared up by a distinction in mechanism between failure at shallow depth and failure at great depth.

At shallow depth the environmental or confining pressure is small and the stress distribution is strongly influenced by the proximity of a free boundary (the earth's surface). At great depth, confining pressure increases the strength of the material (or so experiments would suggest) and the influence of the free boundary at the earth's surface is practically negligible.

Accordingly, failure at shallow depth takes place predominantly along joints, bedding planes and other surfaces of weakness and assumes the form of simple collapse of the overlying and adjacent material under its own weight. But at depths beginning at 3000 to 5000 feet, failure partakes more of the nature of slabbing from walls and crushing of both horizontal and vertical pillars. It is determined more by the shape of the opening than by pre-existing surfaces of weakness.[7] As pressure effects tend to be all-sided, rather than merely vertically downward, failure occurs from the sides and floor as well as from the roof.

It is convenient, therefore, to describe effects of these contrasting modes of failure under the two separate headings, "Subsidence" and "Rockbursts," even though at intermediate depth they overlap and merge, and even though failure at depth is not always as violent as the term "Rockbursts" might suggest.

[6] Graton, L. C., in symposium: Rock Bursts, *A.I.M.E. Tech. Pub. 1468*, p. 3, 1942.
[7] Welker, K. K., *Rock Failure in Deep Mines:* Ph.D. Thesis, Harvard University, 1931 (unpublished).

Subsidence
(by S. A. Tyler)

When the equilibrium of nature is disturbed by man through surface or underground mining operations, gravitational readjustments of the earth materials must occur to meet the new conditions, and a new equilibrium is established. These readjustments which take place over a period of time involve settling, slumping, and sliding of the earth toward the area of disturbance, namely the mining operation. Underground mines are usually failing structures; in fact mining is often conducted upon the principle that the roof will fail and the problem is to carry on the operation in such a manner that the failure can be more or less controlled so that it will not interfere with the mining operation. The removal of support by mining entails caving and surface subsidence which generally extends over a greater area than that excavated in mining.

Subsidence is a serious problem today because of the increasing scale of mining operations and because, as the mines become older, deeper, and more extensive, earth movements are more likely to be initiated. Shafts, main haulage levels, and other underground workings that must remain undisturbed during the period of ore extraction, as well as structures on the surface, are commonly endangered or destroyed by subsidence. Damage of surface improvement, buildings, roads, and drainage, caused by subsidence has led to extensive and costly litigation and to expenditures of large sums of money for damages or for correcting conditions. Moreover, the public is inclined to the belief that subsidence of the surface is the result of carelessness in mining or the greediness of the mine operators in "robbing the pillars." This belief is fostered by the common-law requirements that the owner of the surface is entitled to full support of the surface. Court decisions have upheld this point of view even when the owner has sold or leased the underlying mineral rights, unless a clause in the sale or lease contract specifically exempts the mining company from paying the owner of the surface for damages that may result from mining. On the other hand, the practice of leaving from one-third to one-half of the ore permanently in the mine in the form of pillars so that the surface may be supported is wrong from the point of view of conservation of mineral resources. The mining geologist and engineer must educate the public that subsidence is the natural and inevitable result of complete extraction of the ore unless expensive methods of back-filling are employed to support the surface.

Mining geologists are called upon in many instances to determine the surface area which will be affected by subsidence and the amount of movement which may be expected if an orebody of a given size at a given depth below the surface is mined. This factor is of great importance when large orebodies are mined by caving methods, for it is necessary to determine in advance the outermost limits of fracture on the surface in order that improvements such as mills, shops, and office buildings may be located on ground which will not be disturbed by mining operations in the future.

The character of the subsidence, its extent, and the time when it will develop over an underground opening seems to depend upon many factors, the most important of which are the size and shape of the opening and its depth below the surface; the number and attitude of incompetent beds, bedding planes, faults, and joints; the method of mining and the rate at which mining operations advance; and the composition, physical character, and shearing strength of the material.

In general, the character and extent of subsidence will vary with the size of the underground opening, diminishing progressively from large open stopes through small or filled stopes to undisturbed formation. When the opening lies relatively close to the surface, the overlying rock may collapse soon after the removal of the ore, although the strength of the rock and the size of the opening are modifying factors. If the opening is located a greater distance below the surface, an appreciable period of time may elapse between the mining of the ore and the first evidence of surface subsidence. During this period the rock slabs off and caves from the roof of the stope, developing an arch which gradually migrates upward toward the surface. Two tons of broken rock in the stopes occupy about the same space or volume as three tons of rock in place. Thus, if the opening is rather small, the increase in volume of the broken rock may be sufficient to fill the developing arch and partially or wholly support the surface. If the supports of the arch are competent and the keystone is maintained, nothing further may happen. However, if the opening is large, the arch may migrate upward and finally break through to the surface with attendant surface subsidence. The volume of the surface subsidence is usually less than the volume of the broken material. However, in cases where the block subsides as a unit, the volumes may be nearly equal.

The character of the material in which the opening is developed is important. Moulton [8] classifies materials into three general groups:

[8] Moulton, H. G., Earth and rock pressures: *Trans. A.I.M.E.*, vol. 63, pp. 327–351, 1920.

The first class includes the materials from moist sands to the firmest rock, all of which act as solids. In surface excavations all homogeneous materials within this group stand with a vertical face to a given depth; below that depth they fail in shear with a characteristic shape of bank after failure.

The second class comprises any granular material, such as dry sand or gravel, that occurs as separate grains and lacks cohesion. The angle of repose controls the manner in which materials within this group stand in surface excavations.

The third class includes semi-liquid materials; quicksand, wet clays, and, in general, all saturated ground that develops pressures of a hydrostatic nature. At critical depths these materials become plastic and flow in such a manner as to develop pressures proportional to the depth.

Many mines, both open-pit and underground, are developed in materials which act as solids. According to Moulton, if the depth of the opening is sufficiently great that the resistance of the material to shearing stresses is overcome by gravity, and if the material is homogeneous and free from planes of weakness, the bounding, surface-subsidence cracks may be determined by drawing a line of one-half to one slope (63°26') from the lowest point on the side of the excavation to the surface. The actual plane of rupture extends vertically downward from the surface to one-half the depth of the excavation below the surface and then curves inward as a segment of a sphere to the bottom of the opening. Haines [9] points out that failure will occur in that form which allows the greatest possible weight to be opposed by the smallest possible resistance, in other words a sphere. This accounts for the one-half to one slope and the curved or hemispherical form of the lower half of the fracture. The fact that the upper portion of the fracture is generally vertical probably results from the condition that the tangent from the sphere to the surface of the earth is shorter than the arc in the upper quadrant.

Crane [10] points out that in many cases the earth is not homogeneous and that planes of weakness such as incompetent beds, bedding planes, schistosity, joints, and faults control to a large extent the manner of subsidence and the area affected by subsidence. The number, spacing, and attitude of the planes of weakness vary from one locality to another and even from one rock formation to another at the same locality, so

[9] Haines, E. G., Discussion of H. G. Moulton's paper on earth and rock pressures: *Trans. A.I.M.E.*, vol. 63, pp. 351–356, 1920.

[10] Crane, W. R., Subsidence and ground movement in the copper and iron mines of the Upper Peninsula, Michigan: *U. S. Bureau of Mines Bull.* 295, pp. 1–66, 1929.

that it is not surprising that no two cases of subsidence are exactly alike. Other factors, such as folding and the presence of dikes and sills of igneous rock, affect the situation only inasmuch as they contribute planes of weakness.

Vanderwilt [11] describes a typical case of subsidence in the intensely fractured ground at Climax. The subsidence fractures produced by block caving are steeply-dipping tension cracks, as proved by crosscuts beneath the ground which is fractured at the surface. Shear fractures have not been observed. The steep, subsidence-tension cracks occur in an upward-widening zone extending 100 feet from the caved ore at the bottom of the caved block (600 feet below the surface) to 500 feet from it at the surface, where the cracks divide the rocks into detached upright slabs and columns. These blocks topple, slide and roll toward the caved area. Vanderwilt believes that this mechanism rather than slipping on shears is of general application in subsidence attending mining by block caving. The discrepancy between this behavior and that which would be expected on theoretical grounds may be attributed to the fact that theoretical discussions of subsidence on shear planes presuppose homogeneous ground free from planes of weakness. The relative strengths of the material in shear and in tension may be an additional controlling factor.

Where openings are developed in flat or gently-dipping beds, joints and faults, if present, are generally controlling factors in subsidence, but in more steeply dipping beds movement commonly occurs on the bedding planes which dip toward the opening.

The method of mining and the rate at which mining operations advance influence subsidence. Block caving and top slicing require that subsidence shall more or less keep pace with the extraction of ore below. Block caving involves dividing the orebody into blocks by workings in both the horizontal and vertical dimensions and attacking each block as a unit. The block is undercut and allowed to drop, thus breaking the ore. Top slicing entails removing slices of the ore from the top of the orebody and allowing the overlying cover to subside more or less gradually as the mining progresses downward. Any overlying material which is reluctant to subside is brought down by blasting. When these methods of mining are used, surface subsidence usually develops shortly after the mining operations begin, particularly if the orebody is located fairly close to the surface.

Square set stoping is employed where the enclosing rock and the ore

[11] Vanderwilt, John W., Ground movement adjacent to a caving block in the Climax Molybdenum Mine: *A.I.M.E. Tech. Pub. 2000*, pp. 1–10, 1946.

are rather weak and need support during mining operations. Timber square sets are used to maintain the opening during ore extraction. Subsidence usually develops in heavy ground shortly after mining ceases, but in some cases the openings are maintained for a long period of time, especially if the stopes are filled with waste rock.

The shrinkage stoping method and the room and pillar method of mining are used where the ore and rock are strong. Subsidence usually does not develop for long periods of time unless the pillars are weakened or removed prior to the abandonment of the mine. However, in extremely deep mines the pillars are often not able to withstand the great pressures developed by the weight of the overlying rock. They shear off with explosive force, producing minor earthquakes.

The long-wall method used particularly in mining coal seams consists of taking out all the coal along the working face and filling the ground behind with loose broken rock to support the roof partially. The weight of the roof is carried in part by the working face and assists in breaking the coal. Compaction of the loose fill takes place, and subsidence slowly works its way through to the surface. Where large tonnages of coal are mined from thin, gently dipping beds, extensive areas are subjected to slow subsidence which gradually results in considerable damage to the surface. Subsidence over mined coal seams in gently dipping strata takes place through sagging of the beds which behave like cantilever beams supported at both ends and sagging in the middle.[12] The bending sets up tensile stresses near the margins of the subsiding area, especially near the surface, causing vertical tension cracks to form. An imaginary line from the outermost surface cracks down to the outer margin of the underground excavation has a dip ranging in numerous examples from 65 to 75 degrees in the direction of the underground excavation. Only very exceptionally is it as flat as 45 or 50 degrees or as steep as 80 degrees. (The complement of this angle is known as the "angle of draw.") Although Professor Briggs does not offer the suggestion, it would seem that tension on the lower side of the beam could account for the "Fayol effect"—loosening and down-dropping of a dome-shaped or wedge-shaped block bounded by ragged fractures which converge upward and do not (at first, at least) reach through to the surface. Briggs discusses the mechanics of caving bounded by shear planes, but his examples are fewer and less specific than those of tension cracks.

The length of time which elapses between mining of a given orebody and the subsequent subsidence of the surface, as well as the area in-

---

[12] *Cf.* Briggs, Henry, *Mining Subsidence.* London: Edward Arnold and Co., 1929.

volved, is determined in many cases by placing monuments on the surface and underground, and surveying the monuments at regular intervals. Observational data such as the date of appearance of new cracks and the character of the surface movement are recorded, for although the subsiding area seems to move as a unit, in detail, differential block movement is likely. The subsiding ground usually moves slowly and sporadically with periods of sudden movement alternating with periods of quiescence. Although records of the amount of surface subsidence and the time of such movements may be of little value in interpreting conditions underground, such records are of great value in predicting the time, character, and extent of future movements and in litigation.

A novel system for determining the rate and the amount of subsidence as it works upward toward the surface was developed by Rice.[13] Vertical test holes are drilled to a depth necessary to penetrate the cavity. The holes are cased through the over-burden and cemented to the ledge. The distance from the top of the cavity to the collar of the casing is recorded and then the drill is lowered through the cavity until the top of the caved material in the stope is encountered. The difference in depth gives the height of the opening. The hole is then plugged above the cavity and grouted for ten to fifteen feet above the plug. Water is run into the hole to determine if large cracks are present above the plug. Small cracks may be sealed by grouting the hole, but if large cracks occur it may be necessary to plug the hole closer to the surface. In order to provide a means of measuring the subsidence of the ground in which the plug is located, a line of one-half inch pipe is inserted in the hole with the bottom resting on the plug and top projecting four to five feet above the top of the casing. A record is then made of the distance which the small pipe projects above the collar of the hole. When subsidence takes place, this interval is again measured and an accurate record of the movement of the block in which the plug is located is obtained. The pipe is then withdrawn and a new plug is cemented in closer to the surface and the procedure repeated. Thus the rate of caving and cracking of the subsiding ground is obtained, and warning is given of impending danger to surface structures.

Depressions over subsiding areas tend to collect water, and the broken nature of the ground allows the water to pass downward into the mine workings. The added weight as well as the lubricating effect of the water, on clays especially, tends to promote subsidence and in some cases acts as the trigger which sets off sudden movements. Unconsolidated beds of sand near the surface, in the presence of more water than is

[13] Rice, G. S., Ground movement from mining in Brier Hill Mine, Norway, Michigan: *Trans. A.I.M.E.*, vol. 109, pp. 118–144, 1934.

necessary to fill the pore spaces, may flash into a liquid state and rush through the broken ground into the mine. This situation has been encountered in many mines and not uncommonly results in heavy damage and loss of life. Surface drainage should be diverted from areas of subsiding ground so that as little water as possible may enter the ground. Swamps and low lying ground over the orebody should be thoroughly drained before mining is undertaken. This is particularly essential if top slicing or block caving methods of mining are to be employed.

Much of what has been said concerning subsidence over underground openings applies with equal force to open pit mines and other surface excavations. If the earth materials act as solids (are homogeneous and free from planes of weakness), and if the excavation is sufficiently deep so that the shearing strength of the material is overcome by gravity, a one-half to one slope of the bank will be established, with the rupture vertical in the upper portion and approximating a circular curve in the lower portion. However, in steam shovel operations other factors often limit the banks of an open pit to a much lower slope. Blasting on successive benches of the bank produces granular material lacking mass cohesion which assumes an angle of repose of approximately forty-five degrees.

The excavation tends to remove the toe support of the bank where incompetent beds, bedding planes, and joints dip into the excavation at angles from thirty to sixty degrees. Bank slides are apt to develop during periods of excessive rainfall; the water increases the weight of the bank as well as acting as a lubricating agent. Excessive loading of the banks with stripping material may add the extra weight necessary to start a slide.

Rock-Bursts

Whereas failure at shallow depth is usually gradual and is preceded by ample warning to those who are able to read the signs, failure in deep workings is often violent, taking the form of rock-bursts. According to their effects, bursts may be described as "strain bursts" and "crush bursts," although there is probably little fundamental difference in cause between the two.[14] Strain bursts are of minor proportions. Fragments of the walls of drifts, stopes, and especially of pillars spall off with explosive violence. Although the fragments are small, they sometimes fly with such speed as to kill or injure a man who is so unfortunate as to be in their way. *Crush bursts* are major failures. As described by Weiss, "the footwall appears to rise and the hanging wall to descend.

[14] Weiss, Oscar, in symposium on Rock bursts: *A.I.M.E. Tech. Paper 1463*, p. 20

Lights are extinguished, props are shattered, pigsties [15] and packs are compressed, and rocks burst from faces of stopes, from pillars, . . . and from the sides and roofs of levels. Tracks are buckled and displaced and pipelines bent and broken." [16]

Although rock-bursts occasionally occur at shallow depth, they are most common and severe in extremely deep mines. They are especially notorious in the deep mines of the Witwatersrand in South Africa and the Kolar Goldfield in India.

The frequency and intensity of rock-bursts vary with the kind of rock. Bursts are most common in brittle rocks, a fact which is understandable from the analogy to a block of glass which, if squeezed in a vise, will shatter and fly whereas a lump of hard clay will crumble gradually. Thus, in the Porcupine district at depths of 4000 feet, the tough, non-brittle greenstone schist fails gradually with little violent spalling. The Sunshine mine in Idaho experienced no serious trouble while the workings were in the St. Regis formation (slates and thin-bedded quartzites) but suffered from rock-bursts after entering the more massive, brittle Burke quartzite. In the Teck-Hughes mine at Kirkland Lake one major group of bursts was distinctly localized in a body of indurated tuff which is harder and much more brittle than the surrounding syenite porphyry.[17]

Rocks that stand well so long as excavations are small may develop rock-bursts after large amounts of ore have been stoped out. Thus the Teck-Hughes mine experienced no serious bursts even though a shaft had reached over 6000 feet, until stoping had progressed at higher levels. Since then many bursts have occurred at depths of 4000 to 5000 feet. Meanwhile the adjoining Lake Shore mine which was stoping a section of the same vein system between its deeper neighbors, Teck-Hughes and Wright-Hargreaves, had many rock-bursts at depths of only 2300 to 4000 feet.[18] A major contributing influence here was the system of mining, then in use, which left behind many isolated small pillars.

Cause

Our understanding of the physics of rock-bursts is far from perfect. From what we know, it is evident that violent bursts are due to a sudden

[15] Pigsties are artificial pillars built of timber, log-cabin style, and filled with packed waste rock.

[16] Weiss, Oscar, The theory of rockbursts and the possibilities of geophysical methods in predicting rockbursts on the producing mines of the Witwatersrand: *Journal Chem. Met. and Mining Society of South Africa*, January, 1938, p. 31.

[17] Christian, J. D., Rock-bursts at the Teck-Hughes Mine: *C.I.M.M. Bull. No. 331*, 1939, also *Transactions*, vol. 42, pp. 555 and 558, 1939.

[18] Robson, W. T., Adamson, J. C., and Selnes, W. E., Rock-bursts at Lake Shore Mines: *C.I.M.M. Bull. No. 333*, 1940; also *Transactions*, vol. 43, 1940, p. 13.

release of strain; the potential energy stored in the form of elastic strain converts itself into kinetic energy. Some observers maintain that certain rocks, as a result of their past geologic history, are in a state of internal strain like that in poorly annealed glass or in an overloaded spring, ready to snap if weakened by boring a hole.[19] This theory may explain why rock-bursts occur occasionally at shallow depth, but it can hardly be more than a minor contributing cause in major bursts at great depth. In these the motivating cause is without question the gravitative load of overlying rock, though this force acts indirectly rather than directly.

Stress in Rocks at Depth

Environmental Stress. If you think of a rectangular prism of rock a mile high you will realize that, due to the weight of the upper part of the column, an imaginary cube at the base is shortened vertically by compression. If the cube is not supported at its sides, it will expand laterally by an amount equal to some fraction of the vertical shortening. The fraction, on the order of 1/10 to 1/3, is determined by the value of Poisson's ratio for the material under the specified conditions. But in a prism of rock in equilibrium in the earth's crust, the adjoining rock furnishes side-support, prevents failure, and inhibits lateral expansion. Being thus constrained, a mass of rock at depth is under compressive stress laterally as well as vertically. In simple elastic strain under the conditions just described, the lateral stress would be somewhere between 1/9 to 1/2 of the vertical stress.[20] This follows from Hooke's law:

$$\varepsilon_2 = \frac{1}{E} \left\{ S_2 - \nu(S_1 + S_3) \right\} = 0$$

Where ε_2 = horizontal strain S_1 = stress in the vertical axis
    ν = Poisson's ratio S_2 = stress in one horizontal axis
    E = Modulus of elasticity S_3 = stress in a second axis taken as
                                        equal to S_2

Consequently, $S_2 = S_3 = S_1 \nu / (1 - \nu)$
Thus, if Poisson's ratio (ν) is 0.10,* S_2 is 1/9 S_1
    "   "   "   " 0.25, S_2 is 1/3 S_1
    "   "   "   " 0.33, S_2 is 1/2 S_1

* For most rocks, Poisson's ratio ranges from 0.1 to 0.27 at ordinary pressures and temperatures. It appears to increase with stress; *e.g.*, for Rockport Granite it increases from .08 at zero stress to 0.172 at 202 kg./sq. cm.—Birch, Francis, in *Handbook of Physical Constants*, G.S.A. Special Paper No. 36, 1942, pp. 73–79.

[19] Bursts of this nature have been termed "inherent bursts" as contrasted with "induced bursts" which are due to localization of stress by artificial openings.—Yates, A. B., and Shenon, P. J., in Symposium on Rock-bursts, A.I.M.E. *Tech. Pub. 1468*, p. 28, 1941.
[20] *Cf.* Bucky, P. B., in Rock Bursts, A.I.M.E. *Tech. Pub. 1468*, p. 52.

While the stress at depth must have horizontal components, it has not been proved that, at say 4000 to 10,000 feet, these are much smaller than the vertical component (S_1). In fact there is some reason to believe that through long lapse of time major stress differences have been relieved by permanent "set" or by adjustment along joint planes. Accordingly the assumption, made by some writers, that stress is hydrostatic seems permissible as one of a number of possible alternatives, although the actual conditions have not been determined.

Regardless of whether or not the stress is hydrostatic, the rock is under a state of elastic compression, which we may term the environmental stress, and is in equilibrium or nearly so.

Stress Adjoining Openings. When the miner makes a hole in the rock, he disturbs this condition of equilibrium, and, since the rock is then locally unsupported, an undue share of the pressure has to be carried by the portions of the rock adjoining the hole. The stress at the periphery of the hole is not merely the equivalent of the overlying load but reaches high local concentrations. Thus it is not necessary to call on failure of the rock along fractures or faults in the walls to account for local stress concentrations, although such features, when and if they occur, will modify and in some cases augment the stress distribution at the periphery of the opening.

To illustrate the magnitude of these stresses, let us take a slab of material, stand it on one of its edges, compress it both vertically and laterally by a load of say 4,000 p.s.i. and bore a horizontal hole through it to represent a drift. We will find that at the periphery of the hole there is a compressive stress of 8,000 p.s.i. acting on all planes normal to the perimeter.[21] Accompanying this compressive stress there is shearing stress [22] whose maximum value is 4,000 p.s.i. on planes (or rather curved surfaces) making angles of 45 degrees with the circumference of the hole.

The value of this localized stress is independent of the size of the hole. What does vary with the size of the hole is the distance into the walls to which the localized high value of the stress extends; for in-

[21] This and succeeding examples are based on mathematical calculations assuming a body of homogeneous material of infinite vertical and lateral extent. Photoelastic tests agree with the theoretical calculations within 5%, provided the test block is at least 6.25 times the diameter of the hole.—Durelli, A. J., and Murray, W. M.: Stress distribution around a circular discontinuity in any two-dimensional system of combined stress. *Proc. 14th Semi-annual Eastern Photoelasticity Conference,* Dec. 6, 1941.

[22] Shearing stress is half the difference of the two principal stresses; *i.e.,* $\frac{1}{2}(S_1 - S_2)$. At the edge of the hole, one of the principal stresses is in the direction of the radius and equal to zero, since there can be no stress across a free boundary. The other principal stress is in the direction of the tangent. In this case the shearing stress is $\frac{1}{2}(8000 - 0)$ or 4000 lb./sq. in. Away from the influence of the opening where the stress is hydrostatic, the shearing stress disappears.

stance, at a distance from the periphery equal to the diameter of the hole, the compressive stress has declined to 4,999 p.s.i.

For a hole whose cross section is other than circular, the stress is not uniformly distributed around the periphery.[23] For example, in a hole whose cross section is an ellipse with one axis ten times the other (not unlike the cross section of a stope in a vein or a bed) the compressive

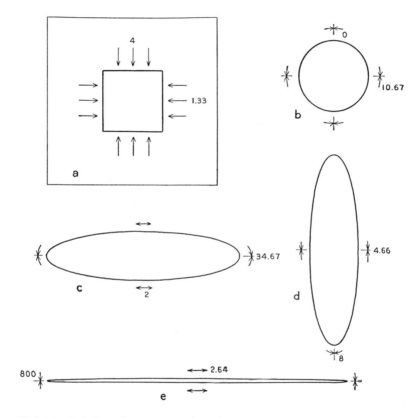

Fig. 147—Relation of stress around a discontinuity to "environmental stress." *a:* Scheme of "environmental stress" for all figures. *b:* Circular opening. *c:* Elliptical opening with horizontal axis 4 times vertical axis. *d:* Elliptical opening with horizontal axis ¼ of vertical axis. *e:* Elliptical opening with horizontal axis 100 times vertical axis.

stress at the ends of the ellipse is 80,000 p.s.i. So long as the environmental stress is such that its horizontal and vertical components are equal, the long axis of the ellipse can be vertical, horizontal, or inclined without causing any difference in the magnitude of stress concentration at its ends.

[23] Durelli, A. J., and Murray, W. M., Stress distribution around an elliptical discontinuity in any two-dimensional, uniform and axial system of combined stress. *Experimental Stress Analysis*, vol. 1, no. 1, Cambridge: Addison-Wesley Press, Inc.

But if the horizontal component of the environmental stress is different in magnitude from the vertical component, the positions and degrees of stress concentration depend on the attitude of the hole with respect to the stress-axis. Figure 147 shows the value of compressive (or in some cases, tensile) stress at the peripheries of openings having the shape of horizontal cylinders of circular and elliptical cross section if vertical pressure is taken as 4,000 lb. per square inch and horizontal pressure is taken as one-third this amount. (This would correspond to a depth of about 3,500 feet with the assumptions that material is under elastic strain, that horizontal pressure is due solely to the effect of side-support, and that Poisson's ratio is .25.)

Under these conditions, an opening which experiences the same stress in all portions of its periphery would have to be not a circle but an ellipse whose axes are proportional respectively to the vertical and horizontal stress, *i.e.*:

$$\frac{\text{Length of horizontal axis}}{\text{Length of vertical axis}} = \frac{\text{horizontal pressure}}{\text{vertical pressure}}$$

In ellipses of other proportions, the high, local stress-concentrations are evident. In the exaggerated case of an opening shaped like a flat stope ten feet high and 1000 feet broad, the side walls would have to support a compressive stress of 800,000 lb. per square inch. As this is far in excess of the strength of any known rock, the opening would collapse, of course, before it reached these dimensions.

For holes whose cross section is neither circular nor elliptical, the stress distributions are not readily calculable but have been determined by experiment for certain shapes. It has been found, for example, that extremely high stress concentrations exist at sharp corners and re-entrants. Stresses in pillars depend on the shape of the pillars with respect to that of the surrounding opening but increase rapidly with the ratio of size of room to size of pillar.

The foregoing calculations neglect the influence of the component of stress in the third dimension, *i.e.*, parallel to the geometrical axis of the hole. This leads to no serious error in regard to stresses on surfaces parallel to this axis, inasmuch as the stress distribution, except near the ends of the hole, closely approximates that of plane strain for which the calculations are valid. At most points the stress axis parallel to the long dimension of the hole will be a mean axis but where stress on radial planes approaches zero or becomes negative, the longitudinal axis becomes a principal axis. As a result, the planes of maximum normal stress at such points become normal to the axis instead of radial and the planes of maximum shearing stress stand locally at 45 degrees to the longitudinal direction.

The results of the calculations are hardly applicable in a quantitative way because, in the first place, we do not know the value of the environmental stresses and because, furthermore, we have assumed that the material behaves elastically and is homogeneous. Nevertheless, they serve to demonstrate the approximate positions and the order of magnitude of the stresses that may be expected.

Mode of Failure

In rocks the condition of elasticity is not perfectly fulfilled; yet where rock-bursts occur the rocks are clearly in an elastic rather than a plastic state. "Homogeneous," of course, does not describe any rock except perhaps certain volcanic glasses, yet granular rocks, such as uniform intrusive masses, can probably be regarded as statistically homogeneous if the dimensions under consideration are much larger than those of the mineral grains. But fractures, schistosity, bedding, etc., will modify the stress distribution.

Although most authorities have assumed that failure occurs by shear, it seems probable both from theory and observation that failure on tension (or rather, perhaps, "extension") fractures plays a dominant role, as it does in all failure of brittle rocks where there is space for increase in volume. In bursts of minor, yet explosive, violence, the fragments that fly from the walls are slab-like and flake-like, bounded by surfaces that would correspond to planes of maximum normal stress rather than planes of maximum shear. Weiss,[24] it is true, attributes flaking to loss of elasticity on exposed surfaces due to absorption of water, and this theory may explain why surface flaking is deterred by coating the walls with gunite. Nevertheless, splitting and spalling along surfaces of maximum normal stress (in this case, parallel to the surfaces of openings) can and do occur without the aid of chemical changes.

Slabbing and loosening of rock at the surface of an opening have the effect of moving the periphery back into the rock mass and thus transferring the points of high stress concentration to new positions. This is a progressive process and takes time, but eventually a zone surrounding an opening becomes a fractured and shattered mass whose shape depends on the stress distribution. Some authorities term this shattered or potentially shattered zone a "pressure dome," but the assumption of

---

[24] Weiss, Oscar, Theory of rockbursts: *Journal Chem. Met. & Mining Soc. of So. Africa*, p. 31, Jan., 1938.

dome-like shape finds little confirmation either in theory or experiment.[25]

Weakening of rock in one place transfers the load to another and may trigger off a rock-burst in a surprisingly remote working place. Weakening of pillars nearly always begins by slabbing, spalling, and splitting, but when their diameter has been sufficiently reduced they may fail by shear. Removal of support, either through mining or through weakening by progressive shattering, may induce slipping on pre-existing fault planes. In fact, shearing movement on fractures appears to be a major mode of failure in the Kirkland Lake District.[26, 27]

Probably the most baffling feature of rock-bursts is their tendency to occur without any visible, immediate cause. A pillar or face may fail suddenly in a part of a mine where neither mine work nor noticeable spontaneous fracturing has occurred for many months. Whether or not either progressive shattering behind the walls or advance of mining at a remote place is adequate to explain such behavior is not known. Weiss attributes it to "elastic hysteresis," the property of rocks which causes them to adjust themselves gradually rather than instantaneously to relief of stress. In this gradual adjustment, strains would be transferred from the body of the rock to portions adjoining the workings where, on reaching critical values, they are able to touch off a sudden collapse. Whether or not this is the underlying cause, the problem of delayed failure still awaits more explicit explanation.

Prediction and Prevention

There is no accurate way of predicting the time or the place in which a rock-burst will occur, but it is often possible to recognize places where the danger is greatest. Sometimes the rocks themselves sound a note of warning by cracking, popping, and "talking." Timbers may show signs of "taking weight" and a sudden increase of weight is especially menacing. But these premonitory signs are not always present; many rock-bursts give no warning whatever. Various geophysical instruments have been devised to measure sag, accumulating strain, and vibrations, and although they seem promising, they have so far been more useful in investigating fundamental principles than in actual prediction.[28]

[25] Weiss, Oscar, in symposium on Rock bursts: *A.I.M.E. Tech. Pub. No. 1468*, p. 17, 1941.

[26] Robson, W. T., Rock-burst incidence, research and control measures at Lake Shore Mines Ltd., *Can. Mining & Met. Bull.* no. 441; *Trans.*, vol. 49, pp. 347–374, 1946.

[27] Hopkins, Harold, Faulting at the Wright-Hargreaves Mine with notes on ground movements, *Can. Mining & Met. Bull.* no. 343; also *Trans. Can. Inst. Min. & Met.*, vol. 43, pp. 700–701, 1940.

[28] Yates, A. B., and Shenon, P. J., in Rock Bursts, a Symposium: *A.I.M.E. Tech. Pub. No. 1468*, 1942, p. 35.

Robson, W. T., Rock-burst incidence, research and control measures at Lake Shore Mines, Ltd., *Can. Inst. Min. & Met. Bull.* no. 441; also *Transactions*, vol. 44, pp. 371–374, 1946.

Calculations based on experimental measurements of the strength of rocks and the weight of overlying load involve certain assumptions and can hardly be expected to yield more than generalized results. For one thing, the shapes of most workings are too irregular to lend themselves to mathematical calculation. Therefore models give the best indication as to vulnerable points. Bucky[29] recommends a model built of the same material as the prototype and subjected to centrifugal force by rotation in a centrifuge.

For detailed studies of stress distribution, models using the photoelastic principle have proved extremely useful. The model is made of a transparent plastic, which in the absence of strain is optically isotropic. When stressed it becomes anisotropic and behaves toward light like a uniaxial crystal. Thus, when the unstressed model is viewed between two crossed polarizers (Nichol prisms or polaroid plates) it remains dark like the rest of the field. If it is stressed uniformly it takes on a uniform color which changes to higher and higher orders as the stress is increased. When, as in most experiments, the stress is not uniformly distributed, curving color-bands appear and each band, like a contour line, connects all points that experience the same shearing stress. To determine the shearing stress at any particular point, one needs merely to count the color bands just as one would determine the height of a hill by counting the contours on a map. It is a useful fact that in the cases of plane stress and plane strain the distribution of stress within a body depends entirely on the shape of the body and the manner of loading and is independent of the absolute magnitude of the stress or the elastic constants of the material[30] so long as the material is homogeneous and behaves elastically. In this way a replica in which the mine openings are cut to scale will show the points of greatest stress-concentration and therefore the places where there is greatest danger of rock-bursts. Trial will indicate the most stable shapes for stopes and pillars. The model does not of course take into account the variations from uniformity that appear when different rock-types are present in the same mine, nor can it very readily be induced to show the effects of joints, cleavage, or bedding planes. These irregularities can be handled only by making allowance for them in a qualitative way, with experience as the main guide.

No sure way of preventing rock-bursts has been discovered, but some methods of mining invite failures, whereas other methods reduce their frequency and minimize their disastrous effects. Each mine presents its

[29] Bucky, P. B., Use of models for the study of mining problems: *A.I.M.E. Tech. Pub. No. 475*, 1931.

[30] Timoshenko, S., *Theory of Elasticity*, p. 24. New York: McGraw-Hill, 1934.

own problems, depending on the openings already in existence, on the nature and structure of the rocks, and on the nature, attitude, and shape of the orebodies. In each case, economic conditions may of course limit the choice of mining methods that can be used. A few general principles have emerged from experience, however. One is that pillars are danger spots, not only because the pillars themselves are likely to fail, but because they induce concentrated stresses in the rock above and below them. Another is that support of the roof or hanging wall, while unlikely to prevent collapse, may help to retard it. Supports consisting of stulls with cushion blocks are of some help but are ineffectual under severe conditions. Closely spaced "pigsties," built of timber and filled with rock, are much more effective. Flexible steel linings, made of arched railroad iron, are used to keep travel ways open in the deep Indian gold mines. Circular steel drift sets have proved effective in the Lake Shore mine.[31] They are insulated from direct contact with the rock by a cushion of broken waste on the floor, a foot of sand filling between the lagging and the side-walls and about a foot of open space below the back. For stopes, filling with sand or rock is most essential, especially in steeply dipping openings. It is always subject to compaction amounting to ten or twenty percent of its volume, but it does have a tendency to retard sagging.

The critical counter measures against rock-bursts have been summarized by Yates[32] as follows:

1. For the safest and most efficient extraction of an oreshoot, adopt a properly planned sequence of stoping for the whole shoot.

2. Adopt a plan as nearly approaching the longwall ideal as possible.

3. Avoid the merging of two large excavations in depth.

4. Eliminate pillars or reduce them to minimum numbers. (At the Teck-Hughes mine the practice is to recover large pillars by drilling them with diamond drills and breaking the entire pillar with a single blast. This avoids the dangerous procedure of nibbling at a pillar until its size is reduced to the bursting point.)[33]

5. Distribute stresses as evenly as possible along all solid faces surrounding an excavation. This may be accomplished by keeping the faces straight.

6. Stope parallel veins singly, the hanging wall vein first, and where veins branch, begin stoping at the intersection and move away from it one branch at a time.

7. If possible, stoping should proceed away from a fault or other plane of weakness.

[31] Robson, W. T., Adamson, J. C., and Selnes, W. E., Rock-bursts at Lake Shore Mines: *Can. Inst. Min. & Met. Bull. 333;* also *Transactions,* vol. 43, p. 28, 1940.

[32] Rock bursts, A Symposium: *A.I.M.E. Tech. Pub. No. 1468,* 1942, p. 38.

[33] Christian, J. D., Rock-bursts at the Teck-Hughes Mine: *Can. Inst. of Min. & Met. Bull. No. 331;* also *Transactions,* vol. 42, p. 563, 1939.

8. Stoping should proceed at a sufficient rate to take advantage of rock hysteresis.

9. Avoid openings within pillars as far as possible.

10. Footwall drives under pillars are considered more dangerous, in some mining districts, than reef drives (*i.e.*, drives on the vein or orebody) if the latter are reasonably well supported.

11. Inasmuch as sagging begins as soon as excavations are opened, put in supports as soon as possible and as near the face as mining will permit. The initial supports should be permanent, as replacements allow another period of sagging. If filling is used for support, it should be tightly packed.

12. The supports are not a local matter and the need for them does not end when a stope is worked out; the need depends on the relationship of the stoped-out areas to the mine as a whole.

SOURCES OF MINERAL RAW MATERIAL

A mining and smelting operation uses a number of mineral raw materials besides the ore. Fuel, being one of the most important, should not escape mention, especially since some geologists, entering the employ of a metal mining company, have found themselves spending a large share of their time examining coal prospects. But coal, as well as petroleum and natural gas, are subjects in themselves and beyond the province of this book. Other materials, notably concrete aggregate, fluxes, and clay, are often to be found within convenient reach of the base of operations, and the geologist who, in the course of his work, becomes familiar with the local rock formations, both consolidated and unconsolidated, can often unearth new sources if he is acquainted with the requirements.

Concrete Aggregate

Every large mining company uses significant quantities of concrete in surface construction and for lining shafts and stations underground. Aside from Portland cement, the concrete calls for fine aggregate (sand) and coarse aggregate (gravel or crushed stone).

For fine aggregate, pure quartz sand is the most desirable and should be uniform in grain size. Marine sand is likely to be the best sorted, both mineralogically and as to size. River sand is more variable, and glacial sand is poorly sorted. However, sand from the water-laid parts of glacial deposits, such as kames, eskers, and outwash plains, is satisfactory, and a knowledge of glacial geology is helpful in prospecting for it.

Crushed stone for coarse aggregate should be uniform, durable, and correctly graded as to size. Weakness, porosity, and the presence of clay, gypsum, and anhydrite are very undesirable; thus, argillaceous limestone, shale, and slate are usually poor.   The temptation to use soft rock easily crushed and quarried or, because it is always readily accessible, waste from mine dumps, is likely to lead to poor economy in the end. While some mine waste is highly satisfactory, the wall rock of most orebodies contains not only sulphides which are very deleterious but soft sericite or kaolin.   Better, though somewhat more expensive, sources which will be evident to the geologist who has mapped the rocks, should be available in most mining districts.

For gravel, the best material is that made up of pebbles of quartz or quartzite, although pebbles of other hard rocks are very satisfactory. Pebbles of shale, schist, and decomposed rock are objectionable.   The sources of gravel are similar to those of sand but include disintegrated quartz conglomerate.

The aggregate, whether coarse or fine, should be clean.   One impurity which is easily overlooked is organic matter in the form of weak organic acids which may form transparent and virtually invisible coatings on pebbles and sand grains.   It seriously impairs the setting qualities of the concrete [34] but can be removed by washing with a 3% solution of caustic soda.   Fortunately it is absent from sand in limestone districts.

Limestone

Limestone is used as a flux in at least small amounts in smelter charges of almost all types and in large proportions when the smelter charge would otherwise contain an excess of silica.   Limestone for this purpose should carry as little silica as possible.

For iron furnaces, the sulphur and phosphorus content should be low; S should not exceed 0.5% although few limestones carry this much; P should be under 0.1% for basic iron and under 0.01% for low-phosphorus iron.[35]

Quicklime is used to neutralize acid pulps in cyanide plants and, where necessary, in flotation mills.   It is made by "burning" limestone in a kiln.   Limestone is so common that suitable supplies are available within convenient distance of most milling and smelting plants, but the geologist's knowledge of local stratigraphy and structure may enable him to locate sources more convenient for quarrying than those currently in use.   In some districts where limestone is absent, calcite vein-matter is used as a source of lime.

[34] Legget, Robert, *Geology and Engineering*, p. 633.   New York: McGraw-Hill, 1939.
[35] Patterson, Seely B., Crushed stone and broken stone; in *Industrial Minerals and Rocks*: A.I.M.E., 1937, p. 806.

Silica Flux

In most modern base-metal smelters, a high proportion of the feed consists of concentrate which is low in silica and in many cases high in pyrite and chalcopyrite. Since the iron in the concentrate has to be removed in the form of slag, the addition of silica to the charge is necessary in order to form iron silicates. Some silica flux comes to the smelter in response to a premium for quartz-rich ores, but if there is not enough of this type of material, silica must be added deliberately. The two commonest forms of silica flux are vein-quartz and sandstone or quartzite. If vein-quartz can be found which contains even a small content of gold or silver, so much the better. Quartzites for fluxing purposes should be low in the oxides of calcium, magnesium, iron, and aluminum, as these elements counteract part of the fluxing value of the silica. The geologist from his knowledge of the geology of the district may be able to locate sources of pure sandstone or quartzite conveniently situated for quarrying and thus save the cost of buying and transporting silica flux from a remote source.

Clay

Clay is used underground for tamping the dynamite charge and about the blast-furnace for plugging the tap holes. For both purposes local clay is usually used. The chemical composition of the clay is of minor importance—the chief consideration is proper consistency.

A large smelter uses a substantial amount of firebrick and some smelters, especially those remote from industrial centers operate their own brick plants. Clay for firebrick should be high in aluminum silicate and low in iron, calcium, and magnesium. A nearly white clay consisting of virtually pure kaolinitic minerals is best. Geologically there are two types of clay—residual and transported. Residual clays are to be sought in the weathered zones of shales and slates. Some good residual clays are found in the subsoil overlying limestones whose calcium and magnesium carbonates have been leached out, thus concentrating the insoluble aluminum silicate which existed as an impurity in the rock.

Transported clays are decomposition products carried, sorted, and deposited by water. They are to be sought in alluvial valleys, alluvial terraces, or in the clay layers of unconsolidated marine or lacustrine sediments. Glacial clays are usually less suitable if chemical purity is important, since they consist partly of ground rock that has escaped weathering and sorting.

Clays suitable for first-quality brick carry 36% to 42% Al_2O_3 and

50% to 57% SiO₂ with CaO and MgO, each under 0.5% and iron oxide under 2%. Alumina brick is made from clays containing 50% to 80% Al₂O₃ and 13% to 45% SiO₂ with less than 1.5% iron oxide.[36]

Grinding Pebbles

Pebbles formerly used as a grinding medium in ball-mills and tube-mills have been largely displaced by forged steel balls but are still used in some mills for special reasons. "Danish pebbles" from the countries bordering the North Sea and the English Channel are the standard. They are composed of flint which is hard and especially tough. Although flint and chert pebbles, weathered from chalk and limestone, are preferred, quartz and quartzite and even pebbles of granite and other rocks are used.

SELECTED REFERENCES

Engineering Geology

Fox, Cyril S., *Engineering Geology*. New York: D. Van Nostrand Company, Incorporated; London: Technical Press, Limited, 1935.

Legget, Robert, *Geology and Engineering*. New York: McGraw-Hill Book Company, Incorporated, 1939.

Ries, H., and Watson, T. L., *Engineering Geology*, 2nd Edition. New York: John Wiley and Sons, Incorporated, 1947.

Hydrology

Meinzer, Oscar (Editor) *Hydrology* (Physics of the Earth, vol. 9.) New York: McGraw-Hill Book Company, Incorporated, 1942.

Tolman, C. F., *Ground Water*. New York: McGraw-Hill Book Company, Incorporated, 1937.

Subsidence

Briggs, Henry, *Mining Subsidence*. London: Edward Arnold and Company, 1929.

Crane, W. R., *Subsidence and Ground Movement in the Copper and Iron Mines of the Upper Peninsula, Michigan*. U. S. Bureau of Mines, Bulletin No. 295, 1929.

Lane, W. T., and Roberts, J. H., *Principles of Subsidence and the Law of Support*. London: Alfred A. Knopf, Limited, 1929.

Moulton, H. G., Earth and rock pressures, *Transactions, American Institute of Mining and Metallurgical Engineers*, vol. 63, pp. 327–351, 1920.

Vanderwilt, John W., Ground movement adjacent to a caving block in the Climax Molybdenum Mine, *Transactions, American Institute of Mining and Metallurgical Engineers*, Technical Publication 2000, 1946.

[36] Tyler, Paul M., and Heuer, R. P., Refractories, in *Industrial Minerals and Rocks*, p. 614. A.I.M.E., 1937.

21

Writing and Reading Reports

Most reports . . . representing geological results have a common major theme—the possibility and cost of commercial ore.
—Augustus Locke [1]

No matter how much satisfaction the geologist may derive from gathering his information and drawing his conclusions, the results of his work are of little practical value unless they are translated into action by the operating staff. Depending on the magnitude of the problem, the geologist will make his report to a mine superintendent, a general manager, or a board of directors. The report may take the form of a conversation with the mine captain while waiting for the cage, or it may be a formal presentation around the table in a board room. It may be a letter written by carbide light in a log cabin and illustrated by pencil sketches, or it may be a thick typewritten tome, leatherbound, with carefully drafted and colored illustrations. Whatever form the report may take, its purpose is to present conclusions in a definite manner and submit recommendations in convincing form.

Often the most persuasive and convincing reports are oral, but even then there should be a supplementary written record, which is likely to belong to one of three types:

> Progress report,
> Periodical report,
> Final or special report.

Progress Reports

The geologist, when making an examination in the field, will wish to keep his principals informed of the progress of his work. He does this

---

[1] The profession of ore-hunting: *Econ. Geol.*, vol. 16, p. 256, 1921.

either by formal reports once a week or once a fortnight, or by frequent letters written whenever there is an opportunity to send them or at such times as definite results become available. The home office is always intensely interested in the work of its men in the field, even though reports may not be acknowledged as regularly as the field man might wish. Besides such routine questions as how much money he is spending and how many men he is employing, the home office will want to know how he is conducting his examination, what problems he is encountering, how long it will take him to finish and, particularly, how the mine looks to him at the moment. In conveying his impressions, the geologist has to steer a careful course between committing himself only to what has been confirmed (and thereby appearing very uninformative) and, on the other hand, suggesting conclusions and predictions that he may have to retract when full information is assembled. This is largely a matter of the personalities of the people for whom he is working. A sympathetic and understanding superior will realize that early reports are tentative and will be ready to revise his own impressions as the geologist's view becomes more mature, so that periodical reports present an opportunity to build up a mental picture and lay a better foundation for recommendations than could be presented in a single final report. Some executives are of the critical type, however, and want to cast early predictions in the geologist's teeth if later facts reverse the first impressions. Under these conditions the field man needs to be very cautious, especially in presenting opinions which have an optimistic flavor.

PERIODIC REPORTS

The geologist who is attached to the staff of an operating mine or who is conducting a long examination usually makes regular reports at monthly intervals. These reports present a considerable amount of routine data, such as feet of development work accomplished, results and averages of sampling, and tons of ore in sight, but they also offer an opportunity to present opinions and discuss problems. It is not a bad plan to take space in each monthly report to summarize a particular topic or explain some aspect of the geology. The geologist will command more attention and will be in a better position to get action on his recommendations if he can make his report interesting as well as factual, explaining the significance of his facts and observations, the bearing they have on development, the problems they raise, and the steps that can be taken to solve them. The succession of reports constitute a continued story, and the reader awaits the next installment with interest.

In periodic reports it is well to present successive topics in the same order in each report. This has certain disadvantages, as will be seen, but since one must so often go through the accumulated reports of a year and take out all of the information bearing on a single topic, it is convenient to find this topic in the same position in each report. No one outline will serve for all mines or for all companies, but one form which has proved serviceable on a particular job may be given as an example.

Examplar Mining Company
Geological Department

Monthly Report No. 18   January, 1946

1. Work accomplished
   a. Geologic Mapping
   b. Sampling
2. Results of Previous Recommendations
   a. Development work
      (Here tabulate footage of winzes, raises, shafts, drifts, crosscuts)
   b. Sampling (give average over stated intervals)
      (1) old workings
      (2) new development
3. Discussion of Results
   (Here describe any new ore that has been opened up or indicated by sampling and explain its significance and its relation to the development problem as a whole. Discuss any new geological disclosures or ideas)
4. Plans for Future Work   (Sampling and geological investigation)
5. New Recommendations
6. Status of Prospects
   Tabulate:
      Prospects completed during the month (list by number)
      Prospects in progress
      Prospects not started
      Prospects newly recommended

Maps and sections should accompany the periodic report to show the locations in which development work has been carried out and where it is still recommended. For most purposes, small-scale maps which can be bound with the report are the most convenient. A plan or longitudinal section on the scale of 500 or 1000 feet to the inch is usually sufficient. You can save labor by using a set of tracings which you bring up to date each month for making the prints. On the prints you may, for example, use yellow to show development work completed during the month and red to show development recommended.

In addition to these maps you may wish to include detailed plans of selected parts of the mine to illustrate topics or descriptions which you presented in the text.

FINAL AND SPECIAL REPORTS

A final report, submitted after an investigation is completed, is a comprehensive summary of all the pertinent observations, conclusions, and recommendations that result from the entire examination. It need not reiterate such details as have already been submitted in progress reports, but it should summarize them in such a manner that the final report will be complete in itself without reference to other documents.

A special or topical report is similar in nature but is submitted in the course of work at an operating property when occasion arises. For example, if you propose a program for developing some part of the property, you will wish to summarize all of the facts that bear on the project and give the reasons for your recommendations. You may well include with this an estimate of the proposed expenditure and a time schedule giving the date at which each phase of the development should be finished.

The ensuing suggestions apply chiefly to final and special reports.

SUGGESTIONS FOR PREPARING REPORTS

PRIVATE REPORTS

When to Write the Report

Complete the report as soon as possible, while the facts are still fresh in your mind. Indeed, it is a good plan to start writing before the field work is more than half finished, even though you will have to rewrite it later on. The attempt to put your ideas and conclusions on paper will call attention to any gaps in your observations before it is too late to fill them. It will start you looking for evidence that will support or destroy your tentative conclusions

Always allow plenty of time for preparing the report. Some people need more time than others, but my own experience is that it takes nearly as long to write the report and draw up the maps as it does to make the field investigation. Of course this period is shortened if some of the office work has been done concurrently with the field work, but when there is a deadline to be met, it always seems to come too soon.

Arrangement

Summary and Table of Contents. Every report of more than a few pages should begin with a summary and table of contents. The summary, although it is not prepared until after the report is written, should appear at the very beginning, immediately after the title-line or title-page. If you put it there the reader will see it immediatly; you can make sure that he will not miss your main points even if he does not read the whole report. The summary need not be an abstract, nor is it necessarily a condensation of all the matter presented in the report. It should merely list the chief conclusions and recommendations. Above all, it should answer the first questions that the reader is likely to ask, and if the reader is a business man, the questions are: What kind of mine is it? What do you think of it? Is there any ore? Can any more ore be found and how? How much will it cost to find it? What profits will it yield? In a short report the summary should not exceed a single page; in a report of fifty pages, the summary might extend to four or five pages if necessary.

The table of contents should come after the summary and before the body of the report. It should list the headings and subheadings in exactly the same wording that you use in the report itself, with subheadings indented to indicate their relationship to the main headings. A table of contents or an outline, aside from assisting the reader, is likely to reveal to the writer any faultiness in arrangement.

Order of Topics. As contrasted with the table of contents which, by its nature, cannot be set down in final form until the body of the report has been written, an outline, prepared before the writing begins at all, serves continuously as a guide to the order of topics. There is no need to adhere to it rigidly; in fact you should change and revise it whenever a better arrangement suggests itself. The order of topics that you will eventually use will be the one that allows you to present the critical problems most effectively and to state your conclusions most clearly and convincingly. This order will not be the same for every mine. For example, such a topic as "Water Supply" may be the critical consideration for a mine on the Chilean desert and will, therefore, deserve early discussion, whereas the same topic would be of only secondary concern among the myriad lakes of the Canadian Shield. Similarly, stratigraphy may be the key to ore distribution in one district but of negligible importance in another. Therefore, the outlines [2] that appear in some of the texts and handbooks, though useful as a check against omissions, are not always conducive to the most desirable arrangement. If they are followed too closely they may result in a stodgy presentation

[2] Westervelt, William Young, Mine examinations, valuations and reports, in *Mining Engineers' Handbook*, Robert Peale, Ed. New York: John Wiley & Sons, 1941. Section 25, p. 30.
Hoover, Theodore Jesse, *The Economics of Mining*, p. 213. Stanford: Stanford University Press; London: Oxford University Press, Humphrey Milford, 1933.

and compel the reader to plow through endless irrelevant information before he can find the crux of the matter.

Above all, the report should never be a chronological recital of your own experiences during the examination. The reader is superbly unconcerned as to whether you saw Locality *A* before or after Locality *B;* he wants to read about all matters of one sort at the same time, regardless of the order of your observations. Nor is the body of the report the place in which to record the itinerary of your trip. You may wish to give your employer a statement of what you did each day in order to assure him that you spent your time profitably, but the place for such a statement is in a covering letter, not in the body of the report itself.

The location of the mine or district is always important and should be specified early in the report unless it is certain to be familiar to the reader. Obviously the directors of the Climax Molybdenum Company would hardly need to be told that their mine is in Colorado, but the vice-president of an investment house in New York is naturally interested in knowing whether the Carmen prospect is in Cuba or Chile. The writer should take the reader into his confidence also to the extent of disclosing what metal the mine aspires to produce. Odd as it may seem, I have read reports in which I could discover this interesting detail only by searching the pages for a table of assays. Aside from these obvious matters, the writer should give himself complete freedom to place emphasis on the topics that are of first importance.[3]

Tables and Appendices. In arranging the text, give every consideration to the long-suffering reader. When you present such supporting data as petrographic descriptions which the reader can omit without losing the thread of the discourse, have them typed in single space (if the body of the report is double-spaced) or block the paragraphs out by indenting the left-hand margin. Whenever you submit numerical information, set it up in the form of a table which the reader can scan or study exhaustively as he prefers. If you are going to describe several geological formations, preface your descriptions with a stratigraphic column, and if you are discussing a complex series of geological events, present a chronological table in order to give the reader a quick preview.

In any long report there is likely to be a good deal of supplementary information—cost data, tables of assays, calculations and even geological description—that is worth placing on record for its possible value but which is not essential to the main discussion. Material of this sort can

---

[3] As already explained, these remarks regarding order of topics do not apply to periodic reports.

very properly appear in an appendix, keyed to the report by references at the appropriate places in the text. No harm will result if the appendix turns out to be more voluminous than the report itself.

Style

Although "style" may suggest the ornate writing of an eighteenth century novelist, the word applies equally well to the manner, whether good or bad, in which a geologist expresses himself. Since his aim is to describe his observations lucidly and to present his opinions convincingly, he can accomplish his purpose best by using a style that is simple and straightforward. To do so is not as easy as it might seem, and the technical writer finds scope for all the artistry and ingenuity he possesses when he sets down his ideas in wording that is accurate and unambiguous yet direct and easy to follow. I have found these few hints helpful in trying to avoid the involved and awkward phrasing that is too common in geological reports:

Use the active instead of the passive voice wherever possible. Instead of "the veins are displaced by faults which have been mineralized," say "mineralized faults displace the veins." However, if you have been talking about veins rather than faults, it may be permissible to use the passive in order to avoid changing the subject. It seems pardonable also to say "the veins are stoped by caving methods" for no one cares who, in particular, performs the stoping. But the entanglements of the passive lie in wait for you if you follow a roundabout path in order to avoid the first person singular. Although your observations should be impersonal and objective, there is no need to be afraid of the capital I when occasion calls for it; too many I's are not so much a sign of bad writing as of egocentric thinking. "I believe" is much more direct and no more egotistical than "It is the considered opinion of the writer" and it is certainly less ambiguous than saying "it is believed" without disclosing who does the believing. There is a school of thought, less influential than it used to be, which contends that scientific papers should be written in the third person. Whether or not this is the best form for published writings, it is quite unnecessary in a professional report where the client is paying good money for your personal opinion.

After writing the first draft, go through it and weed out unnecessary words. Consider, for example, the introduction to a recent report: "The mines pertaining to this company lie two hundred kilometers in a southwesterly direction from the city of Cordoba." Why not simply: "The company's mines are two hundred kilometers southwest of Cordoba."?   Geologists seem to derive some subtle pleasure (not shared by the reader) from saying "The veins lie in close proximity (or juxtaposition) to one another" instead of "The veins are close together."   An equally pedantic practice is to record strikes in the form "N35E–S35W," as though, when the strike is N35E, it could possibly be other than S35W if viewed in the opposite direction.   That this mode of expression can be ambiguous as well as clumsy is evident from this sentence taken from the report of an otherwise estimable geologist: "The deposit occurs in a northwest-southeast band of dolomite enclosed on either side by shales.   The strike of the dolomite progressively changes in the neighborhood of the orebodies from northwest-southeast to east-west and finally 10 or 15 degrees north of east by south of west."   Anyone who attempts to sketch the outcrop of the dolomite from this description will be reminded of Stephen Leacock's frantic king who mounted his horse and rode off rapidly in all directions, for there are definitely two, and conceivably, six different shapes which would meet these specifications.   If the writer had been content to pursue the outcrop in one direction at a time, he could have expressed his meaning unequivocally by saying, "The strike . . . progressively changes from northwest to west and finally . . . to S 75 or 80 W"—if that perchance is what he meant.

If cumbersome and ambiguous phrases make the reading difficult, the over-use of technical terms makes a report positively unintelligible so far as the non-scientific reader is concerned.   Technical terminology has its use, of course; it is the scientist's shorthand and, from one geologist to another it may save space, explanation, and qualification.   But even the geologically literate reader bogs down in a paragraph in which technical terms are too thickly concentrated.   This sentence, from a government report, is more commendable for its terseness than for its ready comprehensibility: "The texture is subhedral, inequigranular, inequant and diverse."   The young graduate, especially, needs to curb his inclination to use technical terms gratuitously in the subconscious desire to display his learning.   It is not a bad plan to go through a report with a blue pencil and see how many common words you can substitute for ten-dollar technical ones.   This will make the going easier, even for the scientific reader and, embarrassingly enough, it is likely to expose any vagueness of ideas that may be hiding behind impressive double-talk.   If the report is to be read by a company official who happens not to be a technical man, express yourself in words as simple as may be used without insulting his intelligence.

The reader will be grateful also if, in addition to using simple phrasing and intelligible wording, you will arrange the sentences and paragraphs in such a way that he will have an inkling as to what you are about to discuss, before you regale him with a feast of otherwise indigestible facts.   To this end the familiar rhetorical device known as the topic sentence is most helpful.   In particular it is a good rule never to begin a paragraph with "at" or any other designation of locality, for such words automatically launch a description of an outcrop or prospect before telling the reader why he is asked to read about it.   What could make duller plodding than a series of paragraphs each beginning in some such manner as: "At latitude 30, 760 N, 7497 E, 500 feet south of the northeast corner post of the Wild Ass claim, there is an exposure of partly decomposed diabase . . ."?   Of course, it is permissible and even necessary to describe localities, and the "anti-at" rule does not apply if an entire series of locality-paragraphs is prefaced with an introductory or summary statement.

Finally, a wealth of sound advice is available in the volume [4] known familiarly among Survey geologists as the "sex appeal bulletin."   Every writer will profit by reading it religiously even though in places it may seem to lean over a bit in the direction of purism.

Length

The length of a report ranges from a page or less, for a brief examination of a hopeless prospect, to a hundred pages or even more for a prolonged investigation of an important property.   The proper length depends not on how much the writer can think of to say but on how much information or discussion is really worth setting down.   There is no true merit in length for length's sake.   Unfortunately there are some geologists who believe that a long report is more impressive than a short one, and there are business men who would feel that they were not getting their money's worth if they paid a thousand dollars for a five-page report even though it represented weeks of hard work.   But these are not the usual reasons for undue length; the more common cause is betrayed in the famous epigram, "I am writing you a long letter because I have not the time to write a short one."   The first draft, especially if it is dictated, is likely to be wordy and rambling; only by revising and condensing can a writer squeeze repetition and circumlocution out of the text.   The beginner, especially, needs to rearrange and rewrite much in the spirit of Lew Wallace, who wrote Ben Hur on slates.   One may

[4] Wood, George McLane, Suggestions to Authors of Papers Submitted for Publication by the United States Geological Survey, 4th edition by B. H. Lane. U.S.G.S. Administrative Publication, 1935.

well take as a model the student of mathematics at a Swedish university who presented a doctoral thesis consisting of a page and a formula and, despite opposition from a few conventional faculty members, received his merited degree. In the same vein is Josh Billings' quip: "I don't care how much a man talks as long as he says it in a few words."

For despite the advantages of a leisurely and logical development of an idea, the writer has to remember that only a reader who is intensely interested in the subject or has nothing else of importance to do will wade through a treatise that is overly wordy. A report designed for the thorough indoctrination of the reader defeats its own purpose if it is so lengthly that nobody reads it through.

This does not mean that the report should be brief to the point of neglecting any of the necessary facts, of failing to explain the reasoning behind the conclusions, or of leaving any doubt as to what the writer means. All information that can possibly be of use ought to be included, and, with topics treated in logical order and the text supplied with plenty of subheadings, a long report is as easy to "read" as a short one. A report can be long without being long-winded.

Illustrations

Maps. Information of certain kinds presents itself much more lucidly in the form of maps and diagrams than in words. All too frequently one has to read reports that consist largely of description like this: "The second level at 2013 feet below the shaft collar is opened by drifts north and south 103 ft. and 207 ft. long respectively. In the north drift no. 1 crosscut to the east at 37.3 ft. is 93 ft. long," etc., etc., for page after page. This conveys no picture to the reader unless he reconstructs a map for himself, and it usually gives the impression that the engineer could think of nothing more important to put in his report. A few small-scale maps would tell the story much more quickly and efficiently. They should be placed where the reader can make the best use of them while he is reading, either paged in with the text or grouped at the end of the report. For this purpose they should be relatively small, preferably the standard 8½" x 11" size. If this size does not give sufficient space to show the necessary detail, a map 11" x 14", which can be bound along with the manuscript by folding it only once, will cover a surprising amount of ground. Most field maps will have to be reduced to bring them to these sizes, but the reduction is usually possible without loss of essential detail. Larger maps are justified only when smaller ones would fail to convey the information, and not merely because the writer does not want to take the trouble to reduce them. If large maps are absolutely necessary, they can be folded and placed in a pocket in the back of the report, or for an exhaustive report in which many large maps are needed, they may be bound separately into an atlas.

Large rolled maps accompanying a report are an abomination. Most readers, not being handily equipped with table space, paperweights, and thumbtacks, simply will not bother to unroll the plans unless they are intensely interested in the subject matter. Then the rolls get separated from the report so that nobody can find them when they are needed, and as a report that is written to be read with maps in hand is well-nigh unintelligible without them, nothing is more baffling than a copy of the report without copies of the maps. Too often when reports are copied, the maps are omitted in order to save trouble and expense. Remember that if a report is worth copying at all the maps are worth reproducing.

But when maps are presented as a part of a report, remember that business men and executives who lack an engineering training find it difficult to grasp the significance of plans and sections especially where visualization in three dimensions is required. Composite maps are especially confusing. For this reason, block diagrams are particularly useful (see p. 177). But no matter how terrifying a white-print may be to a layman, it requires less visual imagination than does the same information presented in words.

Photographs. Good photographs add to the interest and clarity of a report. Unfortunately, however, a mine is a difficult subject to portray photographically, and the examiner finds that most of the pictures he has taken show mills, headframes, and landscapes, but little geology or ore. Yet these convey some impression of the condition of the property and the nature of the terrain. Good pictures of specimens, outcrops and underground exposures require considerable skill and practice. For underground photography, flashlight bulbs are commonly used, but electric flood-lights or even carbide lamps [5] have been found satisfactory if the time exposure is long enough. For the exposure to be long enough, the camera must be mounted on a tripod or some other kind of support. For photographing outcrops, Lahee [6] offers some useful suggestions: "It is best to photograph irregular rock surfaces on a dull day, for the shadows made by projecting edges and corners on sunny days appear on the print as black patches. Not infrequently contact lines

[5] Graton, L. C., Underground photography without flashlight: *Econ. Geol.*, vol. 22, pp. 388–399, 1927.
[6] Lahee, Frederic H., *Field Geology*, pages 417–418. McGraw-Hill, New York, 4th Edition, 1941.

and other rock structures are exposed on granular, pitted, ribbed or scratched surfaces. If one's aim is to bring out the grain, ribs, etc., take the picture on a bright day when the sun is rather low so that these minor irregularities will cast shadows; but if the structures are to be emphasized, the photographs should be made on a cloudy day."

Pictures taken with a miniature camera are entirely satisfactory when enlarged. Color photographs are excellent for bringing out rock tints, but until lately the necessity of viewing them with a stereopticon has limited their use. Recent advances in the technique of making colored prints open a wide field for illustrating reports not only with colored photographs but with colored maps.

Physical Appearance

A report that is well gotten up is sure to prejudice the reader in its favor.

A few years ago in the New York office of a mining company, one of the officials handed me a neatly bound folder. "This will interest you; it's a splendid report that Dr. Hade just sent in from Alta Baja. At least it looks like a good report—I haven't read it yet." As it happened it was a very good report, but for all Mr. Ryanheim knew it might have been atrocious. Dr. Hade's neat draughtsman, his careful typist, and a good photographic studio had conspired to produce a favorable impression before Dr. Hade's own geology had had a chance to register. On the other hand, I have always, probably unjustly, harbored doubts about the proficiency of a certain engineer of national reputation because I once had to read one of his reports that was illustrated by maps that looked as though they had been drawn by a schoolboy who lettered them with his left hand.

Appearance alone does not make a report good any more than clothes make the man, but it is conducive to a cordial reception.

PAPERS FOR PUBLICATION

Many of the rules for writing reports apply to the preparation of manuscripts for publication. Beyond these a few hints may be helpful to the novice:

Most journals and bulletins have their own editorial style as regards captions, footnotes, abbreviations, etc., and some editors return manuscripts for rewriting if they do not conform to these specifications.

There are various methods of presenting references to previous publications. For reasons of economy the present trend is toward placing all bibliographic references at the end of the article, where they may be listed either in the order in which the text refers to them, or arranged alphabetically. In the latter case they are referred to by the author's name, thus: "Husenheimer, p. 387" or, if there is more than one title by the same author, "Husenheimer, '29, p. 387," designating the article by the year of publication. There is still much to be said for the older practice of placing the reference in a footnote, where it may be found without thumbing through to the end of the article. Although the purpose of references is to give credit (or place responsibility, as the case may be) for the information that is used, another and more valuable function is to call the reader's attention to an article that might interest him. Therefore, the considerate author quotes the title in full and saves the reader the frustration of tracking down the reference in the library only to find that the article is on a subject which holds no interest for him.

Illustrations are often the most informative part of an article. It is advisable wherever possible to draw sketches to scale from actual maps or exposures, because idealized sketches are likely to be untrue to nature in some respect, and if the reader uses them for a purpose which the author did not intend, they may prove quite misleading. It is sometimes desirable, nevertheless, to publish a diagram to clarify a discussion just as one might draw a sketch on the blackboard while lecturing. But then it should be distinctly labeled "diagramatic" lest the reader take it as a faithful portrayal of observation.

Drawings for publication may be made in India ink on smooth-surface white paper, tracing cloth, or Bristol board. In applying patterns such as those used to designate rock formations, a series of ready-printed designs to be cut out and cemented to Bristol board can save labor in drafting. A helpful discussion of these methods will be found in articles by Ives.[7] Line drawings should be at least twice the size that they will take when they are reproduced, since the process of photographic reduction used in making the cut subdues any irregularities in the original drafting and increases the neatness of the picture. Allowance should be made for this reduction in selecting the size of lettering. Maps should show their scales graphically rather than in words. A note: "1 inch equals 200 feet" will not be true after reduction.

Photographs are reproduced by means of half-tone cuts from prints or enlargements on glossy paper. The original photographic prints

---

[7] Ives, Ronald L., Shades and screens for isometric block diagrams: *Econ. Geol.*, vol. 34, pp. 419–436, 1939. Additional aids to illustration: *Econ. Geol.*, vol. 35, pp. 668–670, 1940. Fabricated diagrams: *Jour. Geol.*, vol. 47, pp. 517–545, 1939. Production of broken line patterns with standard Ben Day," *Econ. Geol.*, vol. 39, pp. 152–157, 1944.

must be used, since previously published half-tones do not reproduce satisfactorily.   All photographs lose some of their definition and contrast in reproduction, therefore only really good pictures are worth reproducing, though retouching may help prints which are not of quite the best quality.[8]

READING REPORTS

A geologist often has occasion to form a preliminary opinion of a mine or prospect by reading a report written by someone else.   How much credence you may place in such a report depends largely on the competence of the person who prepared it.   If you are personally well acquainted with the writer, you will know how to interpret his statements; if you have complete confidence in him, you can accept his facts even though you may have to allow for the personal factor depending on whether he is habitually bullish or bearish; or if you know him to be incompetent or dishonest, you will probably not bother to read his report at all.   But if the report is prepared by a stranger, you will have to appraise the writer as well as the mine, judging his ability and integrity from internal evidence in the report.

INTERNAL EVIDENCE OF DEPENDABILITY

Literacy of Author

Bad grammar, misspelling, and incorrect use of technical terms are the most common earmarks of the ignoramus.   For example, you would hardly wish to spend much money on the recommendation of the following letter: [9]

Lincoln, Ga.

Esperance Mining Company
39 Tall Street,
New York,   City,
    Dear Sers,
        Seeine that You Alle Wos Miners, I thout I mite, Bee Able to Interest you ine A Good Prospeck, I hole A longe, Lease one this Property, I have Had Sevel Analeses Made of it, and the Naleses Rune Frome $9 to $129 Per Tone, Cane Furnih Copyes of thes Analese, and Foole Deetailes, if intresed, the Vaine is Fore Feat Wide, Fore Hundre Acores, of Land ine the Bondry of Land, One Good Rhodes, I bleave, it Will Deevelpe ine to a Big Mine, I thinke it Wille, Stand Eney inginyears investigation, I will

---

[8] Ridgway, J. L., *Scientific Illustration*, Stanford University Press, 1938.   (Retouching Photographs, p. 56.)
[9] This is a verbatim copy of an actual letter, with only names and addresses disguised.

Turne Over this, Mine For Short Prefet, as I have Other Thinges to Looke After,

Wille Bee Glad to Heare Frome you Regardine Same, and Wille Give you Foole Deetailes if intresed

Youers Very Truly,

(Signed)   A. A. Blest

Lincoln, Ga.

Box 203

Fortunately or unfortunately, few reports display quite such a refreshing innocence of the conventions of the English language, but the lack of technical training often gives itself away by misspellings such as "silicious," "pyrrotite," and "ignious" and I have even seen "hypergene," "fisher veins," "quarts," and "porphory." Although only purists are likely to remember that "data" and "phenomena" are plural, there are few if any trained geologists who would talk about "this strata."

Spelling in itself is hardly an infallible index, since there are excellent scientists who are congenitally poor spellers and even a few who are hopeless grammarians, but most of these realize their own shortcomings and either submit their writings for editing or employ competent secretaries. Although a good typist can eliminate errors, a poor one can introduce mistakes in spelling and grammer which make the best report read as though it were written by a dolt. The careful writer guards against this by proofreading, but unfortunately he is deprived of this protection when copies of his report are made without his knowledge. Therefore, he should always have the privilege of stipulating that his reports must not be copied without his permission, and some engineers even take the precaution of having their reports copyrighted.

Earmarks of Scientific Inadequacy

On the other hand, good spelling and grammar are not in themselves a guarantee that the writer knows his business, for educated men who lack technical training occasionally attempt to write mining reports. When they do, they are likely to give themselves away by indulging in sweeping generalities. The mine is "in the heart of a great district whose vast mineral wealth has hardly been scratched." The layman can usually be depended on to use "formation" without knowing what it means, to think that "conglomerate" is any old kind of a mixture, and that "shale" is a synonym for talus. He will usually betray his misconception of geological processes by speaking of "upheavals" and "blowouts." Since he fails to appreciate the work of erosion, he thinks of the ore deposit as related to the present surface and is prone to predict an improvement at depth without presenting any geological reasons for expecting it.

Treatment of Assay Data

The most common failing of the layman or untrained engineer is ignorance of the significance of sampling. If his report states that samples ran "up to $20," you may conclude that the best sample assayed $20 and ask "and down to what?" Sometimes a report states that the vein can be traced for x thousand feet and proceeds to estimate millions of tons on the evidence of two or three samples. Anyone who describes a "mountain of ore" on the basis of anything short of many hundred systematically taken samples immediately discredits himself unless he gives excellent reasons for belief in the uniformity of the material. The statement "not a single sample gave a blank" means nothing because worthless rock in any well-mineralized district will return assays of at least .01 oz. in gold or comparable values in other metals unless the assayer by request takes special precautions. But these are glaring examples.

If assays are listed without a record of width, you may assume that they are specimen samples and not entitled to much weight in estimating ore. Statements that "all samples are five feet wide" or "drift width" are suspect except in ore deposits which are wider than the drift. When samples are averaged without weighting for width, you may assume that the writer does not understand the principle of weighted assays and, therefore, cannot make a creditable ore estimate, and when high erratics are not reduced, you may likewise beware unless there is a plausible explanation for such treatment.

Reticence Regarding Ore

Ore, of course, is the *sine qua non* of a mine. It is on the prospects for ore that the trained engineer or geologist fixes his attention, and, until he is satisfied on that score, he does not concern himself with the excellence of facilities for operation. If the report has a great deal to say about the excellent roads, the cheap power, the abundance of labor, the timber and water supply, the good fishing, and the enjoyable hunting, with relatively little about the ore deposit, you may conclude that either the ore itself or the writer's ability to judge it is negligible. And if the report discusses the metallurgy exhaustively and with seeming competence without much concern about the ore-reserve, you may surmise that the writer is a metallurgist whose ability to size up an ore deposit may perhaps require checking.

Fact Amid Fancy

While you must always guard against gullibility, you should not allow your healthy suspicion to obscure valuable facts. Many a report on an excellent prospect has been written by the horny hand of an honest but illiterate prospector, and while betraying every evidence of gross, if unintentional, exaggeration and most deplorable methods of calculation, nevertheless contains facts which stamp the prospect as worth examining. The art is to sift the wheat from the chaff, to read between the lines, to discount exaggerated and improbable statements and find the grain of truth if it is there.

RESUME

When you read a report, you will judge the competence of its author by the appearance, arrangement and content. By the same token the reader of your own report will judge you by similar criteria. Unless your report conveys the impression that you are thoroughly competent, your opinions and conclusions will not carry the weight that you wish them to carry. In a sense, your report is the culmination of all your geological study; it is your instrument for translating your observation and reasoning into action. Therefore, it merits thought and care commensurate with the work that you have put into the investigation. If the report is to be presented orally, think over the subject matter, select the facts that are most important, eliminating all boring and beclouding detail, and plan the order in which you will present your explanations and conclusions. If the report is written, give plenty of care to the arrangement and the subject matter, and dress the document in Sunday clothes with good typing, well-drawn illustrations, and neat binding. This is no less than it deserves.

SELECTED REFERENCES

Agg, Thomas R., and Foster, Walter L., *The Preparation of Engineering Reports.* New York: McGraw-Hill Book Company, Incorporated, 1935.
Harbarger, S. A., *English for Engineers.* New York: McGraw-Hill Book Company, Incorporated, 1934.
Hoover, Theodore J., *The Economics of Mining*, Chapter 11, pp. 205–221. Stanford University, California; Stanford University Press, California; London: Humphrey Milford, Oxford University Press, 1933.

Lahee, Frederic H., *Field Geology*, 4th Edition, Chapter 22, Preparation of geologic reports, pp. 702–712. New York: McGraw-Hill Book Company, Incorporated, 1941.

Park, C. W., *English Applied in Technical Writing*. New York: F. S. Crofts and Company, 1937.

Rickard, T. A., *Technical Writing*, 3rd Edition. New York: John Wiley and Sons, Incorporated, 1931.

Ridgway, J. L., *Scientific Illustration*. Stanford: Stanford University Press, 1938.

Wood, George McLane, *Suggestions to Authors of Papers Submitted for Publication by the United States Geological Survey*. 4th Edition by B. H. Lane, 1935. U.S.G.S. Administrative Publication.

PART FOUR

TECHNOLOGICAL CHARACTERISTICS
OF ORES

22

Amenability of Ore to Treatment

. . . for since Nature usually creates metals in an impure state, mixed with earth, stones and solidified juices, it is necessary to separate most of these impurities from the ores as far as can be before they are smelted.
—Agricola de Re Metallica, 1556 [1]

To predict how much ore is likely to be found on a mining property is, of course, one of the main purposes of a geological examination, but in order to decide what *is* ore (in the technical sense) one must consider the question of what can be done with the material when and if it is mined. The answer depends partly on such economic conditions as the cost of labor, power, chemicals, and transportation, and even on such political considerations as local laws and taxes; but in large degree it depends on the nature of the ore itself. In what mineral is the metal contained? What minerals are associated with it? What is the grain size and texture of the mineral aggregate? These questions are really aspects of the geology of the ore deposit, and after answering them the geologist should be able to make a shrewd guess as to which of a variety of treatment processes will be applicable. In order to do this he needs to have some understanding of the principles of metallurgy.

He should not, however, attempt or pretend to be a skilled metallurgist. The final decisions as to what method of treatment is best suited to the ore, what portion of the metal can be recovered, and how much its recovery will cost require not only specialized knowledge but thorough laboratory tests often followed by pilot plant operations. These are the jobs of the metallurgist. The geologist's responsibility is to recognize a metallurgical problem when he sees one and to determine the stage in the development program at which professional metallurgi-

[1] Translation by Herbert Clark Hoover and Lou Henry Hoover, p. 267. London: The Mining Magazine, 1912.

cal advice is required.   For example, if an ore consists of argentite and other rich silver-bearing sulphides in a clean quartz gangue, the geologist may rest assured that it will respond to flotation, or perhaps, alternatively, to cyanidation.   Which of the two methods will be preferable and what will be the results are not critical questions until the existence of a reasonable tonnage is demonstrated.   But, if ore of the same silver content contains no visible silver minerals and is high in manganese dioxide, a preliminary metallurgical test is needed before any substantial expenditure on geological examination or development can be justified. There are, indeed, cases in which a difficult metallurgical problem is a sound reason for early rejection of a prospect.

On the other hand, the seriousness of the metallurgical obstacle depends somewhat on the magnitude of the deposit.   It is safe to assume that if an orebody is large enough and rich enough metallurgical genius will sooner or later find a way to treat it; but only a substantial deposit offers a sufficient reward to warrant the expense of the research and experimentation that is involved in pioneering in the metallurgical field. New processes, even though simple enough in the laboratory, always turn out to be full of "bugs" when full-scale operations begin.   Only a strong company can afford to be the guinea pig for testing them out. The small mine that cannot operate on thoroughly proved methods is a poor risk.   The dumps of many a prospect are littered with novel machinery which gullible mine-owners have bought from glib salesmen in the hope of getting better extraction and cheaper costs than standard equipment could provide.   In short, for small deposits a metallurgical problem may be a stop-light; for large ones the problem is merely a challenge to bold perseverance and ingenuity.

TREATMENT PROCESSES

Recovering a metal from its ore involves two kinds of processes.   One is purely physical—the separation of the metallic mineral from its gangue.   The other is chemical—breaking down the metallic mineral itself to recover the metal and get rid of the other elements that are combined with it.   Both processes are illustrated by the usual steps in treating a galena ore that occurs in calcite gangue.

First the galena is separated from the calcite; then the concentrated galena is smelted to drive off the combined sulphur and recover the metallic lead.   When the chemical part of the treatment is carried out at high temperature, as it is in the case of a lead ore, the process is described as *pyrometallurgical*; when it is accomplished by dissolving the mineral in a reagent (usually at room temperature) and precipitating a metal from the solution, the process is *hydrometallurgical*.

The metal that either of the processes yields is rarely completely free from undesirable impurities. Therefore it needs refining before it is ready for the market. The refining process consists either of remelting with the proper fluxes or of some wet chemical treatment. Of wet methods the commonest is electrolytic, *i.e.*, plating across from an anode to a cathode in an electrolyte. Thus refining methods, like reduction methods, may be classified under the headings pyro- and hydrometallurgical. Some authorities consider the electrometallurgical methods as a separate category.

Physical concentration, reduction, and refining are the three standard steps in the treatment of a typical ore, but one or even two of these steps can be omitted in special cases. If the ore is to be reduced by smelting, it usually pays to concentrate it at the mine before shipping it to the smelter; but if the smelter is close at hand concentration accomplishes no saving in freight, and, although diminishing the tonnage of ore that is smelted and reducing smelting charges, the saving may not compensate for milling costs and the inevitable losses in tailings. Therefore, concentration is often omitted if the smelter is within convenient shipping distance. Moreover, there are some ores—high-grade iron ores and some unusually rich non-ferrous ores, for instance—whose grade cannot be greatly improved by physical methods.

When wet methods of reduction are used, they usually render both concentration and smelting unnecessary. Since plants for cyaniding and for copper leaching can be built close to the mines, there is no occasion for concentrating to save transportation charges, although some ores are concentrated in order to get rid of constituents that would interfere with the chemical process. Thus gold ores that contain graphite are commonly concentrated by flotation and only the concentrate is cyanided. Most products from wet chemical treatment are ready for final refining, although some may be so impure as to require smelting. Copper that is precipitated electrolytically does not need further refining but may be sold as finished metal.

The standard metallurgical processes may be grouped as follows:

CONCENTRATION (Physical beneficiation)
   Handpicking
   Gravity methods
   Flotation [2]
   Amalgamation [2]

[2] Flotation and amalgamation, although classed here as physical methods, are partly dependent on chemical principles. Amalgamation owes its effectiveness to surface processes (whereby the gold or silver adheres to mercury) rather than to complete solution of the precious metal in mercury. Gaudin, A. M., *Principles of Mineral Dressing*, p. 477, New York: McGraw-Hill, 1939.

Magnetic concentration
REDUCTION
  Pyrometallurgical
    Smelting
    Volatilization
  Hydrometallurgical
    Cyaniding
    Other leaching methods
REFINING
  Fire refining
  Electrolytic refining
  Chemical refining

CONCENTRATION

Purposes

As already indicated, the primary reasons for concentration are to avoid paying freight on valueless rock and to reduce the tonnage of material that is to be treated by the smelter. An additional reason is that metals in certain complex ores can be separated from each other more economically by milling than by smelting. Thus at Salt Lake City the U. S. Smelting Refining and Mining Co. operates a mill next door to its smelter to separate its own and customer's ores into (1) lead concentrate, (2) zinc concentrate, and (3) copper concentrate, each of which goes to a different furnace or plant.

Calculations

The ores that are fed to a mill are known as *millheads* or simply *heads*. The product from the mill is *concentrate* and the material that is discarded is known as *tails* or *tailings*.

The effectiveness of mill operation is indicated by two factors: percentage recovery and ratio of concentration. The meaning of these terms will be evident from the following example:

Suppose that during a day's run a mill treats 100 tons of lead ore assaying 4% Pb and produces 6 tons of concentrate assaying 60% Pb. The ratio of concentration is 100:6 or 16.67:1. The recovery is calculated as follows:

	Tons	*%Pb*	*Lead contained*
Millheads	100	4	4.0 tons
Concentrate	6	60	3.6 tons

The recovery is 3.6 divided by 4.0, or 90%. The 0.4 ton of lead unaccounted for was presumably lost in the tailing which should have a weight of 94 tons (excluding water) and therefore assay 0.42% Pb.

In a well managed mill the heads and concentrates are systematically weighed and sampled as a matter of routine. The tailings are sampled also, but, as they will have been diluted by a large volume of water, their weight is difficult to determine directly; therefore it is estimated by deducting the weight of concentrates from the weight of millheads. The results of these samples should check: that is,

(weight of concentrates $\times$ assay of concentrates) *plus*
(weight of tailings $\times$ assay of tailings) *ought to equal*
(weight of millheads $\times$ assay of millheads)

If this equation does not balance there is something wrong with the sampling or weighing, or with both. In small mines the discrepancy is likely to be found in the figures for millheads; where there is no automatic sampler the millheads are often sampled casually, and where there is no mechanical weighing device their weight is commonly estimated from the assumed weight of a carload or skipload of ore, a factor that may lead to cumulative error unless it is checked periodically. Any recurring error in the weight and grade of daily millheads should be rectified at once, because it leads to deceptive conclusions in regard to the whole economics of mine and mill operation.

METHODS OF CONCENTRATION

Hand-Picking

There are many primitive mining operations in various parts of the world where groups of men, women, and children break up pieces of ore with hand hammers on hard stones or blocks of steel and, by sorting and re-sorting, discard the gangue and garner pieces of valuable mineral into separate piles. Primitive as it is, hand-sorting can be the most economical method of ore-dressing when circumstances favor it. In its more modern form, hand-picking is facilitated by mechanical aids: the ore, after coarse crushing, goes over a screen to separate the fines and under a spray to wash off dust and mud. Then a broad conveyor belt, or, less commonly, a revolving table, carries it in front of the pickers.

Used alone, hand-picking is likely to be wasteful. If the gangue is picked out of the ore, the remaining product will still be low in grade; if the ore is picked out of the waste, there will be excessive loss in the residue. But, as a preliminary to mechanical concentration, hand-sorting is often the cheapest method of separating ore from waste at coarse sizes. It may be employed either to get rid of part of the gangue and wall rock or to collect pieces of high-grade ore for direct shipment.

In either case it reduces the bulk of the ore that has to be milled and so, in effect, increases the capacity of the existing treatment plant.

Hand-sorting can be economical even in large operations.   The Alaska Juneau gold-mining enterprise owed a large part of its success in treating ore assaying only 0.035 oz. at the amazingly low mining and milling cost of 56 cents [3] per ton to the fact that the gold is confined to white quartz stringers in dark slate.   This made it possible to reject about half [3] of the run-of-mine ore by hand-sorting before mechanical milling.

In the course of mine examination, the engineer, as he sees the ore in place and in muck piles, is in a position to decide whether or not it is likely to be susceptible to hand-picking, whereas the laboratory metal-lurgist, if he receives the samples in crushed form, may have no op-portunity to form such an opinion and may even fail to investigate this possible source of economy.

Gravity Concentration

Gravity methods are mechanical refinements of the simple processes of washing and panning.   Their effectiveness depends on the difference in specific gravity between different minerals; naturally, the greater the difference the better the separation.   Since a liquid buoys up a body by the weight of the liquid displaced, a particle immersed in water has its apparent specific gravity reduced by 1.   That is, if the specific gravity of a gangue mineral is 3 and that of a metallic mineral is 5, their relative weights in water are as 2 to 4.

But the size as well as the specific gravity of a particle affects its be-havior in a liquid.   Large particles of light minerals settle as fast as small particles of heavy minerals; thus a quartz particle 4 mm. in di-ameter settles at about the same rate as a galena particle of 1 mm.   For this reason separation is imperfect unless the particles all have the same size.   Uniform sizing becomes especially important among fine particles. Thus a quartz particle .05 mm. in diameter settles at the same rate as a galena particle of half rather than one-fourth its diameter.   Among particles of very small size, gravity separation is not efficient.   There-fore, brittle minerals that tend, on grinding, to yield a high proportion of slime give poor separation by gravity methods.   Fortunately, the finer size-range is the effective field of flotation.

A great variety of machines has been used in gravity concentration,

---

[3] The percentage discarded has varied during different periods. Figures of 33%, 46%, and 53% are mentioned in the literature.   The cost of 56 cents per ton of ore trammed to the mill is for the year 1934, reckoned before any book-charges or taxes.   Croston, John J., The effect of revaluation on the gold-mining industry: *A.I.M.E. Tech. Pub. No. 907*, p. 25, 1936.

but much the commonest are jigs and vibrating tables. Auxiliary to these are boxes and cones of various forms designed to permit settling in an ascending current of water.

Gravity concentration, pure and simple, is no longer widely used except for relatively coarse ores of simple mineralogy and for ores that do not respond to flotation. But various types of gravity concentrators are used in combination with other treatment processes. Thus, ore in a relatively coarse state may pass through jigs before flotation or cyanidation. The jigs take out large grains of heavy mineral (*e.g.*, gold or galena) and save the added expense and the possible tailing loss that would be incurred if this fraction of the material went through the complete process. Tailings from flotation or cyaniding are sometimes passed over slime tables to pick up valuable particles that have escaped recovery.

Heavy-Fluid Separation

Laboratory workers who have used heavy liquids, such as acetylene tetrabromide, in which light minerals float and heavy minerals sink, have often dreamed of such a liquid cheap enough to use in full-scale ore concentration. This dream has recently partially materialized as the "sink-and-float" process (not to be confused with flotation). Substituted for the heavy fluid is a pseudo-liquid consisting of a finely-ground heavy solid in suspension in water. Galena and ferrosilicon are the solids most commonly used. For lead ores, galena is convenient as a medium because it is readily available and the portion that becomes too fine for further use can be recovered and sold along with the concentrate. Ferrosilicon has the advantage of being ferromagnetic so that it can be recovered and cleaned for re-use by means of a magnetic separator. Ferrosilicon containing 15% Si is brittle enough to be grindable to the proper size and has a density of 6.7 to 7.0. As used for cleaning iron ore on the Mesabi Range, ferrosilicon of size 65% minus 200 mesh[4] is mixed with water to a density of 2.5 to 3.4.

The sink-and-float process operates most successfully on coarse ore from 2″ down to ¼″, but it has been used on some types of ore as fine as 48 mesh (0.116″)[5] which is about the coarser limit for flotation. Thus it competes with jigging, hand sorting, and the coarser ranges

[4] Holt, Grover J., Sink-and-float separation applied successfully on the Mesabi: *E. & M. J.,* vol. 141, no. 9, pp. 33–38, Sept., 1940; *also,* Development of sink-and-float concentration on the iron ranges of Minnesota: *A.I.M.E. Tech. Pub. 1621,* 1943.

[5] Heavy media separation processes: *Ore Dressing Notes.* American Cyanamid Co., 30 Rockefeller Pl., N. Y., no. 11, July, 1942.

of tabling. The sink-and-float method is best adapted to ore that breaks in such a way that the valuable mineral or the gangue, or both, occur in chunks of fairly large size.

For most ores it is a preliminary to further concentration by flotation or other methods. On iron ores, however, since a coarse product is desired, it may be used alone. When used as a pre-concentration process it may serve either to recover a coarse marketable product, leaving a tailing that can be further concentrated, or to reject coarse waste and recover a low-grade concentrate for additional treatment. Thus, at Mascott, Tenn.,[6] a heavy-medium separation unit rejects 60% of the run-of-mine as a tailing at a size ranging from 2″ down to ⅜″. Only the remaining 40% needs to be ground and treated by flotation.

As the sink-and-float process is relatively new, its possibilities are not yet fully explored nor are its limitations clearly defined.

Flotation

The principle of the flotation process is illustrated by the parlor-trick of floating a sewing needle on water. The water is reluctant to "wet" the needle, especially if it has gathered a little oil from the fingers, so the surface of the water is locally depressed by the weight of the needle yet does not allow the needle to sink completely through it. Similarly a particle of sulphide, suitably treated, would float at the surface of the water while a particle of quartz would sink. This is because the quartz, unlike the sulphide, is "wetted" by the water. Or, stated differently, the sulphide adheres to air and the quartz to water. This same preferential adherence applies not only to mineral particles at the top of the liquid but also to particles that are submerged, thus sulphide particles adhere to bubbles of air and are buoyed upward as the bubbles rise to the surface.

Although each mineral behaves in its own way with regard to adherence to air or water, the natural tendencies may be modified almost at will by introducing suitable chemicals into the pulp.[7] According to modern conceptions of surface chemistry, a mineral particle immersed in a solution surrounds itself with a layer of molecules or of ions, and the nature of the coating determines its susceptibility to flotation.

Practice is to mix the appropriate reagents into the pulp and cause air

[6] Heavy-mineral separation processes: *Ore Dressing Notes*, no. 11, July, 1942.
[7] Pulp: the mixture of water and finely ground ore. In flotation its density ranges from 15% or less of solids to 35% or, at most, 40%. Gaudin, A. M., *Principles of Mineral Dressing*, pp. 403–404, New York: McGraw-Hill, 1939.

to bubble up through the mixture. The sulphide particles rise with the air-bubbles to form a froth which overflows the tank or "cell." This froth, or rather the suspension that results when the bubbles collapse, is filtered to recover the mineral-bearing concentrate.

The reagents used in flotation are classed as (1) frothers, such as pine oils or cresylic acids to promote the formation of bubbles and froth, (2) collectors, such as xanthates, which promote the adherence of air-bubbles to the mineral grain, and (3) conditioners, mostly inorganic salts, which modify the surface of the mineral particle and make it either more susceptible (activators) or less susceptible (depressants), whichever is desired. Only small quantities of reagent are required—from less than a pound to, exceptionally, ten pounds per ton of ore.

Early methods of flotation, developed before the first World War, were devoted essentially to separating all of the sulphide minerals as a group from the associated gangue (*collective* flotation). In the early 1920's the process of *selective* flotation came into use for separating the sulphide minerals from each other. By careful control of the process, any designated sulphide can be separated from its associates. Which mineral or minerals will float is decreed by the reagents that are used and by the hydrogen-ion concentration (pH) of the solution. Thus galena may be floated away from sphalerite by using sodium cyanide and zinc sulphate as controllers to depress the sphalerite and ethyl xanthate as a collector for the galena. In a succeeding step, sphalerite may be "activated" by adding copper sulphate which forms a very thin coating of copper sulphide on the particles and renders them easy to float.[8]

In this way, flotation can separate almost any sulphide not only from gangue but from other sulphides. A type of complex ore that is found in many places throughout the Cordilleran region consists of (1) galena, which carries silver in the form of minute inclusions of argentite and tetrahedrite, (2) pyrite which may contain tiny blebs of native gold, (3) tetrahedrite, which is likely to be silver-bearing, (4) sphalerite which is essentially free of gold and silver, and (5) chalcopyrite, which may carry a little gold. From such an ore the products are: a silver-bearing lead concentrate, a silver-bearing copper concentrate, and a zinc concentrate. The pyrite may be separated as a gold-bearing iron concentrate or may be shipped along with the copper.

Although the sulphide minerals are the most susceptible to flotation, native gold is also recoverable under proper control. Scheelite and a

[8] Gaudin, A. M., *Principles of Mineral Dressing*, p. 417, New York: McGraw-Hill, 1939.

number of non-metallic minerals have been floated successfully, but wolframite and cassiterite have not proved economically amenable to the process.   Oxidized ores of the base metals generally give poor recovery, although lead carbonate can be made to float by sulphidizing it; *i.e.*, treating it with alkali sulphide to coat it with a film of artificial galena.   Oxidized gold and silver ores usually respond better to other methods of treatment than to flotation.

Intimate intermixture of sulphides is not a bar to flotation, since the process works well with finely ground ore.   The normal operating sizes are 48 to 65 mesh (.3 to .2 mm.) for sulphide ores and 100 to 150 mesh (.15 to .1 mm.) for free gold.   Flotation becomes inapplicable only when a substantial portion of the grains are so extremely small that the cost of grinding fine enough to liberate them is excessive.

Amalgamation

Mercury forms an amalgam with metallic gold and silver.   This principle is utilized in the recovery of precious metals by passing a layer of pulp over a table consisting of a plate of silvered copper which has been coated with mercury.   The mercury holds and partly absorbs the particles of precious metals, while gangue and sulphides pass onward.   Instead of using a plate, the ore and mercury may be brought into contact inside a revolving barrel.   The mercury and gold are later separated from each other by distillation of the amalgam.

Amalgamation is a cheap and simple process and yields a product in the form of directly marketable bullion.   But it is suited only to ores in which the gold or silver occurs in native and fairly coarse particles, as is the case in placers and in many oxidized deposits.   Gold that is "locked up" in grains of pyrite or other minerals escapes recovery.   Hence in modern lode mining (as distinguished from placer mining) amalgamation is chiefly an auxiliary process used to recover coarse gold before cyaniding or flotation or to recover free gold from flotation concentrates.   It no longer has wide application in treating silver ores, since the proportion of silver occurring in native form is small.

Magnetic Separation

Magnetic methods have long been used for concentrating magnetite iron ores.   The other iron oxides (hematite and goethite) as well as the carbonate, siderite, are virtually non-magnetic, but they may be converted into artificial magnetite by controlled roasting.   They are thus made amenable to magnetic separation.   Magnetic methods may be used "in reverse" to purify non-ferrous ore by removing the undesired magnetic minerals. Such methods are used on a large scale for removing magnetite from the titanium ore at Lake Sanford, N. Y.[9]

Many other minerals—for example, chromite, manganese oxides, and garnet—are weakly magnetic and can be concentrated by machines using a strong field. Wolframite or tantalite can be separated from cassiterite by this means, and garnet can be eliminated from scheelite concentrates. Although pyrite can be removed from cassiterite or from sphalerite by roasting followed by magnetic separation, the same purpose is accomplished more effectively by flotation.[10] In summary, magnetic separation occupies a limited but useful field chiefly in the concentration or cleaning of ferrous ores and for separation of other magnetic minerals that do not respond to flotation.

HYDROMETALLURGY

Some ores can be treated economically by taking the valuable metal into solution and precipitating it in relatively pure form. Certain of the ores of gold, silver, copper, and zinc are amenable to these processes. Lead ores are not treated by these wet methods, partly because most lead salts are insoluble and partly because lead is especially welcome at the smelter as a collector of precious metals. Nor are zinc ores treated at the mines by wet methods; zinc is mentioned here only because the electrolytic refining of zinc concentrate is a wet metallurgical process.

The common wet chemical methods involve (1) crushing and grinding, (2) dissolving, either by allowing the solvent to percolate through the ore or by agitating the ground ore in the solution (3) filtering to remove insoluble residue (4) precipitation of the metal either by electrolysis or by contact with a metal higher in the electromotive series.

HYDROMETALLURGICAL METHODS

Cyaniding

The cyanide process is applicable commercially only to ores of gold and silver. Any base metals in the ore are not recovered. The solvent is a weak solution of sodium or calcium cyanide [11] which, when aerated, readily dissolves the precious metals. They are then recovered by agi-

---

[9] Staff of National Lead Co., The MacIntyre development at Tahawus, N. Y., *Mining and Metallurgy*, vol. 24, pp. 512–513, Nov., 1943.

[10] Gaudin, A. M., *Principles of Mineral Dressing*, p. 457. New York: McGraw-Hill, 1939.

[11] In the original MacArthur-Forrest process, potassium cyanide was used, but sodium cyanide and Aero-brand cyanide (about half calcium cyanide and the balance sodium chloride and lime) are cheaper in terms of dissolving power. It is still customary to discuss the chemistry of the process in terms of KCN. Equation for solution: $4Au + 8KCN + O_2 + 2H_2O = 4KAu(CN)_2 + 4KOH$. Precipitation: $KAu(CN)_2 + Zn + 2KCN + H_2O = K_2Zn(CN)_4 + Au + H + KOH.$

tating the "pregnant" solution with zinc or aluminum in the form of shavings or dust and filtering out the precipitate which is then melted and cast into bars (bullion).

Although native gold is readily attacked by cyanide solutions, gold tellurides give a poor extraction. Telluride ores at Kalgoorlie, W. A., have either to be roasted (after concentration) before cyaniding or to be treated by a solution containing bromocyanide. The telluride-bearing ore of Kirkland Lake, Ont., gives a good extraction without resorting to these methods, but it contains only 0.1% [12] of tellurides and these mostly tellurides of lead rather than of gold.

The gold in some ores, although it occurs in native form, is in very fine particles, included in grains of pyrite and other sulphides. Such ores must be ground fine enough to expose all of the gold particles to the attack of the solution. Where the gold is as fine as 1 to 3 microns, it is not released even at −325 mesh, which is about the economic limit of grinding.[13] Here again, roasting may render cyaniding possible but it adds, of course, to the cost of treatment.

Most silver minerals are attacked and dissolved by cyanide solutions. Native silver, argentite, and most of the sulphantimonides and sulpharsenides are easily treated, but silver chlorides and bromides are not. Oxidized silver ores[14] containing much manganese dioxide are likely to be resistant to cyanide and require special and often expensive methods of treatment.

Some ores contain undesirable compounds that react with cyanide solutions and thus increase consumption of the reagent, sometimes to such an extent that the expense is prohibitive. These substances, known as cyanicides, are especially common in oxidized and semioxidized ore. Oxidized copper minerals are objectionable on this account; hence, ore that shows copper staining may prove unsuitable for cyaniding. Free sulphuric acid, if present in the ore, decomposes cyanides but can be neutralized with lime or alkalies. Other cyanicides are:

Carbonates and sulphates of zinc and copper,
Soluble sulphides, arsenates and sulphates, including gypsum and ferric sulphate,
Some arsenical and antimonial minerals.

---

[12] Dorr, John V. N., *Cyaniding and Concentration of Gold and Silver Ores*, p. 273. New York: McGraw-Hill, 1936.

[13] Anon., The Role of the microscope in ore dressing: *Ore Dressing Notes*, American Cyanamid Co., No. 5, Oct. 1935, p. 14.

[14] Unsigned article, Recovery of silver from manganiferous ore: *Chem. Eng. & Mining Review* (Melbourne), p. 159, Jan. 10, 1939. *Also* Clevenger, G. H., and Caron, M. H., The Treatment of Manganese-Silver Ores, *U. S. Bureau of Mines* Bull. 226, 1925. Contains a bibliography *re* treatment of manganiferous silver ores.

Hydrocarbons and graphite are said to increase cyanide consumption but cause trouble chiefly by prematurely reprecipitating gold from solution. Most sulphide minerals are not attacked appreciably by cyanide. The sulphides of copper, nickel, cobalt, lead, and zinc do not interfere with cyaniding, especially if the pH is properly controlled; nor does pyrite, but pyrrhotite may cause difficulty, perhaps because it is readily oxidized.

Leaching of Copper Ores

Some copper ores can be treated by leaching, using as a solvent either ammonia, ferric sulphate, or sulphuric acid, according to the nature of the ore. Ammonia in the presence of CO_2 dissolves native copper and is used in retreating tailings in the Lake Superior copper country. Ammonia also dissolves copper carbonate and has been used at Kennecott, Alaska, on carbonate ores.[15]

Sulphuric acid readily dissolves copper carbonates and sulphates but is uneconomical for ores with limestone gangue because of the high acid consumption. This rules out sulphuric acid for most malachite deposits, but it is used along with ferric sulphate on malachite-chrysacolla ore in schist at Inspiration, Arizona, and, as long as the oxidized ore lasted, it was employed on similar malachite-chrysacolla ore in porphyry at Ajo, Arizona. At Chuquicamata, Chile, where the chief mineral is the hydrous copper sulphate, anterlite, sulphuric-acid leaching is highly successful. The copper is precipitated electrolytically and yields metal of high purity.

A chemically similar process takes advantage of the sulphuric acid and ferric sulphate that are generated when pyritic ores oxidize spontaneously. In the method known as "heap-leaching" the ore is placed in piles and irrigated with water; the percolating water is collected for precipitation of the copper. It is a slow process and is used in only a few places. In a unique method known as "leaching in place," water is introduced into the caved stopes of the mine itself, and the drainage is collected for precipitation on scrap iron (usually de-tinned cans). It works best when the orebody has a well defined water-tight footwall. Similarly, the natural drainage from some copper mines contains enough copper sulphate to warrant passing the water through precipitation boxes.

SMELTING

Gravity and flotation concentrates are ordinarily shipped to a smelter for reduction to metal. A few mines, most of them exceptionally large,

[15] Bateman, Alan M., *Economic Mineral Deposits*, p. 411. New York: Wiley, 1942.

have smelters of their own; but since a profitable smelter requires a
longer life and larger ore supply than the ordinary mine is blessed with,
a smelter usually serves a group of mines or a whole district rather than
a single property.   Thereby it is not only assured of a larger and longer
ore supply but gains the advantage to be derived from blending a variety
of ores into a desirable smelting mixture.   It is usually located in an
accessible place with good rail connections rather than close to the mines,
because the tonnage of fuel and flux is likely to be fully as great as that
of the ore itself.   For these reasons, the mine sells its concentrates to the
smelting company rather than smelting and refining them on its own
account.   Even when the same company owns both mine and smelter,
the mining department usually receives credit for its concentrates and
ore very much as though they were sold to an independent concern.
Beyond the stage at which the product is sold, the mine management is
less interested in the exact process of further treatment than in the price
received.

REFINING

The final metallurgical step is to remove impurities from the smelted
metal.   Silver and gold are recovered from base bullion at this stage.
The arrangements for refining copper, lead, and zinc are made by the
smelting company, and the cost is taken account of in the smelter settlement.

CHOICE OF A TREATMENT METHOD

Precious metal ores offer a choice between cyaniding and flotation, either
of which may be preceded by gravity concentration or amalgamation.
Cyaniding has the advantage that its product is a precipitate that can
easily be melted down into ingots and sold directly to a mint, thus by-
passing custom smelting.   The bullion is so valuable that freight charges,
even by airplane, are almost negligible compared with the price of the
product.   Furthermore, cyaniding is more foolproof than flotation.
On the other hand, it entails a higher capital cost, more plant space, and
a somewhat higher operating cost which is increased still further if the
ore contains objectionable constituents or if the precious metal is in such
small particles that reasonably fine grinding fails to make it accessible to
solutions.   Flotation, besides being cheaper to install and operate, is
adaptable to a wider variety of ores and offers less temptation to thievery.
Aside from requiring a higher degree of operating skill, its greatest disadvantages are that its product is a concentrate which may or may not
be low in grade but at best is never as valuable, weight for weight, as

bullion and that it has to go to a smelter for extraction of the metal. By the same token, however, flotation permits recovery of any base metals that may be present in the ore.

Considering these facts, a precious-metal mine in a remote or inaccessible locality is likely to find cyaniding the more economical process. In fact, the cost of transporting concentrate may rule out flotation as a competitor. Even where freight charges are not high, the probability is that cyaniding will be preferable, provided there are no complicating factors. But if the ore contains enough copper, lead, or even zinc, to pay at least part of the freight and smelting charges, flotation becomes a strong competitor, and the balance in its favor increases with the amount of base metal present.

Sulphide ores of copper, lead, and zinc call for treatment by flotation unless they are so simple mineralogically or so coarse-grained that gravity concentration is adequate. Oxide and carbonate ores of these metals present special problems because they respond poorly to flotation. Gravity concentration may improve their grade, but it will usually do so with a low recovery. Some oxidized copper ores can be treated economically by leaching processes, but oxidized lead and zinc ores cannot. As a rule, oxidized base-metal ores are economical only if they can stand transportation to the nearest smelter or if the deposit is huge and warrants a smelter of its own. Where oxide and carbonate ores are present, however, the possibility of finding sulphides at greater depth demands investigation.

The importance of the mineralogical nature of an ore is illustrated by the development of the copper deposits in Central Africa. Oxidized ores in the Belgian Congo are exceptionally rich and readily stand the cost of treatment by direct smelting. Somewhat similar oxidized ores, though of much lower grade, had long been known to exist across the border in Northern Rhodesia, but since they could not be concentrated easily they aroused little interest. However, when it was found, first at N'Change [16] late in 1925 and then at Roan Antelope in 1926,[17] that these oxidized cappings were underlain at depths of a very few hundred feet by chalcocite ores which would yield a high-grade flotation concentrate, the great Northern field developed very rapidly.

[16] Brooks, Raymond, Other factors in the success of Rhodesian exploration: *E. & M. J.*, vol. 145, No. 7, p. 95, 1944.

[17] Joralemon, Ira B., *Romantic Copper*, p. 265. New York: Appleton, 1934; *and* Bateman, Alan M.; The unexpected in the discovery of orebodies (Discussion): *Mining and Metallurgy*, vol. 12, p. 328, July, 1931.

23

MARKETABLE FORMS OF METALS AND ORES

Res tanti valet quanti vendi potest.
—ROMAN LAW [1]

THE more common and familiar metals, when in finished form and ready for the manufacturing industry, are readily salable in the open market at prices which are quoted daily or weekly in the press. Small or medium-sized producers usually sell them through metal brokers or selling agencies that receive a brokerage fee for their efforts. This applies to electrolytic copper, blister copper, electrolytic zinc, spelter (zinc metal prepared by other than electrolytic methods), pig lead, and mercury. But gold bullion and, in some countries, silver bullion are sold to a government treasury or mint.

Most mines, however, do not prepare finished metal but sell their products in the form of crude ore or concentrates. The chief exceptions are those which use the cyanide process (for precious metals) and those which have copper-leaching plants or own their own smelters. The producer of crude ore or concentrate containing the common precious and base metals has no difficulty in ordinary times in selling his product to a custom smelter. In fact the competing smelting companies employ ore-buyers to drum up trade.

The many less common or less familiar metals, such things as tantalum, molybdenum, or titanium, present problems of their own. Being specialties rather than common staple articles of trade, the market for them is more restricted and in some cases the specifications are quite rigid.

[1] Quoted by Louis, Henry, *Mineral Valuation*, p. 2. London: Charles Griffin & Co., Ltd., 1923.

Ores and Concentrates of Precious and Base Metals

Ores (and to save words the term will include concentrates) are sold as copper ore, lead ore, or zinc ore, depending on the predominant metal, and are treated in separate smelting plants or at least in separate furnaces,[2] each of which is designed to obtain the most economical recovery of its own metal.   Any metal other than the principal one in the ore is paid for at a relatively low rate, if at all.   This statement does not apply to gold and silver contained in the ore; these metals are paid for in ores of any of the standard types.   Precious metal ores without base metal content may be treated at either a lead smelter or a copper smelter.

The best way to calculate the liquidation value of an ore is to obtain a schedule from the nearest smelter or, better, from all plants within shipping range if by great good fortune there should be more than one. All custom smelters have "open" schedules on which they are prepared to buy any ore that is offered and which are useful for preliminary calculations.   Most regular shippers, however, obtain special contracts and receive considerably better rates than those of the open schedule.   Just how much better the rates are depends on the quality of the ore, the smelter's need for it, and the shipper's bargaining power.   Although individual contracts vary widely, often in accordance with what the traffic will bear, there are established practices in the trade that may serve as a guide.

Smelters' Payments

The amount that the producer receives from the smelter in payment for ore is likely to be very different from the gross value of the contained metal, a fact which many a shipper has learned only too late.   The liquidation value ranges from as little as 30% of the gross in certain zinc ores carrying high freight charges to 75% or 85% for some copper and silver ores.   Rarely, though, does it exceed 80%.   The smelter must be compensated for costs and metallurgical losses, and it must earn a profit on its operations.

The manner in which the smelting company takes its "margin" varies widely under different modes of settlement.   The margin may take the form of a treatment fee per ton of ore, it may constitute a deduction of so many cents per pound from the quoted price of the metal or it may enter through payment for less than 100% of the contained metal. Most schedules embody all three types of "cuts," and a few use addi-

---

[2] Most of the newer zinc-treating plants use the electrolytic process rather than smelting.

tional and less straightforward bits of mathematics in adding to the take. In fact the small shipper often considers himself the victim of brigandage and not always without reason, although he usually fails to appreciate the expenses and the risks that a smelting company incurs.

For *lead* ores, the methods of settlement are especially divergent. Settlement is usually based on the lead content, as determined by the wet method, less 1 to 1½ units.[2a]   (This deduction is ostensibly to bring the content in line with that obtained by the old-fashioned fire assay.) Then payment is made for 90% of the lead at a price which in the United States is either 1 to 1½ cents per lb under the New York price or is 90% of the New York price.   It is customary to pay for 95% to 100% of the contained gold at one to three dollars an ounce below the government price and for 90% to 95% of the silver at government or Handy and Harman quotations.   From the payment for metals a charge of $3 to $5 per ton is usually made for smelting, and deductions are debited or premiums credited for accessory elements in the ore.   To pay for roasting to remove sulphur the charge is 15 to 25 cents per unit of S in excess of 2% or 3%.   The sum of As, S, and Bi is penalized at $1 a unit if over 0.5%.   At some smelters, however, antimony is desired and commands a premium.   Since a fixed ratio of iron-plus-lime to silica is necessary to the formation of a slag, it is customary to pay a premium for any iron in excess of silica, or to penalize either a deficiency of iron or an excess of silica.   Zinc above 5% to 8% carries a penalty of 25 cents to 50 cents per unit.

Sampling is usually charged for at $1 to $3 for each carload or smaller lot.   Freight from mine to smelter is paid at the smelter but charged to the shipper.

In *copper* ores the content paid for is 1 to 1½ units under the wet assay determination, and the price is 2½ to 3 cents per pound less than the New York quotation for electrolytic metal.   Gold and silver are paid for in copper as they are in a lead ore.   The smelting charge is usually $3 to $4 a ton of ore.   Premiums, penalties, and charges are about the same as in lead ores except that there is no penalty for sulphur since this element is required to make a matte.   Arsenic, however, may be penalized, and zinc usually carries a penalty.

In *zinc* settlements there is little uniformity, and schedules are complicated.   In the Tri-state district, zinc concentrates are sold at a flat price per ton for standard 60% ore, and the Joplin quotation serves as a rough guide, although concentrates from other regions usually bring

[2a] For definition of "unit," see Glossary.

less than the Joplin price.   In general the liquidation value of zinc concentrate is considerably less than that for a lead concentrate of equal grade when the market prices of the two metals are the same.

SMELTING AND REDUCTION PLANTS [3]

A. COPPER SMELTING PLANTS

United States

WASHINGTON
American Smelting and Refining Company   Tacoma
MONTANA
Anaconda Copper Mining Company   Anaconda
NEVADA
Kennecott Copper Corporation   McGill
UTAH
American Smelting and Refining Company   Garfield
International Smelting and Refining Co.   Tooele
ARIZONA
American Smelting and Refining Company   Hayden
International Smelting and Refining Co.   Miami
Magma Copper Company   Superior
Phelps Dodge Corp. (Copper Queen Branch)   Douglas
    "   "   " (Morenci Branch)   Morenci
    "   "   " (United Verde Branch)   Clarkdale
NEW MEXICO
Kennecott Copper Corporation   Hurley
TEXAS
American Smelting and Refining Company   El Paso
MICHIGAN
Calumet and Hecla Cons. Copper Company   Hubbell
Copper Range Co., Smelting Department   Oskar
Quincy Smelting Works (idle 1946)   Hancock
NEW YORK
Phelps Dodge Refining Corporation   Laurel Hill, L. I.
NEW JERSEY
American Metal Company, Ltd.   Carteret
TENNESSEE
Tennessee Copper Company   Copperhill

Canada

BRITISH COLUMBIA
Consolidated Mining and Smelting Company   Trail

---

[3] Data from various listings; supplementary data, especially for foreign plants from Yearbook, American Bureau of Metal Statistics, 1946 Issue, 33 Rector Street, New York.   Additional information from staffs of U. S. Smelting Refining & Mining Co. and Kennecott Sales Corporation.

MANITOBA
Hudson Bay Mining and Smelting Co., Ltd.   Flin Flon
ONTARIO
Falconbridge Nickel Mines, Limited   Falconbridge
International Nickel Co. of Canada, Ltd.   Copper Cliff
    "   "   "   "   "   Coniston
QUEBEC
Noranda Mines Limited   Noranda

Mexico

BAJA CALIFORNIA
Cie. du Boleo (in liquidation, 1946)   Santa Rosalia
COAHUILA
American Metal Co., Ltd.   Torreon
SONORA
Cananea Consol. Copper Co., S. A.   Cananea
ZACATECAS
Mazapil Copper Company (idle 1946)   Concepcion del Oro
SAN LUIS POTOSI
American Smelting and Refining Company   San Luis Potosi

South America

ECUADOR
Cotopaxi Exploration Co.   Macuchi
PERU
Cerro de Pasco Copper Corporation   Oroya
CHILE
Cia Minas de Gatico (idle 1946)   Gatico
Andes Copper Mining Company   Potrerillos
Braden Copper Company   Caletones
Societe des Mines de Cuivre de Naltagua   El Monte, Santiago
Cia. Minas y Fundicion de M'Zaita   Chagres

Europe

GREAT BRITAIN
Rio Tinto Company, Ltd.   Port Talbot, S. Wales
Bede Metal & Chemical Co.   Hebburn-on-Tyne
NORWAY
Raffineringsverket A/S   Kristiandsand
Röros Kobberverk   Röros
A/S Sulitjelma Gruber   Sulitjelma
SWEDEN
Reymersholms Gamla Industri Actiebolag   Hälsingsborg and Oskars-hamn
Bolidens Gruv Actiebolag   Rönnskär
FINLAND
Outokumpu Oy   Harjavalta

BELGIUM
  Soc. Gen. Met. de Hoboken   Hoboken and Oolen
GERMANY
  (Present status of smelters not available.)
SPAIN
  Rio Tinto Co., Ltd.   Rio Tinto, Huelva
YUGOSLAVIA
  Cie. Français des Mines de Bor   Bor (Moravska Banovina)
    (Believed to have been nationalized)

Asia

BURMA
  Burma Corporation, Ltd.   Namtu
INDIA
  Indian Copper Corporation   Moubhandar, Chota Nag-
JAPAN   pur
  (Information *re* present status not available)
TURKEY
  Turkiye Bakir Isletmeleri Müessesesi   Ergani-Maden

Africa

BELGIAN CONGO
  Union Miniere du Haut Katanga   Lubumbashi
    "   "   "   "   "   Panda
NORTHERN RHODESIA
  Mufulira Copper Mines Ltd.   Mufulira
  Rhokana Corporation   N'Kana
  Roan Antelope Copper Mines Ltd.   Luanshya
SOUTHWEST AFRICA
  Otavi Mines and Railway Co.   Otavi
TRANSVAAL
  Messina (Transvaal) Development Co., Ltd.   Messina
CAPE COLONY
  O'Okiep Copper Co., Ltd.   O'Okiep, Namaqualand

Australia

QUEENSLAND
  Mount Isa Mines Ltd.   Mt. Isa
  Mount Morgan Ltd.   Mt. Morgan
  Chillagoe State Smelters   Chillagoe
NEW SOUTH WALES
  Electrolytic Refining & Smelting Co. of Austr. Port Kembla
TASMANIA
  Mount Lyell Mining & Railway Co.   Queenstown

B. PRIMARY LEAD SMELTING AND REFINING PLANTS[4]

(S-Smelter; R-Refinery)

United States

CALIFORNIA
American Smelting & Refining Co. (S and R)   Selby

IDAHO
Bunker Hill & Sullivan Mining & Refining Co.
(S and R)   Kellogg

MONTANA
American Smelting & Refining Co. (S)   East Helena

UTAH
American Smelting & Refining Co. (S)   Murray
International Smelting & Refining Co. (S)   Tooele
U. S. Smelting Refining and Mining Co.   Midvale

COLORADO
American Smelting & Refining Co. (S)   Leadville

NEBRASKA
American Smelting & Refining Co. (R)   Omaha

TEXAS
American Smelting & Refining Co. (S and R)   El Paso

ILLINOIS
American Smelting & Refining Co. (S and R)   Alton

MISSOURI
St. Joseph Lead Co. (S and R)   Herculaneum

NEW JERSEY
American Smelting & Refining Co. (R)   Perth Amboy

KANSAS
Eagle-Picher Mining & Smelting Co.   Galena

Europe

GREAT BRITAIN
Britannia Lead Co.   Northfleet
H. J. Enthoven & Sons, Ltd.   Rotherhithe
Walkers, Parker & Co.   Newcastle-on-Tyne

SWEDEN
Bolidens Gruv A. B.   Rönnskär
Svenska Ackumulator AB Jungner   Fliseryd

BELGIUM
Cie. Met. de la Campine   Beersse
Soc. Gen. Met. de Hoboken   Hoboken
Cie. des Metaux d'Overpelt-Lommel et de Cor-
phalie   Overpelt
Soc. Anon. des Mines et Fonderies de Zinc de la
Vieille Montagne   Baelen-Wezel

[4] Data verified by Francis Cameron, Vice President St. Joseph Lead Co.   Supplemented by information from American Bureau of Metal Statistics, Yearbook, 1946.   New York.

FRANCE
Cie. Met. Franco-Belge de Mortagne   Mortagne
Soc. Anon. des Mines et Fonderies de Pontgibaud   Couëron
Soc. Min. et Met. de Peñarroya   L'Estaque
"   "   "   "   "   "   Noyelle Godault
GERMANY, AUSTRIA, CZECHOSLOVAKIA
(Information re present status not available)
SPAIN
Cia. La Cruz   Linares (Jaén)
Cia. Minera Met. Los Guindos   Malaga
Soc. Min. et Met. de Peñarroya   Peñarroya
Minas de Priorato   Bellmunt de Ciurana
Cie. Royale Asturienne des Mines   Renteria
Cia. Sopwith   Linares (Jaén)
Soc. Minera Metalurgica "Zapata Portman"   Portman (Murcia)
ITALY
Soc. de Monteponi   Monteponi, Sardinia
Soc. Min. & Met. di Pertusola   Pertusola
Soc. Italiana del Piombo e dello Zinco   S. Gavino Monreale, Sardinia
GREECE
Cie. Française des Mines du Laurium   Laurium
RUSSIA, POLAND, ROUMANIA
(Information re present status not available)

Asia

BURMA
Burma Corporation, Ltd.   Namtu
JAPAN
(Information re present status not available)
TURKEY
Soc. des Mines de Balya-Karaydin   Balya
Koc Ticaret Turk Anonim Sirketi   Sirketi Anamur

Africa

MOROCCO
Soc. des Mines de Zellidja   Zellidja
TUNIS
Soc. Anon. Française du Djebel Hallouf   Souk-el-Khemis
Soc. Min. et Met. de Peñarroya   Mégrine
Mines et Fonderies Tunisiennes   Bizerte
NORTHERN RHODESIA
Rhodesia Broken Hill Development Co.   Broken Hill
SOUTHWEST AFRICA
Otavi Mines & Railway Co.   Tsumeb

Australia

QUEENSLAND
    Mount Isa Mines, Ltd.   Mt. Isa
SOUTH AUSTRALIA
    Broken Hill Associated Smelters Pty. Ltd.   Port Pirie

Canada

BRITISH COLUMBIA
    Consolidated Mining & Smelting Co. of Canada
      (S and R)   Trail

Mexico

CHIHUAHUA
    American Smelting & Refining Co. (S)   Chihuahua
COAHUILA
    American Metal Co., Ltd. (Mexican Division)
      (S)   Torreon
NUEVO LEON
    American Smelting & Refining Co. (R)   Monterrey
    Cia. Minera de Penoles (S and R)   Monterrey
SAN LUIS POTOSI
    American Smelting & Refining Co. (S)   San Luis Potosi
ZACATECAS
    American Metal Co.   La Fe plant

C. ZINC SMELTING AND REFINING PLANTS

United States

MONTANA
    Anaconda Copper Mining Company (electro-
      lytic)   Anaconda
    Anaconda Copper Mining Company (electro-
      lytic)   Great Falls
IDAHO
    Sullivan Mining Company (electrolytic)   Silver King
TEXAS
    American Smelting and Refining Company
      (electrolytic)   Corpus Christi
    American Smelting and Refining Company   Amarillo
    American Zinc Co. of Illinois   Dumas
ARKANSAS
    Athletic Mining and Smelting Co.   Fort Smith
OKLAHOMA
    Blackwell Zinc Company (Inc.)   Blackwell
    Eagle Picher Mining and Smelting Company   Henryetta
    National Zinc Inc.   Bartlesville

Illinois
  American Zinc Co. of Illinois (electrolytic)   Monsanto
    "   "   "   "   "   Fairmount City
  Hegeler Zinc Company   Danville
  Mathiessen and Hegeler Zinc Co.   La Salle
  New Jersey Zinc Co.   Depue
Pennsylvania
  St. Joseph Lead Company   Josephtown
  American Steel and Wire Co.   Donora
  New Jersey Zinc Co. (Ores and Cons.)   Palmerton
    "   "   "   "   (Refining Ops.)   Palmerton
West Virginia
  E. I. du Pont de Nemours and Co.   Meadowbrook

Canada

British Columbia
  Consolidated Mining & Smelting Co., Ltd.
    (electrolytic)   Trail
Manitoba
  Hudson Bay Mining & Smelting Co., Ltd.
    (electrolytic)   Flin Flon

Mexico

Coahuila
  Mexican Zinc Co. (A. S. & R.)   Rosita

Europe

Great Britain
  Northern Smelting & Chem. Co., Ltd. (Im-
    perial Smelting Corp.)   Seaton Carew
  Improved Metallurgy, Ltd. (Imperial Smelting
    Corporation)   Avonmouth
  National Smelting Co., Ltd. (Imperial Smelting
    Corporation)   Avonmouth
  National Smelting Co., Ltd. (Imperial Smelting
    Corporation)   Swansea, Wales.
Norway
  Det Norske Zinkkompani A. S. (electrolytic)   Eitrheim, near Odda
Belgium
  Soc. Métallurgique de Boom   Boom (Anvers)
  Cie. des Metaux d'Overpelt-Lommel et de Cor-
    phalie   Corphalie
  Cie. des Metaux d'Overpelt-Lommel et de Cor-
    phalie   Overpelt
  Cie. des Metaux d'Overpelt-Lommel et de Cor-
    phalie   Lommel
  Soc. Anon. Métallurgique de Prayon   Prayon-les-Trooz
    "   "   "   "   "   Engis

Soc. Anon. de Rothem	Rothem
Soc. Anon. de la Vieille Montagne	Angleur
" " " " "	Flone
" " " " "	Valentin-Cocq
Soc. Anon. de la Vieille Montagne (electrolytic)	Baelen

FRANCE

Cie. Franco-Belge de Mortagne	Mortagne (Nord)
Soc. Minière et Métallurgique de Peñarroya	Noyelle-Godault (Pas de Calais)
Soc. Anon. de la Vieille Montagne	Creil (Seine et Oise)
" " " " " " (electrolytic)	Viviez, Aveyron
Cie. Royale Asturienne des Mines	Auby (Nord)

GERMANY, CZECHOSLOVAKIA, POLAND
  (Information re present status not available)

SPAIN

Cie. Royale Asturienne des Mines	Arnao, near Avilés
Soc. Minière et Métallurgique de Peñarroya	Peñarroya (Cordoba)

ITALY

Soc. di Monteponi	Vado Ligure
" " " (electrolytic)	Monteponi (Sardinia)
Soc. Min. e Met. di Pertusola (electrolytic)	Crotone
Soc. Italiana del Piombo e dello Zinco (electrolytic)	Porto Marghera

YUGOSLAVIA

Cinkarna d.d.	Celje

NETHERLANDS

Zincs de la Campine	Budel

Asia

INDO-CHINA

Cie. Min. et Met. de l'Indochine	Quang Yen, Tonkin

JAPAN
  (Information re present status not available)

Africa

NORTHERN RHODESIA

Rhodesia Broken Hill Development Co. (electrolytic)	Broken Hill

Australia

TASMANIA

Electrolytic Zinc Co. of Austr., Ltd. (electrolytic)	Risdon

ORES AND CONCENTRATES OF THE RARER OR LESS FAMILIAR METALS

The smelter schedules that have just been discussed apply to the ores of the common precious and base metals. The geologist, when he encounters deposits containing any of the less familiar metals, will need some information from which he can decide whether or not the ore is of commercial interest.   In particular, he wants to know what metal content is required in a marketable concentrate, what impurities are objectionable, and in what terms the product is quoted.   The actual price will fluctuate, of course, from year to year and, in an active market, from day to day.   Current quotations will be found in such periodicals as *The Engineering and Mining Journal* and *The London Mining Magazine*.

A prospective producer of any but the common metals should consult dealers [5] and consumers before investing any substantial amount in developing or equipping a property.   The processors who specialize in some of these products are few, and they supply their requirements either from their own mines or through contracts with existing producers.   Therefore no open market may exist, in which case the quotations in the journals have only a nominal significance.

METALLIC ORES—MINERALOGICAL NATURE AND COMMERCIAL STANDARDS

Aluminum

The principal commercial ore is bauxite, an intimate physical mixture of $Al_2O_3.H_2O$ and $Al_2O_3.3H_2O$.   Alunite and certain clays have been used as sources of alumina under war conditions.   Bauxite for aluminum manufacture should contain a minimum of 50% Al_2O_3 and a maximum of 6% SiO_2, 10% Fe_2O_3 and 4% TiO_2.   For chemical purposes, bauxite should contain not over 3% each of iron and titanium oxides.   Bauxite for abrasives should carry not over 5% each of Fe_2O_3 and SiO_2.   Bauxites of the three respective grades are quoted per long ton.[6]

Antimony

The common ore is stibnite, Sb_2S_3 but enough metal to supply normal demands is recovered as a by-product from smelting copper, silver, and lead ores.   However, there is a small regular market for antimony oxide ores.   In times of abnormal demand, stibnite concentrates are purchased.   Even so, only rich antimony ore can compete with Chinese stibnite.

The ordinary marketable forms are antimony slabs and oxides.

---

[5] A directory of buyers appears in *Metal Statistics*, a volume published annually by American Metal Market, 18 Cliff Street, New York 7, N. Y. ($2).   This publication also gives production statistics and prices by years.

[6] Bateman, Alan M., *Economic Mineral Deposits*, p. 228, New York, Wiley, 1942.

Arsenic

The commonest mineral is arsenopyrite but there is rarely a market for it as an arsenic ore.   Adequate arsenic to supply normal demands is recovered as a by-product from smelting gold, copper, and other ores containing arsenopyrite, enargite, and tennantite.   In fact, large stocks of flue dust and Cotrell dust accumulate at times because it is unprofitable to process them.   Disposal of this poisonous material becomes a problem, and it is said that in Sweden the difficulty was solved by sealing the arsenic compounds in concrete blocks and dumping them in the sea.

The common marketable form is refined white "arsenic," 99.5% pure As_2O_3.

Beryllium [7]

The only important commercial ore is beryl ($3BeO.Al_2O_3.6SiO_2$). Chrysoberyl ($BeO.Al_2O_3$) is acceptable but less common.   Helvite ($Mn_4Be_3Si_3O_{12}S$) [8] might be a commercial ore if deposits could be found sufficiently rich to justify solving metallurgical problems.   It is quite possible that such deposits may exist, because the mineral occurs in contact metamorhpic zones and has probably been overlooked because it so closely resembles green garnet.

Consumption of beryllium ore increased rapidly during the war—from 459 tons in the U. S. in 1939 to 4,840 tons in 1943.[9]

Standard specifications for beryl ore call for 10 to 12% BeO (theoretically, beryl contains 14%).   Quotations are per short ton unit of contained BeO.

Bismuth

The principal supplies of the metal are obtained as by-products of copper and lead smelting.   Minor amounts are recovered in tin smelting. In a few places, notably Peru and Bolivia, bismuthinite (Bi_2S_3) and other ores are mined.   Only rich ores are of commercial interest.

Cadmium, Indium, Germanium, Gallium [10]

All of these metals are by-products of treating zinc ore.   No ore is mined primarily for its cadmium content but zinc ores rich in cadmium

---

[7] Information from J. S. Baker.

[8] Isomorphous with helvite are danalite, in which Fe takes the place of Mn and genthelvite in which Zn takes the place of Mn.   Helvite may be distinguished from garnet by the Gruner staining method which consists of boiling the mineral with arsenic trioxide in dilute sulphuric acid.   Glass, J. J., Jahns, R. H., and Stevens, R. E., Helvite and Danalite from New Mexico and the Helvite Group, *American Mineralogist*, vol. 29, p. 172, 1944.

[9] *Minerals Yearbook 1945*, U. S. Bureau of Mines, p. 818, 1947.

[10] Information from J. S. Baker.

are treated preferentially and command a premium. Indium has important industrial uses and may become still more important. Little germanium and gallium are used at present but they are said to have future possibilities.

Cobalt

The ores are cobaltite (CoAsS), Smaltite (CoAs$_2$) and a number of sulpharsenide minerals, which can be concentrated by gravity and flotation, but the ore in the Belgian Congo consists of hydrous black oxides. Concentrates are quoted per pound of contained cobalt and should carry at least 10% Co. The mines in the Belgian Congo are so productive that few small producers can compete.

Chromium [11]

The only commercially important chromium mineral is chromite, a member of the spinel group. The general formula is R″O.R‴$_2$O$_3$.[12] Practically speaking the formula for chromite is best written (Fe,Mg)O.-(Fe,Al,Cr)$_2$O$_3$. Part of the ferric iron is usually replaced by magnesium and some of the chromium by alumina or ferrous iron with the result that the average pure chromite contains from 45% to 55% Cr$_2$O$_3$ and in many places the chromium content is even much less.

In considering the quality of a chromium ore the important variables are Cr$_2$O$_3$ content, chromium-iron ratio, SiO$_2$ content, content and ratio of Al$_2$O$_3$ and MgO and sometimes the minor constituents such as sulphur, phosphorus and others if they exceed a fraction of 1%.

The physical characteristics of the ore are likewise extremely important particularly with respect to metallurgical lump ore and refractory lump ore. Lump ore is defined as that in which all lumps will pass a 6 inch screen and not more than 25% will pass a $\frac{1}{2}$ inch mesh screen.

From a market and usability basis, chrome ores are divided into three classes namely metallurgical, chemical and refractory. The primary distinction between metallurgical and chemical ores is the chrome-iron ratio which must be above 2.5 to 1 in metallurgical ores and which is 2.0 to 1 or less in chemical ores. This chemical distinction is accentuated by a marked price difference between the two classes. Refractory ores are characterized by a lower Cr$_2$O$_3$ content, higher Al$_2$O$_3$, FeO, MgO and particularly by their physical characteristics. Lime is especially

[11] By Horace J. Fraser.

[12] Stevens, Rollin E., Composition of some chromites of the Western Hemisphere, *American Mineralogist*, vol. 29, pp. 1–34, 1944.

detrimental in refractory ores.   Standard specifications of these three types are as follows:

Chemical	Composition	Metallurgical Standard	Metallurgical Minimum	Chemical	Refract.
Cr_2O_3	Minimum	48%	45%	44.5%	30%
Chrome-Iron Ratio	Minimum	3 to 1	2.5 to 1	None	None
FeO	Maximum	Depends on ratio		No Max	11%
SiO_2		6%	7%	6%	5%
S		0.50%	0.50%	—	—
P		0.20%	0.20%	—	—

Metallurgical ore is used in making ferrochrome.   Under standard American practice, the ore fed to the standard reduction furnace must contain a minimum of 70% lump, the balance being fines or concentrates.   Certain processes can use a higher percentage of concentrates. The price of such ore is usually based on 48% Cr_2O_3 at a ratio of 3 to 1 with premium and penalties on Cr_2O_3, chrome-iron ratio, and penalties on silica.

Chemical ore is used in the manufacture of chrome chemicals.   Prices are based on contained units of Cr_2O_3 with a penalty on silica.

Refractory ores are used in the manufacture of refractory bricks and refractory patching compounds.   Prices are on a per ton basis depending on the known characteristics of a given ore.

Copper

The common ores are chalcocite (Cu_2S), bornite (Cu_5FeS_4) chalcopyrite ($CuFeS_2$), and enargite (Cu_3AsS_4).   Native copper is important only in the Lake Superior District.   Oxidized ores contain malachite ($Cu_2(OH)_2CO_3$) and minor amounts of azurite and chrysacolla, with cuprite and other oxides.   Since oxidized copper minerals do not respond to ordinary methods of flotation, it is important in assaying to determine "soluble copper" (*i.e.*, copper which is not in sulphide form) as well as total copper, especially in low-grade ores of the porphyry type. Copper is sold to smelters in the form of crude ore or concentrates. Plants using hydrometallurgical processes sell cement copper or electrolytic copper.   Treatment methods are discussed in Chapter 22.

Gold

The chief ore mineral is native gold.   Tellurides of gold with or without silver occur in a few districts.

Gold is purchased by government mints in the form of bullion—bars or bricks consisting of gold with more or less silver and minor amounts of impurities. Nuggets and "dust" collected from placer deposits by washing are readily marketable. Gold contained in base metal concentrate or in pyritic concentrate is paid for by smelters.

Methods of treating gold ores are discussed in Chapter 22.

Iron [13]

The principal ore minerals are magnetite (Fe_3O_4), hematite, (Fe_2O_3), "limonite" (field term for hydrous oxides) and siderite ($FeCO_3$). The sulphides, pyrite and pyrrhotite, are ores of sulphur rather than of iron but the sinter that remains after roasting them may be marketable as iron ore.

Merchantable iron ore should carry 50% or more of Fe although ore as lean as 25% may go to furnaces under especially favorable conditions. Ore of Bessemer quality must be low in phosphorus (not over 0.045% P). Non-Bessemer ores which sell at a lower price may contain up to 0.18% P. Sulphur in excess of 0.025% is usually undesirable although iron ore containing as much as 0.20% may be marketable. Arsenic and zinc, even in very small amounts are highly objectionable. Manganiferous ores up to 10% Mn and titaniferous ores up to 1.5% TiO_2 are ordinarily acceptable.

As iron ore commands a relatively low price per ton, the amount that can be spent in concentrating it is limited. Magnetite ores, however, are cheaply concentrated and some hematite ores can be improved by washing or sink-and-float treatment.

A small iron mine, to be profitable, should have a low freight rate to a merchant furnace. Recent developments in the manufacture of sponge iron may modify this requirement in isolated regions where fuel and power are readily available and where there is a market for the product.

There is an increasing market for high grade iron ore in Europe and the United States, which will normally be supplied by mines close to tidewater and to port facilities. Iron ore has been transported economically by sea over distances as great as 4500 miles and this range will probably be extended.

The more important steel companies of the world own or control iron mines, coal mines, limestone deposits and other sources of the raw materials they need. Some of them control railways and shipping. There-

---

[13] Information supplied by Andrew Newberry.

fore published quotations are apt to be nominal and a prospective producer needs to assure himself of a market before proceeding too far
with a venture.

Lead

The principal ore mineral is galena (PbS) but oxidized ores contain
cerussite ($PbCO_3$), anglesite ($PbSO_4$) and a number of less common
minerals.   Some lead is sold to smelters in the form of high-grade crude
ore but most of it is in the form of concentrate.   Treatment methods
are discussed in Chapter 22.

Manganese

Most manganese ores consist of a mixture of black oxides, the commonest of which [14] are pyrolusite (MnO_2), cryptomelane [15] (a potash-
bearing oxide of variable composition) and psilomelane (which contains
barium and sometimes cobalt).   Braunite, a black silicate, often accompanies the oxides.   Rhodochrosite, the pink carbonate is the only
commercial mineral other than the oxides.   In Montana, it is recovered
by flotation and prepared for the market by calcining.

Most oxide ores are shipped as mined, although a successful flotation
process has been developed by the Cuban-American Manganese Company.[16]   Manganese ore for metallurgical use is quoted per long ton
unit (weight adjusted to a moisture-free basis) for standard ore of
48% Mn content, sometimes with a premium for additional percentages
of Mn.

"High grade ore" must carry at least 48% Mn, with impurities not
in excess of: 7% Fe, 0.18% P, 11% combined SiO_2 + Al_2O_3 and 1%
combined base metals.   "Low grade ore," down to 40% or even less,
with a slightly more liberal tolerance of impurities, brings a lower price.[17]

Ore for making spiegeleisen may carry a still lower content and in
times of strong demand iron ores containing as little as 5% Mn are segregated for special use in steel furnaces.

14 Fleischer, Michael, and Richmond, Wallace E., The Manganese Oxide Minerals: A Preliminary Report, *Econ. Geology,* vol. 38, pp. 269–286, 1943.

15 Richmond, Wallace E., and Fleischer, Michael, Cryptomelane, a New Name for the Commonest of the "Psilomelane" Minerals, *American Mineralogist,* vol. 27 pp. 607–610, 1942.

16 Norcross, F. S., Jr., Development of the Low-Grade Manganese Ores of Cuba, *Tr. A.I.M.E.,*
vol. 153, pp. 93–110, 1943.

17 Information regarding specifications was supplied by H. C. Burrell.

Mercury (Quicksilver)

The only important mineral is cinnabar (HgS) although some ores contain metacinnabarite (also HgS) and native mercury as well. Livingstonite (HgS.2Sb$_2$S$_3$) has been mined in Mexico. The product marketed is the liquid metal which is produced by roasting the ore and condensing the vapor. The process is so simple and inexpensive that ore containing as little as .25% can be treated without prior concentration. In accordance with an old Spanish custom quicksilver is quoted in terms of flasks of about 76 lbs.[18] net weight.

Molybdenum

The only important ore is molybdenite (MoS$_2$), although wulfenite (PbMoO$_4$) has been mined in a few places for its molybdenum content.

Molybdenite responds very readily to flotation and can easily be recovered as a concentrate of good grade. If ores contain chalcopyrite or other copper minerals the concentrate may carry undesirable amounts of copper unless special ore dressing methods are used.

In the oxidized zone of a deposit, part of the molybdenum may be present in the form of ferrimolybdite (see page 259) which cannot be recovered by ordinary flotation processes. Therefore any estimate of the grade of partially oxidized ores should indicate the amount of Mo present in sulphide, as distinguished from oxide, form.[19]

Standard grade concentrate contains 90% MoS$_2$ although concentrates containing as low as 85%, or exceptionally 80% are marketable under special conditions. Impurities should not exceed 0.5% Cu, 0.3% Pb and 0.1% P.

Quotations are in cents per pound of contained MoS$_2$. Small shippers are likely to receive several cents less than the published quotations.

Nickel

The principal ore mineral is pentlandite (Fe,Ni)S, which, at Sudbury, Ontario and elsewhere occurs in bodies of pyrrhotite along with varying quantities of chalcopyrite. Oxidized ores, typified by garnierite (Ni,-

---

[18] In United States markets the flask is 76.0 lbs. although 76 lbs. 1 oz. is sometimes used in contracts. The European flask contains 34.5 kg. (76.17 lbs.) and this weight is also used in Mexican contracts when written in Spanish.—Neil O'Donnel, personal communication.

[19] Michell, Wilson D., Oxidation in a Molybdenite Deposit, Nye County, Nevada, *Economic Geology*, vol. 40, p. 113, 1945.

Mg) $SiO_3.nH_2O$, occur in serpentines in New Caledonia, Nicaro, Cuba and in a few other places.

The sulphide ores can be concentrated by flotation, recovering a pyrrhotite-pentlandite concentrate and a separate chalcopyrite (copper) concentrate. The nickel concentrate is treated by a process similar to copper smelting.

The oxidized ores do not respond readily to physical methods of concentration. The garnierite ore in New Caledonia is reduced by direct smelting, using gypsum as a source of sulphur to form a matte. The Cuban ore, which is low-grade is treated by a leaching process. To be commercially interesting, oxidized ore would have to be rich enough to stand long shipment (and such ores are very rare), or extensive enough to support its own treatment plant.

There are only a few nickel smelters in the world and most of them do little if any custom business. The principal ones are: at Copper Cliff, Ontario, Falconbridge, Ontario, Petsamo, Finland (now under Russian control), Evje, Norway, and on the island of New Caledonia (Societe Caledonickel).

Silver

The commonest ores are silver-bearing galena and silver-bearing copper minerals, principally tetrahedrite and enargite. Silver that occurs in these forms is recovered in the lead or copper concentrate and is paid for by the smelter.

Of the silver minerals proper the most important are native silver, argentite (Ag_2S) stromeyerite ($AgCuS$) and the numerous sulpharsenides and sulphantimonides. Oxidized ores contain native silver, cerargyrite (horn silver) ($AgCl$) and sometimes bromides, iodides and complex basic sulphates. Oxidized ores unless they are amenable to cyanidation or are rich enough for direct smelting, present a serious treatment problem.

Silver recovered by cyaniding or by amalgamation is sold to mints or dealers in the form of bullion, usually containing more or less gold and some impurities. Methods of treatment applicable to silver ores are discussed in Chapter 22.

Tantalum [20]

The principal mineral is tantalite, $(Fe,Mn)(Ta,Cb)_2O_6$. Microlite is a commercial ore-mineral but is much rarer than tantalite. As the

---

[20] Information supplied chiefly by J. S. Baker.

formula indicates, the series tantalite-columbite is isomorphous, hence tantalites vary in Ta_2O_5 content, a critical matter since market specifications are rigid. Yet accurate chemical determination of Ta_2O_5 is so difficult and laborious that only a few laboratories can make reliable assays. The content can be determined roughly from the specific gravity and this method is widely used as a preliminary field test. The following table gives a fair approximation.

Sp. Gr.	% Ta_2O_5	Sp. Gr.	% Ta_2O_5
5.4	5	6.6	52
5.6	13	6.7	56
5.8	21	6.8	60
6.0	30	6.9	62
6.1	33	7.0	65
6.2	37	7.1	67
6.3	41	7.2	70
6.4	45	7.3	72
6.5	49	7.4	75

The table is least accurate near the tantalite end of the series because most "tantalites" with specific gravities above 7 (at least most that have been examined by X-ray methods) prove to be mixtures of tantalite with the tetragonal form tapiolite, which is probably considerably denser, though the specific gravity of neither pure species is accurately known.[21]

Several other minerals whose specific gravity is in the same general range as tantalite are often mistaken for it. These include ilmenite, magnetite, cassiterite, and wolframite.

Tantalite occurs in pegmatites and in eluvial and alluvial deposits derived from them. It is concentrated by gravity methods (tabling, sluicing, etc.) which collect all of the heavy constituents. If too large a proportion of other heavy minerals is present the product will be unsalable. Undesirable ferromagnetic minerals can be removed by magnetic separation however.

Specifications in 1944, provided: minimum 30% Ta_2O_5; a minimum of 60% combined tantalum and columbium pentoxides; maximum 3% SnO_2; maximum of 3% TiO_2. Tin and titanium interfere with treatment of the ores and excess is often severely penalized. Tantalum ore is quoted per pound of contained Ta_2O_5 based on 30% content with a premium for ore of higher grades.

[21] U. S. Geological Survey, Mineralogical Laboratory, personal communication.

Tin

The principal ore mineral is cassiterite (SnO_2) although many of the Bolivian ores contain accessory tin-bearing sulphides such as stannite (Cu_2FeSnS_4), teallite (PbS.SnS) and franckeite[22] ($Pb_5Sn_3Sb_2O_{14}$). In a few mines teallite is the principal ore mineral and from time to time handpicked teallite ore has been marketed in England.[23]   However, tin occurring in any of the sulphide minerals (known as "acid-soluble" tin) is not welcome at most smelters.

Cassiterite, because of its high specific gravity (6.4 to 7.1) yields a high grade concentrate by gravity methods, but recoveries are low— 60% is considered good in Bolivian ores.   Flotation is used to free the ore or concentrate of pyrite and other undesirable sulphides but cassiterite itself does not respond to flotation reagents.[24]   Standard concentrates carry 50 to 60% Sn and are quoted in cents per pound of contained metal.   London prices are in £ per long ton of metal.   One per cent of sulphur and 5% of iron are allowed free but penalties apply to higher content.   Other undesirable constituents are lead, copper, arsenic, antimony and bismuth.

Titanium

The commercial ore minerals are ilmenite ($FeTiO_3$) and rutile (TiO_2). Brookite, which has the same composition as rutile, is equally acceptable. The minerals are concentrated from hard-rock deposits and from placers. Disseminated rutile ore, such as that mined in Amherst County, Va., is readily concentrated but not all ilmenite ore is easy to concentrate; ilmenite is usually intergrown either with magnetite or with hematite. Magnetite can be removed from it magnetically but hematite is practically impossible to separate by physical methods.   Large deposits of ilmenite (the beach sands of southern India[25] and the massive deposit at Lake Sanford in the Adirondacks) are capable of supplying normal demands for this mineral, but there is usually a market for high-grade rutile concentrate.

[22] Frederic Chase, personal communication.

[23] Neil O' Donnell, personal communication.

[24] Experimental work gives promise of developing reagents that will float cassiterite. Cf. Gaudin, A. M., et al., Making tin flotation work, E. & M. J., vol. 147, Oct., pp. 54–59, Nov., pp. 72–74, Dec., p. 68, vol. 148, Jan., pp. 84–87, March, pp. 70–72, 1946–1947.

[25] In the Indian sands, some or all of the titanium is said to occur as arizonite, $Fe_2Ti_3O_9$, which is richer in titanium than ilmenite. Theoretical compositions: arizonite, 60.01% TiO_2; ilmenite, 52.66% TiO_2.

Tungsten [26]

The commercial ores are scheelite ($CaWO_3$) and wolframite (Fe,-Mn)WO_3. Wolframite is an isomorphous series ranging from ferberite ($FeWO_3$) to huebnerite ($MnWO_3$). Tungsten is sold by the miner in form of concentrates. The standard grades are 65% WO_3 for wolframite and 60% for scheelite. Tolerance of impurities varies under different contracts but the maxima allowable without penalty are about as follows: Sn 1.6%, As 0.2%, Cu .10%, P 0.05%, Sb, 0.05%, Bi 0.40%, S 1.0%. Prices for tungsten ores are quoted in the United States per short ton unit (20 lb.) of contained WO_3 and in British countries per long ton unit (22.4 lb.). Tungsten ores are concentrated by gravity methods but with relatively low recovery (65% to 80%). A further recovery can be made from scheelite ores by flotation, but if carbonates are present they float along with the scheelite and yield a low-grade concentrate which requires special chemical treatment. Wolframite concentrates can be purified by magnetic concentration.

Vanadium

The largest single source of ore is the Vanadium Corporation of America's mine at Minasragra, Peru. This deposit is unique geologically; the metal occurs in a number of minerals that are elsewhere rare or unknown, chiefly hydrous calcium vanadates and vanadium sulphides and sulphates. The carnotite and roscoelite ores of Colorado and Utah produce in war time but are relatively low in vanadium. Lead vanadate ores such as those mined at Broken Hill (Rhodesia), and in Southwest Africa need to carry at least 10% V_2O_5 and preferably 18% to 20% in order to be salable. It is the lead vanadate type of ore that is most likely to come to the attention of an itinerant mining geologist. It is quite common in the oxidized zones of lead deposits but is generall erratically distributed; systematic sampling usually shows a lower grade than casual examination might suggest.

Vanadium ores are quoted per pound of contained V_2O_5 but published quotations are nominal. The principal U. S. consumers, Vanadium Corporation of America and U. S. Vanadium Co. have their own sources of ore supply. It would be difficult, except in war times, to bring a new deposit into profitable operation unless it were exceptionally rich.

[26] An exhaustive treatise on the geology, technology and economics of tungsten is, Li, K. C., and Wang, Chung Yu, *Tungsten*, New York, Reinhold Publishing Co., 330 W. 42nd Street, 1943 (325 pages).

Zinc

The most important zinc mineral is sphalerite (zinc blende) (ZnS) which is sold to smelters and refineries in the form of concentrate. Smithsonite ($ZnCO_3$) and hemimorphite (calamine) ($Zn_4Si_2O_7$-$(OH)_2.H_2O$) are marketable but as they are difficult to concentrate they are not profitable to mine unless within easy shipping distance of a smelter.

Treatment methods are discussed in Chapter 22.

Appendices

I: CLASSIFICATION OF ROCKS

A: Igneous Rocks

The following tables and diagrams show the mineralogical compositions of most of the familiar igneous rocks. In most respects the classification follows the Johannsen [1] scheme but is here simplified and recast in order to place emphasis on the relations of the commonest rock-types.

Table A breaks down the whole range of igneous rocks into major groups in accordance with the principal minerals that the rocks contain.

Diagrams B and C (triangular diagrams) subdivide two of these groups in accordance with the species of feldspar present.

Since the rock-names shown in the tables and diagrams are those of the plutonic (Phanerocrystalline) types, Table D gives the names of the corresponding fine-grained and glassy rocks (found in lavas and shallow-seated intrusives).

Table A.

			With Ferromagnesians	Without Ferromagnesians
Without Feldspathoids *	With Quartz	*With Feldspar*	See Diagram C	Aplite Alaskite
		Without Feldspar	——	(Vein quartz)
	Without Quartz	*With Feldspar*	See Diagram B	Albitite Anorthosite
		Without Feldspar	ULTRAMAFIC ROCKS See Note 2.	
With Feldspathoids *		*With Feldspar*	ALKALIC SYENITES See Note 3.	
		Without Feldspar	ALKALIC ROCKS See Note 3.	

* Feldspathoids include nepheline, sodalite, analcite and leucite; also (less common) haüynite, noselite, melilite, cancrinite.

[1] Johannsen, Albert, *A Descriptive Petrography of the Igneous Rocks*, vol. 1, pp. 140–158, University of Chicago Press, 1931.

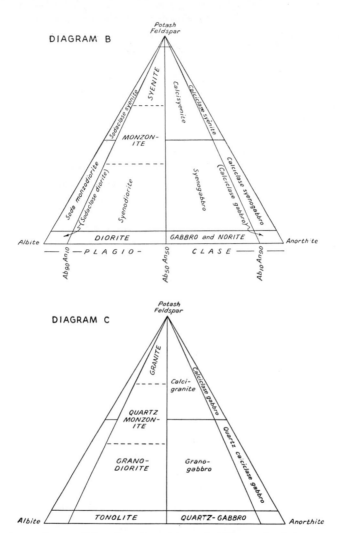

Fig. 148—Rocks containing ferromagnesians and feldspars classified according to nature of feldspar. *Diagram B:* Rocks containing less than 5% quartz. *Diagram C:* Rocks containing 5% to 50% of quartz. The composition (or range of composition) of each rock is indicated by its position in the triangle. The corner of a triangle represents rock consisting wholly of the mineral whose name appears at the corner plus ferromagnesians and, if present, quartz. Distance from any corner represents decrease in the corner-mineral and corresponding increase in the two other corner-minerals.

Notes:

1. GABBRO AND NORITE. Normal gabbro is calcic plagioclase with monoclinic pyroxene. Norite has orthorhombic instead of monoclinic pyroxene. See glossary for related rocks: theralite, essexite.

2. ULTRAMAFIC ROCKS. Consist chiefly of ferromagnesian minerals.
   Common Types:
   Periodotite. A generic name for rocks consisting of olivine with or without other ferromagnesians. Varieties are named by prefix, as: mica-peridotite, enstatite-peridotite, etc.
   Dunite. Chiefly olivine.
   The following rocks are named from their chief minerals: pyroxenite, bronzitite, hypersthenite, diallagite.
   See glossary for compositions of the following related rocks: picrite, saxonite, harzburgite, cortlandite, wehrlite, eclogite, cumberlandite, websterite.

3. ALKALIC SYENITES consist of alkali (potash or soda) feldspar with nepheline (nepheline syenite) and with or without sodalite and leucite. For composition of the following uncommon rocks see glossary: foyaite, ditroite, laurdalite, theralite, lugarite, ijolite, shonkinite.

Table D.

Fine-grained and Glassy Equivalents of Phanerocrystalline
(Plutonic) Rock-Types

Phanerocrystalline Rock	Fine-grained or Glassy Equivalent	Phanerocrystalline Rock	Fine-grained or Glassy Equivalent
Granite	Rhyolite	Syenite	Trachyte
Quartz Monzonite	Quartz Latite	Monzonite	Latite
Granodiorite	Rhyodacite	Diorite	Andesite
Tonolite	Dacite		
Quartz Gabbro	Quartz Basalt	Gabbro	Basalt
		Nepheline	Phonolite
		Syenite	

B: Sedimentary Rocks

Table E.

Original Sediment	Consolidated Rock	Metamorphic Equivalent
GRAVEL (over 2 mm) *	Conglomerate	Conglomerate
SAND (2 to 0.2 mm) 　Chiefly quartz 　Quartz and feldspar 　Fragments of basic rocks and/ 　　or of ferromagnesian min- 　　erals	Sandstone Arkose Graywacke †	Quartzite Arkose Graywacke †
SILT (.02 to .002 mm)	Siltstone	
CLAY (less than .002 mm) 　Laminated 　Unlaminated	Shale Argillite	Phyllite, schist Gneiss (see table of Metamorphic Rocks)
VOLCANIC ASH OR DUST	Tuff	Metamorphic tuff
CALCAREOUS SEDIMENTS 　Chiefly CaCO$_3$ 　Chiefly dolomite	Limestone Dolomite	Marble Dolomite Marble

* Grain sizes are as given by Longwell, Knopf and Flint, *Outlines of Physical Geology.* New York: John Wiley and Sons, 1941, p. 39.

† Graywacke is used in somewhat differing senses by different authorities. *See* Glossary.

C: Metamorphic Rocks

KEY TO TEXTURES

Dense. Compact; individual grains not readily distinguishable; distinct cleavage lacking.

Granular. Individual grains readily distinguishable; distinct cleavage lacking.

Slaty. Cleavable on smooth, usually lustrous surfaces, commonly at an angle to bedding. Grain so fine that individual grains or flakes are not distinguishable except in thin section under the microscope.

Table F.

Minerals	Texture					
	Dense	Granular	Slaty	Phyllitic	Schistose	Gneissic
Quartz	—	Quartzite	—	—	—	—
Quartz and Mica	—	—	—	—	Quartz schist	—
Contact metamorphic minerals *	Hornfels	Hornfels	—	—	—	—
Chlorite	—	—	Slate	Phyllite	Chlorite schist	—
Mica	—	—	Slate	Phyllite	Mica schist	Mica gneiss
Mica with quartz and/or feldspar	—	—	(Slate)	(Phyllite)	(schist)	Gneiss
Hornblende	—	(Amphibolite)	—	—	Hornblende schist or amphibolite	Hornblende gneiss or amphibolite
Calcite	(Marble)	Marble	—	—	—	—
Dolomite	(Marble)	Marble	—	—	—	—
Calcium-bearing † silicates	(Skarn)	Skarn	—	—	—	Skarn
Serpentine	—	Serpentine	—	—	Serpentine	—

* Characteristic minerals of hornfels: cordierite, andalusite, with quartz, feldspar and some mica.

† Characteristic minerals of skarn (alternative term: tactite): garnet, epidote, vesuvianite, wollastonite, diopside, scapolite, with more or less calcite.

Phyllitic. Cleavable on smooth surfaces. Coarser than slate but grains and flakes discernible with difficulty by unaided eye. May contain larger metacrysts, *e.g.* albite or garnet in finer matrix.

Schistose. Coarser than phyllite. Grains and flakes clearly visible. Cleavage surfaces rougher than in phyllites.

Gneissic. Coarse-grained, on the order of one to several millimeters. Cleavable on rough surfaces if at all. If composed of more than one mineral, the minerals are more or less segregated into separate bands or lenses.

Note: Most of the rock names may carry prefixes designating abundant or conspicuous minerals, *e.g.*: albite-chlorite schist, andalusite schist, garnet-muscovite gneiss, biotite gneiss, etc.

II: Genetic Classification of Ore Deposits

(Based on Lindgren's classification as modified by Graton and by Buddington. Some rare or doubtful classes omitted.)

Syngenetic Deposits

In sedimentary rocks. Examples: Clinton and Minette iron ores; placer deposits of gold and platinum.

In igneous rocks. Examples: Most chromite deposits; ilmenite deposits. (Pegmatite deposits may belong here.)

Epigenetic Deposits

Supergene

Due to rock weathering. Examples: Lateritic iron ores; bauxite deposits, nickel silicate deposits (Cuba, New Caledonia, Brazil).

Due to downward sulphide enrichment. Examples: Most porphyry coppers.

Hypogene

Hydrothermal Deposits

Hypothermal. Examples: Homestake gold. Noranda, copper-gold. Sullivan, B. C. lead-zinc. Most pyrometasomatic deposits probably belong here.

Mesothermal. Examples: Veins of the main copper zone at Butte, Mont.

Leptothermal. Examples: Casapalca, Peru. Veins of the silver-lead-zinc zone at Butte, Mont. San Juan region, Colorado.

Epithermal. Examples: Goldfield, Nevada. Tonopah, Nevada. Most quicksilver deposits.

Note re Hydrothermal Ore Deposits

Lindgren designated his class II B 2 b: "Concentration effected by introduction of substances foreign to the rock—origin dependent upon the eruption of igneous rocks—by hot ascending waters of uncertain origin, but charged with igneous emanations." This deference to the theory of lateral secretion seems no longer necessary, since most authorities now agree that the water of ore solutions is of magmatic origin.

Lindgren subdivided this class of deposits (the hydrothermal class) into three sub-classes:

Epithermal—Deposition and concentration at slight depth. Temperature 50–200 degrees C. Pressure moderate.

Mesothermal—Deposited at intermediate depth. Temperature 200 to 300 degrees. Pressure high.

Hypothermal—Deposited at great depth or at high temperature and pressure. Temperature 300–500 degrees. Pressure very high.

More recently three additional subclasses within the hydrothermal group have been proposed (see Chapter 15). The following table, intended to express the possible relationships of the telethermal, xenothermal and leptothermal sub-classes to Lindgren's three, is offered without intending to imply that the authors of the newer terms would necessarily endorse this particular arrangement. In this table "source" does not necessarily represent the ultimate point of origin of the ore solutions but rather the lower limit of conditions favorable to deposition of ore minerals.

Table G.

Surface	Surface	Surface
Telethermal	Epithermal	Xenothermal
(Epithermal?)	Leptothermal	
(Leptothermal?)	Mesothermal	————
(Mesothermal?)	Hypothermal	
Hypothermal		Shallow "source"
	————	
————		
	Moderately Deep "source"	
————		
Deep "source"		

III: Geologic Time-Scale

For North America [2]

Cenozoic Era

Quaternary Period
  Recent Epoch
  Pleistocene Epoch
Tertiary Period
  Pliocene Epoch
  Miocene   "
  Oligocene   "
  Eocene   "

[2] Wilmarth, M. Grace, Geologic Time Classification of the United States Geological Survey Compared with other classifications, U.S.G.S. Bull. 769, 1923 (Table in pocket).

MESOZOIC ERA
  Cretaceous Period
    Upper Cretaceous Epoch
    Lower   "   "
  Jurassic Period
    Upper Jurassic Epoch
    Middle Jurassic   "
    Lower Jurassic   "
  Triassic Period
    Upper Triassic Epoch
    Middle Triassic   "
    Lower Triassic   "

PALEOZOIC ERA

  Carboniferous Period
    Permian Epoch
    Pennsylvanian Epoch
    Mississippian Epoch
  Devonian Period
    Upper Devonian Epoch
    Middle   "   "
    Lower   "   "
  Silurian Period
  Ordovician Period
    Upper Ordovician Epoch
      (Cincinnatian, provincially)
    Middle Ordovician Epoch
      (Mohawkian, provincially)
    Lower Ordovician Epoch
  Cambrian Period
    Upper Cambrian (or St. Croixan) Epoch
    Middle Cambrian (or Acadian)   "
    Lower Cambrian (or Waucoban)   "
PROTEROZOIC (or PRE-CAMBRIAN) ERA
  Algonkian Period
    Keweenawan Epoch
    Huronian Epoch
  Archean Period
    Laurentian (intrusive)
    Keewatin Epoch

For Europe [3] (Some of these terms are in common use in Latin America)

QUATERNARY ERA

  Quaternary Period
    Recent Quaternary (Holocene) Group
    Middle Quaternary (Pleistocene) Group

[3] Haug, E., *Traité de Géologie*. vol. 2. pts. 1, 2, vol. 3, 1908, 1910, 1911, from Wilmarth, Grace, Geologic Time Classification of the U.S.G.S. *U.S.G.S. Bull.* 769, 1925.

      Wurmian (glacial)
      Chellian
      Rissian (glacial)
    Ancient Quaternary Group
      Cromerian
      Mindelian (glacial)
      St. Prestian
      Villafranchian (Calabrian) (glacial)

TERTIARY ERA

  Neogene (or Mediterranian) Period
    Upper Neogene ("Pliocene") Group
      Astian
      Plaisancian
    Middle Neogene Period
      Sahelian (Pontian)
      Vindobonian
    Lower Neogene Group
      Burdigalian (Langhian)
      Aquitanian
  Nummulitic Period
    Upper Nummulitic (or Tongrian or Oligocene) Group
      Chattian
      Rupelian
      Lattorfian
    Middle Nummulitic Group
      Ludian
      Bartonian
      Auversian
      Lutetian
    Lower Nummulitic (or Suessonian or Paleocene) Group
      Londinian
      Thanetian (including Cernaysian)
      Montian

MESOZOIC ERA

  Cretaceous Period
    Upper Cretaceous (or Senonian) Group
      Danian
      Maestrichtian
      Campanian
      Santonian
      Coniacian
    Middle Cretaceous Group
      Turonian
      Cenomanian
      Albian
    Lower Cretaceous (or Neocomian Group)
      Aptian
      Barremian

Hauterivian
Valanginian
Berriasian
Jurassic Period
 Upper Oolithic Group
  Portlandian
 Middle Oolithic Group
  Kimmeridgian
  Lusitanian
 Lower Oolithic Group
  Oxfordian
  Callovian
  Bathonian
  Bajocian
 Upper Liassic Group
  Aalenian
  Toarcian
 Middle Liassic Group
  Domerian
  Pliensbachian
 Lower Liassic Group
  Lotharingian
  Sinemurian
  Hettangian
  Rhetian
Triassic Period
 Upper Triassic (Keuper) Group
  Norian
  Carnian
 Middle Triassic (Muschelkalk) Group
  Ladinian
  Virglorian
 Lower Triassic (Wurfenian, Bunt Sandstone) Group

PALEOZOIC ERA
 Anthracolithic Period
  Permian Group
   Thuringian
   Saxonian (Lodevian)
   Artinskian (Autunian)
 Carboniferous Period
  Ouralian (Stephanian)
  Moscovian (Westphalian)
  Dinantian
 Devonian Period
  Upper Devonian Group
   Famennian
   Frasnian

Middle Devonian Group
  Givetian
  Eifelian
Lower Devonian Group
  Coblentzian
  Gedinnian
Silurian Period
  Gothlandian Group
    Downtonian
    Ludlow (Clunian)
    Wenlock (Salopian)
    Llandovery (May Hill, Valentian)
  Ordovician Group
    Caradoc
    Llandeilo
    Arenig
    Tremadoc
Cambrian Period
  Potsdamian Group
  Acadian Group
  Georgian Group
PRE-CAMBRIAN (OR AGNOTOZOIC) ERA
  Algonkian Period
  Archean Period

IV: Chemical Elements and Their Atomic Weights *

	Symbol	Atomic Number	Atomic Weight		Symbol	Atomic Number	Atomic Weight
Actinium	Ac	89	[227]	Mercury	Hg	80	200.61
[Alabamine]	Ab	85	[221]	Molybdenum	Mo	42	95.95
Aluminum	Al	13	26.97	Neodymium	Nd	60	144.27
Antimony	Sb	51	121.76	Neon	Ne	10	20.183
Argon	A	18	39.944	Nickel	Ni	28	58.69
Arsenic	As	33	74.91	Nitrogen	N	7	14.008
Barium	Ba	56	137.36	Osmium	Os	76	190.2
Beryllium	Be	4	9.02	Oxygen	O	8	16.0000
Bismuth	Bi	83	209.00	Palladium	Pd	46	106.7
Boron	B	5	10.82	Phosphorus	P	15	30.98
Bromine	Br	35	79.916	Platinum	Pt	78	195.23
Cadmium	Cd	48	112.41	Polonium	Po	84	[210]
Calcium	Ca	20	40.08	Potassium	K	19	39.096
Carbon	C	6	12.01	Praseodymium	Pr	59	140.92
Cerium	Ce	58	140.13	Protoactinium	Pa	91	....
Cesium	Cs	55	132.91	Radium	Ra	88	226.05
Chlorine	Cl	17	35.457	Radon	Rn	86	222
Chromium	Cr	24	52.01	Rhenium	Re	75	186.3
Cobalt	Co	27	58.94	Rhodium	Rh	45	102.91
Columbium	Cb	41	92.91	Rubidium	Rb	37	85.48
Copper	Cu	29	63.57	Ruthenium	Ru	44	101.7
Dysprosium	Dy	66	162.46	Samarium	Sm	62	150.43
Erbium	Er	68	167.2	Scandium	Sc	21	45.10
Europium	Eu	63	152.0	Selenium	Se	34	78.96
Fluorine	F	9	19.00	Silicon	Si	14	28.06
Gadolinium	Gd	64	156.9	Silver	Ag	47	107.880
Gallium	Ga	31	69.72	Sodium	Na	11	22.997
Germanium	Ge	32	72.60	Strontium	Sr	38	87.63
Gold	Au	79	197.2	Sulfur	S	16	32.06
Hafnium	Hf	72	178.6	Tantalum	Ta	73	180.88
Helium	He	2	4.001	Tellurium	Te	52	127.61
Holmium	Ho	67	164.94	Terbium	Tb	65	159.2
Hydrogen	H	1	1.0080	Thallium	Tl	81	204.39
Illinium	Il	61	[146]	Thorium	Th	90	232.12
Indium	In	49	114.76	Thulium	Tm	69	169.4
Iodine	I	53	126.92	Tin	Sn	50	118.70
Iridium	Ir	77	193.1	Titanium	Ti	22	47.90
Iron	Fe	26	55.85	Tungsten	W	74	183.92
Krypton	Kr	36	83.7	Uranium	U	92	238.07
Lanthanum	La	57	138.92	Vanadium	V	23	50.95
Lead	Pb	82	207.21	[Virginium]	Vi	87	[224]
Lithium	Li	3	6.940	Xenon	Xe	54	131.3
Lutecium	Lu	71	174.99	Ytterbium	Yb	70	173.04
Magnesium	Mg	12	24.32	Yttrium	Y	39	88.92
Manganese	Mn	25	54.93	Zinc	Zn	30	65.38
[Masurium]	Ma	43	[98]	Zirconium	Zr	40	91.22

* Hopkins, B. Smith, and Bailar, John C., *Essentials of General Chemistry*, D. C. Heath and Co., Boston, 1946.

V: Weights and Measures

a. Metric and English

LENGTH

	Centimeters	Meters	Inches	Feet	Miles
Metric					
1 Ångstrom	10^{-8}	10^{-10}	3.9370×10^{-9}	3.2808×10^{-10}	——
1 millimicron	10^{-7}	10^{-9}	3.9370×10^{-8}	3.2808×10^{-9}	——
1 micron	10^{-4}	10^{-6}	3.9370×10^{-5}	3.2808×10^{-6}	——
1 millimeter	0.1	0.001	0.03937	3.2808×10^{-3}	——
1 centimeter	1	0.01	0.3937	0.032808	——
1 meter	100	1	39.37	3.2808	.0006
1 kilometer	100,000	1000	39,370	3280.8	.6214
English					
1 inch	2.5400	0.0254	1	0.08333	——
1 foot (12 in.)	30.480	0.3048	12	1	.000189
1 yard	91.440	0.9144	36	3	.0005618
1 mile (statute)	160,940	1609.4	63,360	5280	1
Gunter's Chain					
1 link	20.12	0.2012	7.92	.66	.000125
1 rod * (25 links)	502.9	5.029	198	16.5	.003125
1 chain (100 links)	2012	20.12	792	66	.0125
1 mile (80 chains)	160,940	1609.4	63,360	5280	1
Depth					
1 fathom	182.88	1.8288	72	6	.0011364

*Synonyms for rod: pole, perch.

SURFACE AND AREA

	Sq. Centimeters	Sq. Meters	Sq. Feet	
Metric				
1 sq. cm.	1	.0001	.0010764	
1 sq. meter	10,000	1	10.764	
1 hectare	10^8	10,000	1.0764×10^5	2.4710 acres
1 sq. km.	10^{10}	10^6	1.0764×10^7	.3861 sq. mi.
English				
1 sq. inch	6.4514	0.000645	0.006944	
1 sq. ft. (144 sq. in.)	929.00	0.09290	1	
1 sq. yard	——	0.83613	9	
1 acre (160 sq. rods)	——	4047	43,560	.4047 hectares
1 sq. mile (640 acres)	——	2,590,000	27,878,400	2.590 sq. km.

WEIGHT

	Grams	Kilograms	Oz. Troy	Lb. Avoirdupois	Short Tons
Metric					
1 milligram	0.001	10^{-6}	3.215×10^{-5}	2.205×10^{-6}	——
1 gram (1000 mg.)	1	0.001	0.032151	0.002205	——
1 kilogram (1000 g.)	1000	1	32.1507	2.2046223	0.0011023
1 metric ton	10^6	1000	32,151	2204.6223	1.1023
Troy					
1 grain *	0.064799	6.480×10^{-5}	0.0020833	1/7000	7.134×10^{-8}
1 pennyweight (24 grains)	1.55517	0.001555	0.05	.00342857	1.71426×10^{-6}
1 ounce (20 dwt.)	31.10348	0.0311035	1	0.0685714	3.4286×10^{-5}
1 pound	373.24	0.37324	12	0.8228569	0.000411428

	Grams	Kilograms	Oz. Troy	Lb. Avoirdupois	Short Tons
Avoirdupois					
1 grain *	0.064799	6.48×10^{-5}	.0020833	0.00014286	7.134×10^{-8}
1 ounce	28.3495	0.02835	.911453	0.0652	3.125×10^{-5}
1 pound (16 oz.)	453.59	0.45359	14.5833	1	0.0005
1 short ton (2000 lb.)	9.072×10^{5}	907.19	29,166.7	2000	1
1 long ton (2240 lb.)	1.016×10^{6}	1016.05	32,666.7	2240	1.12

* 1 grain troy = 1 grain avoirdupois = 1 grain apothecary's weight.

VOLUME

	Cu. Cm.	Cu. Meters		U. S. Gal.
Metric				
1 cu. centimeter	1	10^{-6}	0.061023 cu in.	——
1 liter	1000.027	.001	0.035314 cu. ft.	0.26417
1 cu. meter	10^{6}	1	35.317 cu. ft.	264.17
English				
1 cu. inch	16.387	1.6387×10^{-5}	0.0005787 cu. ft.	0.004329
1 cu. foot	28,317	0.02832	1728 cu. in.	7.48053
1 cu. yard	7.646×10^{5}	0.7646	46,656 cu. in.	201.9743
U. S. liquid				
1 quart (2 pints)	946.358	9.4636×10^{-4}	57.75 cu. in.	0.25
1 gallon (4 quarts)	3785.4	0.003785	231 " "	1.
Imperial liquid				
1 quart	1136.521	0.001137	69.352 cu. in.	0.30025
1 gallon	4546.1	0.004546	277.410 " "	1.20091

PRESSURE †

	Kg. per Sq. Cm.	Lb. per Sq. In.	Bars
1 kg. per sq. cm.	1	14.2234	0.980665
1 lb. per sq. in.*	0.070307	1	0.068947
1 lb. per sq. ft.	0.004882	0.006944	0.000479
1 normal atmosphere	1.03323	14.6960	1.01325
1 bar	1.01972	14.5038	1

	Kg. per Sq. Cm.	Lb. per Sq. In.	Bars
1 foot of water	0.030480	0.43353	
1 ft. of rock (sp.gr. 2.7)	0.0823	1.17053	
1 inch of mercury	0.034534	0.49119	

* Normal gravity.

† Data from *Handbook of Physical Constants,* Geol. Soc. Am. Special Paper No. 36, 1942, p. 319.

ASSAY VALUES

	Per Cent	Grams per Metric Ton	Oz Troy per Short Ton
1 per cent	1	10,000	291.667
1 gram per metric ton	0.0001	1	0.0291667
1 kg per metric ton	0.1	1,000	29.1667
1 dwt per short ton	0.00017143	1.71426	0.0500
1 dwt per long ton	0.00015306	1.53061	0.0446428
1 oz troy per short ton	.00342857	34.2857	1
1 oz troy per long ton	.00306122	30.6122	0.892859

For Bolivian and Peruvian assay values, see table c.

b. South Africa [4]

	Cape feet	English feet	Meters
1 Cape foot	1	1.033	0.3149
1 Cape rood	12	12.40	3.7879

	Acres
1 Morgan (11.5 erven *)	2.1165
1 claim (60,000 sq. cape feet)	1.5 ±

* Plural of erf.

[4] Letcher, Owen, *The Gold Mines of Southern Africa,* Johannesburg, 1936, p. 531.

c. Spain and Latin America

Note: The metric system is "compulsory" in Spain and all Latin American countries, but weights and measures based on old Spanish units survive locally.

LENGTH

1 Vara (Spain)	0.8359 meters	2.6816 English feet

Other units in terms of varas: pie 1/3; milla (5000 pies), 1666 2/3; legua, 5000 or 8000.

Length of the vara varies in different countries: in meters: Argentina, 0.8666; Brazil, 1.1; Chile, 0.836, Colombia and Venezuela, 0.8; Costa Rica, 0.8393; Guatamala, 0.8359; Honduras, 0.8128; Mexico, 0.838; Paraguay, 0.83856; Peru, 0.83598.

WEIGHT

	Metric	*Oz. Troy*	*Libra*	*Lb. Avoirdupois*
1 marco (Spain)	230.0465 g.	7.39616	0.5	0.507165
1 libra (Spain)	460.093 g.	14.79232	1	1.014331
1 cajon (Bolivia)	2300.4651 kg.	73961.624	5000	5071.654
1 cajon (Peru)	2760.5581 kg.	88753.949	6000	6085.985
1 tonelada (Spain)	920.086 kg.	——	2000	2032.2

Other units in terms of *libras:* adarme, 1/256; onza (16 adarmes), 1/16; libra (16 onzas), 1; arroba, 25; quintal, 100; carga (12 arrobas), 300, tonelada, 2000.

The libra in Spain, Castille and Chile is 460.093 grams (101.43 lb. avoirdupois). Other countries in *grams:* Argentina, 459.4; Brazil, 459.05; Colombia, 500; Mexico, 460.24636; Peru, 460.09; Venezuela, 1000.

A metric quintal is 100 kg. A tonelada in Cuba is 1015.65 kg.

ASSAY VALUES

	Grams per Metric Ton	*Oz. Troy per Short Ton*
1 marco por cajon (Bolivia)	100	2.91667
1 marco por cajon (Peru)	83.333	2.430555

Note: 1 marco por cajon is known in Bolivia as a decimarco (D.M.)

d. Russia [5]

LENGTH

	Metric	*English*
1 archine	0.711200 meters	2.333 ft.
1 totchka	0.254000 mm.	0.010 in.

Other units have following values in terms of *totchka:* ligne, 10; paletz, 50; sotka, 84; duime, 100; verchoc, 175 foute (= 1 English foot), 1200; archine, 2800.

Following values are in terms of *archine:* sagene, 3; verste, 1500.

[5] National Research Council, *International Critical Tables,* New York: McGraw-Hill Book Company, Inc., 1926, p. 11.

AREA

1 square archine	0.5058054 sq. meters	5.444 sq. ft.
1 square ligne	6.451600 sq. mm.	0.010 sq. in.

Other units have following values in terms of *square ligne:* duime, 100; verchoc, 306.25; foute, 14,400; archine, 78,400.

Following values are in terms of *square archine:* sagene, 9; decientine, 21,600; verste, 2,250,000.

VOLUME OR CAPACITY

1 vedro (10 krouchka)	12.29941 litres	3.249 U. S. gal.
1 krouchka (10 tcharka)	1.22994 litres	75.0602 cu. in.
1 tcharka	122.99441 cc.	7.5050 cu. in.

Other units have following values in terms of *tcharka:* chkalik, 0.5; shtoff, 12.5.

Following values are in terms of *vedro:* stekar, 1.5; anker, 3; pipe, 36; fass or botchka, 40.

WEIGHT

	Metric	*English*
1 fount	409.51241 grams	.9028 lb.
1 doli	44.4349403 mg.	.686 grains

Other units have following values in terms of *doli:* sol or zolotnik, 96; lote, 288; once, 576; lana, 768; fount, 9216.

Following values are in terms of *fount:* poud, 40; berkovets, 400; tonne marine, 2400.

e. China [6]

LENGTH

	Metric	*English*
1 hao	0.032 mm.	0.0126 in.
1 pu	1.6 meters	5.249 ft.
1 chang	3.2 meters	10.498 ft.

1 chang = 10 ch'ih = 100 ts'un = 1000 fen = 10,000 li = 100,000 hao
1 pu = 5 ch'ih = ½ chang.

---

[6] Adopted by China in pursuance of the imperial rescript of Aug. 28, 1908. Data from Peele's *Mining Engineers Handbook*, Sec. 45, p. 50, New York, John Wiley & Sons, 1941.

Surface and Area

1 hao	.6144 sq. meters	6.6134 sq. ft.
1 fang pu	2.56 " "	27.556 sq. ft.
1 ch'ing	61440 " "	15.182 acres

1 ch'ing = 100 mu = 1000 fen = 10,000 li = 100,000 hao.
1 fen = 24 fang pu.

Volume

1 shao	10.35 cc.	0.6438 cu. in.
1 hu	51.774 litres	13.678 gals. (U. S.)
1 tan or picul	103.5469 litres	27.356 gals. (U. S.)

1 tan or picul = 10 tou = 100 sheng = 1000 ko = 10,000 shao.
1 hu = 5 tou = ½ tan.

Weight

1 hao	3.7301 mg.	.0576 grains
1 liang	37.301 grams	1.199 oz. troy
1 chin (catty)	596.816 grams	1.316 lb. av.

1 liang = 10 ch'ien = 100 fen = 1000 li = 10,000 hao.
1 chin or catty = 16 liang.

f. Straits Settlements and Netherlands Indies

Weight

1 kati (Straits)	604.79 grams	1.33356 lb. avoirdupois
1 catti (Neth. Ind.) or kati	617.613	1.361837 " "

Following units in terms of *kati* and *catti*:
Straits: tahil, 1/16; pikul, 100; bhara, 300; koyan, 4000.
Neth. Ind.: thail, 1/16; pikol, 100; small bahar, 300.

g. Japan [7]

Length

	Metric	English
1 shaku	0.30303 meters	.9941919 ft.

[7] Data from Peele's *Mining Engineers Handbook*, sec. 45, p. 51, New York, John Wiley & Sons, 1941.

1 shaku = 10 sun = 100 bu = 1000 rin = 10,000 mo = 100,000 shi.
6 shaku = 1 ken, 60 ken = 1 cho, 36 cho = 1 ri = 12960 shaku.

AREA

1 shaku   .033 sq. meters   .9884 sq. ft.

10 shaku = 1 go, 10 go = 1 bu or tsubo. 30 bu = 1 sé.
10 sé = 1 tan, 10 tan = 1 cho.

VOLUME

1 shaku   18.04 cc.   .0180616 U. S. liq. qt.

1 koku = 10 to = 100 sho = 1000 go = 10,000 shaku.

WEIGHT

1 kwan   3.75 kg.   8.267336 lb.

1 kwan = 1000 momme = 10,000 fun = 100,000 rin = 1,000,000 mo = 10,000,000 shi.

VI: Natural Functions of Angles

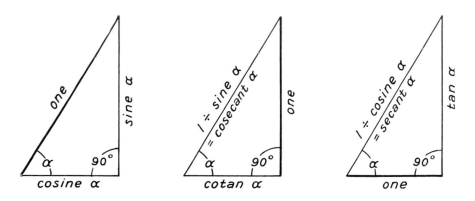

Fig. 149—Use of trigonometric functions in calculating the second and third sides of a right triangle when one side and an angle are known.

Angle	Sin	Cos	Tan	Cot	Sec	Csc
0°00′	0.000	1.0000	0.000	∞	1.000	∞
15′	0.004	1.0000	0.004	229.18	1.000	229.18
30′	0.009	0.9999	0.009	145.59	1.000	114.59
45′	0.013	0.9999	0.013	76.39	1.0001	76.40
1 00′	0.017	0.9998	0.017	57.29	1.0001	57.30
15	0.022	0.9997	0.022	45.83	1.0002	45.84
30	0.026	0.9996	0.026	38.19	1.0003	38.20
45	0.031	0.9995	0.031	32.73	1.0005	32.75
2 00	0.035	0.9994	0.035	28.64	1.0006	28.65
15	0.039	0.9992	0.039	25.45	1.0006	25.47
30	0.044	0.9990	0.044	22.90	1.0008	22.93
45	0.048	0.9988	0.048	20.82	1.0009	20.84
3 00	0.052	0.9986	0.052	19.08	1.0014	19.11
15	0.057	0.9984	0.057	17.61	1.0016	17.64
30	0.061	0.9981	0.061	16.35	1.0019	16.38
45	0.065	0.9979	0.066	15.26	1.0021	15.29
4 00	0.070	0.9976	0.070	14.30	1.0024	14.34
15	0.074	0.9972	0.074	13.46	1.0028	13.49
30	0.078	0.9969	0.079	12.71	1.0031	12.74
45	0.083	0.9966	0.083	12.03	1.0034	12.08
5°	0.087	0.996	0.087	11.43	1.004	11.47
6	0.105	0.995	0.105	9.514	1.006	9.567
7	0.122	0.993	0.123	8.144	1.008	8.206
8	0.139	0.990	0.141	7.115	1.010	7.185
9	0.156	0.988	0.158	6.314	1.012	6.392
10°	0.174	0.985	0.176	5.671	1.015	5.759
11	0.191	0.982	0.194	5.145	1.019	5.241

Angle	Sin	Cos	Tan	Cot	Sec	Csc
12	0.208	0.978	0.213	4.705	1.022	4.810
13	0.225	0.974	0.231	4.331	1.026	4.445
14	0.242	0.970	0.249	4.011	1.031	4.134
15°	0.259	0.966	0.268	3.732	1.035	3.864
16	0.276	0.961	0.287	3.487	1.040	3.628
17	0.292	0.956	0.306	3.271	1.046	3.420
18	0.309	0.951	0.325	3.078	1.051	3.236
19	0.326	0.946	0.344	2.904	1.058	3.072
20°	0.342	0.940	0.364	2.747	1.064	2.924
21	0.358	0.934	0.384	2.605	1.071	2.790
22	0.375	0.927	0.404	2.475	1.079	2.669
23	0.391	0.921	0.424	2.356	1.086	2.559
24	0.407	0.914	0.445	2.246	1.095	2.459
25°	0.423	0.906	0.466	2.145	1.103	2.366
26	0.438	0.899	0.488	2.050	1.113	2.281
27	0.454	0.891	0.510	1.963	1.122	2.203
28	0.469	0.883	0.532	1.881	1.133	2.130
29	0.485	0.875	0.554	1.804	1.143	2.063
30°	0.500	0.866	0.577	1.732	1.155	2.000
31	0.515	0.857	0.601	1.664	1.167	1.942
32	0.530	0.848	0.625	1.600	1.179	1.887
33	0.545	0.839	0.649	1.540	1.192	1.836
34	0.559	0.829	0.675	1.483	1.206	1.788
35°	0.574	0.819	0.700	1.428	1.221	1.743
36	0.588	0.809	0.727	1.376	1.236	1.701
37	0.602	0.799	0.754	1.327	1.252	1.662
38	0.616	0.788	0.781	1.280	1.269	1.624
39	0.629	0.777	0.810	1.235	1.287	1.589
40°	0.643	0.766	0.839	1.192	1.305	1.556
41	0.656	0.755	0.869	1.150	1.325	1.524
42	0.669	0.743	0.900	1.111	1.346	1.494
43	0.682	0.731	0.933	1.072	1.367	1.466
44	0.695	0.719	0.966	1.036	1.390	1.440
45	0.707	0.707	1.000	1.000	1.414	1.414
46	0.719	0.695	1.036	0.966	1.440	1.390
47	0.731	0.682	1.072	0.933	1.466	1.367
48	0.743	0.669	1.111	0.900	1.494	1.346
49	0.755	0.656	1.150	0.869	1.524	1.325
50	0.766	0.643	1.192	0.839	1.556	1.305
51	0.777	0.629	1.235	0.810	1.589	1.287
52	0.788	0.616	1.280	0.781	1.624	1.269
53	0.799	0.602	1.357	0.754	1.662	1.252
54	0.809	0.588	1.376	0.727	1.701	1.236
55	0.819	0.574	1.428	0.700	1.743	1.221
56	0.829	0.559	1.483	0.675	1.788	1.206
57	0.839	0.545	1.540	0.649	1.836	1.192
58	0.848	0.530	1.600	0.625	1.887	1.179

Angle	Sin	Cos	Tan	Cot	Sec	Csc
59	0.857	0.515	1.664	0.601	1.942	1.167
60	0.866	0.500	1.732	0.577	2.000	1.155
61	0.875	0.485	1.804	0.554	2.063	1.143
62	0.883	0.469	1.881	0.532	2.130	1.133
63	0.891	0.454	1.963	0.510	2.203	1.122
64	0.899	0.438	2.050	0.488	2.281	1.113
65	0.906	0.423	2.145	0.466	2.366	1.103
66	0.914	0.407	2.246	0.445	2.459	1.095
67	0.921	0.391	2.356	0.424	2.559	1.086
68	0.927	0.375	2.475	0.404	2.669	1.079
69	0.934	0.358	2.605	0.384	2.790	1.071
70	0.940	0.342	2.747	0.364	2.924	1.064
71	0.946	0.326	2.904	0.344	3.072	1.058
72	0.951	0.309	3.078	0.325	3.236	1.051
73	0.956	0.292	3.271	0.306	3.420	1.046
74	0.961	0.276	3.487	0.287	3.628	1.040
75	0.966	0.259	3.732	0.268	3.864	1.035
76	0.970	0.242	4.011	0.249	4.134	1.031
77	0.974	0.225	4.331	0.231	4.445	1.026
78	0.978	0.208	4.705	0.213	4.810	1.022
79	0.982	0.191	5.145	0.194	5.241	1.019
80	0.985	0.174	5.671	0.176	5.759	1.015
81	0.988	0.156	6.314	0.158	6.392	1.012
82	0.990	0.139	7.115	0.141	7.185	1.010
83	0.993	0.122	8.144	0.123	8.206	1.008
84	0.995	0.105	9.514	0.105	9.567	1.006
85°00′	0.9962	0.0872	11.420	0.0875	11.474	1.0038
15	0.9964	0.0828	12.035	0.0831	12.076	1.0034
30	0.9969	0.0785	12.706	0.0787	12.475	1.0031
45	0.9972	0.0741	13.457	0.0743	13.494	1.0028
86 00	0.9976	0.0698	14.301	0.0699	14.356	1.0024
15	0.9979	0.0654	15.257	0.0655	15.290	1.0021
30	0.9981	0.0610	16.350	0.0612	16.380	1.0019
45	0.9984	0.0567	17.611	0.0568	17.638	1.0016
87 00	0.9986	0.0523	19.081	0.0524	19.107	1.0014
15	0.9989	0.0480	20.819	0.0480	20.843	1.0011
30	0.9990	0.0436	22.904	0.0437	22.926	1.0009
45	0.9992	0.0393	25.452	0.0393	25.471	1.0008
88 00	0.9994	0.0349	28.636	0.0349	28.654	1.0006
15	0.9995	0.0305	32.730	0.0306	32.746	1.0005
30	0.9997	0.0262	38.188	0.0262	38.202	1.0003
45	0.9998	0.0218	45.829	0.0218	45.480	1.0002
89 00	0.9999	0.0174	57.290	0.0175	57.299	1.0001
15	0.9999	0.0131	76.390	0.0131	76.397	1.0001
30	1.0000	0.0087	114.59	0.0087	114.59	1.0000
45	1.0000	0.0004	229.18	0.0044	229.18	1.0000
90 00	1.0000	0.0000	∞	0.0000	∞	1.0000

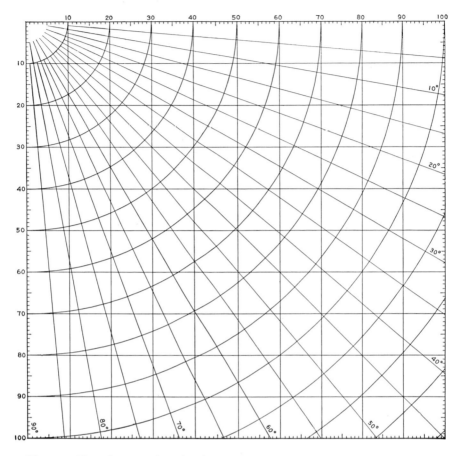

Fig. 150—Chart for conversion of inclined to vertical or horizontal distance. Can be used for approximate calculation of true thickness, depth to an inclined vein or stratum, vertical and horizontal components of dip, etc.

VII: Apparent Dip in Direction Not Perpendicular to Strike [1]

Angle Between Strike and Direction of Section

Angle of Full Dip	5°	10°	15°	20°	25°	30°	35°	40°	45°	50°	55°	60°	65°	70°	75°	80°
10°	1°	2°	3°	3°	4°	5°	6°	6°	7°	8°	8°	9°	9°	9°	10°	10°
15°	1°	3°	4°	5°	6°	8°	9°	10°	10°	12°	12°	13°	14°	14°	14°	15°
20°	2°	4°	5°	7°	9°	10°	12°	13°	14°	16°	17°	18°	18°	19°	19°	20°
25°	2°	5°	7°	9°	11°	13°	15°	17°	18°	20°	21°	22°	23°	24°	24°	25°
30°	3°	6°	9°	11°	14°	16°	18°	20°	22°	24°	25°	27°	28°	28°	29°	30°
35°	4°	7°	10°	13°	16°	19°	22°	24°	26°	28°	30°	31°	32°	33°	34°	35°
40°	4°	8°	12°	16°	20°	23°	26°	28°	31°	33°	35°	36°	37°	38°	39°	40°
45°	5°	10°	15°	19°	23°	27°	30°	33°	35°	37°	39°	41°	42°	43°	44°	45°
50°	6°	12°	17°	22°	27°	31°	34°	37°	40°	42°	44°	46°	47°	48°	49°	50°
55°	7°	14°	20°	26°	31°	36°	39°	43°	45°	48°	49°	51°	52°	53°	54°	55°
60°	9°	17°	24°	30°	36°	41°	45°	48°	51°	53°	55°	56°	58°	58°	59°	60°
65°	11°	20°	29°	36°	42°	46°	51°	54°	57°	59°	60°	62°	63°	64°	64°	65°
70°	13°	25°	35°	43°	49°	54°	58°	60°	63°	65°	67°	68°	69°	69°	69°	70°
75°	18°	33°	44°	52°	58°	62°	65°	67°	69°	71°	72°	73°	74°	74°	74°	75°
80°	26°	45°	56°	63°	67°	71°	73°	75°	76°	77°	78°	78°	79°	79°	80°	80°
85°	45°	63°	71°	76°	78°	80°	81°	82°	83°	83°	84°	84°	84°	85°	85°	85°

[1] Modified after Lahee.

GLOSSARY

GLOSSARY

of mining and geological terms used in this book or otherwise in common use. Includes compositions of igneous rocks and physical properties of ore and gangue minerals.   G. = Specific gravity.   H. = Hardness.

SOURCES OF DEFINITIONS

Names in parentheses after definitions refer to sources as follows:

Billings.   Billings, Marland P., *Structural Geology*, New York: Prentice-Hall, Incorporated, 1942.

Fay.   Fay, Albert H., *A Glossary of the Mining and Mineral Industry*, U. S. Bureau of Mines, Bull. 95.   Washington, 1920.   A number of definitions credited to Raymond, Standard, LaForge, etc., are *via* Fay.

Holmes.   Holmes, Arthur, *The Nomenclature of Petrology*, London: Thomas Murby and Company, 1920.

Hurlbut.   Hurlbut, Cornelius S., *Dana's Manual of Mineralogy*, Fifteenth Edition, New York: John Wiley and Sons, 1946.   Most of the mineralogical data in the glossary unless otherwise acknowledged are from this source.

Leith.   Leith, C. K., *Structural Geology*, New York: Henry Holt and Company, 1913.

Lindgren.   Lindgren, Waldemar, *Mineral Deposits*, New York: McGraw-Hill Book Company, 1933.

Locke.   Locke, Augustus, *Leached Outcrops as Guides to Copper Ore*, Baltimore: Williams and Wilkins Company, 1926.

Longwell.   Longwell, Chester R., Knopf, Adolph, and Flint, Richard F., *Outlines of Physical Geology*, Second Edition, New York: John Wiley and Sons, 1941.

Nevin.   Nevin, C. M., *Principles of Structural Geology*, New York: John Wiley and Sons, 1931.

Palache.   Palache, Charles, Berman, Harry, and Frondel, Clifford, *The System of Mineralogy of James Dwight Dana*, Seventh Edition, Vol. 1, New York: John Wiley and Sons, 1944.

Twenhofel.   Twenhofel, William H., *Treatise on Sedimentation*, London: Bailliere, Tindall and Cox, 1932.

Aa (Hawaiian)   Block-lava consisting of a rough tumultuous assemblage of clinker-like scoriaceous masses.   (Holmes)

Adamellite   A term applied originally to an orthoclase-bearing tonolite, and now used generally for granites in which plagioclase varies from one third to two thirds of the total feldspar.   (Holmes)

Adularia   A colorless and translucent variety of orthoclase (*see* Feldspar) usually in pseudo-orthorhombic crystals.   (Hurlbut)

Aegirite, Aegirine   *See* Pyroxene.

Aegirine-augite, Aegirinaugite   *See* Pyroxene.

Agglomerate　A chaotic assemblage of coarse angular pyroclastic materials. (Holmes)

Aggregate　Sand, gravel, or crushed stone to be bound by cement in order to make concrete.

Alaskite　An igneous rock consisting of quartz and alkalic feldspar with little or no ferromagnesian constituent.

Albite　*See* **Feldspar.**

Allophane　*See* **Clay Minerals.**

Alluvial　(adj.)　Deposited by a stream.　(noun) Deposit of alluvial origin.

Almandite　Subspecies of **Garnet** (*q.v.*)

Alnoite　Dike-rock containing phenocrysts of biotite, olivine, and augite in a groundmass composed of melilite and augite with sometimes perovskite and minor accessories.　(Holmes).　*See* **Lamprophyr.**

Alteration　Change in the mineralogical composition of a rock typically brought about by the action of hydrothermal solutions.　Sometimes classed as a phase of metamorphism but usually distinguished from it because milder and more localized.

Alunite　$KAl_3(OH)_6(SO_4)_2$.　Rhombohedral.　G. 2.6–2.8.　H.4.

Amortization tonnage　*See* Chapter 18.

Amortize　To clear off, liquidate, or otherwise extinguish, as a debt, usually by a sinking fund (Webster).

Amphibole　Name for a group of minerals, silicates of one or more of the following: Mg, Ca, Fe″, Al, Fe‴.　Habit prismatic to fibrous.　Angle of prismatic cleavage about 56 degrees (difference from pyroxenes).　*Principal species:* anthophyllite, cummingtonite, tremolite, actinolite, hornblende, arfvedsonite.

Andesine　*See* **Feldspar.**

Andesite　*See* Tables of Igneous Rocks, Appendix I.

Andradite　Subspecies of garnet (*q.v.*)

Anglesite　$PbSO_4$.　Orthorhombic.　G. 6.2–6.4　H. 3　Lustre adamantine and color white when pure and crystallized.　Otherwise may be dull and gray.

Ångstrom unit　Measure of the wave-length of light and of other very short distances.　10^{-8} cm.

Anhydrite　$CaSO_4$.　Orthorhombic.　G. 2.89–2.98.　H. 3–3½.

Anisotropic　Not **Isotropic** (*q.v.*)

Ankerite　$CaCO_3$ (Mg, Fe, Mn)CO_3.　Rhombohedral.　G. 2.95–3.　H. 3½.　Perfect rhombohedral cleavage.　White to grayish, weathering to brown.

Annabergite　$Ni_3As_2O_8.8H_2O$.　Monoclinic.　G. 3.0.　H. 2½–3.　Light green.

Anorthite　*See* **Feldspar.**

Anorthoclase　Microcline (feldspar) in which sodium replaces potassium and exceeds it in quantity.　(Hurlbut).

Anticline　*See* **Fold.**

Anticlinorium　Major anticline composed of many smaller folds.

Antiguas　(Spanish)　Ancient mines.

Antithetic faults (or shears)　Term proposed by H. Cloos for minor faults standing at a large angle to a master fault and with displacement in the same direction as on a complementary shear; *e.g.*, if the master fault is normal the antithetic faults are also normal.

Antlerite $Cu_3(OH)_4SO_4$. Orthorhombic. G. 3.9±. H. 3½–4. Emerald to blackish green. "Sulphate" taste. Indistinguishable from atacamite or brochantite by inspection.

Apatite $Ca_5(F,Cl)(PO_4)_3$. Hexagonal. G. 3.15–3.20. H. 5.

Apex (of a vein or lode) Term used in U. S. mining law to denote the outcrop of a vein which reaches the surface, or the highest limit of a vein which does not extend upward all the way to the surface.

Aplite A siliceous igneous rock consisting of quartz and feldspar with or without muscovite but with little or no ferromagnesian minerals.

Aquifer A water-bearing layer or formation, *e.g.*, a permeable sandstone which when tapped by a well yields a supply of water.

Argentite Ag_2S. Isometric. G. 7.3. H. 2–2½. Blackish lead-gray. Metallic. Can be cut with a knife like lead.

Arkose Sedimentary rock (grain-size as in sandstone) derived from the disintegration of acid igneous rocks of granular texture. There is usually little sorting of the materials. (Twenhofel). Formed under conditions permitting little mineral decomposition, it contains a considerable proportion of feldspar.

Arroyo (Spanish) Small stream; gutter (Appleton). But usage varies and in some Latin-American countries arroyo includes gorges of major proportions.

Arsenopyrite FeAsS. Monoclinic. G. 6.07±0.15. H. 5½–6. Silver-white, metallic. Usually forms sharp-cut crystals.

Assay (verb) To determine the amount of metal contained in an ore.
(noun) *1.* The act of making such a determination.
2. The result of such a determination.
Note: Difference between assay and analysis: In an analysis all of the chemical constituents are determined; in an assay only certain constituents, usually those of commercial interest.

Assymmetrical fold *See* **Fold.**

Atacamite $Cu_2Cl(OH)_3$. Orthorhombic. G. 3.75–3.77. H. 3–3½. Green.

Attitude Direction and degree of dip of a structural plane (bed, fault, etc.). Attitude may be expressed in terms of **Dip** *and* **Strike** (*q.v.*)

Augite *See* **Pyroxene.**

Axial plane *See* **Folds.**

Axinite $H(Ca,Mn,Fe)_3Al_2B(SiO_4)_4$. Triclinic. G. 3.27–3.35. H. 6½–7.

Axis (of a fold) *See* **Folds.**

Azimuth (of a line) The angle which a line forms with the true meridian as measured on an imaginary horizontal circle. The angle (which may be from zero to 360 degrees) is usually read clockwise from the north point.

Azurite $Cu_3(CO_3)_2(OH)_2$. Monoclinic. G. 3.77. H. 3½–4. Blue.

Back The part of a vein or lode that is on the upper side of a drift or stope. In a vertical vein the back of the drift would correspond to the ceiling of a hallway.

Barite $BaSO_4$. Orthorhombic. G. 4.5. H. 3–3$\frac{1}{2}$. Colorless, white, or tinted. Perfect cleavage on base and prism faces.

Basalt A fine-grained basic rock usually occurring in volcanic flows, dikes, and sills. *See* Tables of Igneous Rocks, Appendix I.

Basanite A basaltic rock, generally porphyritic, containing plagioclase, augite, olivine, and a feldspathoid. (Holmes). Presence of olivine, although not essential in the original usage of the term basanite, distinguishes the type from tephrite.

Batholith A huge intrusive body of igneous rock supposedly enlarging downward into the earth's crust. Minimum size to qualify as a batholith: 40 square miles (Longwell). *Cf.* **Stock.**

Bauxite A mixture of aluminum hydroxides. Amorphous. G. 2.0–2.55. H. 1–3.

Bed Layer in body of a sedimentary rock. Stratum.

Bedding, Bedding Plane Plane of stratification. The surface marking the boundary between a bed and the bed above or below it.

Beidellite *See* **Clay Minerals.**

Beneficiate To reduce, as ores (Standard). As used in the Lake Superior district, beneficiation has the same meaning as concentration, but usually with the added implication that undesirable constituents (such as silica) are eliminated.

Beryl $Be_3Al_2Si_6O_{18}$. Hexagonal. G. 2.75–2.8. H. 7$\frac{1}{2}$–8. Usually green, sometimes yellow or bluish green, rarely white. Usually well-crystallized.

Biotite *See* **Mica.**

Bismuth Bi. Rhombohedral. G. 9.8. H. 2–2$\frac{1}{2}$. Silver-white with distinct reddish tone; metallic. Perfect basal cleavage.

Bismuthinite Bi_2S_3. Orthorhombic. G. 6.78$\pm$0.03. H. 2. Lead-gray, metallic. Perfect cleavage. Resembles stibnite.

Block Caving *See* **Caving.**

Bornite Cu_5FeS_4. Isometric. G. 5.06–5.08. H. 3. Brownish bronze quickly tarnishing to variegated purple and blue. Metallic lustre.

Bostonite A leucocratic alkali-syeniteaplite with trachytic texture; formed almost wholly of alkali-feldspars. (Holmes).

Boulangerite $Pb_5Sb_4S_{11}$. Orthorhombic. G. 6.0$\pm$. H. 2$\frac{1}{2}$–3. Bluish lead-gray; metallic. Prismatic to fibrous.

Bournonite $PbCuSbS_3$. Orthorhombic. G. 5.8–5.9. H. 2$\frac{1}{2}$–3. Steel-gray to black; metallic.

Breccia Rock consisting of fragments, more or less angular in a matrix of finer-grained material or of cementing material. May form by faulting or crushing (tectonic breccia), by erosion (clastic breccia), by collapse, by replacement bordering fractures or by volcanism (volcanic breccia).

Brecciated Converted into a breccia.

Brochantite $Cu_4(OH)_6SO_4$. Monoclinic. G. 3.9. H. 3$\frac{1}{2}$–4. *Cf.* **Antlerite.**

Bromyrite AgBr. Isometric. G. 5.9. H. 1–1$\frac{1}{2}$.

Brookite TiO_2. Orthorhombic. G. 3.9–4.1. H. 5$\frac{1}{2}$–6. Brown; lustre metallic adamantine to submetallic. Found only as crystals.

Bytownite *See* **Feldspar.**

Calamine Synonym for **Hemimorphite** (*q.v.*). In British terminology, calamine is frequently used to denote smithsonite.

Calaverite $AuTe_2$. Monoclinic. G. 9.35. H. 2½. Brass yellow to silver white; metallic. Lacks cleavage

Calcite $CaCO_3$. Rhombohedral. G. 2.72. H. 3. Perfect rhombohedral cleavage. Usually colorless or white, but exceptionally red, yellow, or blue.

Camptonite *See* **Lamprophyr.**

Capping *1.* A rock formation (consolidated or unconsolidated) overlying a body of rock or ore; *e.g.*, rhyolitic volcanics which form mesas and plateaus in S. W. U. S. and Mexico.
2. The oxidized equivalent of disseminated sulphide material. (Locke).

Cassiterite SnO_2. Tetragonal. G. 6.8–7.1. H. 6–7. Brown or black, rarely yellow or white. Lustre adamantine to submetallic. Streak white.

Caving A method of mining in which the ore, the support of a great block being removed, is allowed to cave or fall, and in falling is broken sufficiently to be handled; the overlying strata subside as the ore is withdrawn. (Fay). Variations: *Top slicing:* A horizontal slice of ore is removed, allowing the slice above it to cave. Then, leaving the slice below temporarily intact, a still lower slice is removed, allowing the intervening slice to cave. The process is repeated until the bottom of the orebody is reached. *Block caving:* Similar to top slicing except that the slice which is allowed to cave is of much greater thickness and may, in fact, constitute the full thickness of the orebody. *Pillar caving:* Ore is broken in a series of stopes or tall rooms, leaving pillars between. Eventually the pillars are forced or allowed to cave under the weight of the roof.

Celestite $SrSO_4$. Orthorhombic. G. 3.95–3.97. H. 3–3½. Colorless; white; often faintly red or blue. Resembles barite.

Cerargyrite $AgCl$. Isometric. G. 5.5±. H. 2–3. Distinguished by sectility and horny or wax-like appearance.

Cerussite $PbCO_3$. Orthorhombic. G. 6.55. H. 3–3½. White or gray; often stained yellow when granular or sandy.

Chalcanthite $CuSO_4.5H_2O$. Triclinic. G. 2.12–2.30. H. 2½. Blue.

Chalcedony Cryptocrystalline variety of quartz.

Chalcocite Cu_2S. Orthorhombic. G. 5.5–5.8. H. 2½–3. Shining lead gray, metallic, tarnishing on exposure to dull black. Imperfectly sectile.

Chalcopyrite $CuFeS_2$. Tetragonal. G. 4.1–4.3. H. 3½–4. Brass yellow, often tarnished to iridescent.

Chert Cryptocrystalline variety of quartz. SiO_2 G. 2.65. H. 7.

Chlorite Name of a group of minerals of composition $H_4R''_2R'''_3SiO_9$ where $R'' = $ Fe or Mg and $R''' = $ Al, (Fe) and rarely Cr. (Winchell). *Common species:* Magnesia-alumina chlorites—Penninite, clinochlore, amesite; Iron-alumina chlorites—Thuringite, daphnite. Monoclinic. G. 2.6–2.9. H. 2–2½. Characterized by micaceous habit and usually greenish color. Less elastic than mica.

Chloritoid $(Fe, Mg)_2Al_4Si_2O_{10}(OH)_4$. Monoclinic. G. 3.5. H. 6–7.

Chromite $FeCr_2O_4$. Isometric. G. 4.6. H. 5½. Iron black to brownish black. Metallic to submetallic lustre. Streak dark brown.

Chrysocolla $CuSiO_3.2H_2O$. Usually cryptocrystalline to amorphous. G. 2.0–2.4. H. 2–4. Green to greenish blue.

Cinnabar HgS. Rhombohedral. G. 8.10. H. $2\frac{1}{2}$. Red.

Clay Minerals A family of minerals, most of them hydrous aluminum silicates and all either finely crystalline or amorphous. All those which crystallize are monoclinic. Species are indistinguishable except by laboratory methods (microscopic, X-ray, thermic). Principal species fall into three groups: *Kaolin group:* Kaolinite, nacrite, and dickite all have the same composition: $Al_2O_3.2SiO_2.2H_2O$. Anauxite is $Al_2O_3.3\pm SiO_2.2H_2O$. Halloysite is $Al_2O_32\pm SiO_2.2H_2O$. Allophane is amorphous and has indefinite proportions of alumina, silica, and water. *Montmorillonite group:* Montmorillonite $(MgCa)O.Al_2O_3.5SiO_2.nH_2O$. Beidellite $Al_2O_3.3SiO_2.-nH_2O$. Nontronite $Fe_2O_3.3SiO_2.nH_2O$. Saponite $2MgO.3SiO_2nH_2O$. *Hydromica group:* Hydromuscovite $KAl_2(OH)_2[AlSi_3(O, OH)_{10}]$. Reference: Rogers and Kerr, *Optical Mineralogy*, McGraw-Hill, Incorporated, 1942, pp. 352–359.

Cleavage *Mineral cleavage:* The property of crystals of certain minerals by virtue of which the crystal can be broken or split along smooth planes which correspond to specific crystallographic directions. *Rock cleavage:* The ability of rocks to break along parallel surfaces of secondary origin. Schistosity is the cleavage in rocks that are sufficiently recrystallized to be called schist of gneiss. Bedding fissility is the tendency to part parallel to the stratification. (Billings).

Clinochlore $Mg_5Al_2Si_3O_{10}(OH)_8$. A mineral of the chlorite group.

Clinometer Instrument for measuring inclination, *e.g.*, dip of a bed or vein. Consists of a scale graduated in degrees together with either a level-bubble or a vertically-hanging straightedge.

Clinozoisite $Ca_2Al_3(SiO_4)_3(OH)$. Monoclinic. G. 3.25–3.37. H. 6–$6\frac{1}{2}$. Grayish white, pink, green. Resembles epidote but lighter in color.

Cobaltite CoAsS. Isometric. G. 6.33. H. $5\frac{1}{2}$. Silver white inclining to red. Metallic.

Columbite $(Fe, Mn)(Cb, Ta)_2O_6$. Forms an isomorphous series with tantalite as an end-member. Orthorhombic. G. 5.3–7.3. H. 6. Black. Lustre submetallic.

Complementary shear fractures *See* Chapter 12.

Composite map Map on which several levels of a mine are shown on a single sheet. Horizontal projection of data from different elevations.

Composite section Projection of data from various locations to a single vertical (or inclined) section.

Concentrate (verb) To separate metal or ore from the associated gangue or rock (Murray's Dict.).

(noun) The product of the process cf concentration.

Concentrator Mill or plant in which ore is concentrated.

Conglomerate *See* Table of Sedimentary Rocks, Appendix I.

Conjugate shear fractures *See* Chapter 12.

Contact Bounding surface between two rock units, especially the boundary between an intrusive and its host-rock.

Copper Cu. Isometric. G. 8.9. H. $2\frac{1}{2}$–3.

Cordierite $Mg_2Al_4Si_5O_{18}$. Orthorhombic. G. 2.60–2.66. H. 7–7½.

Core Cylindrical sample of rock cut out by a diamond-drill bit. (*See* Chapter 3.)

Cortlandite Ultrabasic rock consisting of hornblende and olivine.

Corundum Al_2O_3. Rhombohedral. G. 4.02. H. 9. Distinguished by great hardness and high specific gravity. Basal parting planes nearly cubic in angle. White, grayish, or brownish grading to red or blue in gem varieties (ruby and sapphire).

Covellite CuS. Hexagonal. G. 4.6–4.76. H. 1½–2. Blue.

Crest (of a fold) *See* **Folds.**

Cristobalite SiO_2. Tetragonal. G. 2.30. H. 7. Indistinguishable from quartz except by optical properties under the microscope. Characteristically occurs in small lava cavities.

Crocoite $PbCrO_4$. Monoclinic. G. 5.9–6.1. H. 2½–3. Bright hyacinth red, streak orange-yellow.

Cropping Material which crops out, *i.e.*, which is exposed at the surface.

Crosscut A level driven across the course of a vein or in general across the direction of the main workings or across the "grain of the coal." (Raymond).

Cumberlandite Ultrabasic igneous rock composed of olivine, ilmenite, and magnetite with small amounts of labradorite and spinel.

Cuprite Cu_2O. Isometric. G. 6.0. H. 3½–4. Red.

Cyanite *See* **Kyanite.**

Dacite *See* Table of Igneous Rocks, Appendix I.

Dense (of a rock) Compact and fine-grained, lacking appreciable pore-space.

Develop To open up orebodies, as by sinking shafts and driving drifts.

Development work Work undertaken in order to open up orebodies as distinguished from the work of actual ore extraction. Sometimes development work is distinguished from exploratory work on the one hand and from stope preparation on the other.

Diabase A basic igneous rock similar in composition to gabbro characterized by lath-shaped feldspar grains.

Diagonal slip *See* **Faults.**

Diaspore $AlO(OH)$. Orthorhombic. G. 3.35–3.45. H. 6½–7. White, gray, yellowish, greenish. Perfect pinacoidal cleavage.

Dickite *See* **Clay Minerals.**

Differentiation Process whereby two or more rocks of differing chemical composition are derived from a single body of magma.

Dike (British: dyke) Tabular mass of igneous rock that fills a fissure in pre-existent rocks (Longwell). Dikes in layered rocks cut the layers (*cf.* **Sill**).

Diopside *See* **Pyroxene.**

Dip The inclination of a bed, vein, fault, etc., measured from the horizontal, thus the angle between a line in the bed perpendicular to the strike and the horizontal plane.

Dip-fault *See* **Faults.**

Dip-slip *See* **Faults.**

Dip-slip fault *See* **Faults.**

Ditroite   An igneous rock of the alkali syenite group consisting of nepheline and blue sodalite with ferromagnesians.

Dolerite   *1.* A field term for any fine-grained basic igneous rock whose exact identity has not been determined.

   2. (British) A basic rock of the composition of gabbro but finer in grain; thus synonymous with diabase except that diabasic texture is not a necessary characteristic.

Dolomite $CaMg(CO_3)_2$. Rhombohedral. G. 2.85. H. $3\frac{1}{2}$–4. Perfect rhombohedral cleavage. Does not effervesce in dilute HCl (difference from calcite).

Dolomite (rock)   Rock composed essentially of the mineral dolomite. *See* Table of Sedimentary Rocks, Appendix I.

Drag   *1.* Fragments of ore torn from a lode by fault movement and remaining in the fault zone.

   2. Distortion of beds adjacent to a fault.

Drag fold   *See* **Fold.**

Drift   A horizontal underground passage following a vein. It is distinguished from a crosscut, which intersects a vein, or a level or gallery, which may either follow or intersect the vein. (Raymond).

Drift (glacial)   All the material in transport by glacier ice, and all the material predominantly of glacial origin deposited directly by glaciers, or indirectly in glacial streams, glacial lakes, and the sea. (Longwell).

Echelon (en echelon)   An arrangement of faults, veins, etc., in which the individuals are staggered like the treads of a staircase.

Eclogite   A metamorphic rock composed of garnet, pyroxene (omphacite), and sometimes amphibole (smaragdite) with accessories such as sphene and zoisite. (Holmes).

Eluvial deposit   Loose material resulting from decomposition of rock (Lindgren). Eluvial material may have slumped or washed downhill for a short distance but has not been transported by a stream (*cf.* **Alluvial**).

Embolite $Ag(Cl, Br)$. Isometric. G. 5.3–5.4. H. 1–$1\frac{1}{2}$.

Enargite Cu_3AsS_4. Orthorhombic. G. 4.43–4.45. H. 3. Grayish black to iron black. Metallic. Prismatic cleavage.

En echelon   *See* **Echelon.**

Enstatite   *See* **Pyroxene.**

Epidote $Ca_2(Al, Fe)_3(SiO_4)_3(OH)$. Monoclinic. G. 3.35–3.45. H. 6–7. Color, pistachio green or yellowish to blackish green.

Epigenetic ore deposit   Deposit of ore introduced into a pre-existing rock (Lindgren). *Examples:* Ore introduced into a vein by solutions from a magma; ore introduced by solutions and replacing limestone.

Epithermal ore deposit   Deposit formed by hot ascending solutions at slight depth and low temperature.

Erythrite $Co_3(AsO_4)_2.8H_2O$. Monoclinic. G. 2.95. H. $1\frac{1}{2}$–$2\frac{1}{2}$. Pink.

Essexite   A granular igneous rock related to gabbro and containing green and purple pyroxenes and plagioclase (andesine to bytownite) with orthoclase or soda-orthoclase. Soda-amphibole, olivine, and nephelite or analcite may occur in small amounts.

Eutectic (Eutectic Mixture)   Mixture of two (or more) phases (*e.g.,* minerals) that have crystallized simultaneously at the eutectic point. (*See* texts on physical chemistry.)

Exploration The work involved in looking for ore (Rickard). May be done on the surface or may consist of underground work or drilling. Distinguished from exploitation and in some cases from development work.

Ex-solution Pertaining to a product of unmixing from solid solution.

Face In any adit, tunnel, or stope, the end at which work is in progress or was last done (Fay).

Facing (of strata) Direction in which the original top of a vertical or steeply dipping bed now faces.

Faults *Displacement* (on or by a fault)—A general term for the change in position of any point on one side of a fault plane relative to any corresponding point on the opposite side of the fault plane. *Separation*—Distance between two parts of a disrupted horizon measured in any indicated direction, *e.g.*, vertical separation is measured along a vertical line. *Shift* (of a fault)—Displacement on opposite sides of a fault outside the dislocated zone (Billings). The full displacement regardless of drag. *Slip* —Displacement as measured in the fault. Net slip is the total displacement. Dip slip is the component of slip parallel to the dip of the fault. Strike slip is the component of slip parallel to the strike of the fault. *Offset*—Horizontal separation measured perpendicular to the strike of the disrupted horizon. *Heave*—Horizontal displacement measured in a vertical section normal to the strike of a fault. *Throw*—Vertical displacement measured in a vertical plane perpendicular to the strike of the fault. *Normal fault*—One in which the hanging-wall has apparently moved downward with reference to the footwall. *Reverse fault*—One in which the hanging-wall has apparently moved upward with respect to the footwall. *Note.* By usage the terms normal and reverse refer to the apparent displacement, not the true displacement. This is illogical and unfortunate. Usage is trending toward designation by true displacement. Meanwhile it is best to specify the meaning when there is any ambiguity. *Dip fault* —A fault whose strike is approximately at right angles to the strike of the bedding (or the vein). *Strike fault*—A fault having the same strike as the bedding (or the vein). *Oblique fault*—Fault which strikes obliquely to the strike of the bedding (or the vein). *Dip slip fault*—Fault in which the net slip is in the direction of dip (*i.e.*, strike component is lacking). *Strike slip fault*—Fault in which the net slip is in the direction of the strike (*i.e.*, dip component is lacking). *Diagonal slip fault*—Fault in which the net slip is diagonal, *i.e.*, neither vertical nor horizontal. *Hinge fault*—A fault whose displacement is greater at one place than another and diminishes to zero at some point. *Pivotal fault*—A fault of rotary displacement in which the displacement at one place (the pivot) is zero and displacements on opposite sides of the pivot are in opposite directions. Scissors fault. *Trochoidal fault*—Similar to a pivotal fault except that the pivot also slips along the fault surface.

Fayalite *See* **Olivine.**

Feldspar Name for a group of minerals, all silicates of aluminum with po-

tassium, sodium, and/or calcium and rarely barium. G. 2.55–2.75. H. 6.
Principal species:

Orthoclase. $KAlSi_3O_8$ Monoclinic.
Microcline. $KAlSi_3O_8$ Triclinic.
Plagioclase. Triclinic. An isomorphous mixture whose end-members are:
Albite $NaAlSi_3O_8$.
Anorthite. $CaAl_2Si_2O_8$.
Members of the plagioclase series are named according to percentage of albite.

Albite	100–90	Labradorite	50–30
Oligoclase	90–70	Bytownite	30–10
Andesine	70–50	Anorthite	10– 0

Felsite Field term for any fine-grained acid igneous rock whose exact composition has not been determined.

Ferberite *See* **Wolframite.**

Ferromagnesians Minerals containing a high proportion of iron and magnesia, *e.g.*, pyroxene, hornblende, biotite.

Fibrolite Synonym for **Sillimanite** (*q.v.*).

Fissility *See* **Cleavage.**

Fissure An extensive crack, break, or fracture in rock. A mere joint or crack persisting only for a few inches or a few feet is not usually termed a fissure . . . although in a strict physical sense it is one. (Ransome).

Fissure vein A fissure in the earth's crust filled with mineral. (Raymond). As it is now recognized that replacement as well as (or instead of) simple filling has played an important role in the formation of most veins, the term fissure vein has lost much of its meaning.

Float Loose fragments of rock, ore, or grossan found on or near the surface or in stream beds.

Flotation A method of concentrating ore by inducing the particles of ore to float to the surface of water or other solution (usually buoyed up by air bubbles) while the gangue particles sink to the bottom. (*See* Chapter 22.)

Fluorite CaF_2. Isometric. G. 3.18. H. 4. "Purple, red, green, and white are the colors of fluorite."

Flux (metallurgical) A substance charged into a furnace for the purpose of combining with other substances in the ore or charge in order to form slag.

Fold An undulation or wave in stratified, layered, or foliated rock (Billings). Parts of a fold:
Axial plane (or axial surface). Plane (or surface) that divides the fold as symmetrically as possible (Billings). *Axis* (or axial line)—Intersection of the axial plane (or axial surface) with a particular bed. (Billings). *Limb* (or flank). The side of a fold (Billings). That portion of a bed between the crest of an anticline and the trough of a syncline. *Crest.* Line along the highest part of a fold; line connecting the highest points on the same bed in an infinite number of cross sections. (Billings). *Trough.* Line occupying the lowest part of a fold; the line connecting the lowest

parts on the same bed in an infinite number of cross sections. (Billings).
Nose. Place (as shown on a map) where a fold shows the maximum curvature. There is a nose for each stratum. (Billings).
Types of folds:
Anticline. A fold convex upward; arch-like fold. *Syncline.* A fold convex downward. *Monocline.* Fold consisting of a steeper interval between two relatively flat portions of a bed. Local steepening of dip. *Dome.* An anticlinal uplift that has no distinct trend.
Kinds of folds:
Symmetrical. Fold in which the axial plane is essentially vertical. *Assymmetrical.* Fold in which the axial plane is inclined. *Overturned.* One in which the axial plane is inclined and both limbs dip in the same direction, usually at different angles. Synonym: over-fold. The *normal limb* is right side up; the *overturned, inverted,* or *reversed* limb has been rotated through more than 90 degrees to attain its present position. *Recumbent fold.* One in which the axial plane is essentially horizontal. *Isoclinal fold.* One in which the two limbs dip at equal angles in the same direction, *i.e.,* the limbs are parallel or nearly so. *Drag-fold.* Fold produced in an incompetent bed by relative movement of the two enclosing beds in opposite directions with respect to one another.

Foliation 1. More or less pronounced aggregation of particular constituent minerals of a metamorphic rock into lenticles or streaks or inconstant bands, often very rich in some one mineral and contrasting with constituent lenticles or streaks rich in other minerals. (Harker's *Metamorphism,* p. 203).
2. (Foliate structure)—Used in a broad sense includes the textural or structural properties of certain rocks which permit them to be cleaved or parted along approximately parallel surfaces or lines. (Mead, *Jour. Geol.,* Vol. 48, p. 1009, 1940). In this sense the term includes bedding fissility and schistosity.

Formation An assemblage of rock masses grouped together into a unit that is convenient for description or mapping (Longwell).

Forsterite *See* **Olivine.**

Foyaite A nepheline syenite consisting of perthitic orthoclase, microcline, and nepheline with soda-pyroxenes and/or amphiboles. By Rosenbusch the term is applied to all varieties of nepheline syenite which contain dominantly potash feldspars, and this is the common usage of the term. (Holmes).

Fracture A break. Fracture is a general term to include any kind of discontinuity in a body of rock if produced by mechanical failure, whether by shear-stress or tensile stress. Fractures include faults, shears, joints, and planes of fracture-cleavage.

Fracture System Group of fractures (faults, joints, or veins) consisting of one or more sets, usually intersecting or interconnected. System usually implies contemporaneous age for all of the sets, but vein system is sometimes used for all veins in a given mine or district regardless of age or origin.

Franklinite (Fe,Zn,Mn) $(Fe,Mn)_2O_4$. Isometric. G. 5.15. H. 6. Resembles magnetite but less strongly magnetic.   Occurs at Franklin Furnace, N. J.   Reports from other localities doubtful.

Freibergite   Silver-bearing variety of tetrahedrite (*q.v.*).

Gabbro   *See* Table of Igneous Rocks, Appendix I.

Gahnite (zinc spinel) $ZnAl_2O_4$. Isometric. G. 4.55. H. $7\frac{1}{2}$–8. Dark green.   Commonly in octahedral crystals.

Galena   PbS. Isometric. G. 7.4–7.6. H. $2\frac{1}{2}$. Lead-gray. Bright metallic lustre.   Perfect cubic cleavage (inconspicuous in fine-grained steely varieties).

Gangue   Useless minerals occurring in ore.   (Lindgren).

Garnet $R_3''R_2'''(SiO_4)_3$. Isometric. G. 3.5–4.3. H. $6\frac{1}{2}$–$7\frac{1}{2}$. Principal sub-species (intergradational):

Pyrope	$Mg_3Al_2(SiO_4)_3$	G. 3.51
Almandite	$Fe_3Al_2(SiO_4)_3$	G. 4.25
Spessartite	$Mn_3Al_2(SiO_4)_3$	G. 4.18
Grossularite	$Ca_3Al_2(SiO_4)_3$	G. 3.53
Andradite	$Ca_3Fe_2(SiO_4)_3$	G. 3.75
Uvarovite	$Ca_3Cr_2(SiO_4)_3$	G. 3.45

Usually distinctly crystallized; occasionally granular.   Most species dark red to brown but andradite may be yellow or yellowish green to black. Uvarovite is emerald green.

Garnierite $(Ni,Mg)SiO_3.nH_2O$. Amorphous. G. 2.2–2.8. H. 2–3. Apple-green.

Geanticline   Major uplifted area from which sediments are eroded.   *Not a synonym for anticlinorium.*

Geomorphology   *1.* That department of physical geography which deals with the form of the earth, the general configuration of its surface, the distribution of land and water, and the changes that take place in the evolution of land forms.   (Webster).

2. (Geol.).   The investigation of the history of geologic changes through the interpretation of topographic forms.   (Webster).

Geosyncline   Basin in which many thousands of feet of sediments accumulate.   *Not a synonym for synclinorium.*

Gersdorffite   NiAsS. Isometric. G. 5.9. H. $5\frac{1}{2}$. Isomorphous with cobaltite, which it closely resembles.

Gibbsite $Al(OH)_3$. Monoclinic. G. 2.3–2.4. H. $2\frac{1}{2}$–$3\frac{1}{2}$. White or tinted; often stained reddish yellow.   Tabular six-sided crystals; often concretionary.

Goethite   FeO(OH). Orthorhombic. G. 4.37. H. 5–$5\frac{1}{2}$. Yellowish brown to dark brown.   Streak yellowish brown.

Gold   Au. Isometric. G. 15.0–19.3. H. $2\frac{1}{2}$–3.

Gossan   The oxidized equivalent of aggregated sulphide material.   (Locke). (Aggregated sulphide is massive sulphide.   *See* Chapter 10).   Gossan usually consists of ferric oxide and quartz or jasper, sometimes with manganese dioxide, clay minerals, etc.

Gouge   Clay formed by comminution of rock in a fault zone.

Graded bedding   Change of grain-size from the bottom to the top of a bed or succession of beds.   Normally the gradation is from coarse at the bottom to fine at the top, with an abrupt change at the bottom of the overlying bed.   In fine-grained rocks the gradation is sometimes emphasized by change of color from light to dark.

Granite   *See* Table of Igneous Rocks, Appendix I.

Graphite   C.   Hexagonal.   G. 2.3.   H. 1–2.   Black to steel-gray, metallic. Usually foliated or in flakes.

Grauwacke   *See* **Graywacke**.

Gray Copper   Synonym for tetrahedrite.

Graywacke, Greywacke, Grauwacke   *1.* Variety of sandstone (in the broader sense) derived from the disintegration of basic igneous rocks of granular texture and thus contains abundant grains of biotite, hornblende, magnetite, etc.   Thus defined it is the ferromagnesian equivalent of arkose. (Twenhofel).   Twenhofel recommends usage as above rather than *2* or *3*, below:

2. Rock whose grains are fragments of rock rather than fragments of minerals.

3. Ferromagnesian sand where cementation has advanced so far that the rock when fractured breaks across the original grains rather than around them (Van Hise, *Treatise on Metamorphism*, p. 880).   According to this definition graywacke would be a metamorphic rock analogous to quartzite.

Greenockite   CdS.   Hexagonal.   G. 4.9.   H. 3–3½.   Yellow to orange. Usually occurs as a coating on sphalerite or on its decomposition products.

Greywacke   *See* **Graywacke**.

Grit   A sedimentary rock composed of clastic grains coarser than sand but finer than gravel.   Thus a rock intermediate in grain-size between a sandstone and a conglomerate.

Grossularite   *See* **Garnet**.

Gypsum $CaSO_4.2H_2O$.   Monoclinic.   G. 2.32.   H. 2.   Perfect cleavage resembles mica but has two additional cleavages.   Softer than mica.

Hade   (obsolescent)   Inclination of a fault or vein, measured from the vertical.   Complement of the dip.   (The term is unnecessary and confusing.   Fortunately, it is going out of use.)

Halite (rock salt)   NaCl.   Isometric.   G. 2.16.   H. 2½.   Colorless to white.   Distinguished by taste.

Halloysite   *See* **Clay Minerals**.

Harzburgite   Synonym for **Saxonite** (*q.v.*).

Heave (of a fault)   *See* **Faults**.

Hedenbergite $CaFeSi_2O_6$.   Monoclinic.   G. 3.55.   H. 5–6.   A pyroxene.

Hematite Fe_2O_3.   Rhombohedral.   G. 5.26.   H. 5½–6½.   Streak red.

Hemimorphite   (calamine) $Zn_4Si_2O_7(OH)_2.H_2O$.   Orthorhombic.   G. 3.4–3.5.   H. 4½–5.   White or faintly tinted.   Often mammillary.

Hinge fault   *See* **Faults**.

Hornblende $Ca_2Na(Mg,Fe'')_4(Al,Fe''',Ti)_3Si_6O_{22}(O,OH)_2$.   Monoclinic. G. 3.2.   H. 5–6.   An amphibole.

Hornfels   *See* Table of Metamorphic Rocks, Appendix I.

Horn silver   *See* **Cerargyrite**.

Huebnerite   *See* **Wolframite**.

Hyalite   Clear and colorless opal with a globular or botryoidal surface. (Hurlbut).

Hydrology   A science concerned with the occurrence of water in the earth, its physical and chemical reactions with the rest of the earth, and its relation to the life of the earth. (Meinzer).

Hydrothermal   Pertaining to or resulting from the activity of hot aqueous solutions originating from a magma or other source deep in the earth.

Hydrozincite $2ZnCO_3.3Zn(OH)_2$. Monoclinic. G. 3.6–3.8. H. 2–2½.

Hypabyssal   A general term applied to minor intrusions, such as sills and dikes, and to rocks of which they are made, to distinguish them from volcanic rocks and formations on the one hand and "plutonic" rocks and major intrusions such as batholiths on the other.

Hypersthene   *See* **Pyroxene.**

Hypogene   Generated from depth.   Refers to the effects produced by ascending (usually hydrothermal) solutions. *Cf.* **Supergene.**

Hypothermal Ore Deposit   Deposit formed by hot ascending solutions at great depth or at high temperature and pressure.

Iceland spar   A clear, cleavable variety of calcite (*q.v.*).

Idocrase $Ca_{10}Al_4(Mg,Fe)_2Si_9O_{34}(OH)_4$. Tetragonal. G. 3.35–3.45. H. 6½.   Idocrase is synonymous with vesuvianite.

Igneous (adj.)   Related to or derived from molten matter that originated within the earth (Longwell).

Igneous rock   Rock made by the solidification of molten matter that originated within the earth (Longwell).   *Examples:* solidified lava; intrusive granite.

Ijolite   Igneous rock of the alkali syenite group consisting of nepheline and pyroxene (aegerine-augite), granitic texture.

Ilmenite $FeTiO_3$. Rhombohedral. G. 4.7. H. 5½–6. Iron-black. Lustre metallic to submetallic.

Ilvaite $Ca(Fe,Mn)_2Fe'''(SiO_4)_2(OH)$. Orthorhombic. G. 4.0. H. 5½–6.   Black.

Intrusive   In petrology, having, while molten, penetrated into or between other rocks but solidified before reaching the surface (LaForge).

Iodobromite $Ag(Cl,Br,I)$. Isometric. G. 5.71. H. 1–1½.

Iodyrite AgI. Hexagonal. G. 5.5–5.7. H. 1–1½.

Iolite   Synonym for **Cordierite** (*q.v.*).

Iron pyrites   *See* **Pyrite.**

Isoclinal fold   *See* **Fold.**

Isotropic   *1.* Capable of transmitting light with equal velocity in all directions.

2. Having physical properties (*e.g.*, strength characteristics) which do not vary with direction.

Jamesonite $Pb_4FeSb_6S_{14}$. Monoclinic. G. 5.5–6.0. H. 2–3.   Steel gray to grayish black; metallic.   Acicular to fibrous or feathery.

Jarosite $KFe_3(OH)_6(SO_4)_2$. Rhombohedral. G. 3.2. H. 3.

Jasper   Granular cryptocrystalline quartz usually colored red from hematite inclusions (Hurlbut).   *Jasperoid* is a term used in the Tri-state district and elsewhere for finely crystalline quartz, usually dark gray.   *Jaspilite* is a term used in the Lake Superior region for jasper in alternating bands with dark hematite.

Joint A divisional plane or surface that divides a rock and along which there has been no visible movement parallel to the plane or surface (Billings).

Kaolin A general term for a group of clay minerals. *See* **Clay Minerals.**

Kaolinite *See* **Clay Minerals.**

Karst topography Surface typical of limestone country characterized by sinks, solution valleys, and disappearing streams.

Keratophyr (ceratophyr) Porphyry having somewhat the composition of syenite but with phenocrysts of anorthoclase and therefore more sodic.

Kyanite (cyanite) Al_2SiO_5. Triclinic. G. 3.56–3.66. H. 5–7. Bladed crystals often light blue or light green.

Labradorite *See* **Feldspar.**

Laccolith Lens-shaped mass of igneous rock intrusive into layered rocks. Typically a laccolith has a flat floor and a domed roof and is more or less circular in ground plan (Longwell).

Lamprophyr, Lamprophyres A general term for those facies of holo-crystalline dike rocks which differ from the normal types containing the same essential minerals by the abundance of their mafic minerals and the frequent presence of alteration products. (Holmes). Rocks of the lamprophyr group as defined by Harker:

	With biotite	*With Augite or hornblende*
Orthoclase Plagioclase	Minette Kersantite	Vosgesite Camptonite
	With Analcite	*With Melilite*
No feldspar	Monchiquite	Alnoite

Lateritic Extreme type of weathering common in tropical climates. Iron and aluminum silicates are decomposed and silica (along with most other elements) removed by leaching. The product, laterite, is characterized by high content of alumina and/or ferric oxide.

Latite *See* Table of Igneous Rocks, Appendix I.

Laurdalite A variety of nepheline-syenite with rhombic anorthoclase and any of the following: pyroxene, amphibole, and biotite; olivine-bearing varieties also occur. (Holmes).

Lepidolite *See* **Mica.**

Leptothermal Name for a zone or environment of ore deposition in which depth and temperature are moderate. "Comprises a part taken off the top of Lindgren's mesothermal and a part off the bottom of Lindgren's epithermal. . . ." (Graton).

Leucite $KAlSi_2O_6$. G. 2.45–2.50. H. 5½–6. White to gray. Occurs in non-quartz-bearing igneous rocks.

Leucitophyr A variety of leucite-phonolite containing leucite and nepheline or other soda feldspathoid, with generally inconspicuous feldspar; the characteristic mafic constituent is aegirine or aegirine-augite.   (Holmes).

Leucocratic   Adjective for igneous rocks abnormally poor in mafic (dark and heavy) minerals.   Opposite of melanocratic.

Leucoxene   Rutile or sphene resulting from alteration of ilmenite or a titanium-bearing ferromagnesian.   Macroscopically: minute white, yellow, or brown flecks.   Microscopically: patches of grains or gridwork showing high "relief."

Level (in a mine)   Group of workings all at approximately the same elevation.   In most mines levels are spaced at regular intervals of depth, usually 100 to 200 feet apart.

Limb (of a fold)   *See* **Folds.**

Limestone   *See* Table of Sedimentary Rocks, Appendix I.

Limonite   A field term for hydrous iron oxides whose real identity has not been determined.   May consist of lepidochrocite, goethite, or hematite, or any mixture of these, with more or less adsorbed water.   (Palache).   Earthy, fibrous, reniform, or stalactitic.

Liparite   Synonym for rhyolite (*q.v.* in Table of Igneous Rocks, Appendix I.)

Lode   *1.* Composite vein.   Zone of approximately parallel fissures irregularly connected and spaced over a considerable width (up to 100 feet or several hundred feet) and filled with ore and partially replaced country rock.
2. Metalliferous deposit in consolidated rock as distinguished from a placer, thus, lode gold and lode claim as distinguished from placer gold and placer claim.   Not properly used for a flat or stratified mass.
3. In U. S. mining law, lode has a specialized meaning defined by statute and interpreted by court decisions.   (*See* references on mining law cited in Chapter 17.)   In essence (without attempting legal precision) it is a tabular body containing mineral matter and subject to the qualifications mentioned in 2 (above).
4. In British terminology, lode is often used for what an American miner would call a vein or ledge, as Cornish tin lodes, Broken Hill Lode.

Longwall   A system of working a seam of coal in which the whole seam is taken out and no pillars left (except shaft-pillars and sometimes the main-road pillars).   (Fay).   In longwall retreating, mining begins at the outer margin of the tract of coal and retreats toward the shaft, allowing the roof to cave as the coal is removed.   In longwall advancing, mining starts near the shaft-pillar and works outward, maintaining roadways through the worked-out portion of the mine.

Lopolith   A concordant intrusion associated with a structural basin.   In the simplest and ideal case the sediments above and below the lopolith dip inward toward a common center.   (Billings).

Lugarite   An igneous rock of the alkali syenite group consisting of nepheline and analcite (together making 50% of the rock) with augite and amphibole, together with labradorite, ilmenite, and apatite.   (Harker).

Macroscopic, Megascopic   Visible to the unaided eye, as contrasted with microscopic.

Mafic   High in magnesia and iron and correspondingly low in silica.

Magma   Molten rock-matter together with its dissolved gas or vapor.

Magmatic Pertaining to or originating from magma.

Magnesite $MgCO_3$. Rhombohedral. G. 3.0–3.2. H. 3½–5. Perfect basal cleavage. Often earthy or granular.

Magnetite Fe_3O_4. Isometric. G. 5.18. H. 6. Black, metallic lustre. Strongly attracted by a magnet.

Malachite $Cu_2CO_3(OH)_2$. Monoclinic. G. 3.9–4.03. H. 3½–4. Green. Often appears as a stain or as botryoidal radiating masses.

Manganite $MnO(OH)$. Orthorhombic. G. 4.3. H. 4. Steel-gray to iron black. Metallic lustre. Streak dark brown.

Manto (Spanish) A blanket-like layer or stratum, especially one which is minable. In some Mexican districts the term is applied to orebodies having the shape of horizontal pipes.

Marcasite FeS_2. Orthorhombic. G. 4.89. H. 6–6½. According to Buerger contains slightly less S than pyrite, Fe substituting for some of the S atoms. Color usually lighter than pyrite but difficult to distinguish from it except in polished section (marcasite is anisotropic) or by X-ray pattern.

Martite Hematite pseudomorphous after magnetite.

Melanocratic Adjective applied to rocks abnormally rich in mafic (dark and heavy) minerals. Opposite of leucocratic.

Melaphyr A general term for altered and amygdaloidal rocks of basaltic or andesitic types. (Holmes).

Member Group of beds, subdivision of a formation.

Mercury (quicksilver) Hg. G. 13.6. H. O. Liquid. Brilliant metallic lustre.

Meridian A line on a map drawn in a north-south direction. One end may carry the point of an arrow to indicate north.

Mesothermal Ore Deposit Deposit formed by hot ascending solutions at intermediate depth and temperature. (Lindgren).

Metamorphic Pertaining to or resulting from the process of **Metamorphism** (*q.v.*). Metamorphic rocks include quartzite, marble, slate, schist, and gneiss.

Metamorphism Throughgoing change in texture or mineralogical composition of a rock, usually brought about by heat, pressure, or chemically active solutions. Van Hise included under metamorphism (katamorphism), oxidation and hydration by supergene agencies, but most authorities now exclude these effects. Mild changes such as development of sericite or chlorite—especially if local—are usually described as alteration rather than metamorphism.

Metasomatism The process of practically simultaneous capillary solution and deposition by which a new mineral of partly or wholly differing chemical composition may grow in the body of an old mineral or mineral aggregate. (Lindgren).

Mica Name for a group of minerals, all complex aluminum silicates with K and OH, often also Mg, Fe''', and, in some varieties, Na, Li, and Fe'''. Monoclinic. Characterized by perfect basal cleavage. Principal species:
Muscovite, $KAl_3Si_3O_{10}(OH)_2$.
Biotite, $K(Mg,Fe)_3AlSi_3O_{10}(OH)_2$.
Phlogopite, $KMg_2Al_2Si_3O_{10}(OH)_2$.

Lepidolite, $K_3Li_3Al_4Si_7O_{10}(OH,F)_3$.

Microcline *See* **Feldspar.**

Microperthite An intergrowth of the feldspars microcline and albite.

Millerite NiS. Rhombohedral. G. 5.5 ± 0.2. H. $3-3\frac{1}{2}$. Pale brass yellow. Usually in hair-like tufts and radiating groups of slender to capillary crystals.

Mimetite $Pb_5Cl(AsO_4)_3$. Hexagonal. G. 7.0–7.2. H. $3\frac{1}{2}$. Colorless, yellow, orange, brown. Resembles pyromorphite, with which it is isomorphous.

Minette *1.* Jurassic sedimentary iron-ore of the Briey basin and Lorraine.

2. (Rock.) *See* **Lamprophyr.**

Mispickel Synonym for **Arsenopyrite** (*q.v.*).

Molybdenite MoS_2. Hexagonal. G. 4.62–4.73. H. $1-1\frac{1}{2}$. Resembles graphite but slightly bluish rather than brownish black. Greenish streak.

Monazite $(Ce,La,Di)PO_4$. Monoclinic. G. 5.0–5.3. H. $5-5\frac{1}{2}$. Yellowish to reddish brown. Lustre resinous. Occurs in pegmatites and granitic rocks and in sand derived therefrom.

Monchiquite *See* **Lamprophyr.**

Monocline *See* **Folds.**

Monticellite $CaMgSiO_4$. Orthorhombic. G. 3.2. H. 5. An olivine.

Montmorillonite *See* **Clay Minerals.**

Monzonite *See* Table of Igneous Rocks, Appendix I.

Muck (Cornish: mullock) *1.* Useless material, as earth, gravel, or barren rock.

2. To move waste or ore, usually with a shovel.

3. In some districts the term is used to denote ore.

Mugearite A dark finely crystalline rock distinguished from basalt by the occurrence of oligoclase and orthoclase in place of labradorite, by generally containing olivine in greater amount than augite, and by the possession of a trachytic rather than a basaltic texture. (Holmes).

Muscovite *See* **Mica.**

Nagyagite $Pb_5Au(Te,Sb)_4S_{5-8}$. Monoclinic? G. 7.4. H. $1-1\frac{1}{2}$. Blackish lead-gray; metallic. Uncommon.

Nepheline $(Na,K)(Al,Si)_2O_4$. Hexagonal. G. 2.55–2.65. H. $5\frac{1}{2}-6$. White or yellowish. Lustre vitreous to greasy. Massive or in embedded grains in igneous rocks. Hardly ever in quartz-bearing rocks.

Net slip *See* **Faults.**

Niccolite NiAs. Hexagonal. G. 7.78. H. $5-5\frac{1}{2}$. Pale copper red. Metallic lustre.

Nickel bloom A green mineral of oxidized nickel ores, chiefly **Annabergite.** (*q.v.*).

Nontronite *See* **Clay Minerals.**

Norite *See* Table of Igneous Rocks, Appendix I.

Normal fault *See* **Faults.**

Oblique fault *See* **Faults.**

Obsidian Volcanic glass.

Octahedrite Synonym for **Anatase** (*q.v.*).

Offset (of a fault) *See* **Faults.**

Oligoclase *See* **Feldspar.**

Olivine A mineral species representing an isomorphous series whose end-members are:

Forsterite, Mg_2SiO_4. G. 3.2. H. $6\frac{1}{2}$, and Fayalite Fe_2SiO_4. G. 4.14. H. $6\frac{1}{2}$. Orthorhombic.

Option *See* Chapter 17 under Development of Prospects.

Ore A metalliferous mineral, or an aggregate of metalliferous minerals, more or less mixed with gangue, which from the standpoint of the miner can be won at a profit or from the standpoint of the metallurgist can be treated at a profit. The test of yielding a metal or metals *at a profit* seems the only feasible one to employ. (J. F. Kemp, *Trans. Can. Mining Inst.*, 1909, p. 367).

Ore pass An opening in a mine through which ore is delivered from a higher to a lower level. (Fay).

Orpiment As_2S_3. Monoclinic. G. 3.49. H. $1\frac{1}{2}$–2. Lemon-yellow. Resinous lustre. Foliated structure (difference from sulphur).

Orthite Synonym for **Allanite** (*q.v.*).

Orthoclase *See* **Feldspar.**

Ottrelite $(Fe'', Mn)(Al,Fe''')_2Si_3O_{10}.H_2O$. Monoclinic. G. 3.5. H. 6–7.

Outcrop The coming out of a stratum (or vein) to the surface of the earth. That part of a stratum (or vein) which appears at the surface. (Fay.) *Cf.* **Apex.**

Overturned fold *See* **Fold.**

Palladium Pd. Isometric. G. 11.9. H. $4\frac{1}{2}$–5. Resembles platinum and occurs with it.

Pantellerite Igneous rock related to rhyolite. Has a glassy groundmass and phenocrysts of anorthoclase, aegirine augite, and cossyrite (a rare and probably titaniferous amphibole).

Paragenesis *1.* The assemblage of minerals that occur together.
2. The order of deposition or crystallization of the minerals present.

Patronite A vanadium sulphide of indefinite composition from Mina Ragra, Peru.

Pegmatite An igneous rock of exceptionally coarse grain. Most pegmatites have the composition of granite and consist of perthitic feldspar with quartz and muscovite (and/or biotite) but some have the composition of syenite, alkali syenite, or gabbro.

Peneplain "Almost a plain"; surface of low relief resulting from long-continued erosion. Some authors take liberties with W. M. Davis' original spelling and write "peneplane."

Pentlandite $(Fe,Ni)S$. Isometric. G. 4.6–5.0. H. $3\frac{1}{2}$–4. Resembles pyrrhotite but has a cleavage and is non-magnetic.

Perthite An intergrowth of the feldspars microcline and albite.

Petrology Study of rocks, particularly igneous rocks. Adj. Petrologic(al).

Petzite $(Ag,Au)_2Te$. Isometric? G. 8.7–9.0. H. $2\frac{1}{2}$–3. Steel-gray to iron-gray; metallic. Conchoidal fracture, slightly sectile. Occurs in some gold veins usually with other tellurides.

Phlogopite *See* **Mica.**

Phonolite Igneous rock: fine-grained equivalent of alkali syenite.

Physiography Physical geography; more specifically, **Geomorphology,** *q.v.*

Picrite Ultramafic rock consisting of olivine with a small amount of feldspar (usually labradorite).

Pillar A piece of ground or mass of ore left to support the roof or hanging-wall in a mine.

Pillar Caving *See* **Caving.**

Pinite A micaceous alteration product, chiefly muscovite.

Pitch (of an oreshoot in a vein) The angle between the axis of the ore-shoot and the strike of the vein. The pitch is measured in the plane of the vein. The term is used similarly to designate the inclination of any line that lies in a plane, *e.g.,* lineation in a bedding plane or slickensides in a fault plane. (*Not to be confused with* **Plunge,** q.v., *or with* **Dip,** q.v.)

Pitchblende Synonym for **Uraninite** (*q.v.*).

Pivotal fault *See* **Faults.**

Placer Deposit of gold-bearing alluvial gravel. Also applied to similar deposits containing other metals such as tin, platinum, or tungsten.

Plan Representation of features such as mine workings or geological structure on a horizontal plane.

Platinum Pt. Isometric. G. 14–19. H. 4–4½. Steel-gray with bright lustre; metallic.

Plumbago Synonym for **Graphite** (*q.v.*).

Plunge The angle between any inclined line and a horizontal plane. The angle is always measured in a vertical plane containing the line. The term is used to designate the inclination of the axis of an oreshoot, the axial line of a fold, the attitude of lineation, etc. (*Not to be confused with* **Pitch** *or* **Dip,** q.v.)

Plutonic Of igneous intrusive origin. Usually applied to sizable bodies of intrusive rock rather than to small dikes or sills.

Polybasite $Ag_{16}Sb_2S_{11}$. Monoclinic. G. 6.0–6.2. H. 2–3. Steel-gray to iron-black; metallic. Tabular crystals show triangular markings.

Porphyrite (British) A term which has been variously used for pre-Tertiary andesitic rocks, altered andesite rocks, and hypabyssal rocks of marked porphyritic texture and andesitic composition. (Holmes).

Porphyritic Texture in an igneous rock characterized by larger crystals in a finer-grained groundmass. (Does not apply to metacrysts, *e.g.,* garnet, in a metamorphic rock.)

Porphyry *1.* Any igneous rock with a porphyritic texture.
2. (British) A hypabyssal rock containing phenocrysts of alkali feldspar. (Contrast with **Porphyrite.**)

Porphyry copper Copper deposit in which the copper-bearing minerals occur in disseminated grains (or in veinlets) throughout a great volume of rock. The rock need not be porphyry. *Characteristic:* large tonnage and relatively low grade.

Primary Of rock minerals: those originally present in the rock, not introduced or formed by alteration or metamorphism. Of ore: not enriched or oxidized by supergene processes.

Propylitization Alteration characterized by pyrite and chlorite, sometimes with epidote, carbonate, and a little sericite.

Protore *1*. Valueless material which generally underlies ores formed by sulphide enrichment and which would be converted into ore were the enriching process continued to sufficient depth. (Ransome).

2. The unchanged portion of any primary material that locally has been concentrated into ore, and that which by weathering may be so concentrated. (Emmons).

Proustite Ag_3AsS_3. Rhombohedral. G. 5.55. H. 2–2½. Ruby red. Streak vermilion. Lighter in color than pyrargyrite.

Psilomelane $BaR_9O_{18}.2H_2O$ (?) where R is chiefly manganese and cobalt. G. 4.4–4.7. H. 5–6. "Psilomelane type" applies to manganese oxides whose mineral composition is not specifically determined, if massive, hard, and heavy. (Fleischer and Richmond).

Pyrargyrite Ag_3SbS_3. Rhombohedral. G. 5.85. H. 2½. Deep red to black; in thin splinters deep ruby red. Streak Indian red. Darker than proustite.

Pyrite FeS_2. Isometric. Commonly cubes and pyritohedrons; less commonly octahedrons. G. 5.02. H. 6–6½. Brassy yellow with metallic lustre.

Pyrolusite MnO_2. Tetragonal. G. 4.75. H. 1–2. Metallic lustre. Color and streak iron-black.

Pyrometasomatic Contact metamorphic; *see* Chapter 15.

Pyromorphite $Pb_5Cl(PO_4)_3$. Hexagonal. G. 6.5–7.1. Lustre resinous to adamantine. Usually green, sometimes yellow, more rarely—orange, gray, or white.

Pyroxene Name for a group of silicate minerals analogous in composition to members of the amphibole group. Angle of prismatic cleavage about 87 degrees (difference from amphiboles). Principal species:

Enstatite $MgSiO_3$. Orthorhombic.

Hypersthene $(Fe,Mg)SiO_3$ with FeO exceeding 15%. Orthorhombic.

Augite $Ca(Mg,Fe,Al)(Al,Si)_2O_6$. Monoclinic.

Aegirite $NaFe'''Si_2O_6$. Monoclinic.

Spodumene $LiAlSi_2O_6$. Monoclinic.

Note: Acmite is a mineral having the composition of the pure aegirite end-member. Aegirine-augite is augite with the aegirite (acmite) molecule.

Pyrrhotite $Fe_{1-x}S$. Hexagonal. G. 4.58–4.65. H. 4. Brownish bronze darker than pyrite; metallic lustre. Magnetic but varying in intensity. Softer than pyrite.

Quaquaversal dip Dip away from a center in all directions, as in a structural dome. (Hills).

Quartz SiO_2. Rhombohedral. G. 2.65. H. 7. Colorless to white but some varieties smoky, reddish, brown, or amethystine.

Raise (British: rise) An opening like a shaft made in the back of a level to reach the level above (Standard).

Realgar AsS. Monoclinic. G. 3.48. H. 1½–2. Red to orange. Streak more orange than that of other red minerals. Almost invariably associated with orpiment.

Recumbent fold *See* **Fold.**

Rejuvenation Renewal of vigorous erosion as by uplift.

Replacement **Metasomatism** (*q.v.*).

Reverse Fault *See* **Faults.**

Rhodochrosite $MnCO_3$. Rhombohedral. G. 3.45–3.6. H. $3\frac{1}{2}$–$4\frac{1}{2}$. Rose-red to pink, weathering black. Perfect rhombohedral cleavage.

Rhodonite $MnSiO_3$. Triclinic. G. 3.58–3.70. H. $5\frac{1}{2}$–6. Rose-red, pink, or brown sometimes weathering to black. Prismatic cleavage like a pyroxene.

Rhyolite *See* Table of Igneous Rocks, Appendix I.

Riebeckite $Na_3Fe_3''Fe_2'''Si_8O_{23}(OH)$. Monoclinic. G. 3.44. H. 4. An amphibole.

Rise *See* **Raise.**

Rock Crystal Quartz crystal.

Room (mining) A wide working place in a flat bed or vein corresponding to a stope in a steep vein. (Ihlseng).

Room and Pillar A method of mining whereby the ore (or coal) is mined in a series of rooms leaving pillars between.

Roscoelite $K_2V_4Al_2Si_6O_{20}(OH)_4$. Monoclinic. G. 2.97. H. $2\frac{1}{2}$. Micaceous. Brown to green.

Rotational fault *See* **Faults.**

Round *1.* The advance accomplished in a drift or other opening by simultaneously blasting a single set of drilled holes.

2. The set of holes drilled in preparation for the blast.

3. The ore or rock broken by the blast.

Ruby copper Cuprite.

Ruby silver Pyrargyrite and/or proustite.

Rutile TiO_2. Tetragonal. G. 4.18–4.25. H. 6–$6\frac{1}{2}$. Red, reddish brown to black. Lustre adamantine to submetallic.

Sandstone *See* Table of Sedimentary Rocks, Appendix I.

Sanidine A glassy variety of orthoclase (*see* **Feldspar**) found as phenocrysts in some igneous rocks.

Saxonite Ultramafic rock consisting of enstatite and olivine.

Scapolite (wernerite) A silicate of Ca, Na, and Al with chlorine, carbonate, and sulphate radicles. Tetragonal. G. 2.65–2.74. H. 5–6. White or tinted. Imperfect cleavage in four directions at 45 degrees.

Scheelite $CaWO_4$. Tetragonal. G. 5.9–6.1. H. $4\frac{1}{2}$–5. White to amber. Lustre vitreous to adamantine. Most scheelite fluoresces. (*See* Chapter 16).

Schistosity *See* **Cleavage.**

Scorodite $FeAsO_4.2H_2O$. Orthorhombic. G. 3.1–3.3. H. $3\frac{1}{2}$–4. Pale green to liver brown. Usually in pyramidal crystals resembling octahedrons.

Secondary *Of rock minerals:* Minerals introduced into the rock or formed by metamorphism or alteration. *Of ore:* Enriched by supergene processes.

Section Representation of features such as mine workings or geological features on a vertical (or inclined) plane. A longitudinal section is parallel to the strike of a vein or geologic plane. A cross section is perpendicular to the strike.

Sediment Deposit of solid material (or material in transportation which may be deposited) made from any medium on the earth's surface, or in its outer crust under conditions of temperature approximating those normal to the surface. (Twenhofel).

Sedimentary rock Rock which originated as a **Sediment** (*q.v.*). The sediment may have been transported by wind, water, or ice and carried in the form of solid particles (sand, gravel, clay) or in solution (rock salt, gypsum, some calcareous sediments). Sedimentary rocks (unless still unconsolidated) have been indurated by cementation or by recrystallization.

Sedimentation The process of deposition of sediments. In a broader sense, "Sedimentation includes that portion of the metamorphic cycle from the destruction of the parent rock . . . to the consolidation of the products . . . into another rock." (Twenhofel).

Semseyite $Pb_9Sb_8S_4$. Monoclinic. G. 5.8. H. $2\frac{1}{2}$. Metallic. Gray to black. An uncommon mineral rarely identified except in polished sections.

Separation (of a fault) *See* **Faults.**

Sericite A fine-grained or finely flaky variety of muscovite. (*See* **Mica.**)

Serpentine $Mg_3Si_2O_5(OH)_4$. Monoclinic. Crystals, except pseudomorphs, unknown. G. 2.2. H. 2–5. Green. Lustre greasy; silky when fibrous.

Serpentine (rock) Rock composed essentially of the mineral serpentine.

Shaft A well-like downward opening in a mine. Usually a shaft starts from surface; if started from underground workings it is called a winze, though if equipped with a hoist it may be called an underground shaft. A shaft may be vertical or inclined. In some districts a flatly inclined opening is called an incline, "shaft" being limited to vertical openings.

Shear Mode of failure of a body whereby the portion of the body on one side of a plane or surface slides past the portion on the opposite side. (*See* Chapter 12.) Surface on which shearing has occurred.

Shear zone A layer or slab-like portion of a rockmass traversed by closely spaced surfaces along which shearing has taken place. (*See* Chapter 12.)

Shift A day's work for a miner (commonly 8 hours). The group of men who work during a given 8-hour period, hence day shift, afternoon shift, night shift, graveyard shift (the shift beginning at or around midnight).

Shift (of a fault) *See* **Faults.**

Shift-boss The foreman in charge of the men on a shift.

Shonkinite Alkaline igneous rock of granular texture consisting of augite and orthoclase with or without olivine, nepheline, and sodalite.

Shoot, Oreshoot That part of a deposit in which the valuable minerals are so concentrated that their utilization becomes possible. (Lindgren). Body of ore as contrasted with enclosing sub-commercial vein-stuff. (The alternative spelling, chute, is now usually reserved for the mining term— a shaft or trough through which broken ore falls.)

Shrinkage stoping A modification of overhand stoping in which ore is mined beginning on a level and working upward, withdrawing only enough broken ore to leave a space between the broken ore and the back for the men to work. After the stope reaches the next level above (pillars being left to support the floor of the level), the broken ore is drawn from the stope.

Siderite $FeCO_3$. Rhombohedral. G. 3.83–3.88. H. $3\frac{1}{2}$–4. Perfect rhombohedral cleavage. Yellowish or brownish white, weathering to dark brown.

Silica Silicon dioxide, SiO_2. Common mineralogical forms: quartz, chert, jasper, chalcedony.

Silicated Converted into or replaced by silicates, especially skarn minerals. (Distinguish from **Silicified**, *q.v.*) *Note:* Replacement processes under relatively low temperature conditions, as sericitization or chloritization, are not included in silication.

Silicified Replaced by silica or converted into silica.

Sill (geologic) 1. Intrusive sheet of igneous rock parallel with the layers enclosing it. (Longwell).

2. (Mining) A piece of wood laid across a drift to constitute a frame with the posts and to carry the track of the tramway. (Raymond).

3. (Mining) The floor of a passage or gallery in a mine.

Sillimanite Al_2SiO_5. Orthorhombic. G. 3.23. H. 6–7. White, pale green, or brown. Frequently fibrous.

Silver Ag. Isometric. G. 10.5. H. $2\frac{1}{2}$–3.

Skarn Rock resulting from contact metamorphism and characterized by calcium-silicates such as garnet and pyroxene. Tactite.

Slickenside Polished and striated surface resulting from friction on a fault plane. (Billings).

Slip A thin or inconspicuous fracture on which movement has taken place.

Slip (of a fault) *See* **Faults.**

Sludge Cuttings made by a diamond-drill or churn-drill bit. (*See* Chapter 3.)

Smaltite $CoAs_2$. Isomorphous with chloanthite. Isometric. G. 6.5 ± 0.4. H. $5\frac{1}{2}$–6. Tin-white to silver-gray. Metallic. Indistinguishable from arsenopyrite except by chemical test unless in crystals.

Smithsonite $ZnCO_3$. Rhombohedral. G. 4.35–4.40. H. 5. Usually botryoidal or in honeycombed masses; also granular to earthy. Gray to dirty brown. Sometimes white, green, blue, or pink.

Sodalite $Na_4Al_3Si_3O_{12}Cl$. Isometric. G. 2.15–2.3. H. $5\frac{1}{2}$–6. Commonly massive in embedded grains. Usually blue; also white, gray, or green.

Spathic iron Synonym for **Siderite** (*q.v.*).

Specific gravity The weight of a body (*e.g.*, rock or mineral) divided by the weight of an equal volume of water. Standard conditions: distilled water at 20 degrees Centigrade.

Specular iron *See* **Specularite.**

Specularite Micaceous or foliated variety of hematite.

Sperrylite $PtAs_2$. Isometric. G. 10.50. H. 6–7. Tin-white. Metallic.

Spessartite *See* **Garnet.**

Spessartite (rock) A diorite lamprophyr consisting essentially of green hornblende and plagioclase. (Holmes).

Sphalerite ZnS. Isometric. G. 3.9–4.1. H. $3\frac{1}{2}$–4. Commonly rosin-colored to black. Sometimes red; rarely white to green. Lustre resinous to submetallic; also adamantine. Perfect dodecahedral cleavage.

Sphene (Titanite) $CaTiSiO_5$. Monoclinic. G. 3.40–3.55. H. 5–5½. Gray, brown, gray, green, yellow, black. Resinous to adamantine lustre. Prismatic cleavage.

Spile A temporary lagging driven ahead in loose ground (Fay). The lagging is usually a plank sharpened wedge-fashion. Driven ahead horizontally at the elevation of the back or roof of a level, it permits the loose earth to be removed without caving of the material overhead. Sometimes spiles have to be driven parallel to the walls as well as the back.

Spilite A basaltic rock, generally vesicular or amygdaloidal, whose feldspars have been albitized. Pyroxene or amphibole, more or less altered, and sometimes serpentinized olivine may be present. (Holmes).

Spinel $MgAl_2O_4$. Fe″ may replace Mg; Fe‴ and Cr may replace Al. Isometric. G. 3.6–4.0. H. 8. Color varies with composition. Streak white.

Square set A set of timbers consisting of vertical and horizontal pieces all meeting at angles of 90 degrees. A system of square sets forms a three-dimensional lattice-work.

Square-setting (Square-set stoping) Method of mining whereby the stope is filled with square-set timbering as the ore is removed.

Stannite Cu_2FeSnS_4. Tetragonal. G. 4.4. H. 4. Steel-gray to iron-black. Metallic.

Staurolite Fe″$Al_5Si_2O_{12}$(OH). Orthorhombic. G. 3.65–3.75. H. 7–7½. Red-brown to brownish black. Prismatic crystals; sometimes cross-shaped twins.

Stephanite Ag_5SbS_4. Orthorhombic. G. 6.2–6.3. Iron-black. Metallic. More brittle than argentite and softer than tetrahedrite.

Stibnite Sb_2S_3. Orthorhombic. G. 4.52–4.62. H. 2. Lead-gray to black; lustre metallic. Bladed habit; cleavage perfect in one direction.

Stilbite $(Ca,Na,K)_3Al_5(Al,Si)Si_{14}O_{40}.15H_2O$. Monoclinic. G. 2.1–2.2. H. 3½–4. Usually white; perfect cleavage. Crystals often in sheaf-like groups.

Stock (geology) An intrusive body like a batholith but smaller, *i.e.*, less than ten or at most 40 square miles (Longwell).

Stockwork A mass of rock irregularly fractured along which mineralization has spread. (Lindgren).

Stope An underground opening from which ore has been or is being extracted. Usually applied to vertical or highly inclined veins. According to Raymond the term is properly restricted to a series of advancing horizontal faces in step-like arrangement, but this restriction is not in accordance with present-day usage. An *overhand stope* is made by working upward from a level into the ore above. An *underhand stope* is made by working downward beneath a level.

Stratigraphy Study of strata of sedimentary rocks, particularly with reference to correlation or determination of age. Adj. stratigraphic.

Strike The bearing of a horizontal line in the plane of a bed, vein, fault, etc.

Strike fault *See* **Faults.**

Strike-slip (of a fault) *See* **Faults.**

Strike-slip fault *See* **Faults.**

Strike slip *See* **Faults.**

Stringer A veinlet or small vein, usually one of a number which collectively make up a stringer lode or stockwork.

Stromeyerite (Ag,Cu)$_2$S. Orthorhombic. G. 6.2–6.3. H. 2½–3. Dark steel gray, tarnishing blue.

Strontianite SrCO$_3$. Othorhombic. G. 3.7. H. 3½–4. White to gray, yellow, or green.

Stull A platform (stull-covering) laid on timbers (stull-pieces) braced across a working from side to side, to support a workman or to carry ore or waste (Raymond). However, the term is commonly applied to the timbers (stull-pieces) which extend across a stope from hanging wall to footwall.

Sub-outcrop Intersection of a vein (or other structural feature) with an unconformity. What would be the outcrop if the overlying unconformable formation were removed.

Sublevel An intermediate level opened a short distance below a main level. (Fay).

Sublevel caving *See* **Caving.**

Sublevel stoping Stoping by driving a series of sublevels, all advancing horizontally, in steplike arrangement and separated by horizontal pillars. As work advances the pillars are caved progressively, starting with the uppermost. Part of the broken (caved) ore is removed and part is left to support the walls as in shrinkage stoping.

Sulfur S. Orthorhombic. G. 2.05–2.09. H. 1½–2½. Yellow.

Supergene Generated from above. Refers to the effects (usually oxidation and secondary sulphide enrichment) produced by descending groundwater. *Cf.* **Hypogene.**

Syenite *See* Table of Igneous Rocks, Appendix I.

Sylvanite (Au,Ag)Te$_2$. Monoclinic. G. 8.0–8.2. H. 1½–2. Silver white. Brilliant metallic. Good cleavage.

Syncline *See* **Fold.**

Synclinorium Major syncline composed of many smaller folds.

Syngenetic ore deposit Deposit formed by processes similar to those which have formed the enclosing rock and in general simultaneously with it. Examples: a bed of sedimentary iron ore between quartzite and slate; a concordant band of chromite in a stratiform layer of dunite.

System The assemblage of rocks formed during a given geologic period, *e.g.*, the Cambrian system.

System of veins, fractures, etc. *See* **Fractures.**

Taconite (Lake Superior) Iron formation whose iron content has not been sufficiently enriched by natural leaching of silica to constitute ore. Taconite consists of chert with magnetite, martite, siderite, and hydrous iron silicates (greenalite, minnasotaite, and stilpnomelane).

Talc Mg$_3$Si$_4$O$_{10}$(OH)$_2$. Monoclinic. Crystals rare. G. 2.7–2.8. H. 1. Apple green, gray, white, or silver white. Lustre pearly to greasy. Greasy feel.

Talus Mass of rock-fragments at the foot of a cliff. The fragments (of sliderock) have been loosened from the cliff and have reached a position of rest by falling, sliding, or rolling.

Tantalite $(Fe,Mn)Ta_2O_6$. Cb may replace Ta in an isomorphous series ranging to columbite. Orthorhombic. G. $6.5\pm$. H. 6. Black. Lustre submetallic. Often in prismatic crystals.

Tectonic Pertaining to or resulting from physical forces which have been or still are operative in the earth's crust. Tectonics is the study of such forces and their results and is more or less synonymous with structural geology.

Telethermal Zone or environment of ore deposition characterized by lesser intensity than epithermal and in general by remoteness from an igneous source.

Tellurides Minerals which are compounds of tellurium with gold, silver, or other metal.

Template (in drafting) A standard sheet bearing a set of lines which may be traced onto successive tracings. (In mechanical drawing a template is a piece of cardboard cut to a standard shape to be used as a ruler in reproducing the shape.)

Tennantite $(Cu,Fe,Zn,Ag)_{12}As_4S_{13}$. Forms an isomorphous series with tetrahedrite. Isometric. G. 4.6–5.1. H. 3–4½. Indistinguishable from tetrahedrite except by chemical tests.

Tenorite CuO. Triclinic. G. 6.5. H. 3–4. Steel-gray or iron-gray to black. Metallic. Occurs in oxidized copper deposits.

Tephrite *See* **Basanite**.

Tetrahedrite $(Cu,Fe,Zn,Ag)_{12}Sb_4S_{13}$. Isomorphous with tennantite. Isometric. G. 4.6–5.1. H. 3–4½. Grayish black to black. Metallic. Brittle.

Theralite. An igneous rock of the alkali syenite group consisting of predominant pyroxene with basic plagioclase and nepheline. (The type "theralite" from the Crazy Mountains, Mont., proved not to have this composition and thus does not conform to Rosenbusch's definition. *Cf.* Johannsen, Vol. 4, p. 97.)

Thorite $ThSiO_4$. Tetragonal. G. 5.3. H. 5. Black. Otherwise resembles zircon.

Throw (of a fault) *See* **Faults**.

Tin stone Synonym for **Cassiterite** (*q.v.*).

Titanite Synonym for **Sphene** (*q.v.*).

Tonalite A quartz-diorite containing hornblende and biotite as the chief mafic minerals. (Holmes).

Topaz $Al_2SiO_4(F,OH)_2$. Orthorhombic. G. 3.4–3.6. H. 8. Colorless to straw-yellow and other tints. Perfect basal cleavage.

Top slicing *See* **Caving**.

Tourmaline $WX_3B_3Al_3(AlSi_2O_9)_3(O,OH,F)_4$, where $W = Na$, Ca and $X = Al$, Fe''', Li, Mg. Rhombohedral. G. 3.0–3.25. H. 7–7½. Color varies with composition. Commonly black to brown. More rarely pink, green, blue. Usually in prismatic crystals with rounded triangular cross section. No cleavage. Sometimes finely acicular and visible only under the microscope.

Trachyte *See* Table of Igneous Rocks, Appendix I.

Tremolite $Ca_2Mg_5Si_8O_{22}(OH)_2$. Monoclinic. G. 3.0–3.3. H. 5–6. An amphibole. White, varying to green with increase in iron (actinolite). Often shows silky sheen. Perfect prismatic cleavage.

Tridymite SiO_2. Orthorhombic. G. 2.26. H. 7. Indistinguishable from quartz by macroscopic methods. Found chiefly in siliceous volcanic rocks.

Trochoidal fault *See* **Faults.**

Troctolite Igneous rock related to gabbro and consisting of plagioclase and olivine.

Trough (of a fold) *See* **Folds.**

Turquois $Al_2(OH)_3PO_4.H_2O+xCu$. Triclinic. G. 2.6–2.8. H. 6. Blue to green. Usually compact or reniform. Rarely in crystals.

Unit (as used in connection with tenor or price of a metal) The amount of metal (or oxide or other component) contained in a ton of 1% ore; hence: short ton unit = 20 lb; long-ton unit = 22.4 lb; metric ton unit = 10 kg (22.04 lb). *Example:* if the value of tungsten ore is $20 per short ton unit of WO_3, a ton of 60% ore (since it contains 60 units) is worth $1200.

Uraninite (pitchblende) Complex oxide of uranium with small amounts of lead and rare elements. Isometric. G. 9.0–9.7. H. 5½. Black. Lustre submetallic to pitch-like. Usually massive or botryoidal.

Vanadinite $Pb_5Cl(VO_4)_3$. Hexagonal. G. 6.7–7.1. H. 3. Ruby-red, brown, yellow. Lustre resinous to adamantine.

Vosgesite *See* **Lamprophyr.**

Vug (vugh) Cavity within a body of rock or ore, usually lined with crystals.

Wad One of several manganese oxide minerals or a mixture of them. "Wad" is applied to manganiferous material when massive, soft, and of low apparent specific gravity (Fleischer and Richmond).

Waste Valueless material such as barren rock to be thrown on the dump. Material too poor to mine or treat, as distinguished from ore.

Water level; Water table Surface, whether even or irregular, below which rock or soil is saturated with water. Above this surface, pores are incompletely filled and water is percolating downward.

Websterite An ultramafic igneous rock. A variety of pyroxenite composed of both monoclinic and orthorhombic pyroxenes. (Holmes).

Wehrlite A variety of peridotite containing diallage. The name is now extended to include with diallage all other varieties of monoclinic pyroxenes. (Holmes).

Wernerite Scapolite (*q.v.*).

Willemite Zn_2SiO_4. Rhombohedral. G. 3.9–4.2. H. 5½. Various colors; white when pure.

Winze A downward opening like a shaft but starting from a point underground rather than from the surface. It differs from a raise in that it is driven downward rather than upward. After a winze has connected with a level below it is described as a raise if viewed from the lower level. But in some mines the opening when connected through is called a raise no matter how driven originally or how viewed.

Witherite $BaCO_3$. Orthorhombic. G. 4.3. H. 3½. White to gray.

Wolframite An isomorphous series whose end-members are ferberite, $FeWO_4$

and huebnerite, $MnWO_4$. Monoclinic, G. 7.0–7.5. H. 5–5½. Black (ferberite) to brown (huebnerite). Lustre submetallic to resinous. Perfect cleavage.

Wollastonite $CaSiO_3$. Triclinic. G. 2.8–2.9. H. 5–5½. Colorless, white, or gray. Crystals and cleavage like pyroxenes.

Wood tin Cassiterite, when occurring in reniform shapes with radiating fibrous appearance.

Wulfenite $PbMoO_4$. Tetragonal. G. 6.8±. H. 3. Often yellow, orange, or red. Lustre vitreous to adamantine. Tabular crystals.

Wurtzite ZnS. Hexagonal. G. 3.98. H. 4. Macroscopically indistinguishable from sphalerite except by crystal form.

Xenothermal Ore Deposit Deposit formed at high temperature but at shallow to moderate depth.

Zeolite Name for a family of hydrous silicates of aluminum with sodium and calcium. Species include: Heulandite, stilbite, chabazite, natrolite, analcime.

Zinc blende Synonym for **Sphalerite** (*q.v.*).

Zincite ZnO. Hexagonal. G. 5.6. H. 4–4½. Deep red to orange yellow. Very rare except at Franklin Furnace, N. J.

Zinkenite $Pb_6Sb_{14}S_{27}$. Hexagonal. G. 5.3. H. 3–3½. Steel-gray. Metallic. Uncommon.

Zircon $ZrSiO_4$. Tetragonal. G. 4.68. H. 7½. Commonly brown. Adamantine lustre. Usually in crystals or in grains embedded in igneous rocks. Occurs in placer deposits derived from such rocks.

Zoisite $Ca_2Al_3(SiO_4)_3(OH)$. Orthorhombic. G. 3.3. H. 6. Resembles clinozoisite.

Zonal Theory Theory to explain observed zonal arrangement of hypogene mineralization. *See* Chapter 15.

Zone Interval bounded by horizontal or inclined planes or curved surfaces (tangible or imaginary) between which given physical or chemical conditions exist. *E.g.*, *Zone of weathering*—shallow portion of the earth's crust in which oxidation and hydration are active. *Oxidized zone*—near-surface portion of an ore deposit in which the original sulphides and other minerals have been oxidized. *Zone of (supergene sulphide) enrichment*—interval below the oxidized zone in which a metal (usually copper) has been carried down in solution from the oxidized zone and redeposited as sulphide. *Zone of fracture*—relatively shallow environment where rock fails by fracture. *Zone of flow*—deeper environment in which rock fails by flow. *See also* **Zonal Theory.**

Zone, shear *See* **Shear zone.**

Zoning Arrangement of minerals or mineral assemblages in zones.

INDEX

L

M